NEW COORDINATED SCIENCE

3RD EDITION

Physics

for Higher Tier

Stephen Pople

OXFORD
UNIVERSITY PRESS

OXFORD
UNIVERSITY PRESS

Great Clarendon Street, Oxford OX2 6DP

Oxford University Press is a department of the University of Oxford.
It furthers the University's objective of excellence in research, scholarship, and education by publishing worldwide in

Oxford New York

Auckland Bangkok Buenos Aires Cape Town Chennai
Dar es Salaam Delhi Hong Kong Istanbul Karachi Kolkata
Kuala Lumpur Madrid Melbourne Mexico City Mumbai
Nairobi São Paulo Shanghai Taipei Tokyo Toronto

with associated companies in Berlin

Oxford is a registered trade mark of Oxford University Press in the UK and in certain other countries

First published 2001

British Library Cataloguing in Publication Data

Data available

ISBN 0 19 914822 8

10 9 8 7 6 5

Typeset in Palatino by AMR, Bramley, UK

Printed in Spain by Gráficas Estella

Acknowledgements

The publisher would like to thank the following for their kind permission to reproduce the following photographs:
p8 Corbis/Dave G Houser; **p10** OUP; **p12** SPL (left), NASA (right); **p13** SPL/P Parviainen; **p14** Eye Ubiquitous/K Wilton; **p15** SPL/A Tsiaras; **p18** Corbis/Paul A Souders; **p23** Powerstock Zefa/G Montgomer; **p24** Greg Evans; **p26** Austin J Brown; **p30** Allsport/M Hewitt (top), Alton Towers (centre left and right, and bottom left), Crown Copyright (bottom right); **p31** OUP (top and bottom), Volvo Concessionaires (centre); **p32** Rolls Royce; **p33** James Davis; **p34** British Petroleum (top), Rex Features (bottom); **p35** Austin J Brown (top), Porsche Cars Great Britain (centre), Powerstock Zefa (bottom); **p36** Allsport UK (left), Colorsport (right); **p37** Allsport UK (top), Colorsport (bottom); **p40** NASA (top), Allsport UK (bottom left), Ford Motor Company (bottom right); **p41** Allsport UK/D Klein; **p42** Rex Features/Today; **p46** James Davis (left), Corel Professional Photos (right); **p47** Holt Studios/ M Mayer (left), Mary Evans/A Hartingue (top right), Robert Harding/I Griffiths (bottom right); **p50** Corbis/Charles and Josette Lenars; **p54** Colorsport/A Cowie; **p56** Space Frontiers; **p59** Ardea/Y Arthus-Bertrand; **p61** SPL/M Bond (left), SPL/C Molloy (centre), Eye Ubiquitous/Selby (right); **p62** SPL/S Fraser (top), Stone/A Levenson (bottom); **p64** SPL/G Parker; **p66** Eye Ubiquitous/J Burke; **p67** SPL/D Ducros; **p69** Powerstock Zefa; **p72** Barnarby's Picture Library (left), OSF/M Birkhead (right); **p74** Allsport UK/B D Vandystadt (top left), FLPA/S McCutcheon (top right), OUP (bottom left), Derek Fordham (bottom right); **p75** J Allan Cash; **p76** Corel Professional Photos (top left), Colorsport (top right), BMIHT (bottom left and right); **p77** OUP (top left and right), Garden Picture Library/B Challinor (bottom); **p78** Sally and Richard Greenhill (left), Bubbles/J Farrow (left); **p79** British Petroleum; **p82** Corbis/Michael and Patricia Fogden; **p84** Photocall (top left), Oxford Lasers (top right), Ann Ronan/Image Select/US Naval Observatory (bottom left), Robert Harding (bottom right); **p85** Barclaycard (top), OUP (centre), Oxford Lasers (bottom); **p86** OUP; p88 OUP; **p91** SPL/D Parker (left), SPL/Dr K F R Schiller (right); **p92** FLPA/S McCutcheon; **p94** OUP; **p95** OUP; **p101** OUP (left), SPL/A Syred (right); p102 FLPA/H Binz; **p103** Odeon Cinemas; **p104** OUP (top and bottom), Robert Harding (centre); **p105** Environmental Images/M Bond (left), Stock Market (top right), Topham Picturepoint (bottom right); **p106** Redferns/M Hutson (left), Redferns/E Roberts (right); **p107** Eye Ubiquitous/J Waterlow; **p108** Eye Ubiquitous/P Schewt (top left), Eye Ubiquitous/R D Battersby (top right), Eye Ubiquitous/Skjold (bottom left), Eye Ubiquitous/D Woodward (bottom right); **p109** Redferns/L Morris; **p110** OSF/Press-Tige; **p111** SPL/H.Schneebeli; **p115** Dr Tony Waltham; **p116** Dr Tony Waltham; **p120** SPL; **p123** SPL/M F Chillmaid (top), Eye Ubiquitous/R Donaldson; **p124** John Birdsall (left), OUP (right); **p126** Ardea/P Morris; **p128** OUP (top and bottom); **p129** SPL/Tek Image; **p130** Danlers (left), OUP (right top, centre and bottom); **p132** Britstock-IFA/ICS (top), OUP (bottom); **p133** Chris Honeywell; **p137** OUP; **p138** OUP (left and right); **p142** Braun Electric UK; **p144** National Grid (top), Milepost 92 1/2 (centre), FLPA/A J Roberts (bottom left), OUP (bottom right); **p145** OUP (top left and right), Andrew Lambert (centre and bottom); **p146** OUP; **p147** OUP; **p148** OUP (top left); **p150** OUP; **p151** SPL/K Kent; **p154** Corel Professional Photos; **p156** OUP; **p157** OUP; **p159** OUP (left and right); **p160** OUP (left top and bottom), Boxmag Rapid (top right), J P Browett (bottom right); **p162** OUP (left, centre and right); **p164** OUP; **p166** Robert Harding (left), SPL/Eurelios/C Pouedras; **p167** Mary Evans Picture Library; **p169** Redferns/S Stockwell (top), OUP (bottom); **p170** OUP (top, centre and right), Central Electricity Generating Board (lower centre); **p172** OUP (left, centre and right); **p174** National Power; **p176** OSF/M Chillmaid (top left), Powerstock Zefa (bottom right); **p177** North London Waste Authority (top left and right), SPL/J Mead (bottom right); **p180** NASA; **p182** Camera Press/L Wilson; **p185** SPL/Fermilab; **p186** SPL/D Parker; **p188** UKAEA (left), National Radiological Protection Board (right); **p189** James Davis; **p190** Frank Spooner/Gamma (left), J Hoffmann (right), Collections/R Deane; **p199** OUP (top and bottom); **p192** Getty Images; **p194** SPL/M Dohrn; **p195** UKAEA (left); **p196** UKAEA; **p197** SPL/M Bond; **p199** SPL/US Department of Energy (left), NASA (right); **p202** NASA; p204 SPL/J Sanford; **p208** SPL/NASA (top), SPL/L Pesek (bottom); **p209** SPL/J Lodriguss: **p211** SPL/GE Astro Space (top left), SPL/PLI (top right), SPL/NASA (bottom left); **p213** SPL/NASA; **p214** SPL/Celestial Image; **p215** SPL/European Southern Observatory; **p216** SPL/F Zullo (left), SPL/D Nunuk (right); **p218** SPL/US Geological Survey (left), SPL/ESA/PLI (top right), SPL/NASA (bottom right); **p219** SPL/M Bond (left), SPL/V Habbick Visions (right); **p222** Hulton-Deutsch/Corbis; **p226** Allsport UK; **p228** Photographers' Library (left), OUP (right); **p230** James Davis; **p231** SPL/P Goeigheluck; **p232** Camera Press/Curtis; **p234** Image Bank/A Choisnet.

The publisher wishes to acknowledge the help of Brian Arnold with the preparation of the exam-style questions.

The illustrations are by Jeff Edwards, Clive Goodyer, Nick Hawken, Jan Lewis, Art Construction, Chartwell Illustrators and Oxford Computer Illustration.

Cover image by Gary Thompson.

INTRODUCTION

Science is about asking questions. Physics is the science that asks questions about the physical world around you, its practical uses, and some of the social issues it raises.

You will find this book useful if you are studying physics as part of a Single or Double Award GCSE science course.

Everything in this book has been organized to help you find out things quickly and easily. It is written in two-page units called spreads.

- **Use the contents page**
  If you are looking for information on a large topic, look it up in the contents page.

- **Use the index**
  If there is something small you want to check on, look up the most likely word in the index. The index gives the page number where you'll find information about that word.

- **Use the questions**
  Asking questions and answering them is a very good way of learning. There are questions at the end of every chapter. At the end of the book there is a set of further exam-style questions. Answers to numerical questions, and pointers to those requiring short answers, are provided.

- **Helping you revise**
  To help you revise, in addition to the questions, there are some revision notes, a glossary of important terms, and end-of-chapter summaries.

Physics is an important and exciting subject. It doesn't just happen in laboratories. It is all around you: in fairgrounds, fields, farms, and factories. It is taking place deep in the Earth and far out in space. You'll find physics everywhere.

I hope that this book helps you with your studies, that you enjoy using it, and that at the end of your course, you agree with me that physics is exciting!

Stephen Pople

July 2001

Note: The *Further Topics* are included to satisfy the additional statutory requirements of the national curricula for students in Northern Ireland and Wales.

Contents

Chapter 6

Chapter 7

Chapter 8

Routemaps

The order of content provided by a specification does not always suit all students. These 'routemaps' show you different ways to work through the material. They are designed to help you understand the subject in small, manageable chunks by suggesting groupings of spreads relevant to particular topics and highlighting connections between them. They are especially useful when you are revising because they help you to identify and revise logical sections of material at a time, and if you have missed any work, they can also help you to catch up.

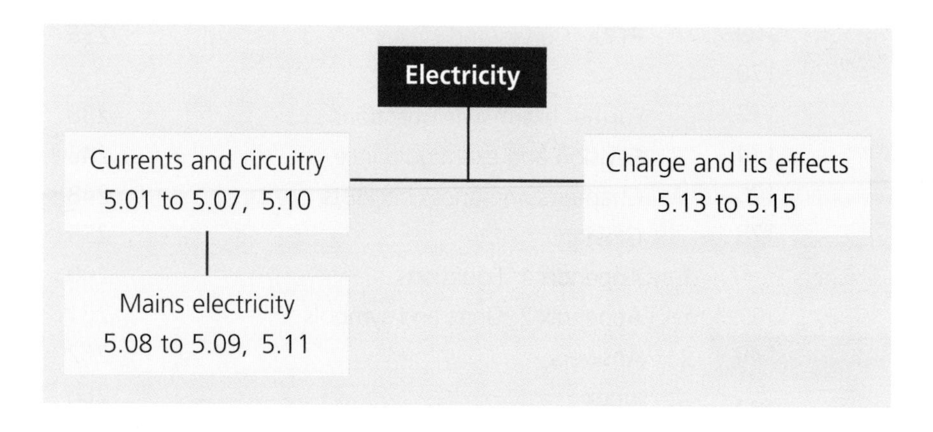

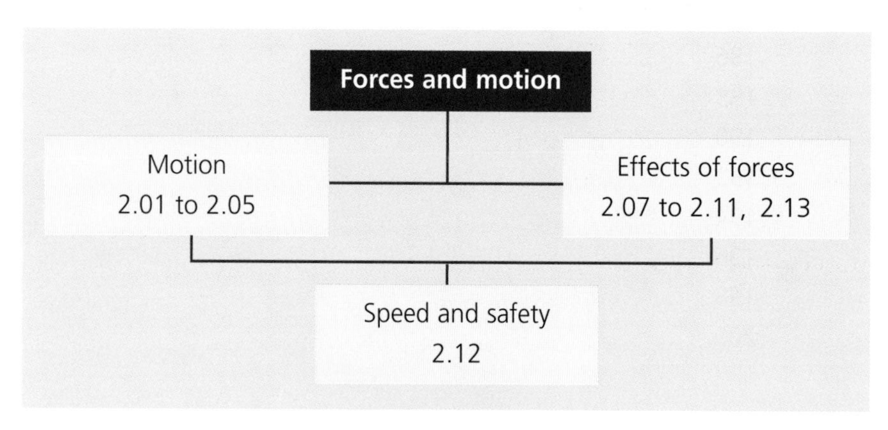

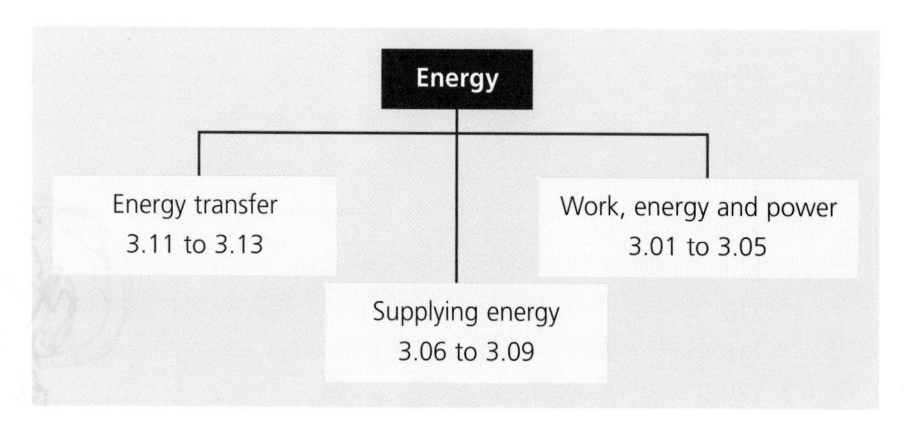

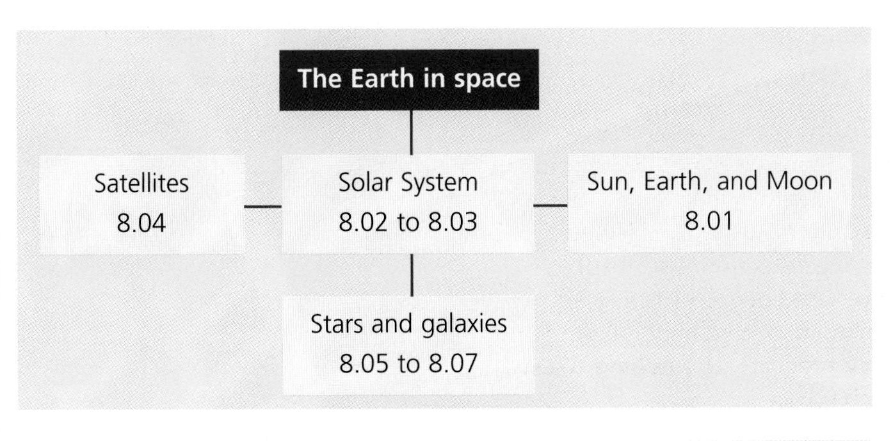
The Earth in space
Satellites
8.04
Solar System
8.02 to 8.03
Sun, Earth, and Moon
8.01
Stars and galaxies
8.05 to 8.07

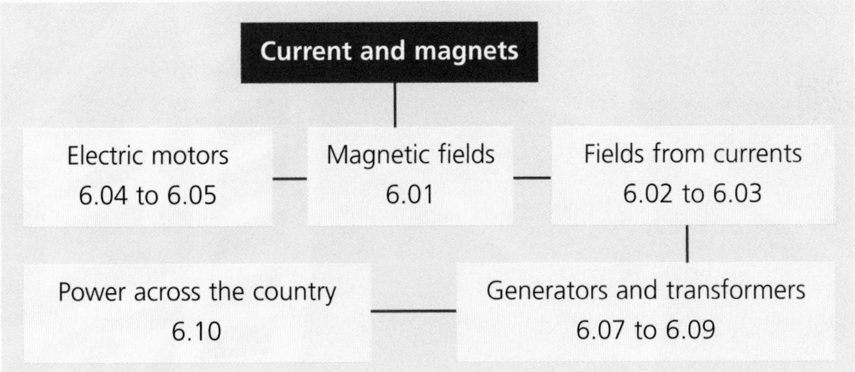
Current and magnets
Electric motors
6.04 to 6.05
Magnetic fields
6.01
Fields from currents
6.02 to 6.03
Power across the country
6.10
Generators and transformers
6.07 to 6.09

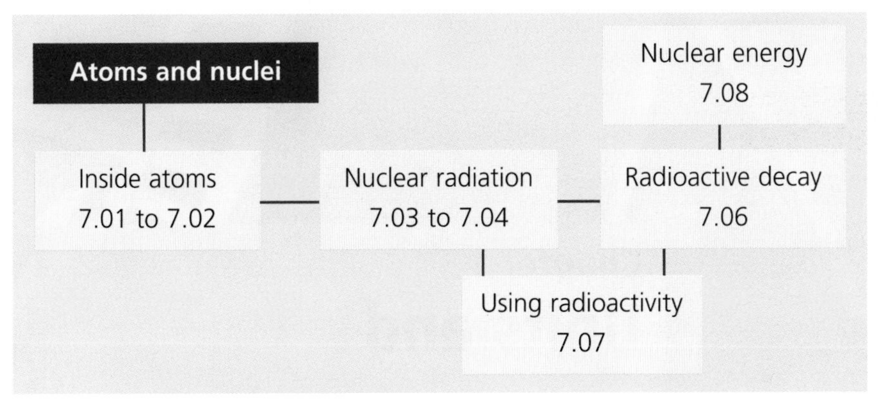
Atoms and nuclei
Nuclear energy
7.08
Inside atoms
7.01 to 7.02
Nuclear radiation
7.03 to 7.04
Radioactive decay
7.06
Using radioactivity
7.07

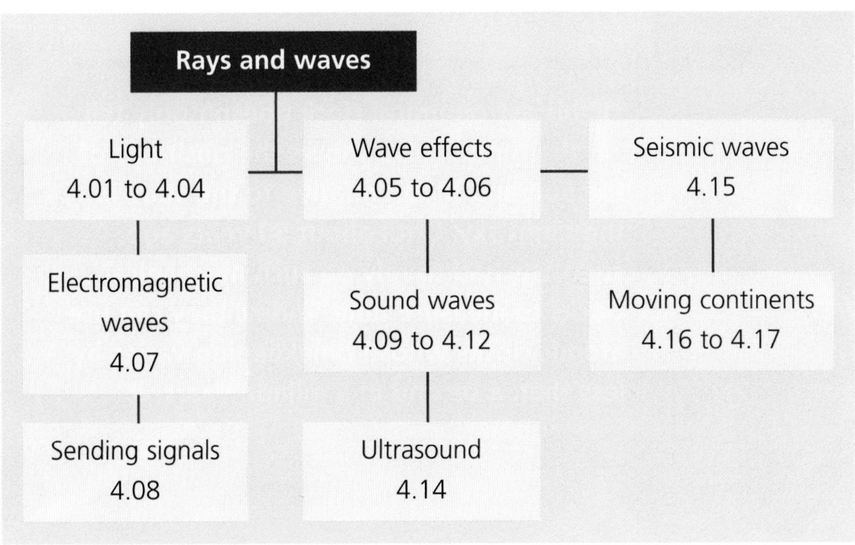
Rays and waves
Light
4.01 to 4.04
Wave effects
4.05 to 4.06
Seismic waves
4.15
Electromagnetic
waves
4.07
Sound waves
4.09 to 4.12
Moving continents
4.16 to 4.17
Sending signals
4.08
Ultrasound
4.14

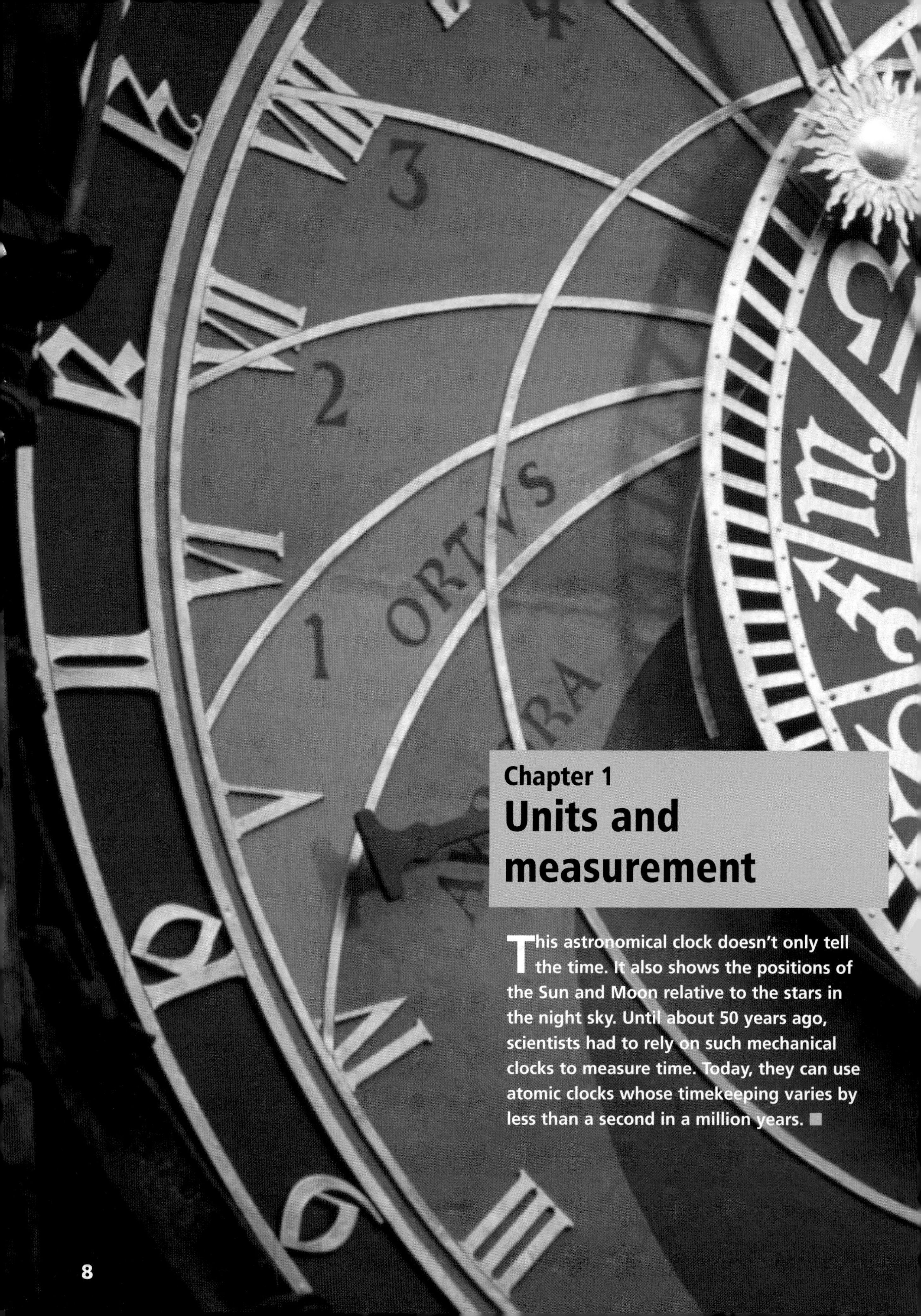

Chapter 1
Units and measurement

This astronomical clock doesn't only tell the time. It also shows the positions of the Sun and Moon relative to the stars in the night sky. Until about 50 years ago, scientists had to rely on such mechanical clocks to measure time. Today, they can use atomic clocks whose timekeeping varies by less than a second in a million years. ■

OCCASVS

1.01 Units for measuring

SI units – a common system of measuring

Which of these units would you use to measure:

- a length?
- or a mass?
- or a time?

There are several possibilities. But in scientific work, life is much easier if everyone uses the same system of units. Nowadays, most scientists use the **SI system** (from the French, Système International d'Unités). This starts with the metre, the kilogram, and the second. Many other units are based on these.

Length

The **metre** (**m** for short) is the SI unit of length.

The chart shows some of the larger and smaller length units based on the metre.

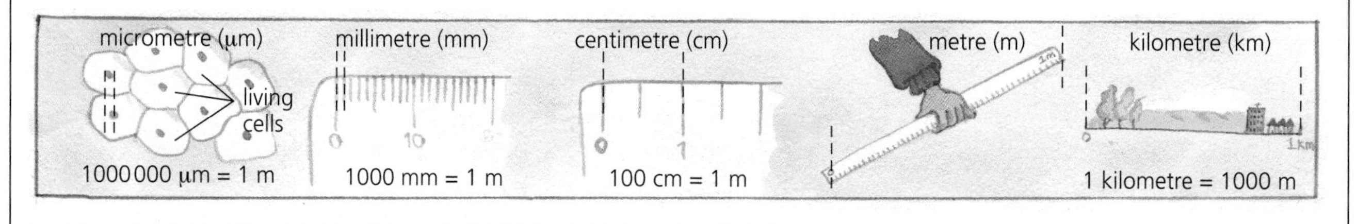

Mass

Mass is the amount of matter in something. In the laboratory, it is often measured using a top pan balance. Mass is sometimes called 'weight'. This is wrong. The difference between mass and weight is explained later on.

The **kilogram** (**kg**) is the SI unit of mass.

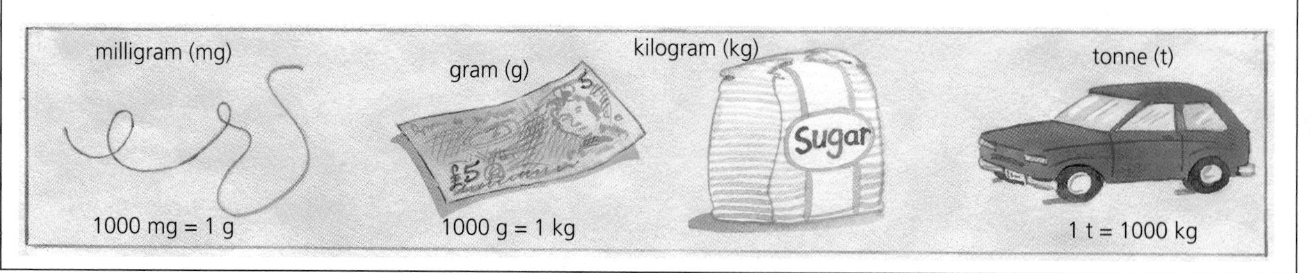

Time

The **second** (**s**) is the SI unit of time.

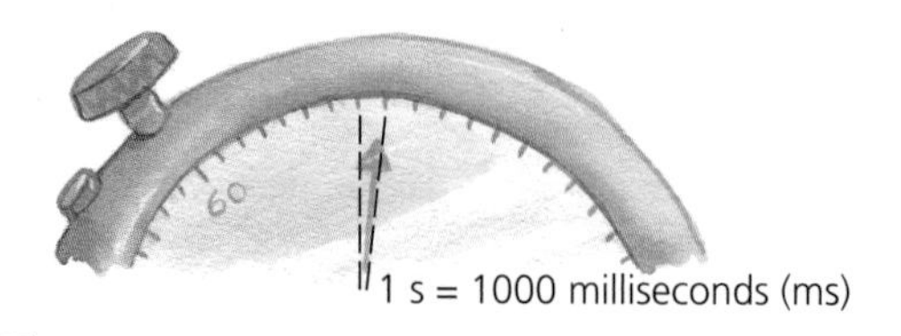

Volume

Volume is the amount of space something takes up. The SI unit of volume is the **cubic metre (m^3)**. This is rather a large unit of volume for everyday use, so the litre, millilitre, or centimetre cubed are often used instead.

There are 1000 millilitres in 1 litre, and 1000 cubic centimetres in 1 litre. So 1 millilitre is the same as 1 cubic centimetre.

Measuring volume

If something has a simple shape, its volume can be calculated. For example:

volume of a rectangular block = length × width × height

Liquid volumes of about a litre or less can be measured using a measuring cylinder. Pour in the liquid, and the reading on the scale gives the volume.

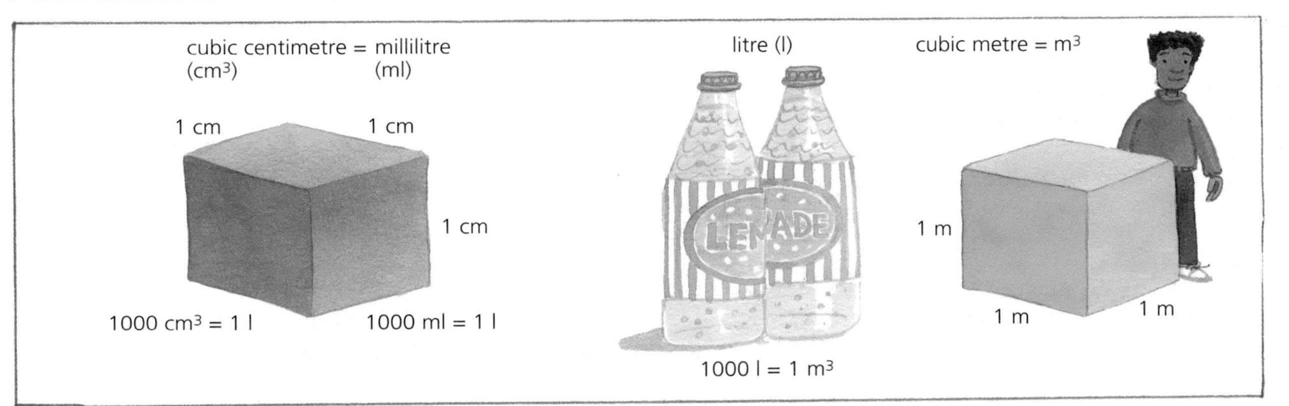

Questions

1 Copy and complete the table:

	Unit	Abbreviation
Length	?	m
?	kilogram	?
Time	?	?

2 What do the following stand for: mm, t, mg, ms, l, cm?

3 Which is the greater?
a 1600 g or 1.5 kg?
b 1450 mm or 1.3 m?

4 *10, 100, 1000, 100 000, 1 000 000*
Which of these is:
a the number of mg in 1 g?
b the number of mm in 1 cm?
c the number of cm in 1 km?
d the number of cm in 1 m?
e the number of mm in 1 km?

5 Write down the value of:
a 1 m in mm
b 1.5 m in mm
c 1.534 m in mm
d 1652 mm in m

6 Write down the values of:
a 2.750 m in mm **b** 1.600 km in m
c 6.500 g in mg **d** 150 cm in m
e 1750 g in kg

7 Which is the odd one out in each of the boxes?

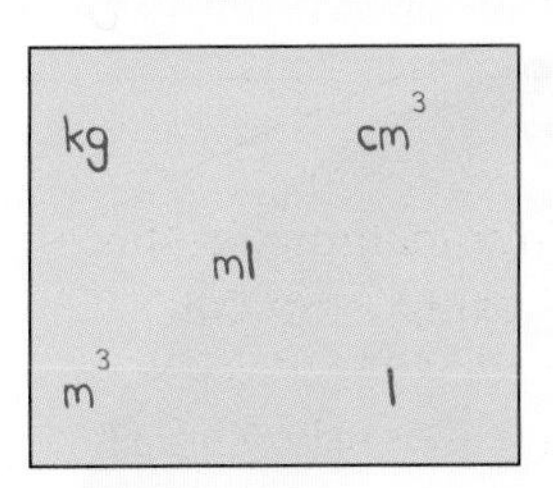

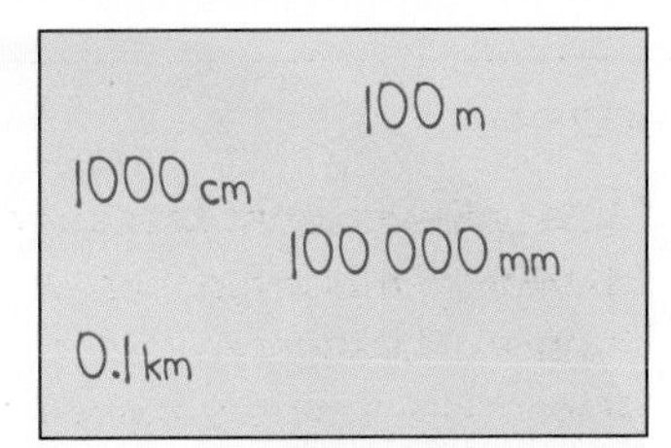

8 What is the volume of the liquid in the measuring cylinder in the diagram? Give your answer:
a in cm^3
b in litres

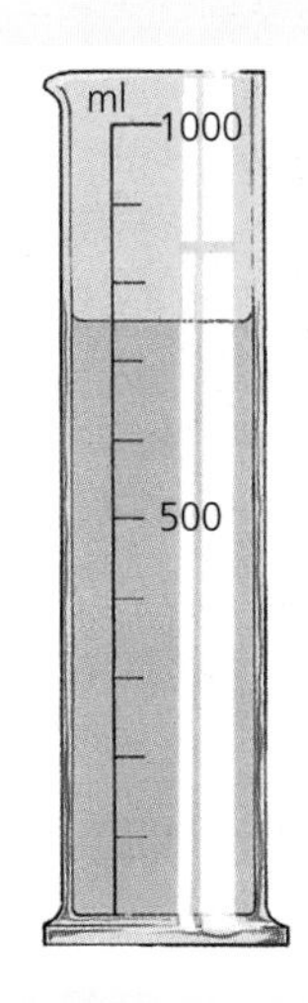

9 What is the volume of a metal block 3 cm long by 2 cm wide by 4 cm high? What would be the volume of a block twice as long, wide, and high?

1.02 More about units

Names and symbols

Units like the metre, kilogram, and second are always written in 'small' letters, without capitals. So are their symbols (the abbreviations, or 'short' versions):

Unit	Symbol (abbreviation)	Measures...
metre	m	length
kilogram	kg	mass
second	s	time

Some units are named after famous scientists – such as Isaac Newton, Blaise Pascal, and André Ampère:

Unit	Symbol (abbreviation)	Measures...
newton	N	force
pascal	Pa	pressure
ampere	A	current

When a person's name is used as a unit, it is *not* written with a capital letter at the start. However the symbol *does* have a capital.

Sir Isaac Newton (1642–1727). The unit of force was named after him.

Density

New units can be made by combining others together. **Density** is one example:

Water has a density of 1000 kilograms per cubic metre (kg/m^3). This means that each cubic metre of water has a mass of 1000 kilograms. The densities of some other materials are given in the chart on the right. The density of air can vary depending on how squashed the air is.

People may say that 'lead is heavier than water'. But that isn't necessarily true. A small piece of lead is lighter than a large beakerful of water! However, lead is more dense than water: it has more kilograms packed into every cubic metre.

The Earth has an average density of 5520 kg/m^3. This is about double the density of the rocks near the surface, so the Earth must have a high-density core – probably mainly iron.

How dense?

The least dense material you are ever likely to see is the dimly glowing gas in the tail of a comet. Millions of kilometres long, the gas is so thin that there is less than a kilogram per cubic *kilo*metre.

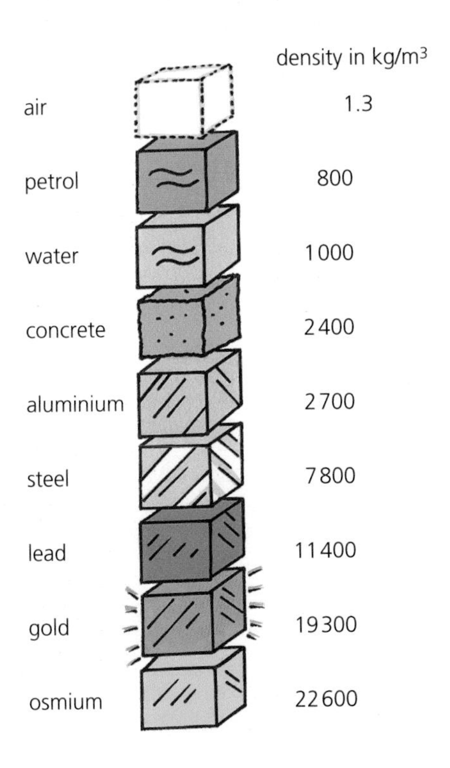

The densest substance found on Earth is the rare metal osmium. It is about twice as dense as lead. If this book were made of osmium, it would weigh as much as a full bucket of water.

Different density units

The kg/m^3 isn't always the easiest unit to use in laboratory work. When masses are measured in grams and volumes in cubic centimetres (millilitres), it is simpler to calculate densities in g/cm^3. Changing to kg/m^3 is easy:

$$1\ \text{g/cm}^3 = 1000\ \text{kg/m}^3$$

For example, water has a density of 1 g/cm^3.

Unit	Symbol (abbreviation)	Measures...
volt	V	voltage
metre	m	length
watt	W	power
kilogram	kg	mass
joule	J	energy

Questions

1 Which of the above units do you think are named after scientists? How can you tell?

2 The density of aluminium is 2700 kg/m^3. What is the mass of:
a 1 m^3 of aluminium? **b** 10 m^3 of aluminium?

3 Use information from the chart of densities on the left to help you answer the following:
a Which has more mass, 1 m^3 of petrol or 1 m^3 of water?
b Which has more volume (takes up more space), 1 kg of petrol or 1 kg of water?

4 Below, which block, X or Y, has the greater:
a mass? **b** volume? **c** density?

5 Use the chart of densities on the left to help you decide which material each of the blocks X and Y below could be made from.

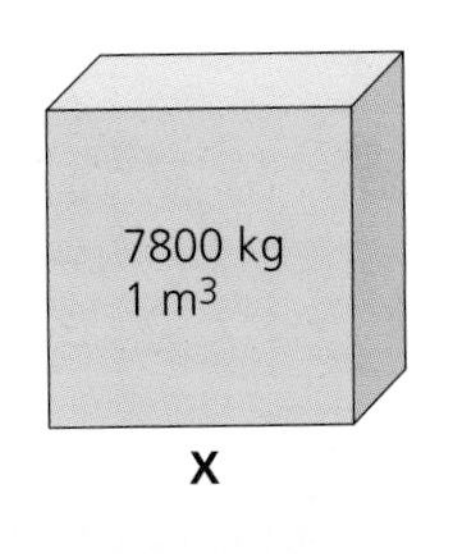

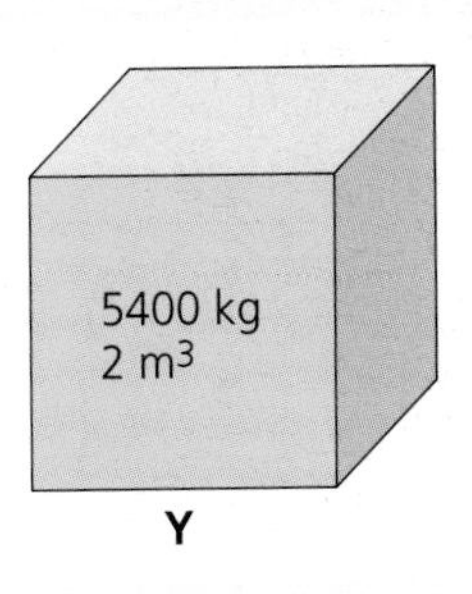

1.03 Measuring matters

Over the centuries, people have used a wide variety of units for making measurements. Here are some examples.

Strange but true

The **foot** (unit of length) was originally the length of a Roman's foot. But some people had much longer feet than others! So, in the 12th century the foot was defined by a law issued by Henry I of England as the total width of 36 ears of barleycorn.

The **knot** (unit of speed) is still used by mariners at sea, and by pilots. It is 1.15 m.p.h., or about 0.5 metres per second. Speed at sea was originally measured by letting a knotted rope out behind the boat, and seeing how many knots floated away from the ship in a set time.

The **acre** (unit of area) was the area of a field that could be ploughed in one day by a team of two oxen.

The **hand** (unit of length) is the width of an average hand. It is still used for measuring the height of horses.

The metric system

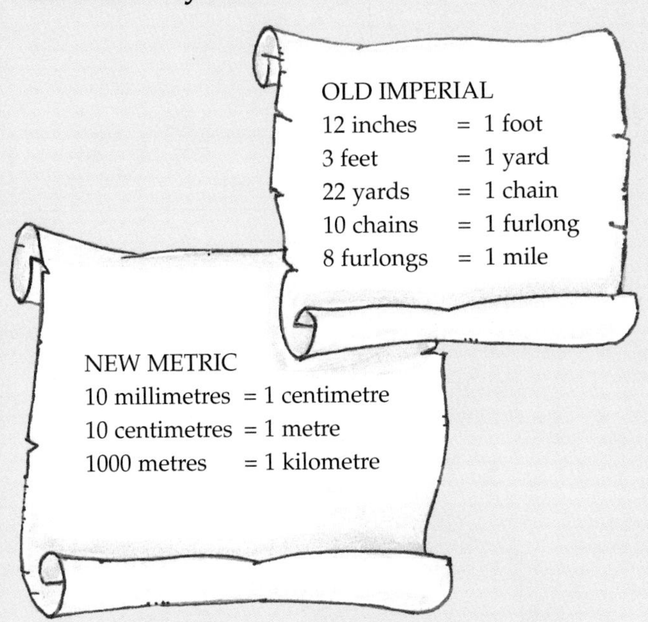

Most scientists now use units based on the metric system. This was introduced by French scientists in the 1790s, after the French Revolution. It sorted out the muddled systems of units used before by basing everything on the number 10.

The **metre** (unit of length) was defined as one forty millionth of the Earth's circumference. The standard metre was a bar with two marks on it, kept in Paris.

The **gram** (unit of mass) was defined as the mass of one cubic centimetre of water.

Units matter

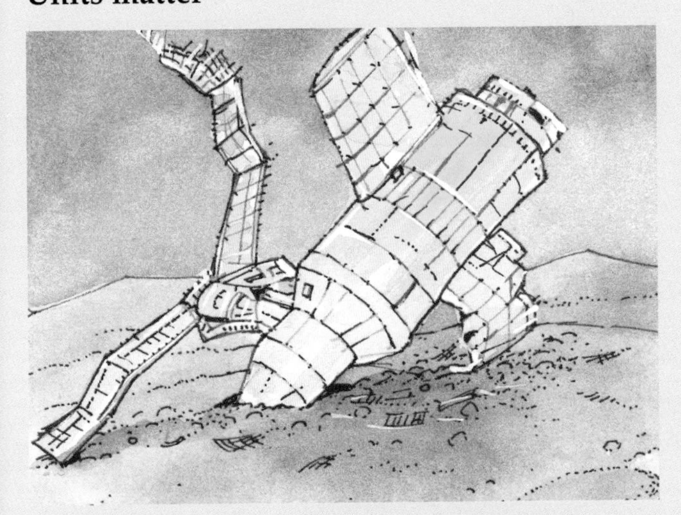

Using the right units is important. A very expensive space probe crashed on Mars because its controllers had fed it landing data in metres, while its computer was programmed for measurements in feet.

Setting new standards

The original definitions of the metric system are not accurate enough for modern scientific work. For example, a 'standard' metre bar will expand and contract slightly if its temperature varies, so it isn't really standard at all! That is why scientists have had to come up with new and better ways of defining units. Here, for example, is the modern definition of the metre:

The metre is the distance travelled by light in a vacuum in a time of $\frac{1}{299\,792\,458}$ seconds.

Of course, to define the metre like this, you have to have an exact definition of the second. That is rather complicated, but it is based on the rate of a particular vibration which can occur in a certain type of caesium atom.

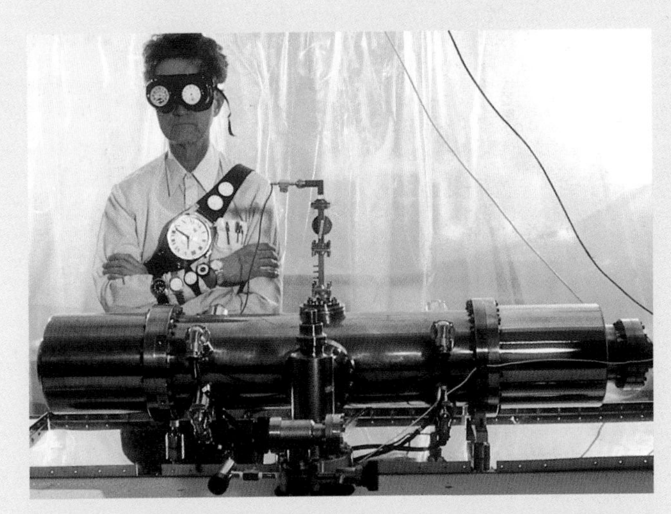

Believe it or not, this is a clock – a caesium atomic clock. You can't tell the time on it at a glance, but it is so accurate that it would gain or lose less than one second in 300 000 years. It is used as the standard for setting all other clocks.

- Scientists use SI units, based on the metric system. For example, the metre is a unit. The *quantity* it measures is length.

  Look up the following units in the index in this book. Find out what quantity each one measures:

  newton joule ampere watt

Questions on Chapter 1

1 Copy and complete the table shown below.

Measurement	Unit	Symbol
length	?	?
mass	?	?
?	?	s
?	ampere	?
temperature	?	?
area	—	?
?	—	m^3
?	newton	?

2 a How many mg are there in 1 g?
b How many g are there in 1 kg?
c How many mg are there in 1 kg?
d How many mm are there in 4 km?
e How many cm are there in 5 km?

3 Write down the values of:
a 300 cm in m
b 500 g in kg
c 1500 m in km
d 250 ms in s
e 0.5 s in ms
f 0.75 km in m
g 2.5 kg in g
h 0.8 m in mm

4 The volume of a rectangular block can be calculated using this equation:

volume = length × width × height

Using this information, copy and complete the table shown below.

Length	Width	Height	Volume of rectangular block
2 cm	3 cm	4 cm	?
5 cm	5 cm	?	100 cm^3
6 cm	?	5 cm	300 cm^3
?	10 cm	10 cm	500 cm^3

5

m	t	g	km	cm^3
kg	ml	kg/m^3	s	

Which of the above:
a are units of mass?
b are units of length?
c are units of volume?
d is a unit of time?
e is a unit of density?

6

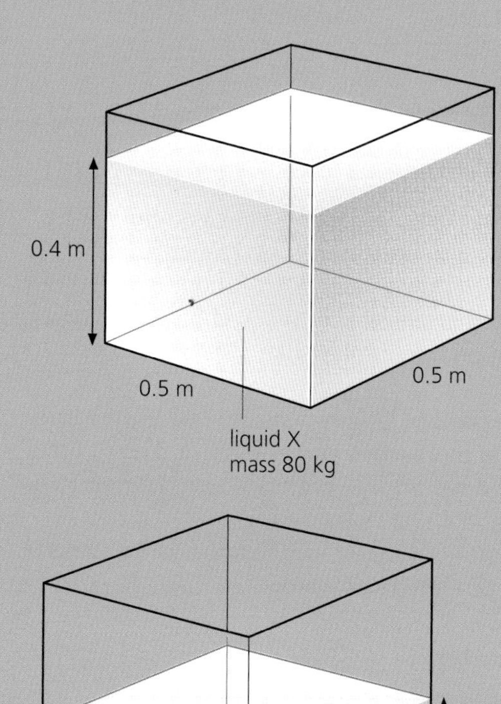

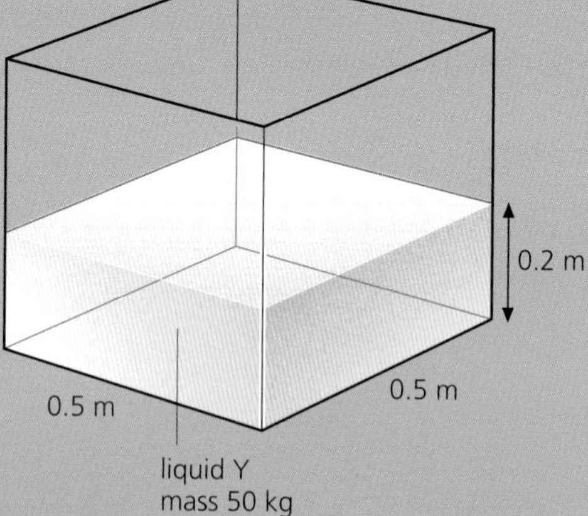

In the diagram above, the tanks contain two different liquids, X and Y.
a What is the volume of each liquid in m^3?
b If you had 1 m^3 of the liquid X, what would its mass be?
c Which liquid has the greater density?
d Use the chart of densities on page 13 to help you decide which liquids X and Y might be.

Chapter 2

Forces and motion

A bungee jumper leaps more than 180 metres from the top of a gorge. With nothing to oppose her fall, she would hit the water after 6 seconds, at a speed of 60 metres per second (135 m.p.h.). However, her fall is slowed by the resistance of the air rushing past her and eventually stopped by the pull of the bungee rope. ■

2.01 On the move

Speed

The police can check the speed of a car with a radar 'gun'. But there's a simpler method. Measure the distance between two points along a road – say, two lamp posts. Measure the time a car takes to travel between these points. Then calculate the speed:

$$\text{average speed} = \frac{\text{distance moved}}{\text{time taken}}$$

For example, a car which travels 50 metres in 5 seconds has an average speed of 10 metres per second – written 10 m/s for short.

On most journeys, the speed of a car varies, so the actual speed at any moment is usually different from the average speed. To find an actual speed, you have to find the distance travelled in the shortest time you could measure.

Velocity

As with speed, the unit of velocity is the metre per second (m/s). Velocity tells you the speed at which an object is travelling. But it also tells you the direction of travel:

$$\text{average velocity} = \frac{\text{distance moved in a particular direction}}{\text{time taken}}$$

In diagrams you can show a velocity with an arrow:

10 m/s →

Or you can use a + or – to give the direction. For example:

+10 m/s (10 m/s to the right)
–10 m/s (10 m/s to the left)

Quantities like velocity which have a direction as well as a value are called **vectors**.

What they mean

A steady speed of 10 m/s	A distance of 10 metres is travelled every second
A steady velocity of +10 m/s	A distance of 10 metres is travelled every second (to the right)
A steady acceleration of 5 m/s^2	Speed goes up by 5 metres/second every second
A steady retardation of 5 m/s^2	Speed goes down by 5 metres/second every second

Acceleration

From a standing start, a rally car can reach a velocity of 50 m/s in 10 s or less. It gains velocity very rapidly. It has a high **acceleration**.

Like velocity, acceleration is a vector. It is calculated as follows:

$$\text{acceleration} = \frac{\text{gain in velocity}}{\text{time taken}}$$

For example, if a car gains an extra 50 m/s of velocity in 10 seconds:

$$\text{acceleration} = \frac{50}{10}\ \text{m/s per second}$$
$$= 5\ \text{m/s per second}$$

which is written as $5\,\text{m/s}^2$ for short.

Retardation is the opposite of acceleration. If a car has a retardation of $5\,\text{m/s}^2$, it is *losing* 5 m/s of speed every second.

How to do calculations

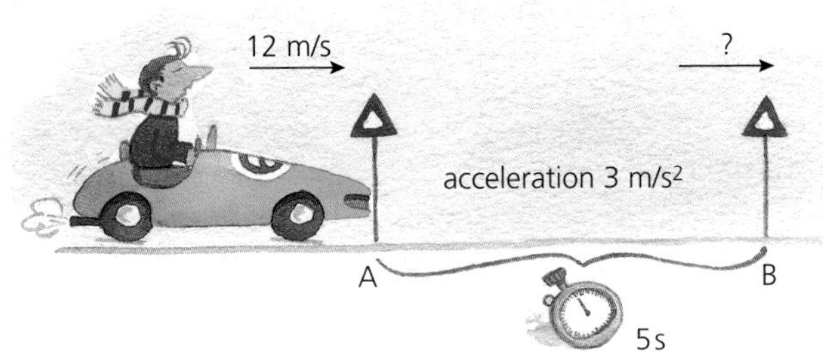

Example *The car in the diagram passes point A with a velocity of 12 m/s.*
The car has an acceleration of $3\,m/s^2$.
What is the velocity of the car as it passes point B 5 s later?

The car is gaining an extra 3 m/s of velocity every second.

So, in 5 s, it gains an extra 15 m/s of velocity on top of its original velocity of 12 m/s.

Its final speed on passing B is therefore 12 m/s + 15 m/s, which equals 27 m/s.

This could be written in another way:

final velocity = original velocity + extra velocity
or

final velocity
= original velocity + (acceleration × time)

The above equation can be written using symbols:

$$v = u + at$$

where
v is the final velocity, a is the acceleration, u is the original velocity, t is the time taken.

In the case of the car,

$$v = 12 + (5 \times 3)\ \text{m/s}$$
$$= 12 + 15\ \text{m/s}$$
$$= 27\,\text{m/s}$$

The equation works for retardation as well. Just call the retardation a negative acceleration. For example, a retardation of $5\,\text{m/s}^2$ is an acceleration of $-5\,\text{m/s}^2$.

Questions

1 a A car travels 500 m in 20 s; what is its average speed?
b Why is the actual speed of a car not usually the same as its average speed?

2 How far does the car on the right travel in **a** 1 s? **b** 5 s? **c** 10 s?
d How long does it take to travel 90 m?

3 A car has steady acceleration. The chart shows how its speed increases. Copy and complete the chart.

After	1 s	2 s	3 s	4 s	5 s	?
Speed	4 m/s	8 m/s	?	16 m/s	?	28 m/s
Steady acceleration = ? m/s^2						

4 Copy and complete:
A motor cycle has a steady _____ of $3\,\text{m/s}^2$. This means that every ___ its _____ increases by _____ .

5 An aircraft on its take-off run has a steady acceleration of $3\,\text{m/s}^2$.
a How much velocity does it gain in 10 s?
b If the aircraft has a velocity of 20 m/s as it passes a post, what is its velocity 10 s later?

6 A motor cycle takes 8 s to increase its velocity from 10 m/s to 30 m/s. What is its average acceleration?

7 A rally driver has 5 s to stop her car, which is travelling at a speed of 20 m/s. What is her average retardation?

2.02 Motion graphs

You can learn a lot from motion graphs. They can tell you how far something has travelled, how fast it is moving, and all the speed changes there have been.

Distance–time graphs

Imagine a car travelling along a road. There is a lamp post on the road. Every second, the distance of the car from the post is measured. Distance and time readings are recorded in a chart, and used to plot a graph.

Here are the results from just four possible journeys. One is hardly a journey at all.

Car travelling at
steady speed of 10 m/s

time in s	0	1	2	3	4	5
distance in m	0	10	20	30	40	50

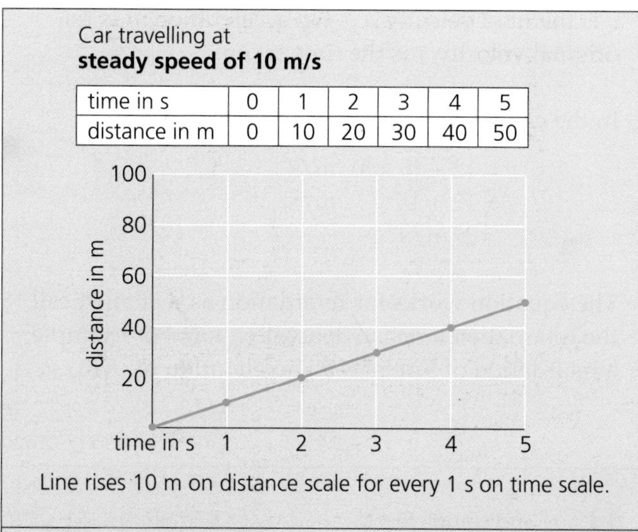

Line rises 10 m on distance scale for every 1 s on time scale.

Car travelling at
steady speed of 20 m/s

time in s	0	1	2	3	4	5
distance in m	0	20	40	60	80	100

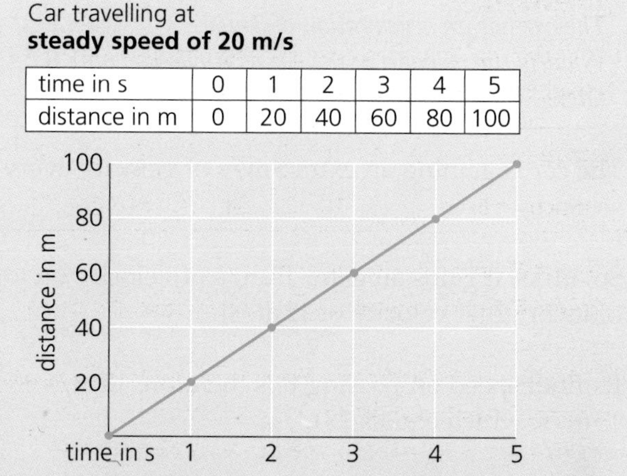

Line is steeper than before. It rises 20 m on distance scale for every 1 s on time scale.

Car **accelerating**

time in s	0	1	2	3	4	5
distance in m	0	10	25	45	70	100

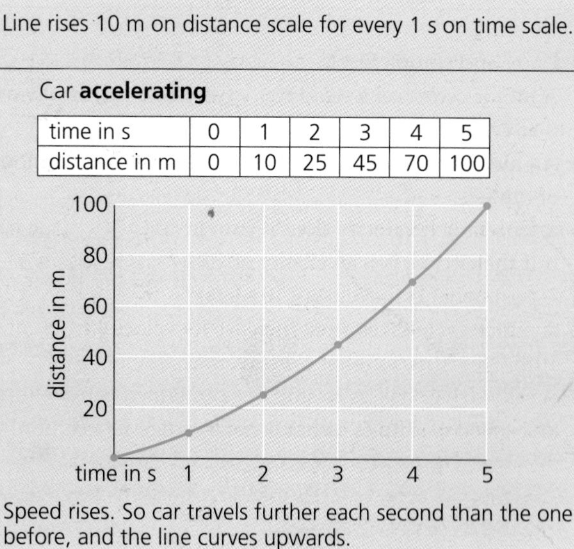

Speed rises. So car travels further each second than the one before, and the line curves upwards.

Car **stopped**

time in s	0	1	2	3	4	5
distance in m	50	50	50	50	50	50

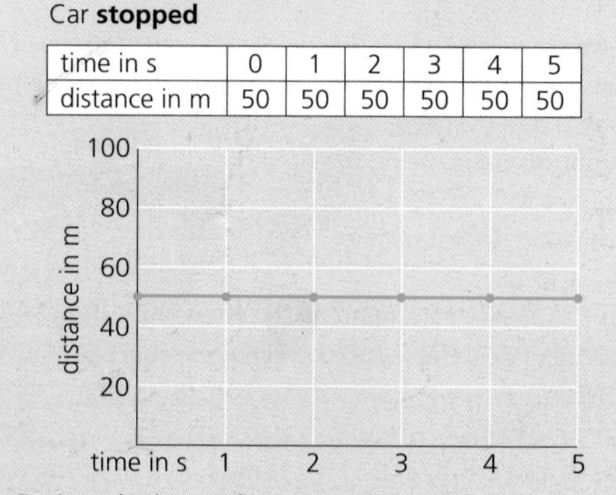

Car is parked 50 m from the post, so this distance stays the same.

Speed–time graphs

Don't confuse these with distance–time graphs. The shapes may look the same, but their meaning is very different.

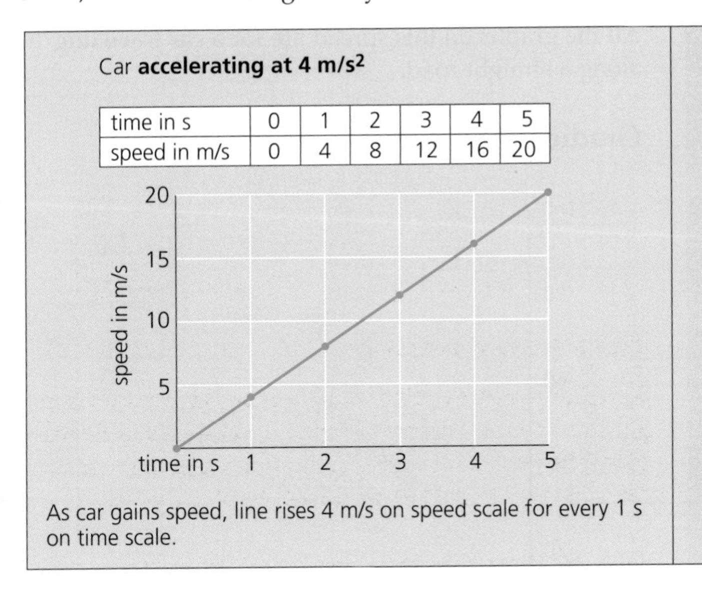

Car **accelerating at 4 m/s²**

time in s	0	1	2	3	4	5
speed in m/s	0	4	8	12	16	20

As car gains speed, line rises 4 m/s on speed scale for every 1 s on time scale.

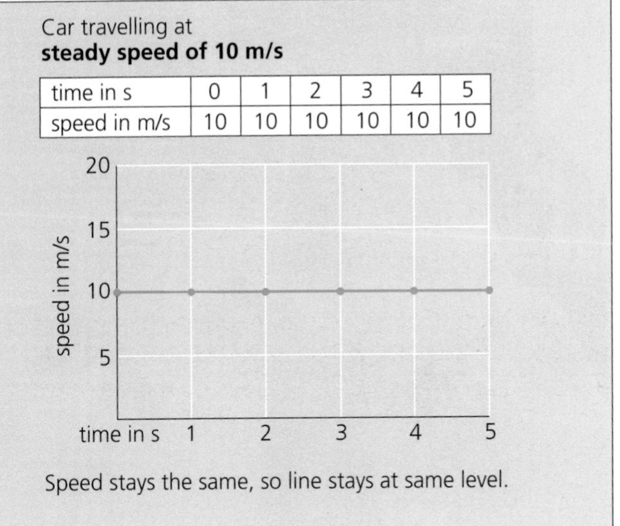

Car travelling at
steady speed of 10 m/s

time in s	0	1	2	3	4	5
speed in m/s	10	10	10	10	10	10

Speed stays the same, so line stays at same level.

Questions

1 A motor cycle passes a lamp post. Every second, its distance from the post is measured:

time in s	0	1	2	3	4	5	6	7	8	9
distance in m	0	3	10	22	34	46	54	56	56	56

a Plot a distance–time graph.

b Mark on your graph the sections where the motor cycle:
has acceleration; is travelling at a steady speed; has retardation; is stopped.

c How far does the motor cycle travel in the first 7 seconds?
What is its average speed over this period?

d How long does it take the motor cycle to travel from 10 m to 46 m? What distance does it cover? What is its average speed over this distance?

2 The graph shows a speed–time graph for another motor cycle.

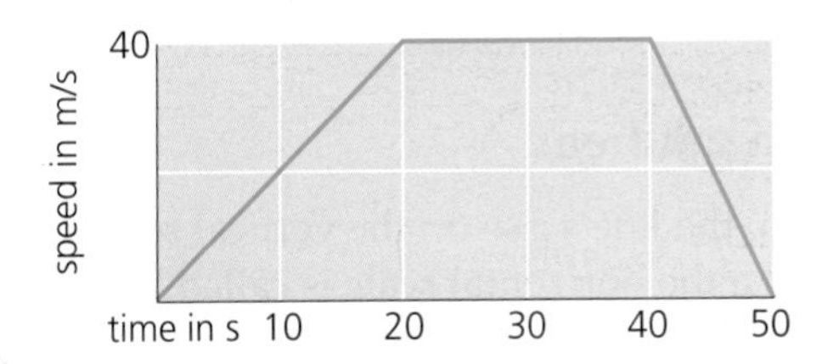

a What is the maximum speed of the motor cycle?

b For how many seconds does the motor cycle stay at its maximum speed?

c For how many seconds is the motor cycle actually moving?

d How much speed does the motor cycle gain in the first 20 seconds? How much speed does it gain every second?

e What is the retardation of the motor cycle during the last 10 seconds?

3 It takes a driver 10 minutes to get to work. She stops to buy a paper on the way, has a set of traffic lights on her route, and a short section of motorway. Sketch a typical speed–time graph for her journey, and don't let her break any speed limits.
(1 m/s is about 2 m.p.h.)

4 An ice skater skates once round an oval rink. He accelerates down the length of the rink, but takes the ends more slowly. He falls over once. Sketch a speed–time graph for him.

2.03 More motion graphs

This slide is steeper in some places than others. Many graphs can be like that as well, although with simple ones, the steepness doesn't change, and it is easy to measure.

Finding a gradient

On a graph, the line's rise on the vertical scale divided by its rise on the horizontal scale is called the **gradient**:

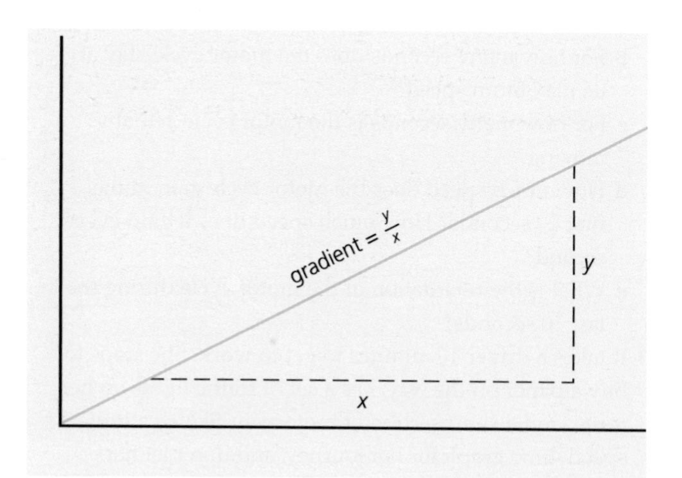

On a straight-line graph like this, the gradient has the same value wherever you measure x and y.
To work out the values of x and y, you must use the scale numbers on the two axes, and not the actual lengths on the paper.

All the graphs on this spread are for a car travelling along a straight road.

Gradient of a distance–time graph

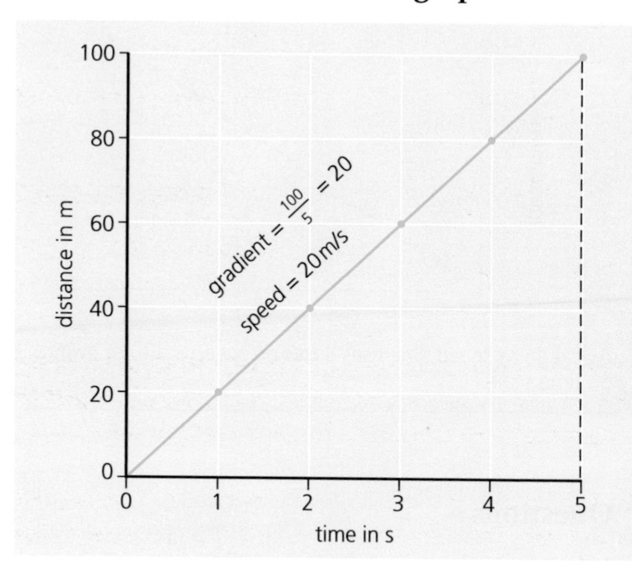

With the graph above, the gradient tells you how much extra distance is travelled every second. So:

The gradient of a distance–time graph gives the speed.

Gradient of a speed–time graph

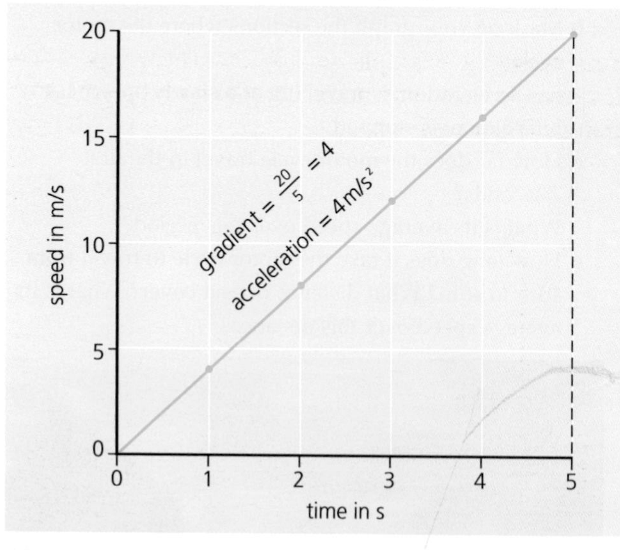

With the graph above, the gradient tells you how much the speed goes up every second. So:

The gradient of a speed–time graph gives the acceleration.

Area under a speed–time graph

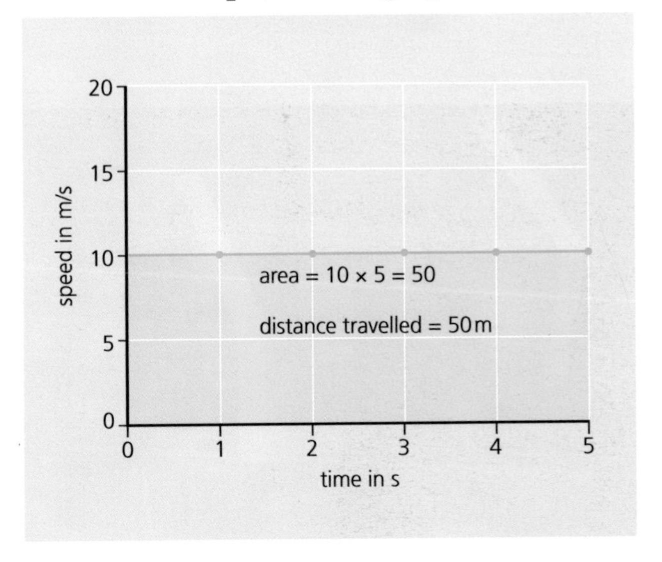

Look at the speed–time graph above. This car travels at a steady speed of 10m/s for 5 seconds. So it covers a distance of 10 × 5m, or 50m.

You could also get this result by calculating the area under the graph. However, when doing this, you must use the scale numbers on the axis. You aren't trying to find the 'real' area on the paper.
The idea also works for graph lines that are sloping or curved:

The area under a speed–time graph gives the distance travelled.

Here is another example. In this case, to find the distance travelled you need to know that the area of a triangle = $\frac{1}{2}$ × base × height:

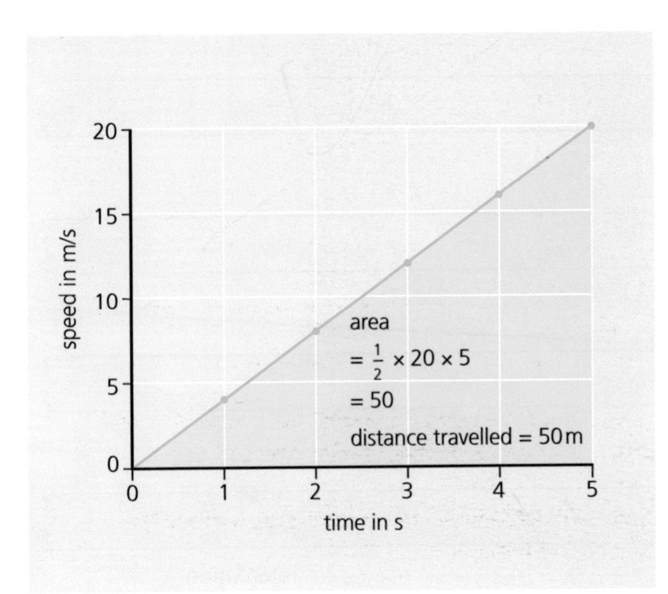

Velocity–time graphs

Speed and velocity are both measured in m/s. The difference between them is that velocity also gives you the direction of travel, often using a + or – .

In simple cases, for example, where a car keeps travelling in the same direction along a straight road, a velocity–time graph looks exactly the same as a speed–time graph. And you can use it to find an acceleration or distance in exactly the same way. The two types of graph only look different if the car changes its direction at some point.

Displacement–time graphs

Distance moved in a particular direction is called **displacement**. Displacement is a vector, and a + or – can be used to show its direction. In simple cases, where there is no change in direction, a displacement–time graph looks exactly the same as a distance–time graph. Its gradient gives the velocity.

Questions

1 What information can you get from:
a The gradient of a distance–time graph?
b The gradient of a speed–time graph?
c The area under a speed–time graph?

2 The speed–time graph below is for a car travelling along a straight road.
a What is the acceleration during the first 10 s?
b What is its retardation during the last 5 s?
c What is the distance travelled during the first 10 s?
d What is the total distance travelled?
e What is the time taken for the whole journey?
f What is the average speed for the whole journey?

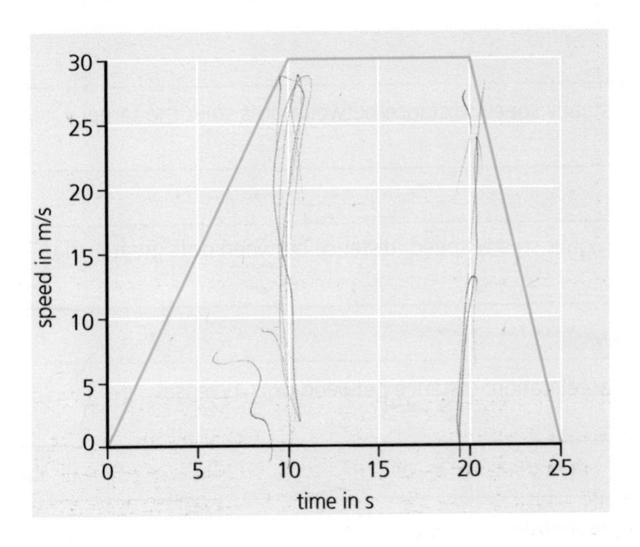

2.04 Timing with tape

The photograph on the right shows a 'black box' flight recorder from an aircraft. It records the motion of the aircraft in its electronic memory.

This spread is about recording motion, but on paper tape. A piece of paper tape is rather like a graph. It can give you a complete record of how something is moving. On these pages, however, it isn't a plane being studied, but a trolley moving on a laboratory bench.

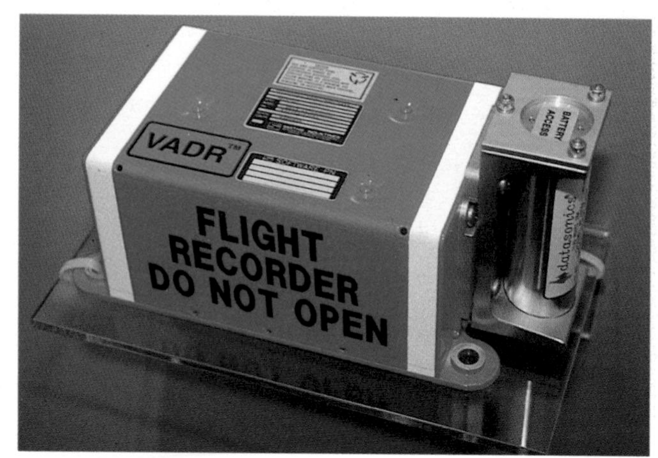

A 'black box' flight recorder records the motion of an aircraft.

Trolley experiments

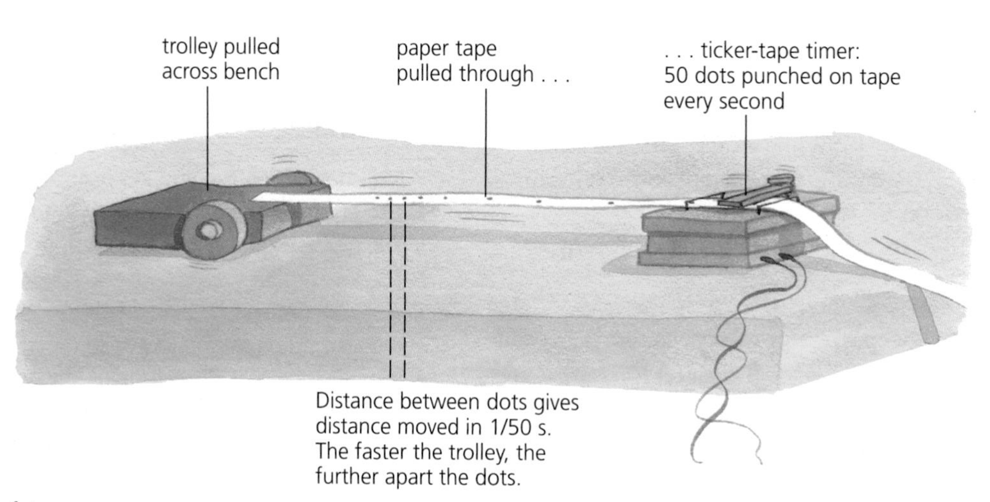

Examples of tapes

start

steady speed: distance between dots stays the same

higher steady speed: distance between dots greater than before

acceleration: distance between dots increases

acceleration — — — — — — — then — — — — — — — retardation

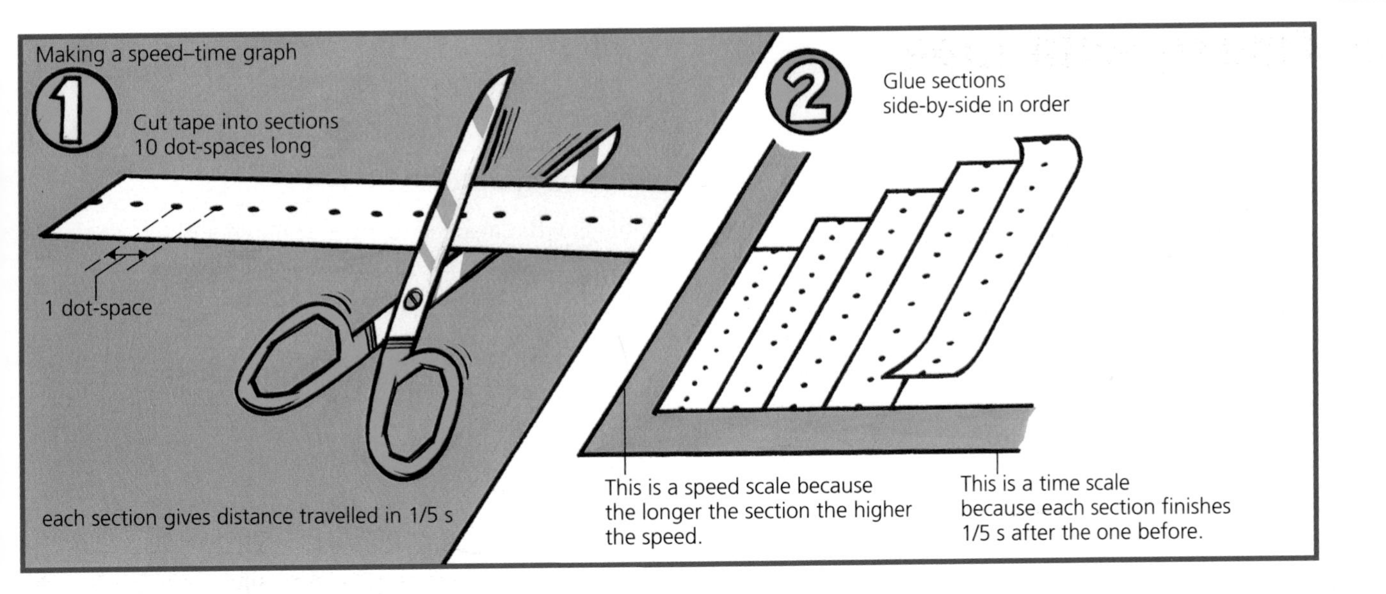

Questions

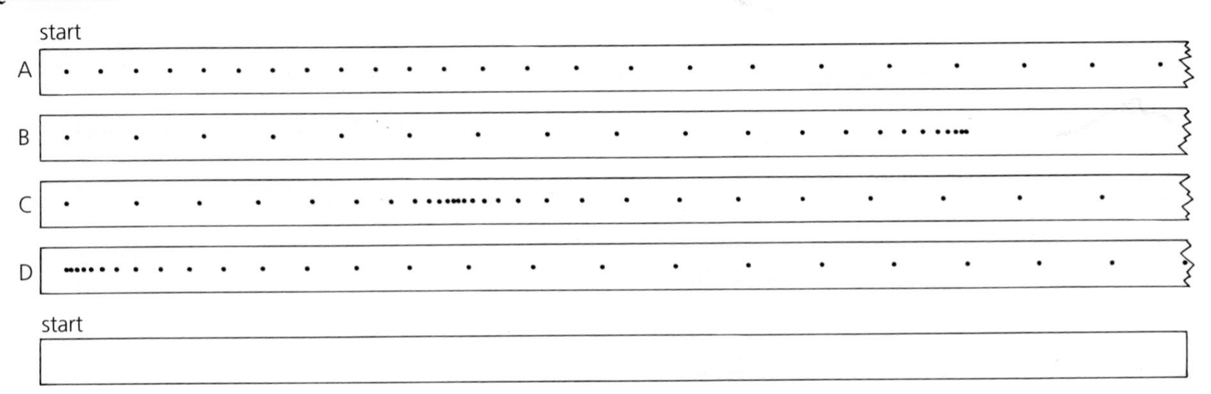

1 Which of the tapes above shows:

a acceleration, then a steady speed?

b retardation until stopped, then acceleration?

c a steady speed, then acceleration, then a higher steady speed?

2 A trolley travelling at a steady speed loses speed, stops, then accelerates. Copy the blank tape above. Mark in the pattern of dots you might expect to see.

3 In the questions which follow, make measurements on the paper tape shown below. The ticker-tape timer made 50 dots on paper tape every second. The distance from one dot to the next is called a **dot-space**.

a How long did it take the timer to make 5 dot-spaces?

b How many dot-spaces are there between A and B?

c How long did it take the tape to move from A to B?

d Use a mm ruler to measure the distance from A to B.

e What was the average speed (in mm/s) of the trolley between A and B?

f Measure the distance from C to D, then work out the average speed of the trolley between C and D.

g Section CD was completed exactly one second after section AB.
By how much did the speed of the trolley increase in this time?

h An acceleration of 1 mm/s² means that the speed increases by 1 mm/s every second.
What was the acceleration of the trolley in mm/s²?

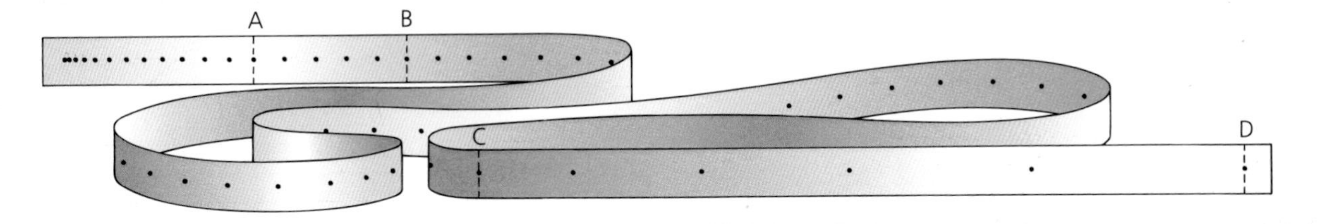

2.05 Falling with gravity

23rd March 1944

Airman survives $3\frac{1}{2}$ mile fall

Miraculous escape from blazing plane

To jump to his death, or be burnt alive. That was the decision facing Flight Lieutenant Nicholas Alkemade when his Lancaster bomber caught fire 10 000 feet above Oberkurchen, Germany. Unable to reach his parachute, he decided to jump. After a fall of nearly $3\frac{1}{2}$ miles, he crashed into the branches of a fir tree at over 100 m.p.h. before coming to rest in a bank of snow. Incredibly, he was able to walk away with only minor bruises.

When Flight Lieutenant Alkemade first left his aircraft, he fell towards the ground with an acceleration of 10m/s^2. Rushing air quickly reduced this acceleration. Otherwise, he would have hit the ground at over 700 m.p.h. (about 300 m/s).

Air resistance slows down some things more than others. It doesn't slow a falling rock very much. But it slows a feather a lot. Without air resistance, all things falling near the Earth would have the same acceleration of 10m/s^2. This is the **acceleration of free fall**, g.

So, without air resistance, anything dropped would speed up like this:

0 s	no speed
after 1 s	10 m/s
after 2 s	20 m/s
after 3 s	30 m/s

and so on.

Motion graphs

This is what a speed–time graph looks like for an object falling freely near the Earth's surface, assuming that there is no air resistance to slow it:

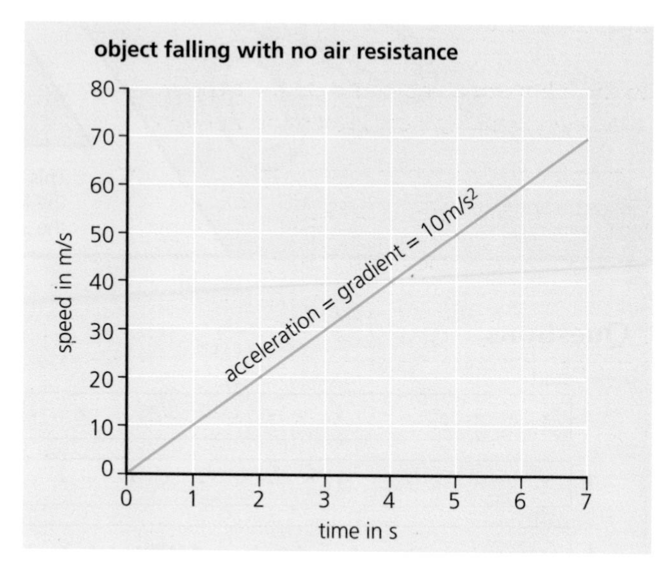

The gradient of a speed–time graph gives the acceleration. In this case, the gradient is g, 10m/s^2.

In practice, there is air resistance. So a falling object starts with an acceleration of g, but this gets less and less as the object gets faster and faster and air resistance increases. Finally, the acceleration falls to zero, and the object reaches a steady speed, called its **terminal speed**. This is shown below. There is more about terminal speed later in the book.

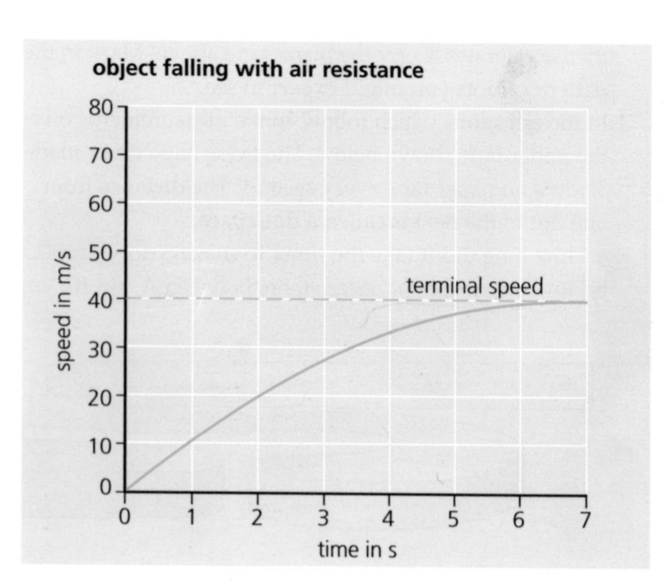

Measuring g

To find a value for g, you could drop a metal ball, measure the height through which it falls, h, and the time taken, t, and then use this information to calculate a result, as shown below.

The calculation below uses typical height and time measurements, and assumes that air resistance has no noticeable effect.

In the laboratory, you could do the experiment more accurately using the equipment on the right.

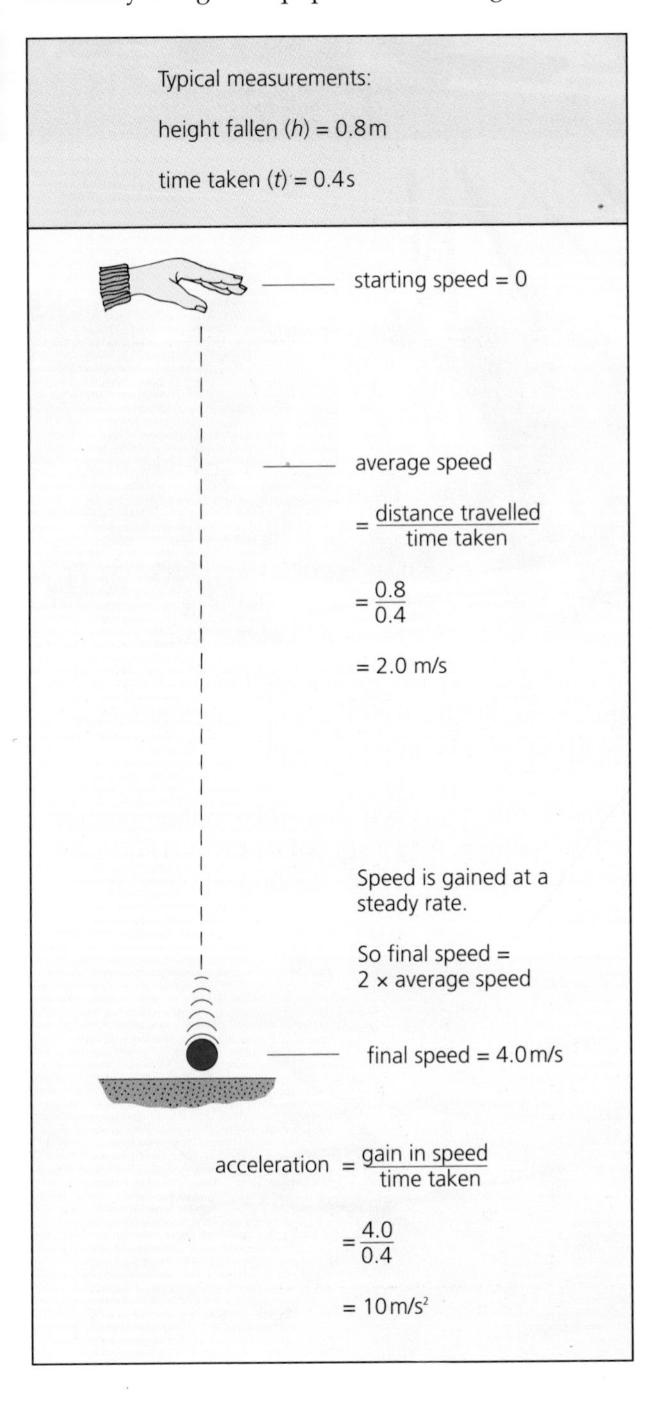

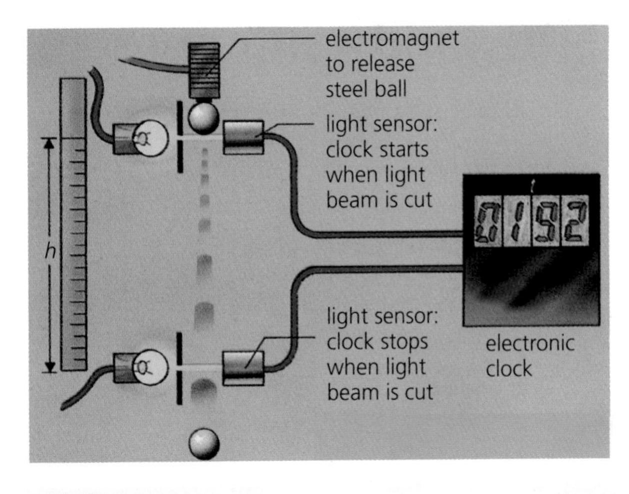

Questions

Assume $g = 10\,\text{m/s}^2$.

1 Is each of the following TRUE or FALSE?
Without air resistance:
- **a** A heavy stone falls more quickly than a light stone.
- **b** Near the Earth, falling things all accelerate at the same rate.
- **c** Dropped from the same height, a heavy stone takes exactly the same time to reach the ground as a light stone.

2 Copy the chart, filling in the missing information about the falling stone:

time in s	0	1	2		?	?
speed in m/s	0	10	?		40	50
speed gained every second = ?						
acceleration = ?						

3 The ball below left has been falling for 5 seconds.
- **a** What is its acceleration?
- **b** What is its speed?
- **c** What is its average speed?
- **d** What height has it fallen?

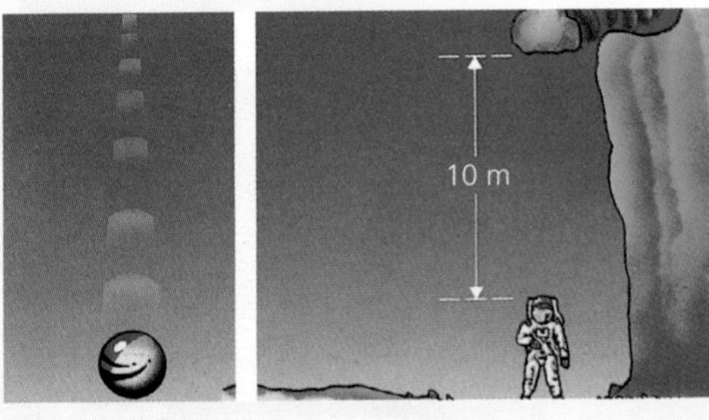

4 The astronaut above right is on a planet where the acceleration of free fall is only $1\,\text{m/s}^2$. It takes him 4 seconds to move sideways. Will he be able to escape the falling rock?

2.06 Thrills and spills

These cars can reach 60 m.p.h. in just three seconds. That's an acceleration of $10\,m/s^2$, the same as the acceleration of free fall, g.

If you were in the driving seat, you would feel the acceleration as a push in the back – a push as strong as your own weight.

These rides give you the effects of high acceleration by making you travel round tight bends very fast.

This roller-coaster ride lasts just over a minute. You experience speeds up to 25 m/s (50 m.p.h.), and acceleration up to $3g$.

High acceleration can drain blood from your head to your feet and make you 'black out'. But not during this ride. Sitting with your knees up stops the rush of blood to your feet.

A $3g$ ride. You may feel most scared at the high point of the swing. But it's near the low point that you are most firmly pushed into your seat.

For this $5g$ ride, you need skill and a million pounds' worth of training. And a special suit which squeezes your limbs tightly to reduce the flow of blood from your head.

If another car crashes into the back of yours, a headrest can save you from serious neck injury. It makes sure that your head accelerates forward at the same rate as the rest of your body.

Why not build cars stronger?
In a crash, it's safer for the passengers if the front of the car *does* collapse. It means lower deceleration and less risk of injury. But the metal body must form a strong 'cage' round the passengers to stop them being crushed.

The safest way to travel is backwards.
If a plane makes a crash landing, the deceleration can be very high. Rear-facing seats give the best chance of survival. This is why the RAF fit them to their transport aircraft. But airlines haven't taken up the idea.

Most thrill machine rides have plenty of built-in safety. If one metal part breaks, there are still others left to support you. But how many fairground rides can you think of where your safety depends on the strength of just one metal part?

If rear-facing seats are safer, why has no airline decided to 'go it alone' and fit them? Can you suggest reasons?

In thrill machine rides, you can experience accelerations of 3*g* or more. But without headrests, accelerations like this wouldn't be safe. Why not?

2.07 Forces in action

A force is a push or a pull. It is a vector. Rolls Royce use a test rig like the one on the right to measure one rather large force – the forward thrust from a jet engine. Other examples of forces include:

- weight – the downward pull of gravity;
- tension – the force in a stretched string or rope;
- friction – the force that tries to stop materials sliding across each other;
- air resistance – one type of friction.

Like all forces, the force from a jet engine is measured in a unit called a **newton** (**N**). Some typical force values are shown below.

A larger unit of force is the **kilonewton** (**kN**):

$$1\,\text{kN} = 1000\,\text{N}$$

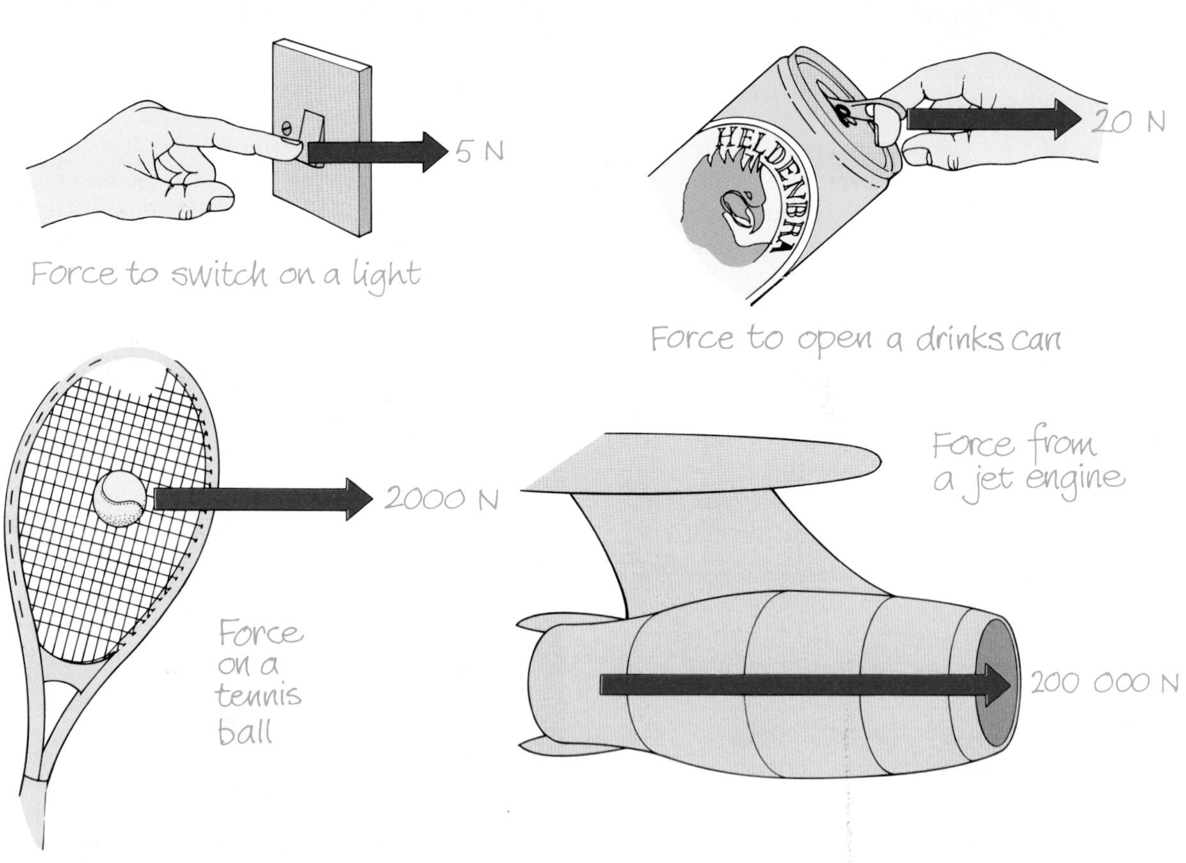

Small forces can be measured with a **spring balance** (or **newtonmeter**). The greater the force, the more the spring is then stretched and the higher the reading on the scale.

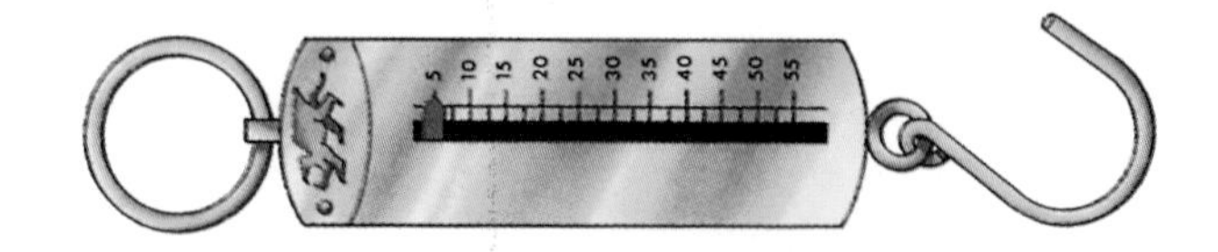

Combining forces

On Earth, very few things ever have just one force acting on them. Usually, there are at least two and often more. When two or more forces act through the same point, their combined effect is called the **resultant force** (or just the **resultant**). In other words, the resultant is the force which, by itself, would have the same effect as all the others acting together.

The chart below gives some examples of the resultant of two forces. In the first one, the two forces are equal but opposite, and cancel each other out. So there is no resultant force.

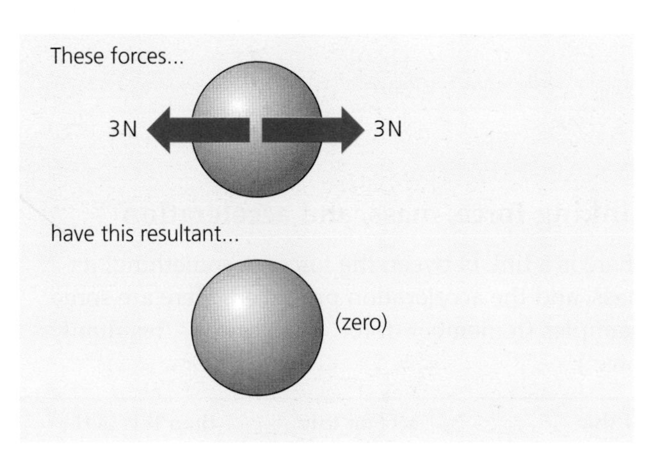

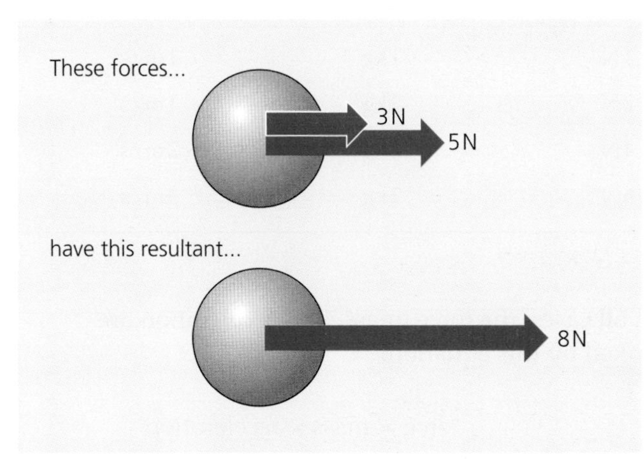

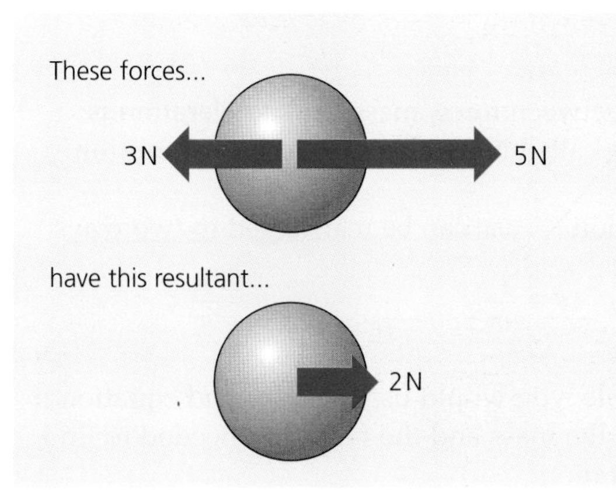

There are several forces acting on this person. Their resultant pulls her forward.

Questions

1 a What unit is used for measuring force?

b In the diagram on the opposite page, what is the force from the jet engine in kN?

2 Work out the resultant of each of the pairs of forces below. (As well as giving the size of the resultant, remember to say what its direction is as well.)

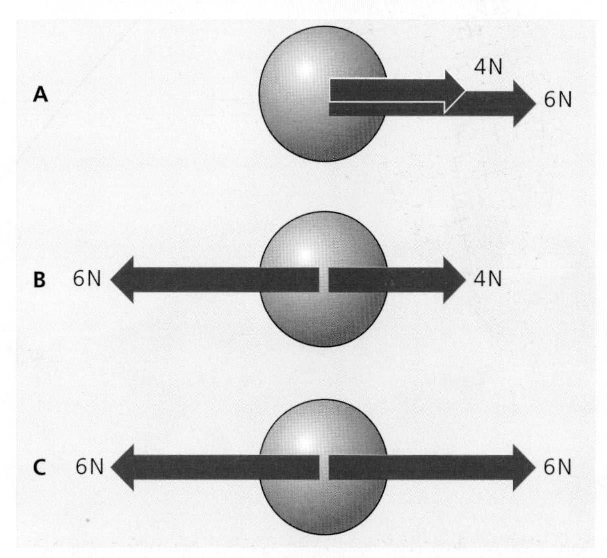

3 Look at the photograph at the top of the page. Write down where all the forces that are acting on the person who is being pulled along are coming from.

2.08 Force, mass, and acceleration

It can take half an hour for a massive tanker like this to reach full speed – and half an hour for it to stop when the engines are put in reverse. Like all masses, the tanker resists any change in velocity – in other words, it resists acceleration. To make a mass accelerate, there must be a force on it.

Of course, most things have several forces on them, so what really matters is the size of the *resultant* force – the single force which has the same effect as all the others acting together.

A small force on a large mass produces very little acceleration.

Force is measured in newtons (N).

Mass is measured in kilograms (kg).

Acceleration is measured in metres per second squared (m/s^2). For example:

If a car increases its velocity by 2 m/s every second, then its acceleration is $2\,m/s^2$.

Linking force, mass, and acceleration

There is a link between the force on something, its mass, and the acceleration produced. Here are some examples (remember 'force' really means 'resultant force'):

If this force...	acts on this mass...	then this is the acceleration...
1 N	1 kg	$1\,m/s^2$
2 N	2 kg	$1\,m/s^2$
4 N	2 kg	$2\,m/s^2$
6 N	2 kg	$3\,m/s^2$

In all cases, the force, mass, and acceleration are linked by this equation:

force = mass × acceleration

In symbols: $F = ma$

This link between force, mass, and acceleration is sometimes called **Newton's second law of motion**.

The equation $F = ma$ can be rearranged in two ways:

$$a = \frac{F}{m} \qquad m = \frac{F}{a}$$

For example, you would use the left-hand equation if you knew the mass and the force, but needed to find the acceleration.

Acceleration problem

Example *What is the acceleration of the model car below?*

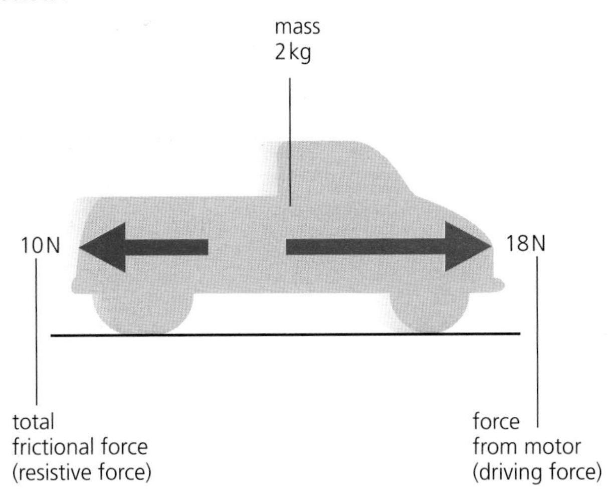

First, work out the resultant force on the car. A force of 18 N to the *right* combined with a force of 10 N to the *left* is equivalent to a force of (18–10) N to the *right*. So the resultant force is 8 N.

Next, use the equation $F = ma$ to find the acceleration, a. To do this, you need the equation in this form:

$$a = \frac{F}{m}$$

So $a = \frac{8}{2} = 4$ (leaving out units for simplicity)

So the car's acceleration is 4 m/s^2.

Defining the newton

A 1 newton force acting on a 1 kilogram mass produces an acceleration of 1 m/s^2. This simple result isn't an accident. The newton was *defined* in that way.

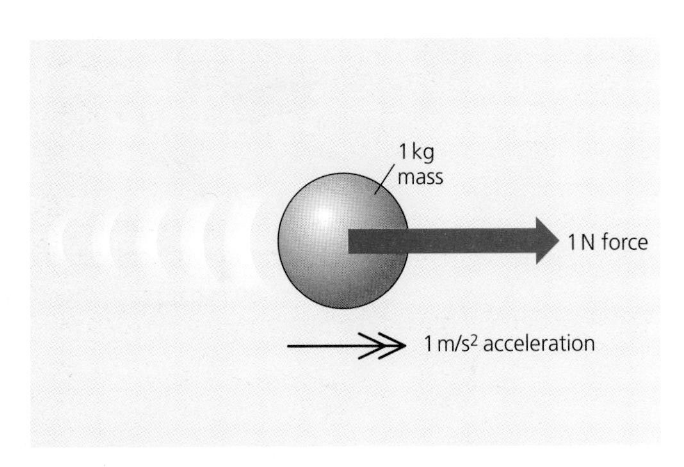

1 newton is the force needed to give a mass of 1 kilogram an acceleration of 1 m/s^2.

Questions

1

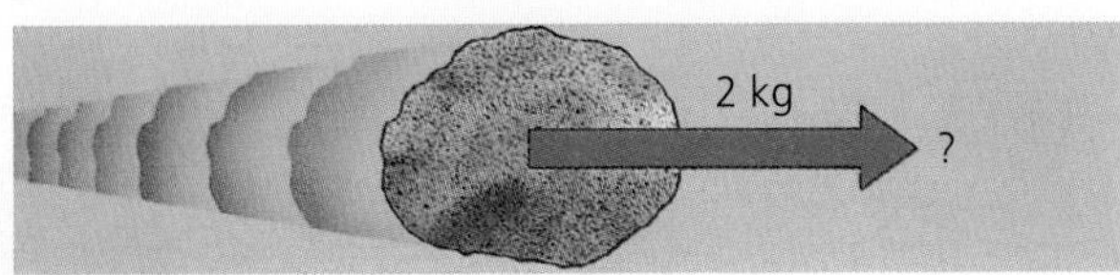

What force is needed to make the rock accelerate at:
a 2 m/s^2? **b** 0.5 m/s^2? **c** 4 m/s^2?

2 In an experiment with a 0.5 kg trolley, someone measures the pulling force, calculates the acceleration, writes down the values '10' and '5', but forgets to note which is which.
Can you decide and add the correct units?

3

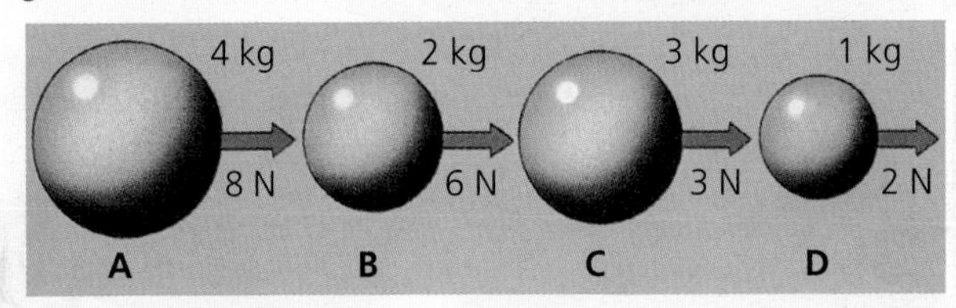

a Which masses have the same acceleration?
b Which mass has most acceleration?
c Which mass has least acceleration?

4 The three vehicles below are among the most powerful of their type. If there is no friction:
a Which wins the contest for the best acceleration?
b Which is the loser?

Boeing 747:
mass 400 000 kg
force from engines 800 000 N

Porsche 911:
mass 1300 kg
force from engines 7800 N

Honda 1000:
mass 300 kg
force from engines 3000 N

5 Look at the model car in the acceleration problem, top left on this page.
What would the acceleration of the car be:
a if there were no resisting force?
b if the resisting force were only 6 N?
c if the resisting force were 18 N?

2.09 Speedy delivery

Out of the way!

This lead blocker plays for the Chicago Bears. His job is to charge through the defence lines, clearing gaps for the running backs to pass through. Mass is the secret of his success. At 145 kilograms, he has more than twice the mass of the average male. And once he starts running he is extremely difficult to stop.

This is someone else who needs mass as well as strength. When she pushes the shot forward, there is a backward push on her body which slows her down and reduces the speed of the shot. The more mass she has, the less effect this backward push has.

Who wins over 1500 metres?

Swimmers lose out because water resistance is much higher than air resistance. Cyclists are fastest of all. And even faster if there's another vehicle in front to reduce the air resistance. The highest speed ever reached on a bicycle was 63 metres/second (140 m.p.h.) – behind a car with a windshield on the back.

Fast service

Could you work out the speed of the racket from this photograph?
If not, why not?

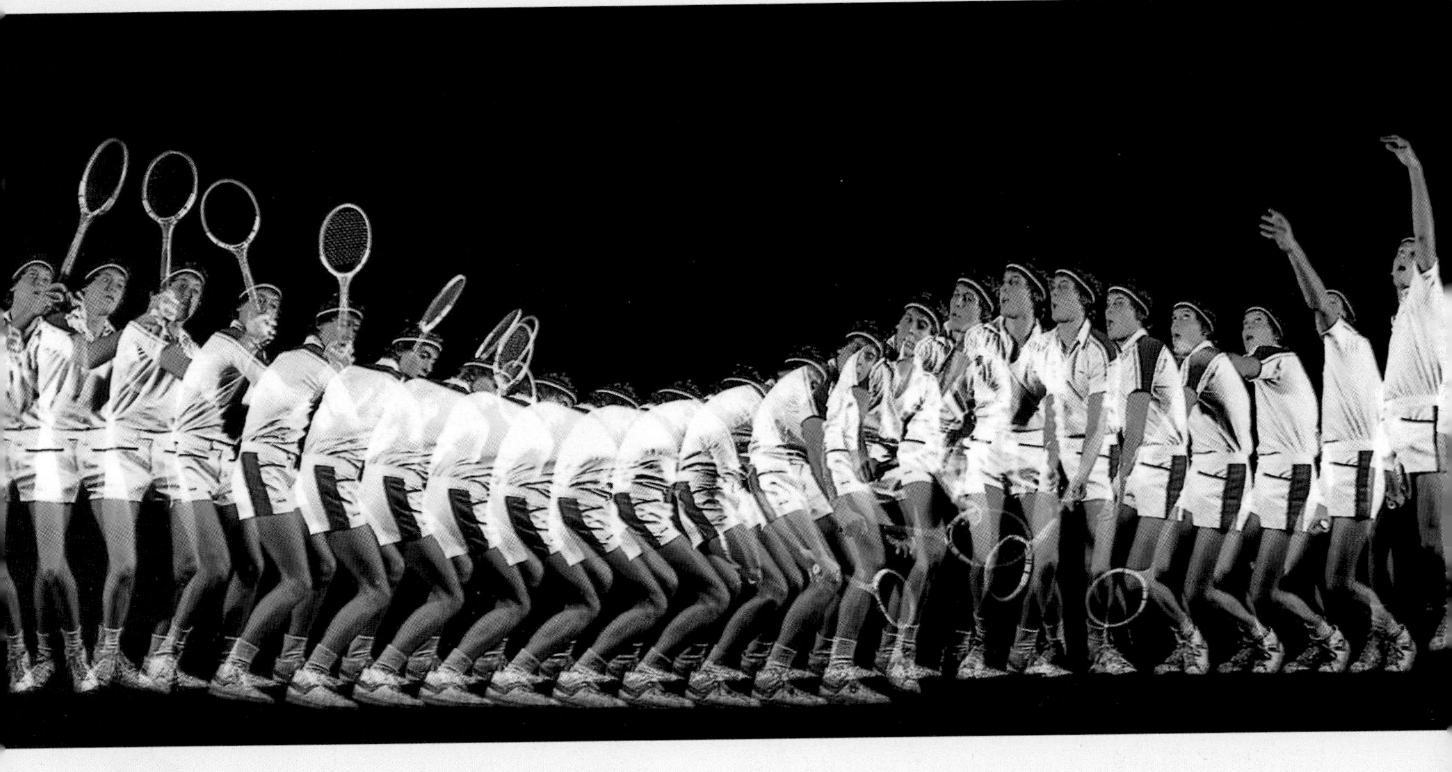

Getting the elbow

A top player uses a racket with tight strings to help him serve the ball really fast. He tries to hit the ball near the centre of the racket. Otherwise, the forces can injure his elbow.

An ordinary player uses racket strings that are less tight. The strings stretch more when the ball is hit, which cuts the speed down. But, if the player hits the ball off-centre, the forces on the elbow are small and not so damaging.

Explain why:

- runners can travel faster than swimmers;
- cyclists can travel faster than runners.

In Olympic speed events, competitors need to keep their air resistance as low as possible. Try to find out how the following reduce their air resistance:

- sprint cyclists;
- speed skaters;
- swimmers.

Describe what happens to the speed of a tennis racket from the beginning of a serve to the end.

Make a list of the games players or athletes for whom plenty of mass is:

- an advantage;
- a disadvantage.

2.10 Weight: the pull of gravity

Does gravity always pull things downwards? Not according to cartoonists. They often use 'plausible impossibles' – things which seem reasonable, but aren't possible because they break the laws of physics. Walking off a cliff is probably the most well known. The character doesn't fall until he realizes that he isn't standing on anything.

Gravitational force

Hang something from the end of a spring balance and you can measure the downward pull from the Earth. The pull is called a **gravitational force**.

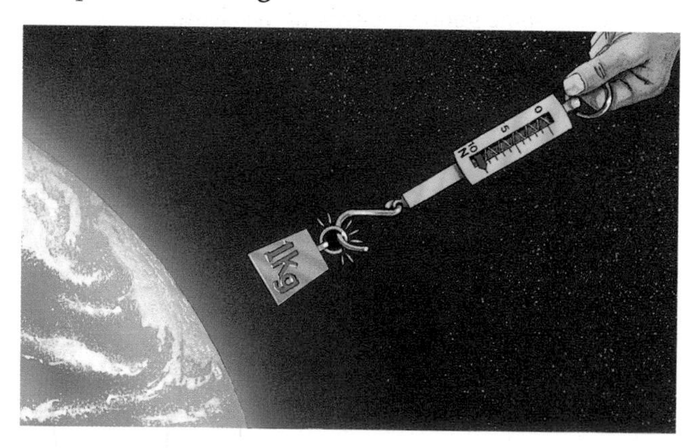

No one knows what causes gravitational force. But several things are known about it:

- All masses attract each other.
- The greater the masses, the stronger the pull.
- The closer the masses, the stronger the pull.

The pull between small masses is far too weak to measure – less than one millionth of a newton between you and the person next to you for example. But the Earth has such a huge mass that the gravitational pull is strong enough to hold most things firmly on the ground.

Weight

Weight is another name for the gravitational force from the Earth. As weight is a force, its unit is the newton. On Earth, each kilogram of matter weighs 10 newtons. The **gravitational field strength**, called g, is 10 newtons per kilogram (N/kg).

weight (N) = mass (kg) × g

People often use the word 'weight' when they really mean 'mass'. The person in the diagram doesn't 'weigh' 50 kilograms. He has a *mass* of 50 kilograms and a *weight* of 500 newtons.

Is there a link?

On Earth, the acceleration of free fall is 10 m/s², there is a gravitational force of 10 newtons on every kilogram.

These two facts are connected.
Try using the equation $F = m \times a$ to work out the acceleration of the two masses below.

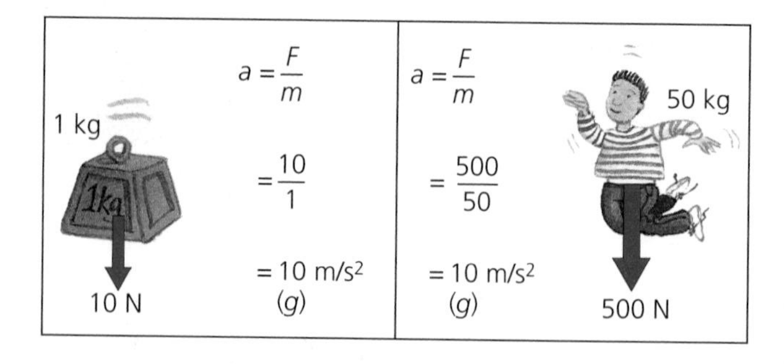

In each case, the acceleration is the same: g.
So you can think of g:
– as an acceleration of 10 m/s².
– as a gravitational field strength of 10 N/kg.

How to lose weight quickly

Go to the Moon. Even better, go deep into space, far away from all planets.

As different planets have different masses and sizes, your weight would vary from one place in the Universe to another. Take the case of a person with a mass of 50 kg:

	mass	weight
deep in space	50 kg	zero
near surface of the Moon	50 kg	80 N
near surface of Jupiter	50 kg	2700 N
near a black hole (a collapsed star whose gravitational pull is so great that even light cannot escape)	50 kg	100 million million N

Travelling around space isn't going to get rid of the kilograms. Weight may vary, but mass stays the same. On the Moon, for example, the gravitational pull is much less than on Earth. But the amount of matter in something is just the same. And it is just as difficult to speed up or slow down.

Questions

1 Copy the following, and fill in the blanks:

a ___ is another name for the gravitational ___ on something.

b Weight is measured in ___.

c All masses ___ each other. The closer the masses, the ___ the pull between them.

2 Write down the weights of the following masses on Earth:

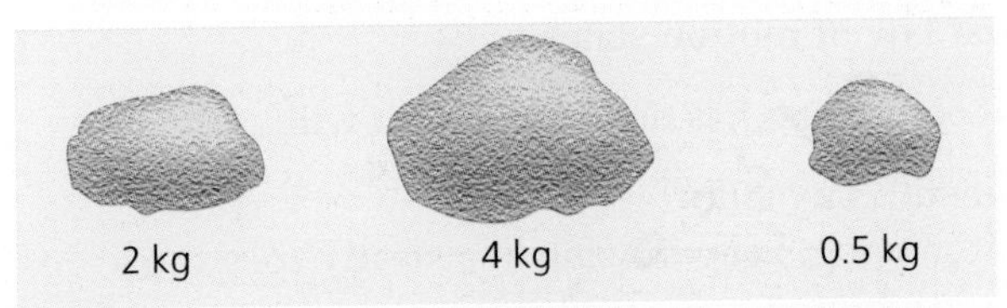

3 'A bag of sugar weighs one kilogram.'
People might say this in everyday language. But the statement is wrong. Why is it wrong? What should it say?

4

A	B
$g = 10\ m/s^2$	$g = 10\ N/kg$

Describe in words what A and B tell you about a mass of one kilogram.

5 Aliens land on several planets, including Earth.
Here is some information about the aliens:

alien	mass in kg	weight in N
A	40	80
B	20	200
C	10	200
D	20	40

a Which alien landed on Earth?

b Which two aliens landed on the same planet?

c The aliens have to jump from their spacecraft when they land.
Which alien will fall with the greatest acceleration?

d If all the aliens came to Earth, which would weigh least?

6 A 10 kilogram lump of rock weighs 16 N on the Moon.

a What is the acceleration of free fall on the Moon?

b What is the gravitational field strength on the Moon?

c How much would the rock weigh on Earth?

2.11 Balanced forces

The spacecraft *Pioneer 10* was launched around thirty years ago. Now deep in space, it doesn't need engines to keep it moving. With no forces to slow it, it will keep moving for ever.

Sir Isaac Newton was the first to describe how things would move if no forces were acting on them. His **first law of motion** states:

> If something has no force on it, it will:
>
> if still, stay still;
> if moving, keep moving at a steady speed in a straight line.

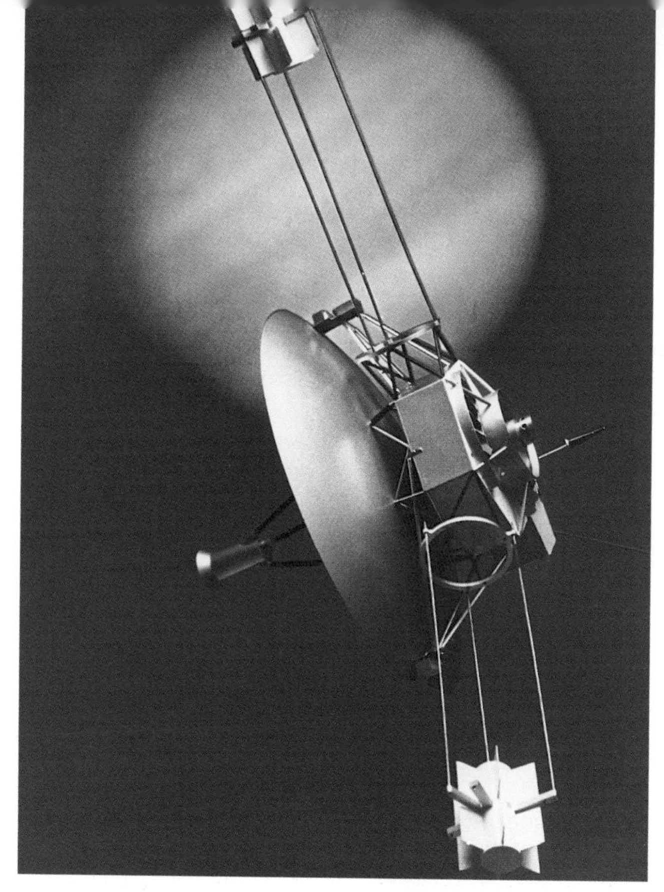

Pioneer 10

Slowed by friction

On Earth, unpowered vehicles quickly come to rest – slowed by the force of friction. **Friction** is the force that tries to stop materials sliding across each other. There is friction between your hands when you rub them together, and friction between your shoes and the ground when you walk on it.

Brakes use friction. If you apply the brakes on a bike, friction between the rubber brake blocks and the wheel rims slows the wheels down. When materials slide across each other like this, friction heats them up. It also wears away their surfaces.

Fluid friction

Liquids and gases are called **fluids**. They can also cause friction. When a car is travelling fast on a motorway, air resistance is by far the largest frictional force pulling against it. Fluid friction increases with speed, so, for a moving vehicle, more speed means more air resistance.

Using friction

Friction is needed to give your shoes grip on the ground.

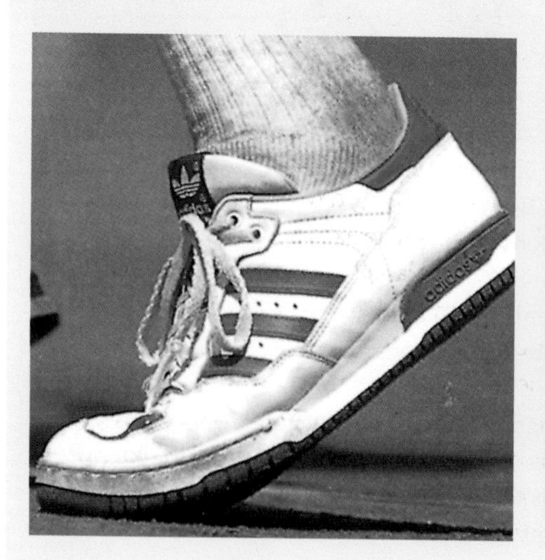

Reducing friction

Car bodies are designed so that the air flow is as smooth as possible. Less air resistance means less wasted fuel.

Forces in balance

Most things have several forces acting on them. For example, everything feels the pull of gravity, and moving things have friction trying to slow them down. Sometimes, the forces on something all cancel each other out. Then it behaves as if it has no force on it at all, and obeys Newton's first law.

When the man stands on the plank, it sags, until the springiness of the wood produces enough upward force to oppose his weight. Then the forces cancel, so the man stays still. The ground isn't as springy as the plank, but it too produces an upward force to equal your weight when you stand on it.

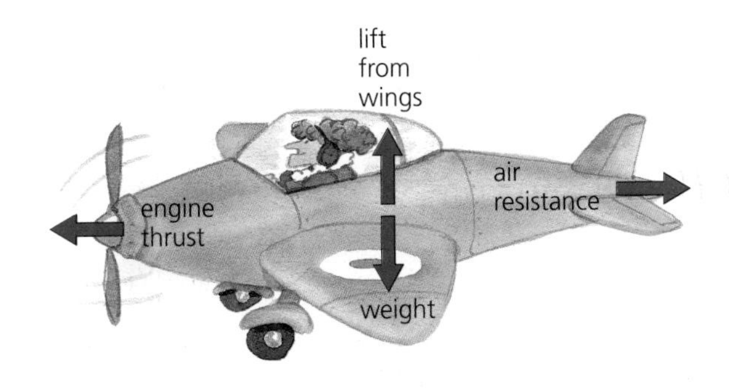

The aircraft is moving through the air at high speed. The weight of the aircraft is balanced by the lift from the wings. And air resistance is balanced by the thrust from the engine. The forces all cancel, so the aircraft keeps moving at a steady speed in a straight line.

If the thrust were *greater* than the air resistance, the aircraft would *gain* speed, and not keep a steady speed.

Terminal speed

As a skydiver falls, the air resistance increases as her speed rises. Eventually, air resistance is enough to balance her weight. If she weighs 500 newtons, then the air resistance rises to 500 newtons. She stops accelerating and falls with a maximum speed called her **terminal speed**. This is usually about 60 metres/second, though the actual value depends on air conditions, as well as her size, shape and weight.

If air resistance balances the skydiver's weight, why doesn't she stay still? There wouldn't be any air resistance unless she was moving.

Surely her weight is greater than air resistance if she is travelling downwards? No. If it were, she would gain speed, instead of keeping a steady speed.

Questions

Assume $g = 10\,\text{N/kg}$.

1 If something has no forces acting on it at all, what happens to it if it is:
a still? **b** moving?

2 Say whether friction is USEFUL or a NUISANCE in each of the following cases:
a a car tyre on the road;
b sledge runners on snow;
c a ship moving through the water;
d brake blocks on a cycle wheel;
e shoes on a pavement;
f a skydiver falling through air;
g someone's hand holding a screwdriver;
h a wheel spinning on an axle.
Which of these are examples of fluid friction?

3 A skydiver weighing 600N falls through the air at a steady speed of 50m/s.
a Draw the diver, showing the forces acting on him.
b What name is given to his steady speed?
c What is the air resistance on him, in newtons?
d What is his mass?
e Why does he lose speed if he opens his parachute?

2.12 Speed and safety

Accidents like this can occur because people are driving too fast for the conditions and too close to the car in front. The performance of the tyres and brakes may also be factors.

Stopping distance

In an emergency, the driver of a car may have to react quickly and apply the brakes to stop the car.
The **stopping distance** depends on two things:

- The **thinking distance**. This is how far the car travels *before* the brakes are applied, while the driver is still reacting.
- The **braking distance**. This is how far the car then travels, *after* the brakes have been applied.

It takes an average driver more than half a second to react and press the brake pedal. This is the driver's **reaction time**. During this time, the car does not slow down. For example:

If a car has a speed of 20 m/s (metres per second), and the driver's reaction time is 0.6 seconds (s):

distance travelled = speed × time

So: thinking distance = speed × reaction time
$= 20 \times 0.6$
$= 12$

So the thinking distance is 12 m.

The chart below shows the stopping distances for a car at different speeds. They are average figures for a dry road. The actual stopping distance may be *greater*. Here are some of the reasons why:

The *driver* may have a slower reaction time, due to:

- tiredness;
- poor weather conditions affecting visibility;
- the effects of alcohol or drugs.

The *brakes* may take longer to stop the car, due to:

- a wet or icy road;
- a heavy load in the car;
- worn brakes or tyres.

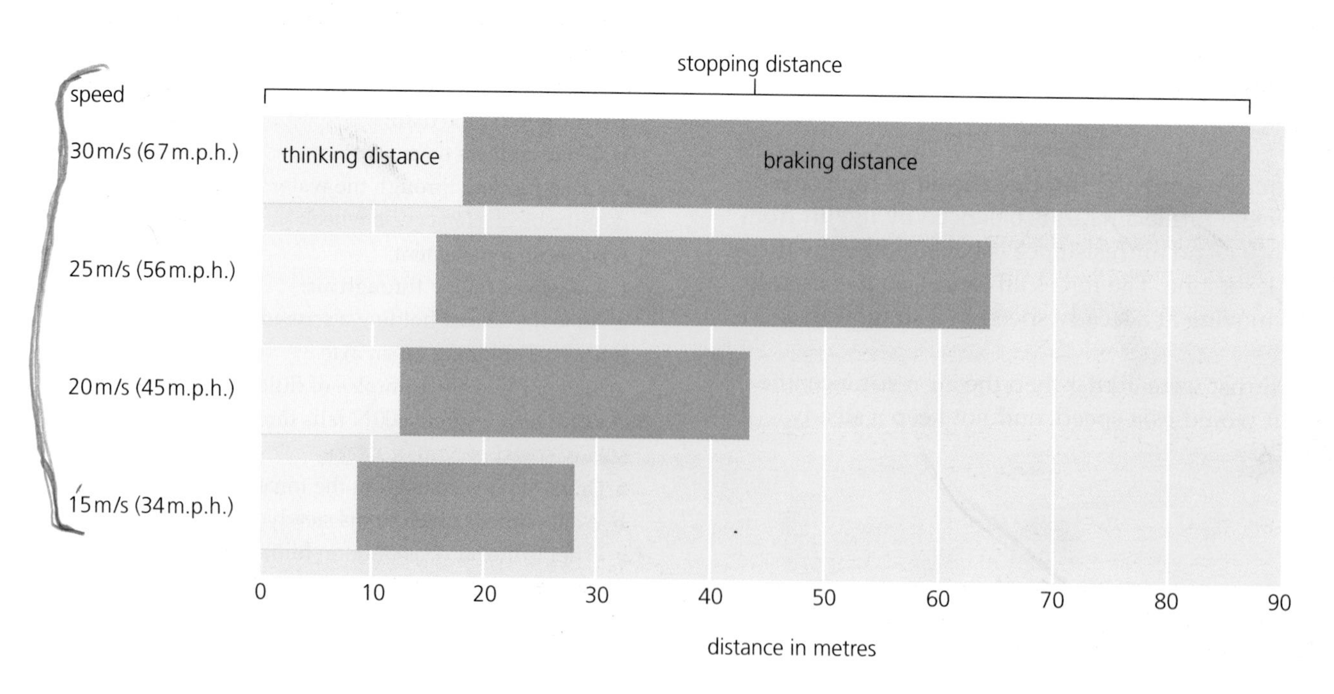

Braking, friction, and skidding

To stop quickly, a car must lose speed rapidly. A high braking force is needed for this. It is provided by the friction between the tyres and the road. But there is a limit to the amount of friction ('grip') that the tyres can supply. If the brakes are put on too strongly, the wheels will 'lock up' (stop turning) and the car will skid.

This car is skidding because there isn't enough friction between its tyres and the road.

Safety features

In a collision, a car stops, but its passengers keep moving...until something stops them as well. The 'something' could be the steering wheel or windscreen, and the impact could cause injury or death. That is why modern cars have these safety features:

Seat belts These stop the passengers hitting the windscreen or other hard parts of the car's inside.

Air bags These inflate in a collision. They cushion the passengers from the effects of any impact.

Crumple zone The front section of a car is a 'crumple zone'. It is designed to collapse steadily in a crash so that the seat belts and air bags can slow the passengers less violently. In other words, their retardation (deceleration) is less.

Losing energy

Like all moving objects, a moving car has **kinetic energy** (energy of motion). To stop, it must lose all that energy – as heat in its brakes or skidding tyres, or by hitting something.

Kinetic energy (in joules) is calculated like this:

$$\text{kinetic energy} = \tfrac{1}{2} \times \text{mass} \times \text{speed}^2$$

The equation shows that if a car doubles its speed, it has *four* times as much kinetic energy to lose. So it needs about four times the braking distance. It is this greatly increased kinetic energy which makes high-speed crashes so destructive.

Questions

1 For a car, what is meant by each of these?
a thinking distance **b** braking distance
c stopping distance

2 Give *two* reasons why the thinking distance may be more than normal.

3 Describe *three* features that a modern car has to make a collision less harmful to the passengers.

4 Cutting your speed is the best safety feature of all. Which of the following are reduced if a car travels more slowly? (You can choose more than one answer.)
A Driver's reaction time
B Thinking distance
C Braking distance
D Risk of serious injury

5 In the chart on the opposite page, what is the thinking distance at **a** 25 m/s? **b** 30 m/s?

6 Alcohol slows people's reactions. If a driver has a reaction time of 2 seconds:
a what will his thinking distance be at 25 m/s?
b Using information from the chart on the opposite page, estimate what his stopping distance will be at 25 m/s.

2.13 Action and reaction

Here are some pairs of forces:

In fact, no force can exist by itself.
All forces are pushes or pulls between *two* things.
So they *always* occur in pairs.
One force acts on one thing. Its equal but opposite partner acts on the other.

Sir Isaac Newton was the first to realize that forces occur in pairs. His **third law of motion** states:

> For every action there is an equal and opposite reaction.

or

> When A pushes on B, B pushes with an equal but opposite force on A.

If forces always occur in pairs, why don't they cancel each other out?
The forces in each pair are acting on two *different* things, *not* the same thing.

Why doesn't the ground move backwards when someone runs forward?
It does. But Earth is so massive that the force has too small an effect to be noticed.

Rocks, rockets, and jets – pairs of forces at work

Moving about in space is no problem if you have a rock handy.

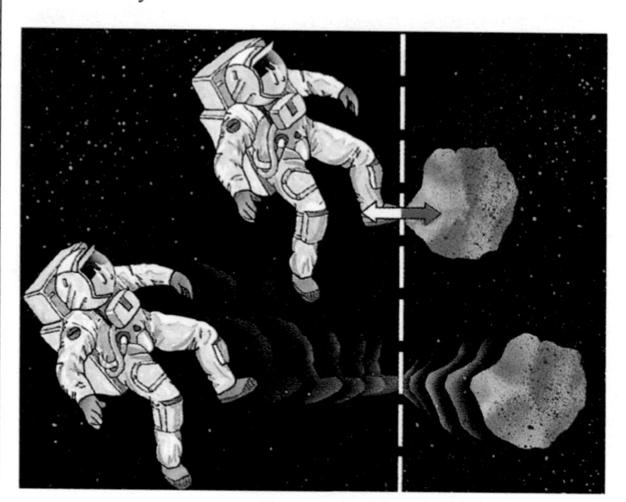

A pair of forces is produced when the astronaut pushes on the rock with her foot.
One force pushes the astronaut to the left.
An equal force pushes the rock to the right.
The astronaut has less mass than the rock. So the force has a greater effect on her.
She gains more speed than the rock.

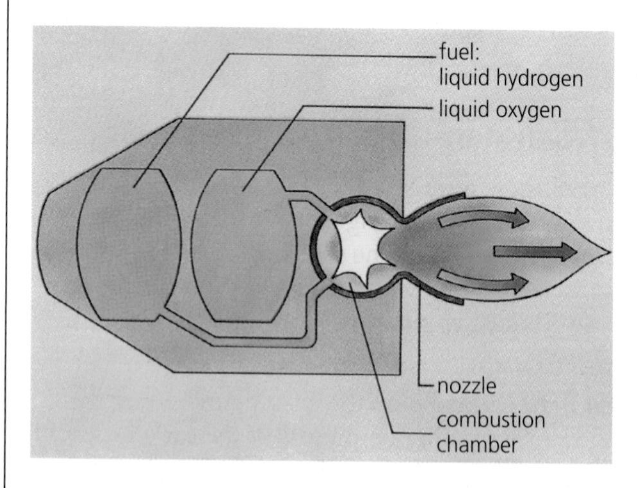

Rocket engines use a similar idea. But they push out large masses of gas, rather than rocks.
In a rocket engine, fuel and liquid oxygen are mixed together in the combustion chamber. The fuel burns fiercely in the oxygen, turns to gas, and expands.

Huge forces are produced, which push engine and burning fuel apart.
One force pushes the burning fuel backwards. An equal but opposite force pushes the rocket forward.

How can a rocket accelerate through space if it has nothing to push against?
It does have something to push against – a huge mass of burning fuel. Fuel and liquid oxygen make up over 90% of the mass of a rocket.

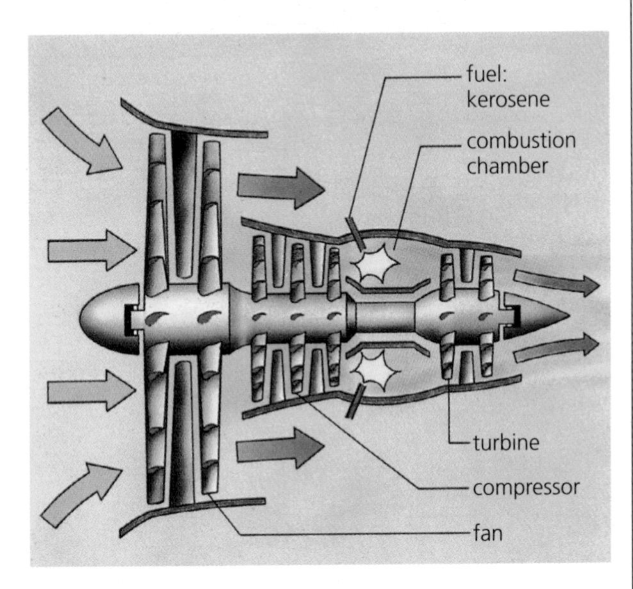

A jet engine doesn't need a supply of liquid oxygen.
Instead, it uses a series of fans, called a **compressor**, to draw in large masses of air from the atmosphere.
The compressor is driven by the turbine.
The turbine is rather like a windmill. It is blown round by the fast-moving gases leaving the engine.

Most of the air drawn in by the jet engine doesn't go through the combustion chambers. It is pushed straight out by the huge fan at the front. This means less noise and better fuel consumption.
A large fan can push out over a quarter of a tonne of air every second.

Questions

1 One force in each pair is missing in the diagrams below. Copy the diagrams. Draw in and label missing forces.

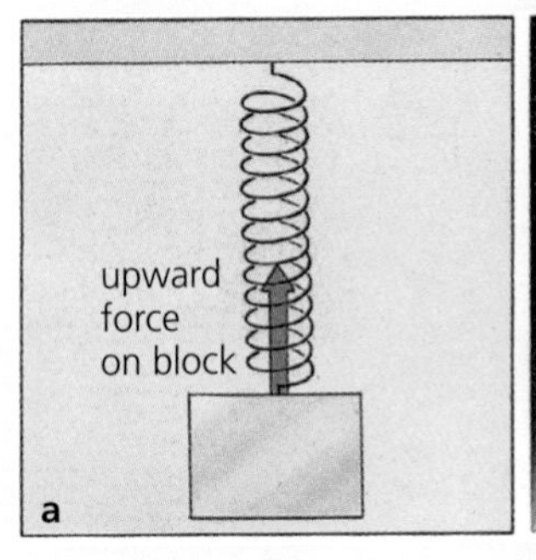

2 Use the first letters of the answers below to make a word. You'll find this whenever there is any action.

- **a** [?] Engine using fuel and liquid oxygen.
- **b** [?] Action and reaction are of ___ strength.
- **c** [?] If there is a reaction, it has to be there.
- **d** [?] It pushes air into the combustion chambers.
- **e** [?] This double page is about the ___ law of motion.
- **f** [?] First name of answer **h**.
- **g** [?] Forces in every pair are equal but ___.
- **h** [?] He put forward the laws of motion.

3 Jet engines and rocket engines both push out large masses of gas. Why can't a jet engine work in space? Why aren't airliners powered by rocket engines?

4 Look at the diagram of the astronaut pushing on the rock. If the astronaut had more mass than the rock, what effect would this have?

5

A woman stands on a plank. Her weight is exactly balanced by an upward force from the plank. Dave says that this is an example of Newton's third law of motion.
Sue says that it isn't.
Who is right? And why?

2.14 Changing ideas

On Earth, everyday experience seems to tell us that a force is needed to keep something moving. Even the curling stone above eventually slides to a halt on the ice. However, friction is confusing the issue. We now know that, with *no* force on it, an object will keep moving at a steady speed in a straight line. Ideas like this took a long time to develop. With them came a new understanding of gravity and the motion of planets and moons.

Ideas from Ancient Greece

Aristotle was born in Greece in 384 BC. Like other philosophers of his time, he based his ideas on what he thought ought to happen in a perfect Universe, rather than on experimental results. However, his ideas became very influential.
Aristotle believed in different forms of 'natural motion'. Matter was made up of four elements: earth, water, fire, and air. Earth and water would naturally sink, fire and air would naturally rise. Nothing was needed to make this happen. It just *happened*. In the 'heavens', the Sun, Moon and planets revolved around the Earth. They were made of a fifth element, the 'aether', whose natural motion was circular.

Galileo challenges Aristotle

Nobody really challenged Aristotle's views until the early 1600s, when Galileo Galilei started to come up with new ideas about the link between force and motion. In a series of experiments, he rolled balls down slopes and deduced that all falling objects, light or heavy, should gain speed at the same steady rate.

It is said that Galileo investigated the laws of motion by dropping cannon balls from the top of Pisa's famous tower. This is almost certainly not true. However, Galileo was born in Pisa, Italy (in 1564), and studied and lectured there.

Using a simple telescope he made himself, Galileo observed the planet Jupiter and saw moons in orbit around it. This was the first evidence that the Earth was not at the centre of all heavenly motion. At the time, this view was highly controversial, and was strongly opposed by the Church.

Newton gets it (almost) right!

Our present-day ideas about motion mainly come from Isaac Newton, who put forward his laws of motion in 1687. Our definition of force is based on his second law: force = mass × acceleration.
Newton also realized that 'heavenly bodies' didn't obey different rules from everything else. The Moon's motion around the Earth is controlled by the same force – gravity – that make objects fall downwards on Earth. In other words, *all* masses attract each other. Newton is supposed to have had this idea while watching an apple fall from a tree.

Newton may have been inspired by an apple falling from a tree, but he produced mathematical equations on gravity that are still used today.

A 'With no force on it, a moving object will keep a steady speed.'

B 'With no force on it, a moving object will lose speed.'

- Which of the two ideas above do you think is correct?
- Which scientist first suggested the correct idea? Was it Aristotle, Galileo, Newton, or Einstein?
- What connection did Newton see between a falling apple and the Moon?

Einstein challenges Newton

Albert Einstein is probably the most famous scientist of all, although most people find his theories extremely difficult to understand!

In 1905, Einstein put forward his special theory of relativity. He developed it in order to explain some experimental observations about the speed of light. One of its predictions is that things gain mass when they speed up. At ordinary speeds this doesn't have a large enough effect to be noticed, but near the speed of light it does. Newton's laws of motion assume that mass doesn't change. However...

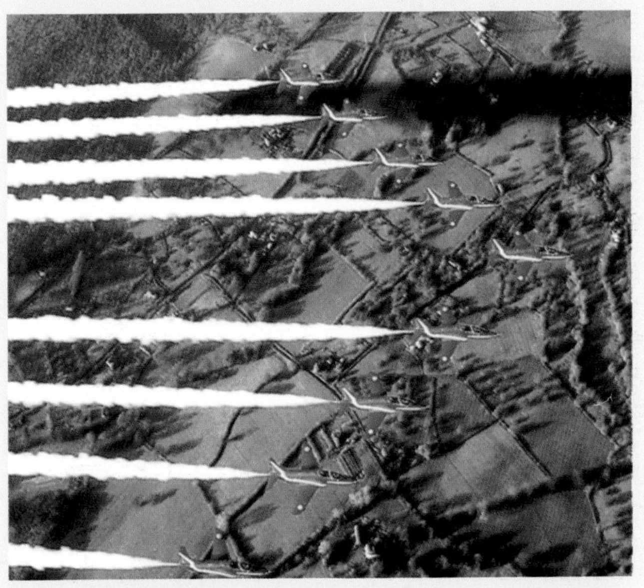

...at speeds like this, calculations based on Newton's laws of motion give results that are quite accurate enough.

Questions on Chapter 2

1 A small object falls from a high building. Choose words from the list to complete the sentences below.

pressure **gravity** **air resistance**
accelerates **falls at a steady speed** **decelerates**

The weight of the object is the force of ___________which acts on it. When the object is first dropped it ____________. The faster it falls, the greater the __________________ which acts on it. Eventually the object ___________________.

2 A car of mass 600 kg accelerates from rest to 25 m/s in 5 seconds.

a Calculate the acceleration of the car.
b Calculate the force needed to cause this acceleration.
c The propulsive force from the car engine will need to be greater than the value calculated in **b**. Explain why this is so.

3 The diagram below shows a bobsleigh team at the beginning of their run.

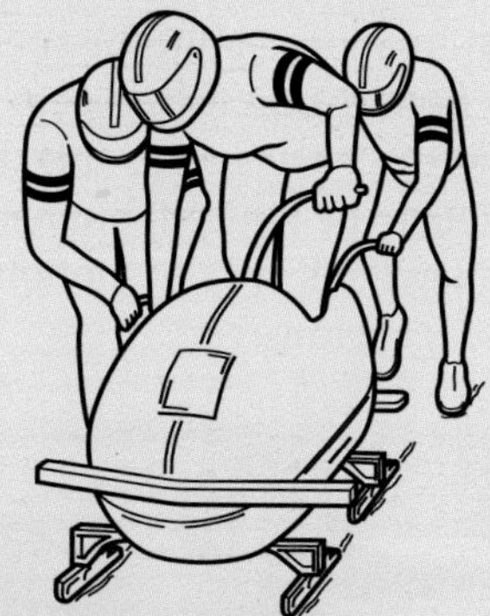

a When the team push the bobsleigh, the forces they apply cause it to accelerate. Name one place where the team need **i** a large amount of friction and **ii** as small an amount of friction as possible.
b What do the team do on their way down the run to reduce any resistive forces?
c Why do the team need a lot of friction at the end of the run?

4 The table below shows how the stopping distance of a car depends on its speed.

Stopping distance (m)	0	4	12	22	36	52	72
Speed (m/s)	0	5	10	15	20	25	30

a Write down TWO factors, apart from speed, that affect the stopping distance of a car.
b Use the information in the above table to draw a graph of stopping distance against speed.
c The speed limit in a housing estate is 12.5 m/s. Use your graph to estimate the stopping distance of a car travelling at this speed.
d Describe how the stopping distance changes as the speed of a car increases.

5 The diagram below shows the horizontal forces acting upon a cyclist.

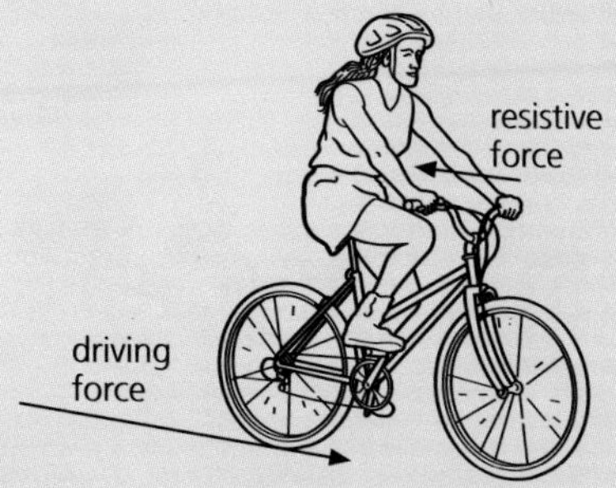

Describe the motion of the cyclist if:

a the resistive force is greater than the driving force.
b the driving force is greater than the resistive force.
c the driving force has the same magnitude as the resistive force.
d Suggest two ways in which the cyclist could reduce the resistive force.

6 A skydiver falls from a hovering helicopter. She waits a few seconds before opening her parachute. The table below shows how her speed changes with time from the moment she jumps:

Time (s)	0	1	2	3	4	5	6	7	8
Speed (m/s)	0		20	30	22	14	12	9	9

a Copy and complete the table, filling in the missing number.
b Plot a graph of speed against time.
c After how many seconds does the skydiver open her parachute? How can you tell from your graph?
d As the skydiver falls, there is a *downward* force acting on her and an *upward* force.
  i What causes the downward force?
  ii What causes the upward force?

iii After 2 seconds, which of these two forces is the larger?

iv After 8 seconds, how do the two forces compare?

e How would you expect your graph to be different if the skydiver's parachute were larger? (You could answer this by drawing sketches to show how the graph changes.)

7 a A car accelerates from 0 to 40 m/s in 20 s. What is the average acceleration of this car? Why is this *average* acceleration?

b A train slows down from 60 m/s to 30 m/s in 20 s. What is the deceleration of the train? What is the acceleration of the train?

c A small rocket on bonfire night accelerates from rest to 40 m/s in 4 s. What is the acceleration of the rocket?

8 a An astronaut of mass 100 kg moves away from his spacecraft by using a small propulsive unit attached to his back. If the maximum force generated by the unit is 20 N, what is the maximum acceleration he can achieve?

b The strings of a catapult exert a total force of 2 N on a stone, causing it to accelerate at the rate of 10 m/s^2. Calculate the mass of the stone.

c A rocket of mass 100 000 kg experiences an acceleration of 2 m/s^2. Calculate the force being developed by the rocket motors.

9 Emma and Jane are having a race. The graph below shows how the speed of each athlete changes with time.

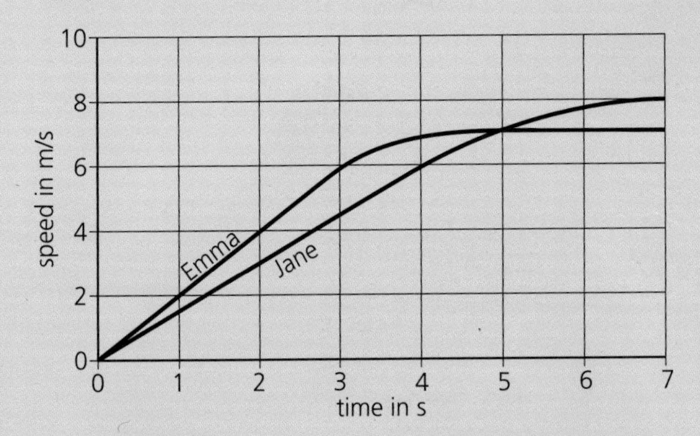

a Which athlete reaches the higher speed?

b Which athelete has the greater acceleration at the start of the race?

c After how many seconds does Jane's speed become greater than Emma's?

d What is Emma's maximum speed?

e To begin with, Emma's acceleration is 2 m/s^2. What does this figure tell you about the way her speed changes?

f What is Jane's acceleration over the first 4 seconds?

g What distance does Jane travel in the first 4 seconds?

10 In each of the following cases, decide whether the frictional forces should be as *low* as possible or as *high* as possible:

a Shoes in contact with the pavement.

b Brake blocks being pressed against the rim of a bicycle wheel.

c Hands holding the handlebars of a bicycle.

d Skis sliding over snow.

e Car tyres in contact with a road surface.

f A wheel turning on its axle.

11 The graph below describes the motion of a bus as it travels from village to village.

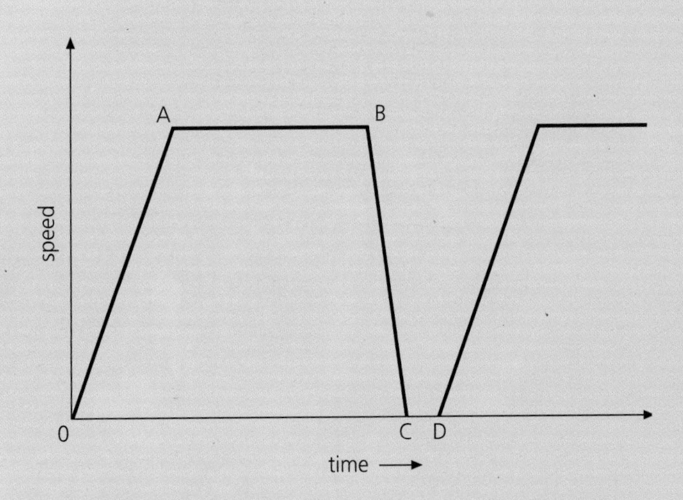

a Describe in detail what is happening between OA, AB, BC and CD.

b Sketch an acceleration/time graph for the bus's journey.

Chapter 3
Energy

The Niagara falls, on the USA–Canada border. The photograph shows the highest section of the falls, where the water tumbles over 30 metres to the river below. Nearly three million litres of water flow over the falls every second. Most of the energy is wasted, but some is harnessed by a hydroelectric power station that generates electricity for the surrounding area.

3.01 Work and energy

Who is doing most work?

In everyday language, 'work' can mean anything from writing an essay to digging the garden. To scientists and engineers, work has an exact meaning:

Work is done whenever a force moves.

The unit of work is the **joule (J)**.

1 joule of work is done when a force of 1 newton moves a distance of 1 metre (in the direction of the force).

There is an equation for calculating work:

work done = force × distance moved
(in the direction of the force)

For example:

6J of work is done when a force of 2N moves 3m
12J of work is done when a force of 4N moves 3m
24J of work is done when a force of 4N moves 6m
and so on.

Larger units of work are the **kilojoule** and the **megajoule**:

1 kilojoule (kJ) = 1000J
1 megajoule (MJ) = 1000000J

Work done . . .	
in shutting a door	5J
in throwing a ball	20J
in climbing the stairs	1kJ
in loading a lorry	1MJ

Energy

Things have energy if they can do work. A tankful of petrol has energy, so does a stretched spring. Each can be used to make something move. In each case, you can think of the energy as a promise of work to be done in the future.

Energy can take different forms:

Kinetic energy

This is 'energy of motion'. All moving things have kinetic energy.

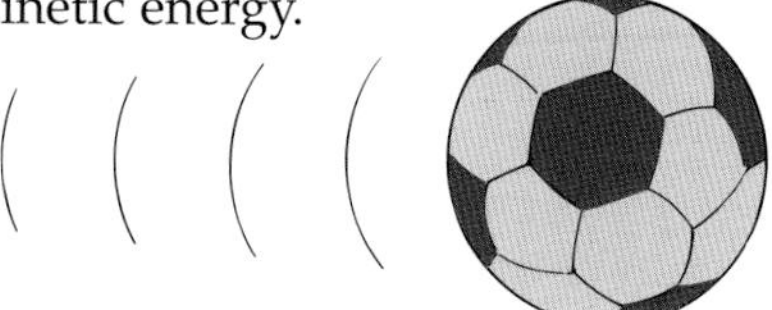

Potential energy

This is stored energy – for example, the energy something has because it has been moved out of its normal position or shape.

On the right, you can see some of the names used to describe the different types of potential energy.

Thermal energy (heat)

This is the energy that comes from hot things when they cool down.

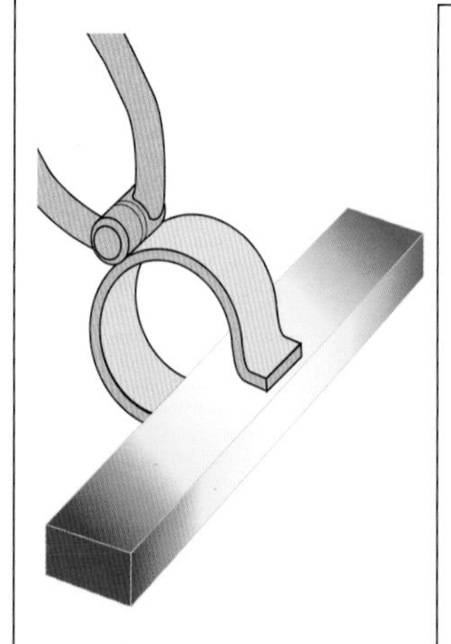

Everything is made of tiny particles (atoms or molecules). These are constantly on the move, so they have energy. The higher the temperature, the faster they move, and the more energy they have.

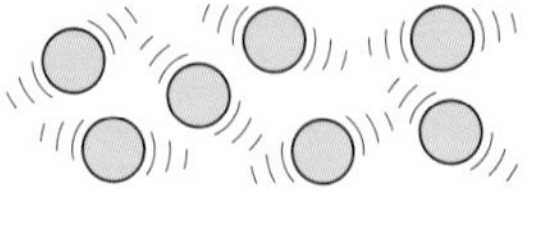

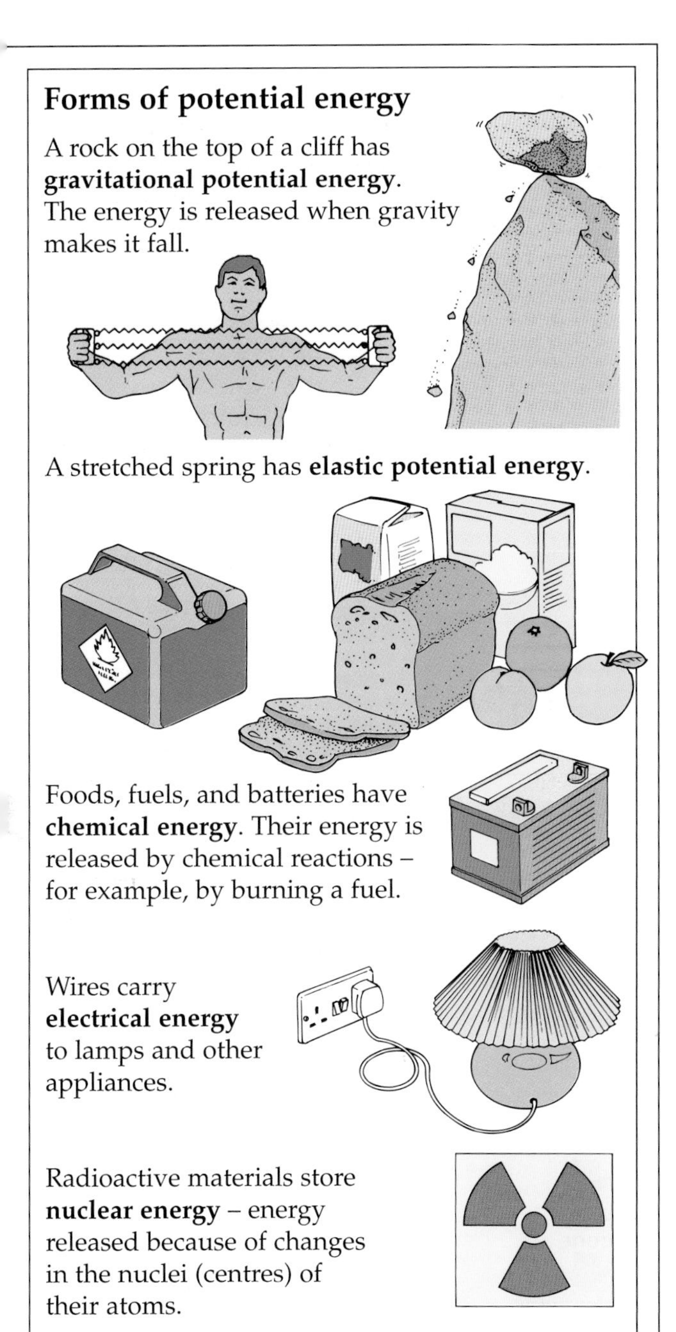

Forms of potential energy

A rock on the top of a cliff has **gravitational potential energy**. The energy is released when gravity makes it fall.

A stretched spring has **elastic potential energy**.

Foods, fuels, and batteries have **chemical energy**. Their energy is released by chemical reactions – for example, by burning a fuel.

Wires carry **electrical energy** to lamps and other appliances.

Radioactive materials store **nuclear energy** – energy released because of changes in the nuclei (centres) of their atoms.

Radiated energy

Light and **sound** are both forms of energy which radiate (spread) from their source.

How much energy?

The unit of energy is the joule (J).
100 000 joules is the energy you could get from . . .

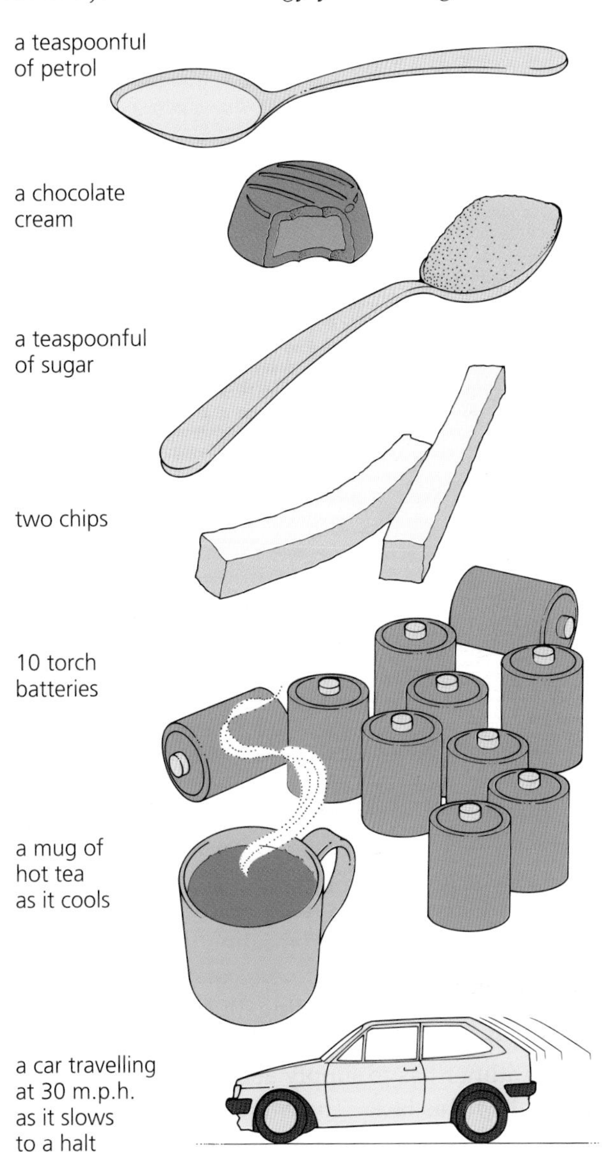

Questions

1 How much work is done when:
- **a** a 6N force moves 3m?
- **b** a 12N force moves 0.5m?
- **c** a 10N force moves 10mm?

2 In the 'How much energy?' chart above, which of the items have (or has):
- **a** CHEMICAL energy?
- **b** THERMAL energy?
- **c** KINETIC energy?

3 Which is likely to release most energy:
- **a** burning a canful of petrol, or dropping it?
- **b** catching a falling apple, or eating it?

3.02 Energy changes

A super-heavyweight and his daily menu:

1 grapefruit	1 bowl of cornflakes
7 pints of milk	12 eggs
8 steaks	1 kg cheese
30 slices of bread	1 kg butter
4 tins of pilchards	2 tins of baked beans
1 rice pudding	1 pot of honey

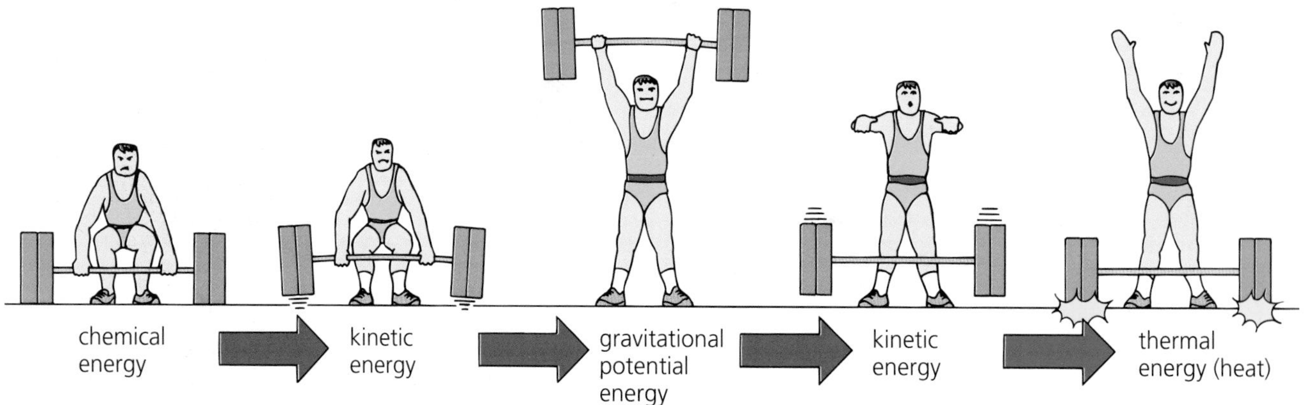

The weightlifter's menu is not a healthy diet for most people but what you might be eating if you were breaking Olympic weightlifting records. Much of the food is used for muscle building. But some provides energy for the lift.

The weightlifter has to supply about 4000 J to lift the weights above his head. The energy is stored in the body as chemical energy. However, during the lift, it is changed into other forms.

When the weights hit the ground, the impact makes the particles (atoms and molecules) move faster. This means that ground, air, and weights are all a little warmer than before. The 4000 J of energy has become thermal energy (heat).

From the first stage to the last, the *type* of energy changes, but the total *amount* of energy stays the same. This is an example of the **law of conservation of energy**:

Energy can change from one form to another, but it cannot be made or destroyed.

Energy change and work

Work is done whenever energy is transformed (changed) from one form to another. For example:

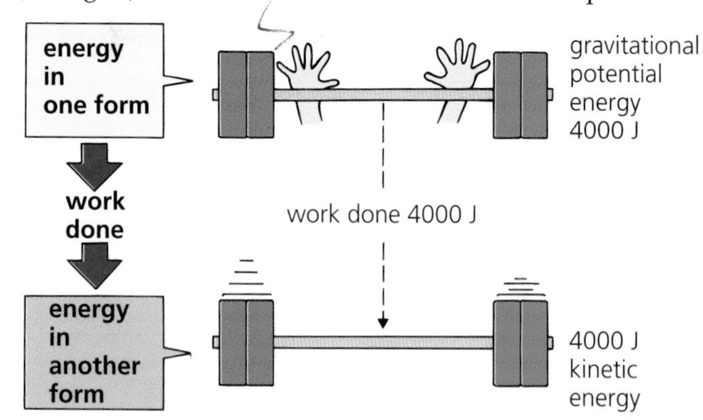

After the weights are dropped, 4000 J of gravitational potential energy is changed into 4000 J of kinetic energy: 4000 J of work is done in speeding up the weights during the fall:

work done = energy transformed

Sometimes, scientists talk about energy being **transferred** rather than transformed, but this means the same thing.

Energy converters

An energy converter changes energy from one type into another.
The weightlifter is an energy converter. So are you. So is each of the following:

an iron changes electrical energy into thermal energy (heat)

brakes change kinetic energy into thermal energy (heat)

telephones change sound energy into electrical energy

. . . into sound energy

a swing changes kinetic energy into potential energy into kinetic energy into potential energy into . . .

Most energy converters lose some of their energy as heat. For example, to do 4000 J of work, the weightlifter has to release about 25 000 J of stored energy by 'burning' food he has eaten. The spare 21 000 J makes him hot – which is why he sweats.

When things move, they often lose energy because of air resistance of friction. The swing slowly loses its energy as heat. As it pushes through the air, it slows down and the air particles (molecules) speed up.

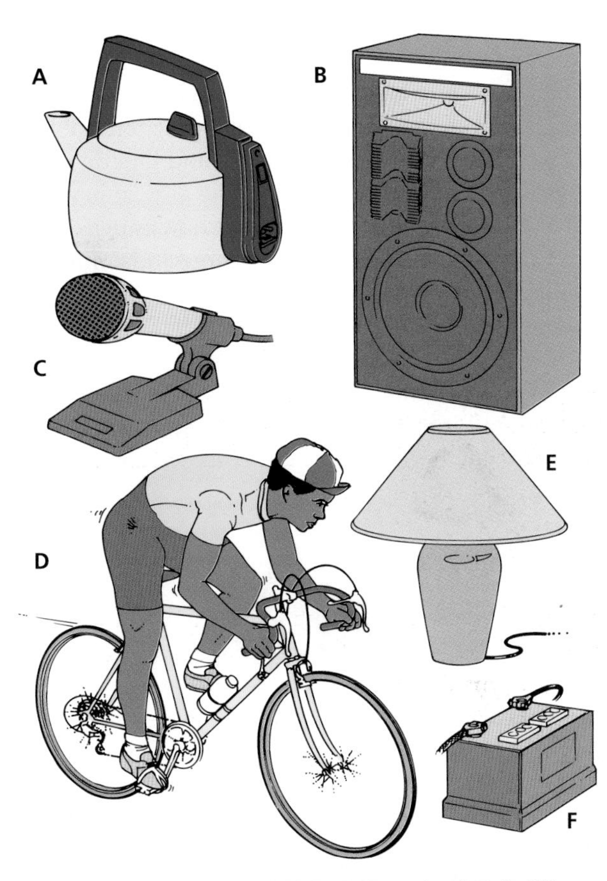

Questions

1 Which of the energy converters above right:

a changes CHEMICAL energy into KINETIC energy?

b changes ELECTRICAL energy into THERMAL energy?

c changes CHEMICAL energy into ELECTRICAL energy?

d changes ELECTRICAL energy into RADIATED energy?

e changes ELECTRICAL energy into SOUND energy?

2 A pole-vaulter has 3500 J of energy when he crosses a bar 7 metres high. How much kinetic energy will he have just before he reaches the ground (assuming no friction)?

3 This is an unusual way of describing the first half hour of someone's day:

gets up at 7:00 a.m.
gains chemical energy
gains thermal energy
leaves house
kinetic energy rises
jumps on vehicle
gravitational potential energy rises
kinetic energy rises
kinetic energy fall to zero
gravitational potential energy falls to zero

Rewrite, to show what could actually be happening to the person.

3.03 Energy calculations

Moving fast, high above the Earth, travelling at around 8 kilometres per second, the Space Shuttle has lots of gravitational potential energy and kinetic energy. When the Shuttle re-enters the atmosphere, that energy is changed into heat. But how much energy? If you were designing the thousands of heat-resistant tiles that protect the surface of the Shuttle, you would need to know.

Gravitational potential and kinetic energies can be calculated, but it is easier to start with something lighter and slower than the Shuttle, like a stone lifted above the ground, or thrown.

Calculating gravitational potential energy (GPE)

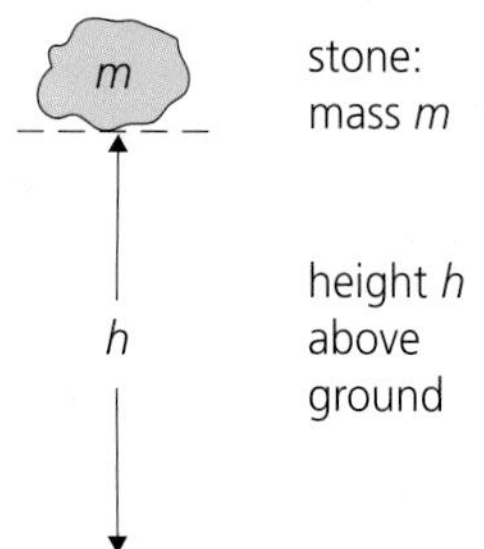

If an object is held above the ground, its gravitational potential energy in joules (J) can be calculated like this:

$$GPE = mgh$$

where
m is the mass of the object in kg
g is the Earth's gravitational field strength (10 N/kg)
h is the height above the ground, in metres (m)

For example, if a stone of mass 2 kg is 5 m above the ground, as in the box on the right:

$$GPE = mgh = 2 \times 10 \times 5 = 100\,\text{J}$$

The same by any route

When calculating gravitational potential energy, it is the height lifted against gravity that matters, not the actual distance moved.

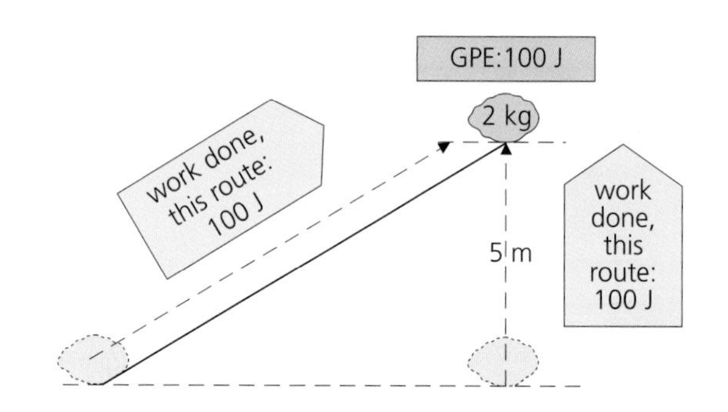

When the stone is lifted above the ground it gets the same potential energy whether it is lifted straight up or pulled up the slope. It takes less force to pull the stone up the slope. But the distance is further. Result: the work done is the same by either route.

Why the equation works

Weight is a force, measured in newtons (N). On Earth, each kilogram (kg) weighs 10 newtons: the Earth has a **gravitational field strength** of 10 N/kg. This value is called g.

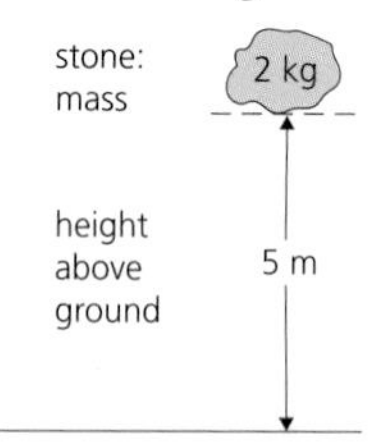

The stone above has a mass of 2 kg.
So its weight = 2 × 10 = 20 N.
Therefore the force needed to lift it is 20 N.

The work done in lifting it 5 m is calculated like this:
work done = force × distance = 20 × 5 = 100 J
so GPE gained = 100 J
To get this answer, you multiplied the mass (2 kg) by g (10 N/kg) and then multiplied the result by the height (5 m). So you multiplied m by g by h.

Calculating kinetic energy (KE)

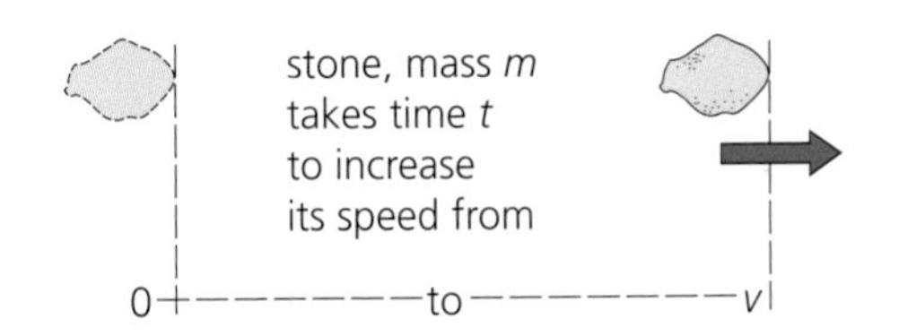

You can calculate the kinetic energy of a moving object with this equation:

$$KE = \frac{1}{2}mv^2$$

where m is the mass of the object in kg, and
v is its speed in metres per second (m/s).

There isn't a simple way of showing why the equation works! But this is how you use it:

If a stone of mass 2kg has a speed of 3m/s:

$$KE = \frac{1}{2} \times 2 \times 3^2 \text{J} = 9\text{J}$$

If a stone of mass 2 kg has a speed of 6 m/s:

$$KE = \frac{1}{2} \times 2 \times 6^2 \text{J} = 36\text{J}$$

So, if something *doubles* its speed, it ends up with *four times* the kinetic energy.

Adding energies

What happens if you lift a 2kg stone 5m above the ground *and* throw it at 6m/s? The stone has 100J of GPE *and* 36J of KE, giving a total of 136J.
The direction of motion doesn't affect this total.

Just before the stone hits the ground, all 136J of this energy will be kinetic energy (assuming the stone doesn't lose energy because of air resistance). The stone ends up with the same kinetic energy – and the same speed – whether it is thrown upwards, downwards, or sideways. The direction of throw makes no difference.

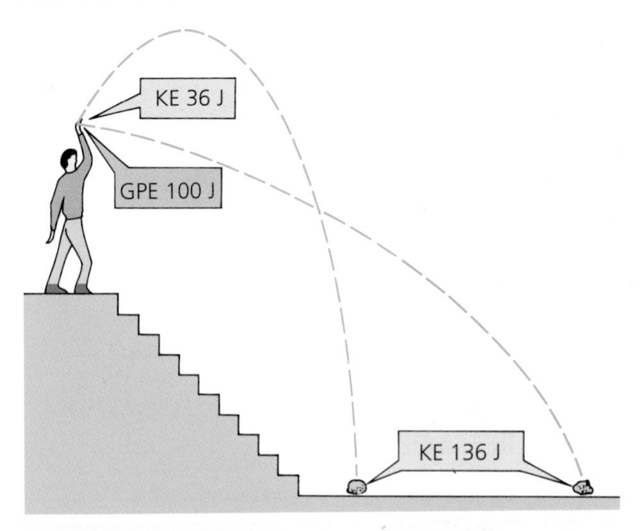

Questions

Assume g = 10N/kg, and there is no air resistance.

1

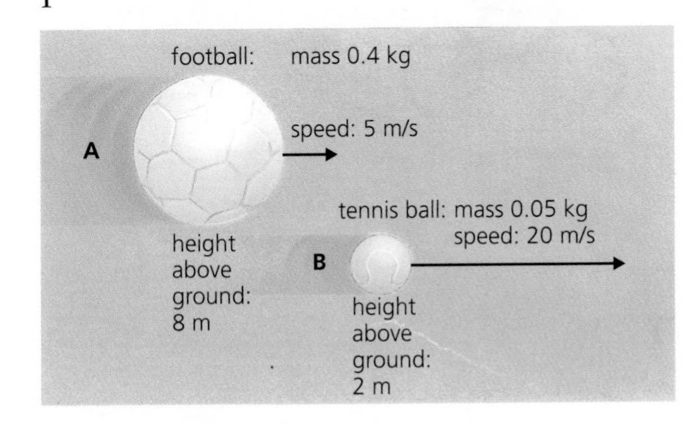

Use the information in the diagram to work out:

a the gravitational potential energy of each ball;
b the kinetic energy of each ball;
c the kinetic energy of each ball just before it reaches the ground.

2 Here is some information about a Space Shuttle in orbit:

mass:	100 tonnes
speed:	8km/s
height above ground:	100km

a What is the mass in kg?
b What is the speed in m/s?
c What is the height above ground in metres?
d What is the gravitational potential energy of the Shuttle?
e What is its kinetic energy?
f How much energy must it lose before coming to a halt on the ground?
g What happens to this energy?

3.04 Efficiency and power I

Efficiency

Like most other engines, the human engine is a wasteful user of fuel. If you are pedalling hard on a bike, for every 100 joules of energy released from your food, you only do about 15 joules of useful work. In other words, for every 100 joules of energy input, your useful energy output is only 15 joules. The rest is lost as heat. Scientifically speaking, your **efficiency** is 0.15, or 15%.

$$\text{efficiency} = \frac{\text{useful energy output}}{\text{energy input}}$$

For every 100 J of energy put into a...	the work done is...	the efficiency is...
petrol engine	25 J	25%
diesel engine	35 J	35%
electric motor	80 J	80%
human engine	15 J	15%

Although the electric motor has a high efficiency, the electricity for it has to be generated, and the efficiency of that process can be as low as 25%.

Low efficiency isn't the fault of engine makers. They constantly seek new ways of reducing engine friction and improving fuel burning. But, because of the way atoms and molecules behave, there are limits to the proportion of heat that can ever be changed into kinetic energy.

Power

A small car engine can do just as much work as a large one, but it takes longer to do it. The large engine has more **power**: it can do more joules of work every second.

Power is measured in **watts (W)**. An engine with a useful power output of 1000 watts can do 1000 joules of useful work every second. In other words, its useful energy output is 1000 joules per second.

$$\text{power} = \frac{\text{work done}}{\text{time taken}}$$

Where power is in watts (W), work in joules (J), and time in seconds (s).

In the above equation, you could replace 'work done' with 'energy transformed'.

For example:

800 J work done ÷ 2 s time taken = 400 W useful power output

Here are two larger units of power:

1 kilowatt (kW) = 1000 watts (W)
1 megawatt (MW) = 1000000 watts (W)

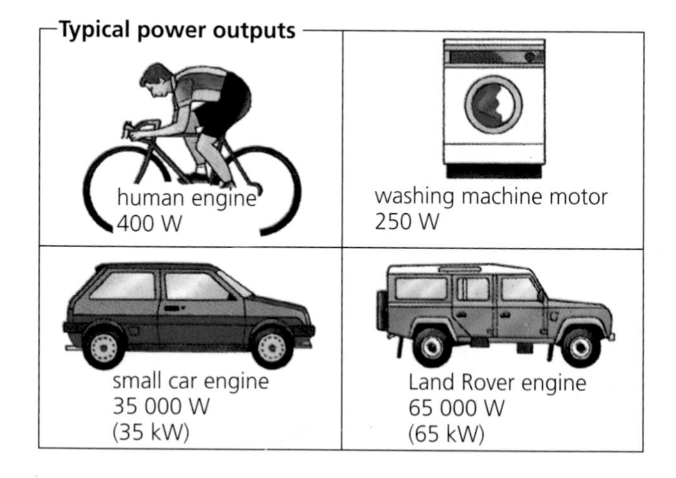

Power values can be used to calculate efficiency:

$$\text{efficiency} = \frac{\text{useful power output}}{\text{power input}}$$

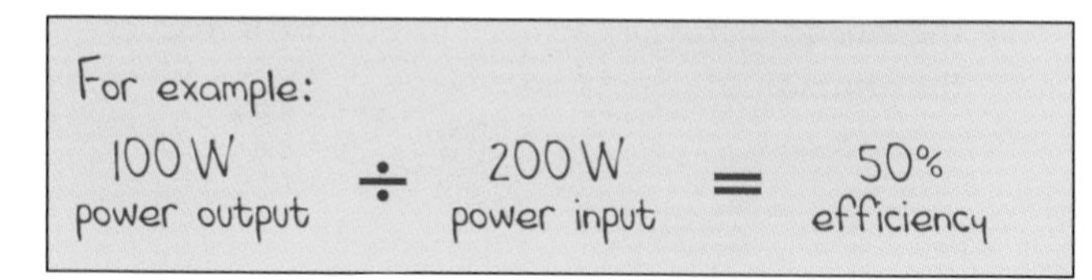

Assume that g = 10 N/kg.
In other words, on Earth, each kilogram (kg) of mass has a weight of 10 newtons (N).

How to measure your power output

		Example
1 Measure your mass . . .	. . . work out your weight Every Kg weighs 10 N	mass = 40 kg weight = 400 N
2 Measure height of stairs . . .	. . . calculate work done when you climb stairs **work done = force × distance** = weight × height lifted	height of stairs = 3 m work done = 400 × 3 m = 1200 J
3 Measure time taken to climb stairs . . .	. . . calculate your average power **power = $\frac{\text{work done}}{\text{time taken}}$**	time taken = 4 s average power = $\frac{1200}{4}$ = 300 W

Questions

Assume g = 10 N/kg.

1 The cheetah is the fastest creature on land. A typical cheetah, at full speed, has a power output of 1000 W, and an efficiency of 15%.

Mike is possibly the slowest creature on land. When he works in the garden (which isn't very often), his useful power output is 100 W, and his efficiency 5%.
Calculate:

a the useful work done by the cheetah in 1 second;
b how long it takes Mike to do the same amount of work.

In unfolding his garden chair, Mike gets 2000 J of energy from the food he has eaten.

c Calculate how much useful work he does.
d Write down what happens to the rest of the energy released.

2 A skier has a mass of 50 kg. It takes her 40 seconds to climb 20 m (vertically) to the top of a slope.
Calculate:

a her weight;
b the work done when she climbs the slope;
c her average power output.
d Why, in reality, will she have to do more work than you have calculated?

3.05 Efficiency and power II

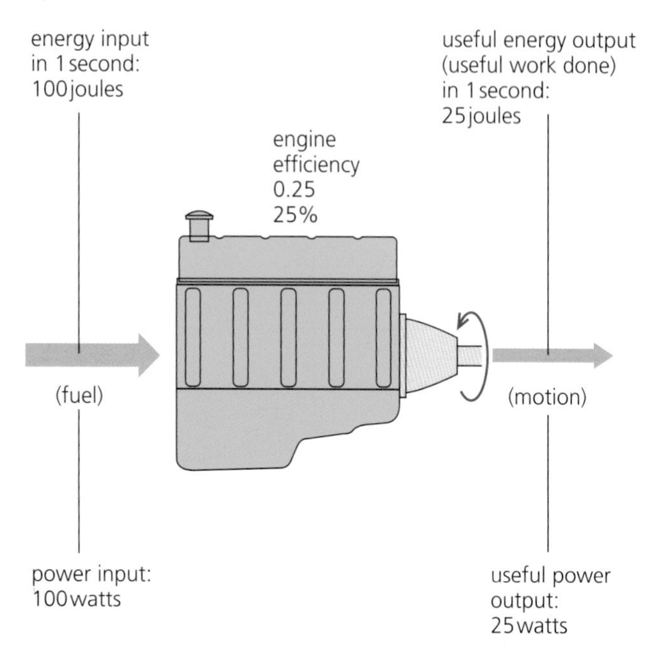

The diagram above is a reminder of the links between work, energy, power, and efficiency.

Wasted heat

Engines get energy from their fuel by burning it. So the energy is released as heat. But not all of this heat can produce motion. In a car engine, for example, the concentrated heat makes gases expand and push on pistons. But as the gases expand, they cool, and their remaining energy becomes too spread out to be useful. So it is wasted.

Engine waste more energy than they deliver as motion. The energy is lost as heat, which is why an engine needs a cooling system.

In the Australian outback, some drivers use the heat from the engine to cook their food.

Efficiency and power problem

Example The crane below lifts a 100 kg block of concrete through a vertical height of 16 metres in 20 seconds. The motor's power input is 1000 watts. Calculate the following (assuming that g = 10 N/kg, and the pulley wheels waste no power):

a The useful power output of the motor.
b The efficiency of the motor.

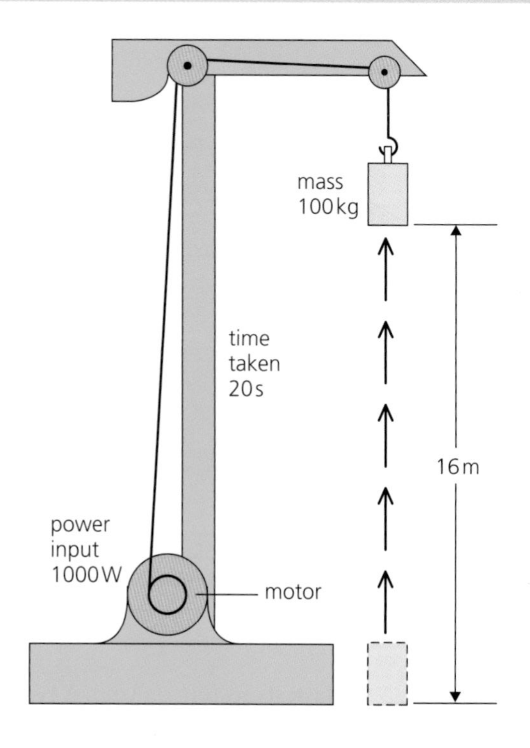

a As g is 10 N/kg, the 100 kg block has a weight of 1000 N. Therefore, a force of 1000 N is needed to lift the block.

When the block is lifted:

work done = force × distance
= 1000 × 16 = 16 000 J

$$\text{useful power output} = \frac{\text{useful work done}}{\text{time taken}} = \frac{16\,000}{20} = 800$$

So the motor's useful power output is 800 W.

b $$\text{efficiency} = \frac{\text{useful power output}}{\text{power input}} = \frac{800}{1000} = 0.8$$

So the efficiency of the motor is 0.8, or 80%.

Low efficiency allowed

With some equipment, low efficiency isn't a problem. A radio is one example. It only delivers a tiny fraction of its power as sound. However, the human ear is so sensitive that very little power needs to come from a loudspeaker for it to sound very loud.

A radio like the one on the right takes only a few watts of power. It would use less energy in a week than a hairdrier would use in half an hour.

The low efficiency of a radio isn't a problem.

Lighting efficiency

These low-energy bulbs have a high efficiency.

This filament bulb has a low efficiency.

Ordinary light bulbs contain a tiny tungsten filament (thin wire) which glows white hot when a current flows through it. Bulbs like this are not very efficient. They give off far more energy as heat than they do as light.

Low-energy bulbs use a glowing gas, rather than a filament. They have a very high efficiency. A 20 watt low-energy bulb gives as much light as a 100 watt filament bulb. Fitting low-energy bulbs is a good way of saving money on your electricity bill – and helping the environment by wasting less energy.

Fluorescent tubes work in the same way as low-energy bulbs. They also have a very high efficiency.

Questions

1 Look at the first diagram on the opposite page.
  a How much energy does the engine waste in one second?
  b What happens to this energy?

2 Someone claims to have invented an engine with an efficiency of 100%. Why shouldn't you believe them?

3 Suggest a reason for each of the following:
  a Light bulbs should have as high an efficiency as possible.
  b Radios have a low efficiency, but this doesn't really matter.

4 Explain why a filament bulb gets hotter than a low-energy bulb of the same brightness.

5 The motor below has a power input of 500 W. It is used to lift a load weighing 600 N through a vertical height of 10 metres in 20 seconds.
  a How much work is done in lifting the load?
  b What is the motor's useful power output?
  c What is the motor's efficiency?

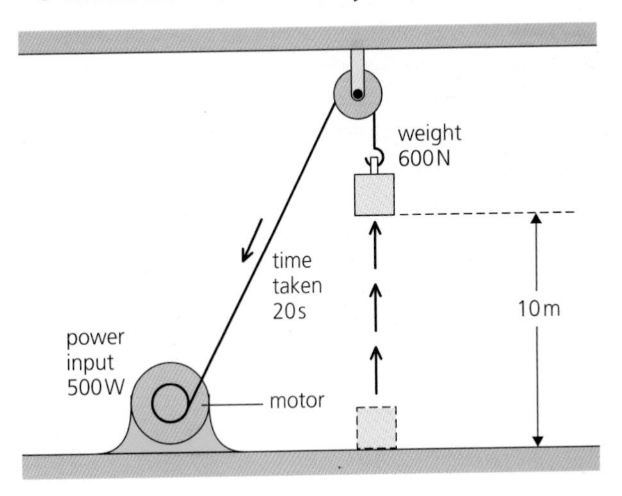

3.06 Energy for electricity I

Clouds of steam coming from the cooling towers at a power station.

Industrial societies need huge amounts of energy. Much of it is supplied by electricity which comes from **generators** in **power stations**.

Thermal power stations

The diagram below shows the layout of a typical large power station. It is called a **thermal** power station because it uses heat.

The generators are turned by **turbines**, blown round by high-pressure steam. To produce the steam, water is heated in a boiler. The heat comes from burning fuel (coal, oil, or natural gas) or from a **nuclear reactor**. Nuclear fuel does not burn. Its energy is released by nuclear reactions which split uranium atoms.

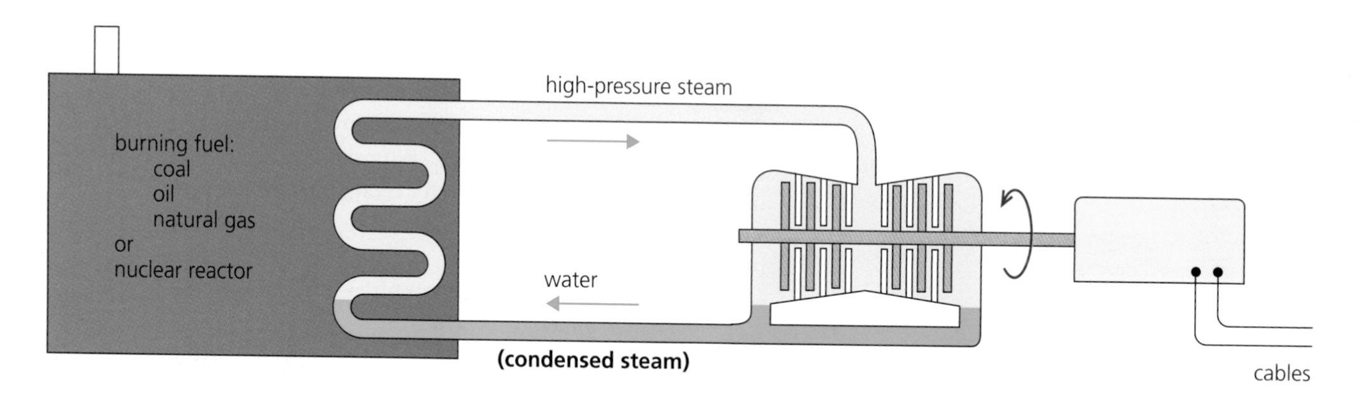

Once steam has passed through the turbines, it is cooled and condensed (turned back into a liquid) so that it can be fed back to the boiler. Some power stations use the cooling effect of nearby sea or river water. Others have huge cooling towers, with draughts of air up through them, like those in the photograph at the top of the page.

A **combined cycle gas turbine power station** is smaller and quicker to start up than the type shown above. It burns natural gas as its fuel. Check the index to see where you can find out more about it in this book.

Turbine from a power station.

Energy spreading

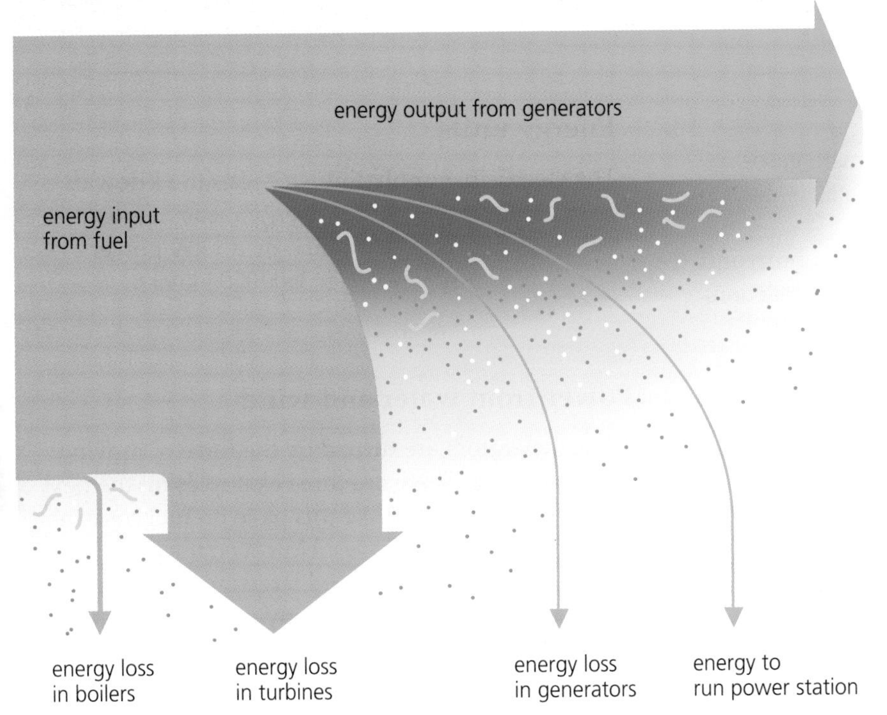

A typical energy-flow chart for a thermal power station. The energy losses are all in the form of heat. A chart like this is called a **Sankey diagram**. The thickness of each arrow represents the amount of energy.

Thermal power stations waste more energy as heat than they deliver as electricity. Most of the wasted heat is carried away by the cooling water. The chart above shows what happens to the energy in a power station and where losses occur.

Engineers try to make power stations as efficient as possible. But once energy is in thermal form (heat), it cannot all be used to drive the generators. Some of it becomes too spread out.

As heat spreads, it becomes more and more difficult to turn it into other forms of energy. In other words, it becomes less and less useful. For example:
The concentrated energy in a hot flame could be used to make steam for a turbine. But if the same amount of energy were spread through a huge tankful of water, it would only warm the water by a few degrees. This warm water could not be used as an energy source for a turbine.

Questions

1 Write down *four* different types of fuel used in thermal power stations.

2 In a thermal power station:
  a what is the steam used for?
  b what do the cooling towers do?

3 The table on the right gives data about the power input and losses in two power stations, X and Y:
  a Where is most energy wasted?
  b In what form is this wasted energy lost?
  c What is the electrical power output of each station? (You can assume that the table shows all the power losses in each station.)
  d Use this equation to calculate the efficiency of each power station:

$$\text{efficiency} = \frac{\text{useful energy output}}{\text{energy input}}$$

W = watt 1 MW = 1000000 watts	power station X coal	 Y nuclear
power input from fuel in MW	5600	5600
power loss in MW:		
– in reactors/boilers	600	200
– in turbines	2900	3800
– in generators	40	40
power to run station in MW	60	60
electrical power output in MW	?	?

3.07 Energy for electricity II

Pollution problems

Fuel-burning power stations give off waste gases which pollute the atmosphere. Natural gas is the 'cleanest' (least polluting) of the fuels.
In a nuclear power station, the fuel doesn't burn and produce waste gases. However, the nuclear reactions do make radioactive waste.

Thermal power stations can cause pollution in a variety of ways:

- Fuel-burning power stations put carbon dioxide gas into the atmosphere. The carbon dioxide traps the Sun's energy and may be adding to **global warming**.
- Some coal-burning power stations give off sulphur dioxide, which causes acid rain. This can damage stonework. One solution is to burn expensive low-sulphur coal. Another is to fit costly **flue gas desulphurization (FGD) units** to the power stations.
- Transporting fuels can cause pollution. For example, there may be a leak from an oil tanker.
- The radioactive waste from nuclear power stations is highly dangerous. It must be carried away and stored safely in sealed containers for many years – in some cases, thousands of years.
- Nuclear accidents are rare. But when they do occur, radioactive gas and dust can be carried thousands of kilometres by winds.

One effect of acid rain.

Energy units

The electricity supply industry uses the **kilowatt hour (kWh)** as its unit of energy measurement: 1 kWh is the energy supplied by a 1 kW power source in 1 hour. (1 kWh = 3600000 joules).

Power from water and wind

Some generators are turned by the force of moving water or wind. There are three examples on the next page. Power schemes like this have no fuel costs, and give off no polluting gases. However, they can be expensive to build, and need large areas of land. Compared with fossil fuels, moving water and wind are much less concentrated sources of energy:

1 kWh of electrical energy can be supplied using...

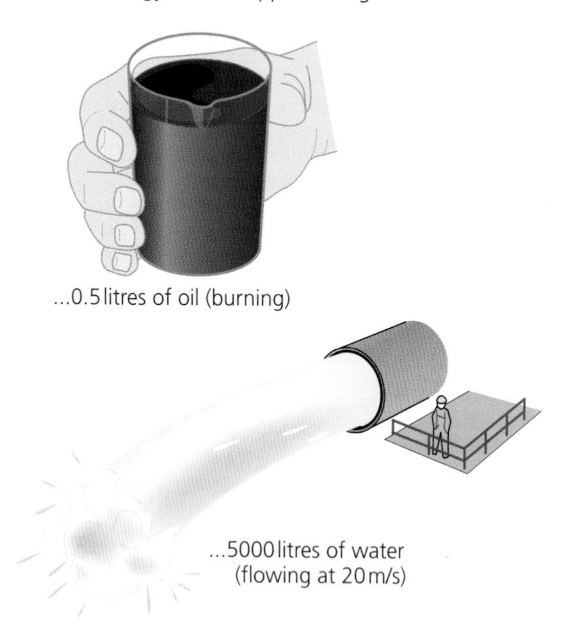

Power stations compared

On the next page, there is a table of data about different types of power station, and the costs of building and running them.

Nuclear power stations have an additional cost: the cost of decommissioning them (closing them down and dismantling them at the end of their working life). This can be almost as much as building them in the first place.

Hydroelectric power scheme River and rain water fill up a lake behind a dam. As water rushes down from the dam, it turns turbines which turn generators.

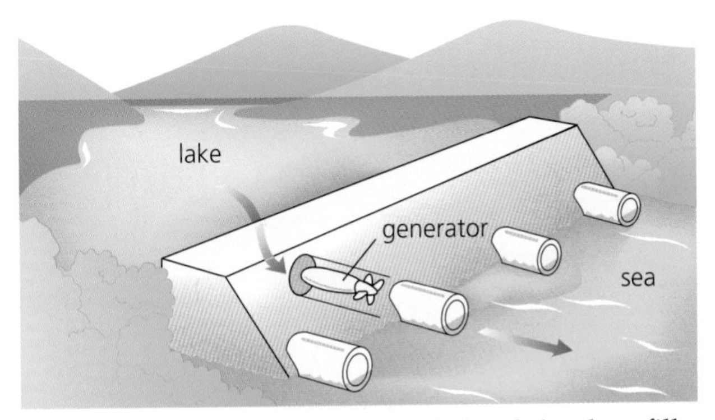

Tidal power scheme The lake behind the dam fills when the tide comes in and empties when the tide goes out. The flow of water turns the generators.

Wind farm This is a collection of **aerogenerators** – generators driven by giant wind turbines ('windmills').

Power station (1 MW = 1000000 W)	**A** coal (non-FGD)	**B** combined cycle gas	**C** nuclear	**D** wind farm	**E** large tidal scheme
power output in MW	1800	600	1200	20	6000
efficiency (fuel energy → electrical energy)	35%	45%	25%	–	–
The following are on a scale of 1–5					
build cost per MW output	2	1	5	3	4
fuel cost per kWh output	5	4	2	0	0
atmospheric pollution per kWh output	5	3	<1	0	0

Questions

1 What is the source of energy in a hydroelectric power station?

2 The table above gives data about five different power stations, A–E.

a C has an efficiency of 25%. What does this mean?

b Which power station has the highest efficiency? What are its other advantages?

c Which power station cost most to build?

d Which has the highest fuel cost per kWh output?

e Which power station produces most atmospheric pollution per kWh output? What can be done to reduce this problem?

f Why do two of the power stations have a zero rating for fuel costs and atmospheric pollution?

3.08 Supply and demand

When people come home from work and start to cook an evening meal, as on the right, the electricity supply companies have to increase their output very quickly. The demand for mains electricity varies from one hour to the next. It is at its peak in the evening, in cold weather, and lowest at night. When more power is needed, generating companies must be able to bring extra generators 'on line' quickly.

Fast and slow

Some power stations can start up (and shut down) faster than others.

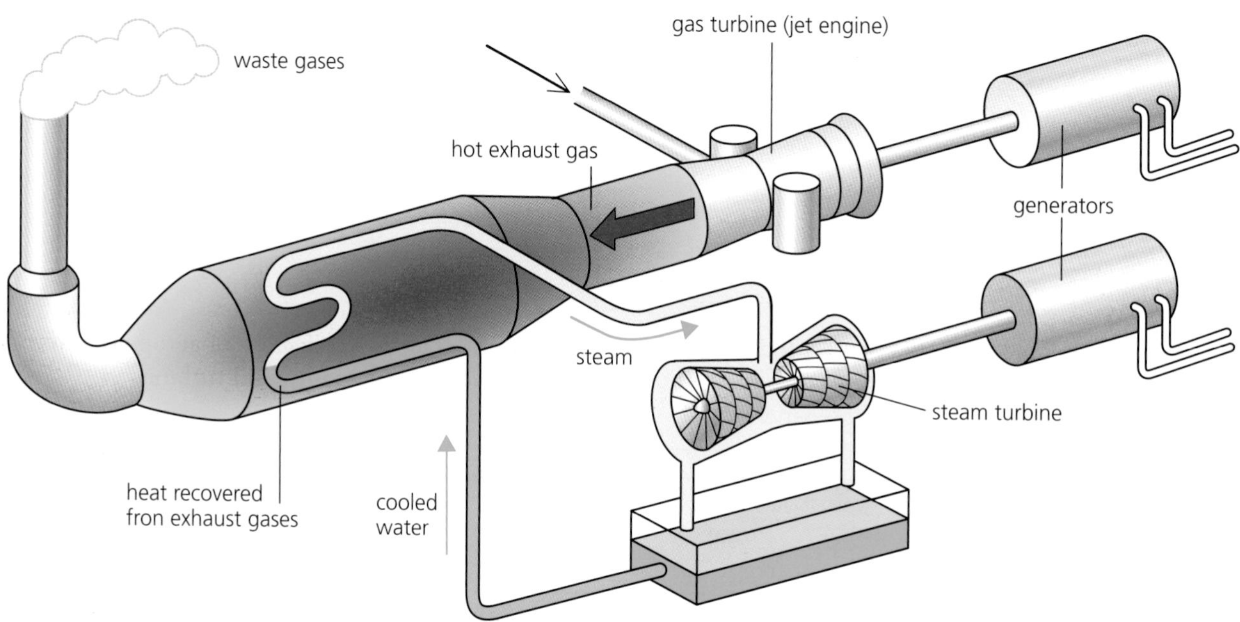

In a **combined cycle gas turbine power station** (above), natural gas is used as the fuel for a jet engine. The shaft of the engine turns one generator. The hot gases from the jet are used to make steam to drive another generator. Units like this give less power than larger types, but can be brought up to speed very quickly.

Hydroelectric power stations use water rushing down from a lake to turn their turbines. They can also start up very quickly.

Large fuel-burning power stations take longer to start up. Nuclear power stations take longest of all. If its reactor is 'cold', a nuclear power station takes about two days to reach full power.

Variable outputs

Some power stations cannot give a steady power output:

Tidal power schemes use the tidal flow of sea water to turn their turbines. Their maximum power depends on the height of the tide, which varies through the month, and from one month to the next. Also, at high tide, when the tide is 'on the turn', they deliver no power.

Wind farms contain giant 'windmills' which turn generators. Even on the most exposed sites, wind speeds can vary, and on calm days, no power is generated.

Solar cells produce electricity when they absorb the energy in sunlight. So their output falls to zero at night. Solar cells are expensive and produce relatively little power. However, in some situations, that doesn't really matter. Banks of solar cells are sometimes used as 'power stations' in remote, sunny areas, such as deserts.

Most satellites get their power from solar cells. The banks of cells look like huge 'wings'.

A pumped storage scheme

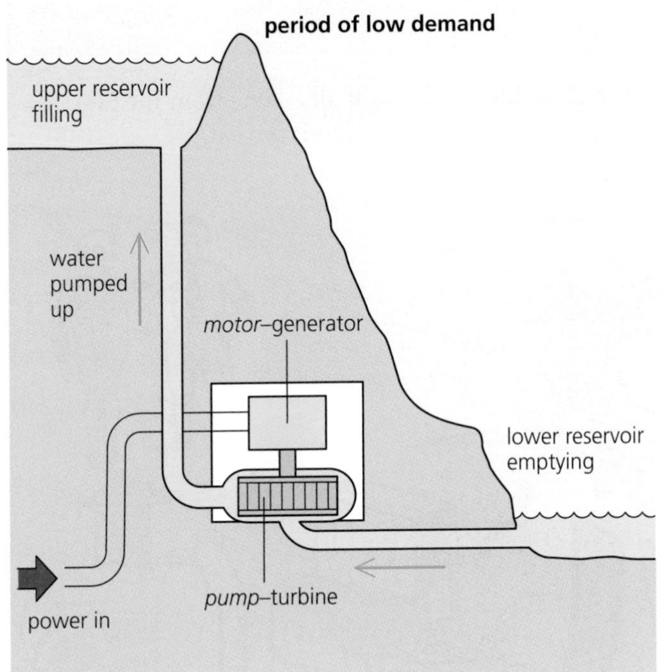

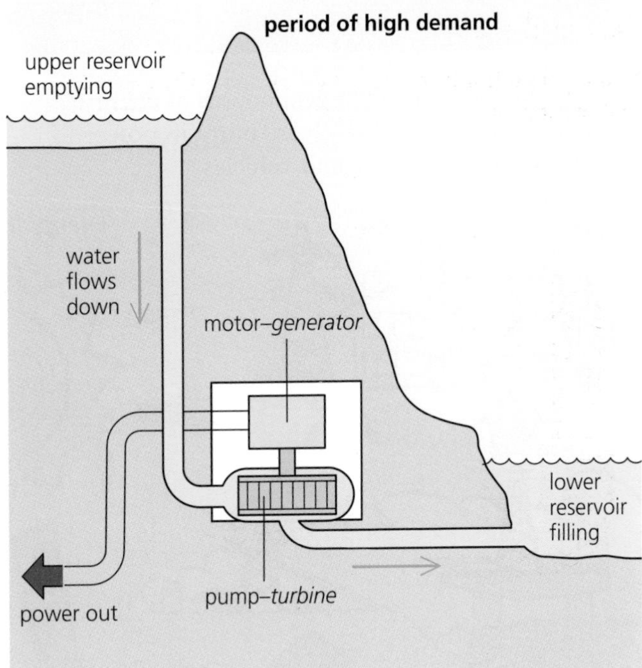

Generating companies must meet peak demand during the day, but at night, their generators may be lying idle. A **pumped storage scheme** like the one above can help solve this problem. When the demand for electricity is low, spare power is used to pump water to the upper reservoir.

When the demand for electricity is high, the water is released so that it flows down to turn the generator. The equipment is designed so that the turbine can be reversed and used as a pump. And when the generator is *supplied* with current, it acts as a motor and drives the pump.

Questions

1 Why is it important that some power stations should have a short start-up time?

2 A Large coal-burning power station
B Combined cycle gas turbine power station
C Nuclear power station
Which of the above power stations has:
a the shortest **b** the longest start-up time?

3 Name *two* types of power station whose output depends on natural conditions, and cannot be guaranteed.

4 Look at the diagrams of the pumped storage scheme above.
a Why is water pumped up to the higher reservoir?
b When is water pumped up to the higher reservoir?
c What happens when water flows down to the lower reservoir?
d What is the reason for building schemes like this?

3.09 Energy resources

How energy is used in the UK

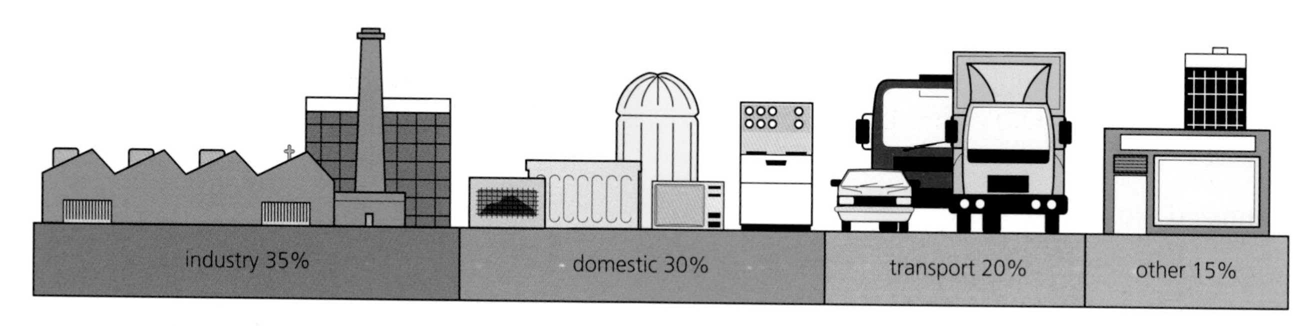

Industrial societies need huge amounts of energy. Most comes from fuels which are burnt in power stations, factories, homes, and vehicles.

The energy in fuels originally came from the Sun. So did the energy in the foods we eat.

Coal, oil, and natural gas are called **fossil fuels** because they formed from the remains of plants and tiny sea creatures which lived millions of years ago. They took millions of years to form in the ground and, when used up, they can't be replaced. They are **non-renewable** energy resources.

At present rates of use, our known reserves, of oil and natural gas should last for 50–100 years, and coal for 200–300 years.

Some energy resources are **renewable**. For example, wood is widely used as a fuel. Once it is used, more can be grown.

Alternatives to fossil fuels: a summary

Wind energy Giant wind turbines (windmills) turn electrical generators. *Aerogenerators* like this can be positioned in a large ground called a *wind farm*.

For: renewable energy resource.
Against: aerogenerators large, costly, and noisy, with relatively low power output. Not enough wind in many areas.

Hydroelectric energy Rivers fill a lake behind a dam. Fast-flowing water from the lake turns generators.

For: renewable energy resource.
Against: few areas of the world suitable.

Tidal energy A dam is built across an estuary. A lake behind the dam fills up at high tide, and empties at low tide. Fast-flowing water turns generators.
The Earth's movement is the source of tidal energy. The Moon's gravitational pull causes 'bulges' of sea water on the Earth's surface. As the Earth rotates, each part passes in and out of a bulge – the tide rises and falls.

For: renewable energy resource.
Against: very expensive to set up: few areas suitable.

Wave energy Generators are driven by the up-and-down motion of waves at sea.

For: renewable energy resource.
Against: difficult to build successfully.

Solar energy Solar **panels** absorb the Sun's energy to heat water. Solar **cells** absorb it and produce electricity.

For: renewable energy resource
Against: continuous sunshine needed.

Nuclear energy Radioactive materials naturally release heat. A nuclear reactor speeds up the process. The heat is used to generate electricity.

For: small amounts of nuclear fuel give large amounts of energy.
Against: nuclear radiation extremely dangerous. High safety standards needed. Waste materials from power stations stay radioactive for thousands of years.

Geothermal energy Water is heated by the hot rocks which lie many miles beneath the Earth's surface. The heat in the rocks comes from radioactive materials naturally present in the Earth.

For: renewable energy resource. Huge quantities of energy available.
Against: deep drilling very difficult and expensive.

Biomass energy Fast-growing plants, or *biomass*, are used to make alcohol. The alcohol is used as a fuel, like petrol.

For: renewable energy resource.
Against: huge land areas needed to grow plants; this may upset the balance of nature.

Questions

1 What is the difference between a renewable and a non-renewable source of energy?

2 COAL, OIL, BIOMASS, WIND, TIDES, NATURAL GAS
Which of these are renewable energy sources, and which are not?

3 The energy from petrol originally came from the Sun. How did it get into the petrol?

4 Which of the energy resources in the chart above depend on the motion of water?

3.10 Saving energy

Escaping heat

Lost heat can cost a family well over £500 a year in fuel bills. The illustration on the right shows how the heat escapes from a house.

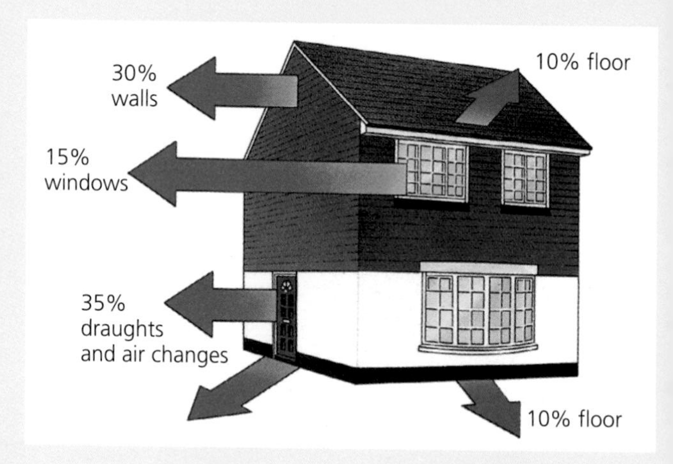

New air for old

Stopping draughts and air changes saves most on the fuel bills. But it can put your health – and even your life – at risk. If rooms are tightly sealed, the oxygen used by people and fires isn't replaced. And dangerous chemicals collect in the air.

For safety's sake, there should be at least one complete change of air in a room every hour. In a draughty house, there may be 15 more. This is good for clearing the air, but it makes the house very expensive to heat.

Low-energy families

The Birkbanks had this low-energy house specially designed and built for them. In winter, the power of a one-bar electric heater is enough to heat the whole house. The house cost them over £500 000, including the land and architect's fees.

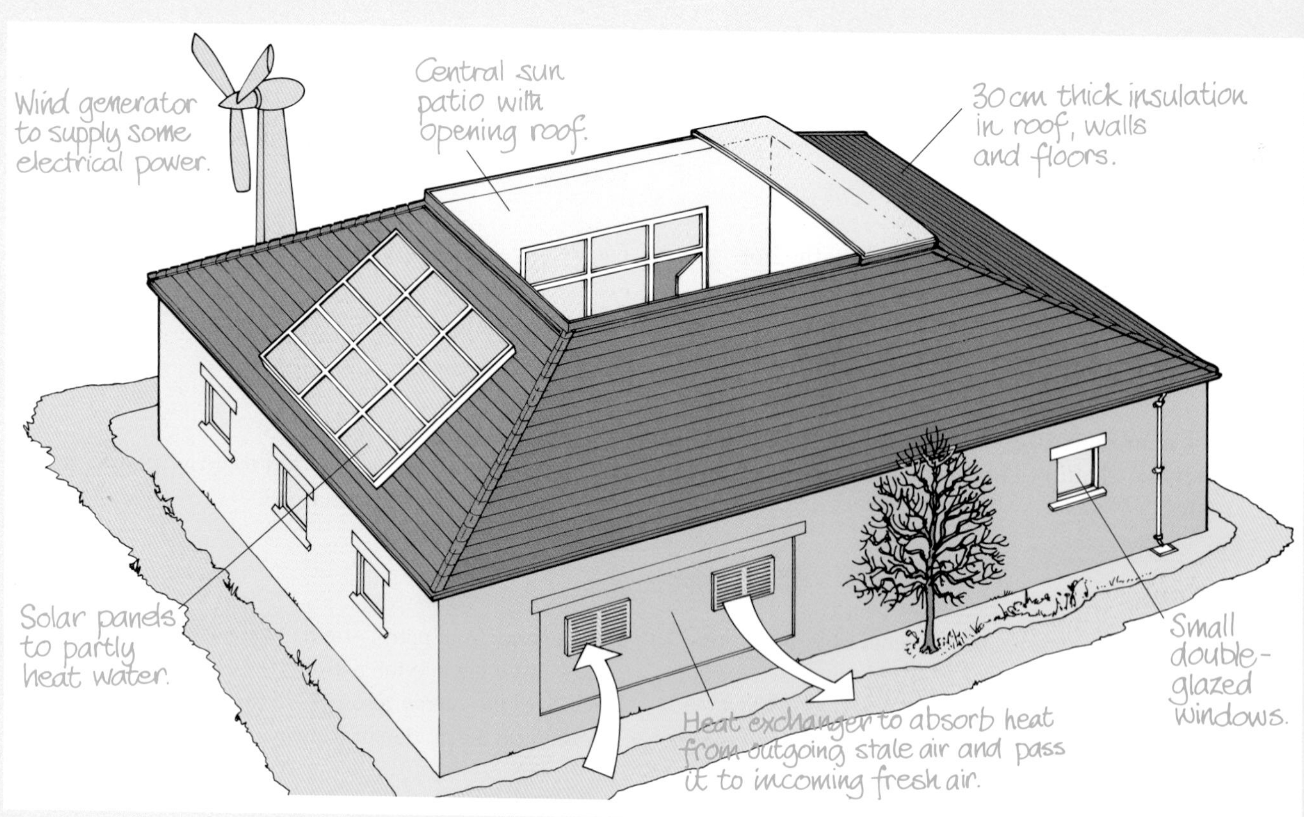

The Cottrells' house is sandwiched between two others. This helps stop some heat loss. But the house is still cold and draughty. They would like to replace the doors and windows with modern ones that fit properly. But they can't afford to. They save energy by heating only one room. It means that their bedroom is very cold in winter, but they can pay the fuel bills.

When power stations generate electricity, much of the energy from their fuels is lost as heat. The heat warms up the cooling water that flows through the power station. Usually, the energy is wasted. But one idea is to use the warmed water to heat buildings nearby.

But there is a problem. Power station water isn't quite hot enough for room heating. To produce hotter water, each power station would have to lose some of its power output. And that would make it more difficult for the electricity companies to stay in profit.

Going to waste

What causes the greatest loss of heat in most houses? Why can it be dangerous to stop this loss completely?

Design a laboratory experiment to find out which loses most heat – a terraced house, a semi-detached house, or a detached house.

How would you set up the experiment and what measurements would you make?

When comparing houses, how would you make sure that your results were 'fair'?

How would you modify your experiment to test whether:

- big houses lose more heat than small houses;
- houses with big windows lose more heat than houses with small windows?

terraced

semi-detached

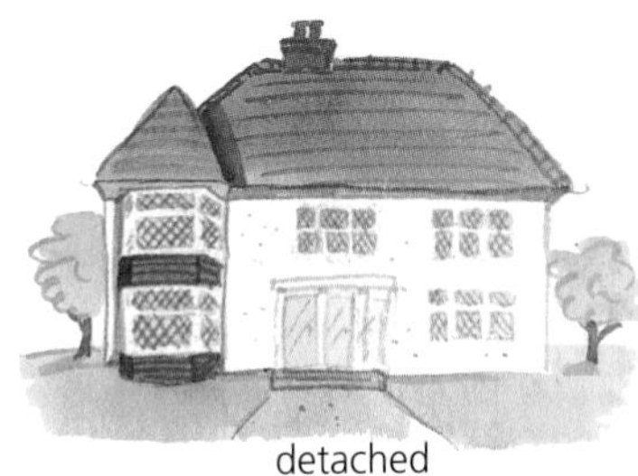

detached

3.11 Thermal conduction

These people are walking over hot coals without getting burned. Is it mind over matter? Not necessarily. It may work because coal conducts heat very poorly. The firewalkers' feet only touch each coal for a short time, so not enough heat flows out to damage the skin.

Conductors and insulators

Some materials are much better **conductors** of thermal energy (heat) than others. Poor conductors are called **insulators**.

Metals are the best thermal conductors. Non-metals like wood and plastic are poor conductors. So are most liquids. Gases are worst of all. You can sometimes tell how well something conducts just by touching it. A metal door handle feels cold because it quickly conducts heat away from your hand. A polystyrene tile feels warm because it hardly conducts away any heat at all.

Poor conductors are called **insulators**. Many materials are good thermal insulators because they have tiny pockets of air trapped in them.

How materials conduct

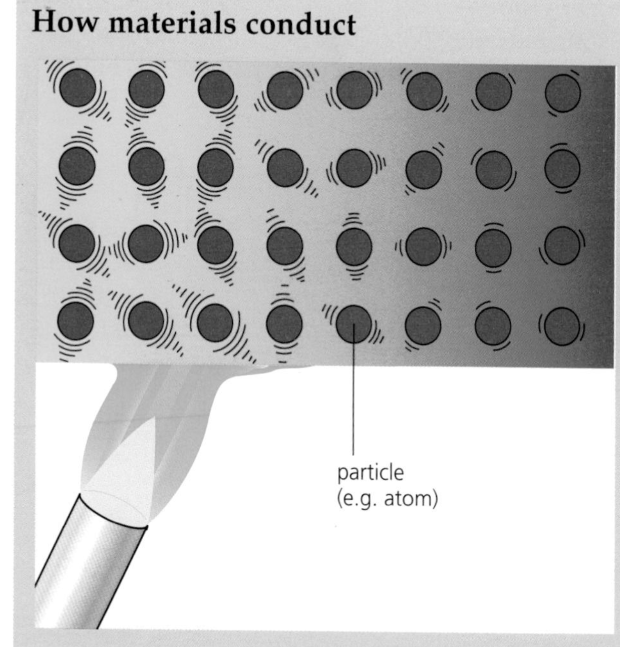

If one end of a metal bar is heated, its atoms gain energy and move faster. They pass on their extra motion to other atoms, so energy is transferred along the bar.

Atoms contain tiny particles called **electrons**. In metals, some electrons are 'loose', and free to move between atoms. When a metal is heated, these free electrons speed up, travel through the metal, collide with atoms, and make them go faster. In most non-metals, the electrons can't move freely, so conduction is a much slower process.

Electricity is a flow of electrons – which is why good thermal conductors are usually good electrical conductors as well.

Good conductors	Poor conductors (insulators)	
best first	glass	
metals, e.g.	water	
copper	plastics	
aluminium	rubber	wool
iron	wood	glass wool (fibreglass)
silicon	materials containing trapped air	plastic foam
graphite	air	expanded polystyrene

Fluffed-up feathers contain trapped air.

Insulating the house

In a house, good insulation means lower fuel bills. Here are some of the ways in which insulating materials are used to cut down heat losses:

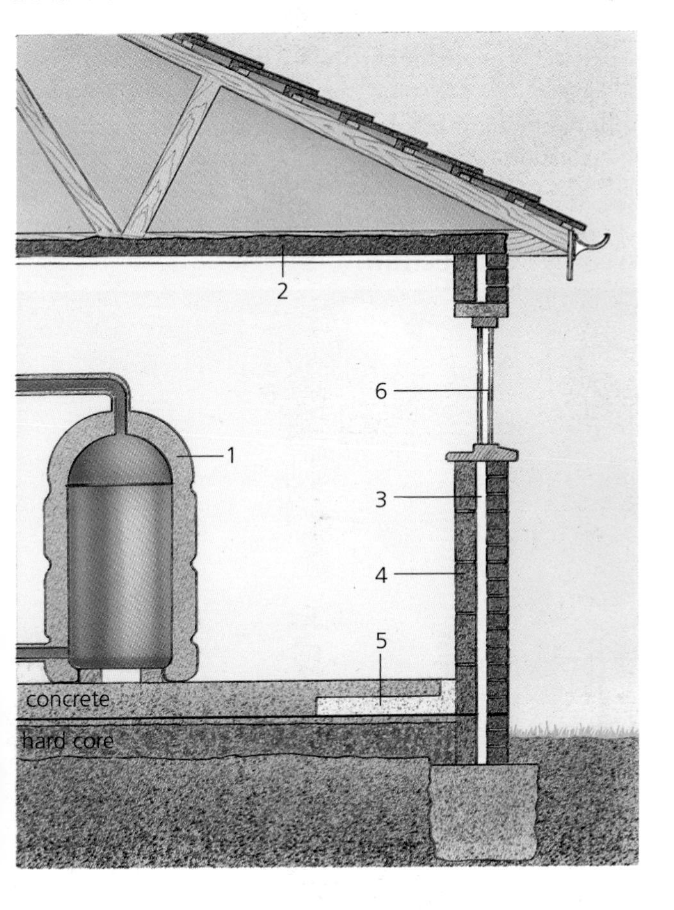

1 Plastic foam lagging round the hot-water tank.
2 Glass wool insulation in the loft.
3 Air cavity between the inner and outer walls.
4 Inner wall built from highly insulating aerated concrete blocks. The concrete has tiny bubbles of air trapped in it.
5 Polystyrene insulation under the edge of the floor.
6 Double-glazed windows: two sheets of glass, with an insulating layer of air between them.

U-values

To calculate likely heat losses from a house, architects need to know the **U-values** of different materials. For example:

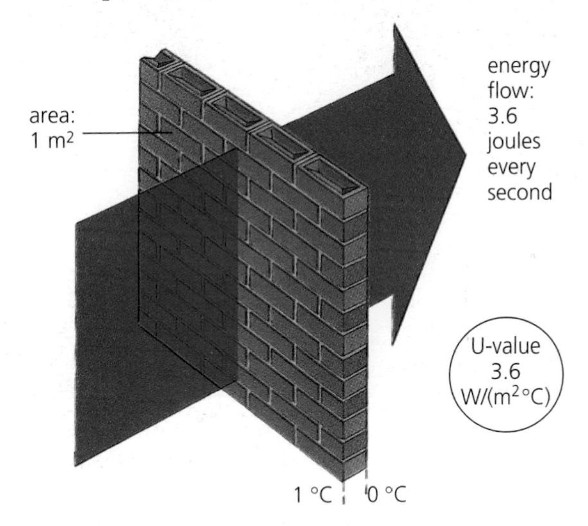

A single-brick wall has a U-value of 3.6 W/(m² °C). This means that the 1 m² wall, with a 1 °C temperature difference across it, will transfer energy at the rate of 3.6 joules every second.

The energy flow would be greater if:
a the temperature difference were higher;
b the area were greater;
c the wall were thinner.

This is how the U-values of different materials compare. The lower the U-value, the better the insulation.

	U-value W/(m² °C)
Single-brick wall	3.6
Double wall, with air cavity	1.7
Double wall, with insulating foam in cavity	0.5
Glass window, single layer	5.7
Double-glazed window	2.7

Questions

1 Explain each of the following:
  a Glass wool is a good insulator.
  b An aluminium window frame feels colder than a plastic window frame when you touch it.
2 Give *three* ways in which insulating materials can reduce thermal energy losses from a house.
3 Why are metals much better thermal conductors than most other materials?
4 Use information from the table of U-values above to help you answer the following.
  a A room has an outer double wall with air cavity. If a single-layered glass window is fitted in the wall, will the heat loss be *more* than it was before, or *less*? Explain your answer.
  b Would your last answer still be the same if the window was double-glazed?

3.12 Convection

Unless the pilot can find a **thermal**, this glider isn't likely to stay airborne for very long. Thermals are rising currents of warm air. They can occur above hilltops, over factories, or under clouds. The problem is finding them. Experienced pilots keep a look-out for circling birds. Birds discovered the secrets of thermal soaring many millions of years before people.
Cooler air sinks, pushing warmer air upwards. The result is a circulating current of air called a **convection current**. Convection doesn't only happen in air. It can occur in all gases and liquids.

Two simple experiments show convection in air and in water:

Cooler air flows in pushing hotter air above the candle. The smoke from the burning straw shows the current of air.

Hot water rises above the Bunsen flame. Cooler water is pushing it out of the way.
Potassium permanganate crystals colour the water so that you can see the current.

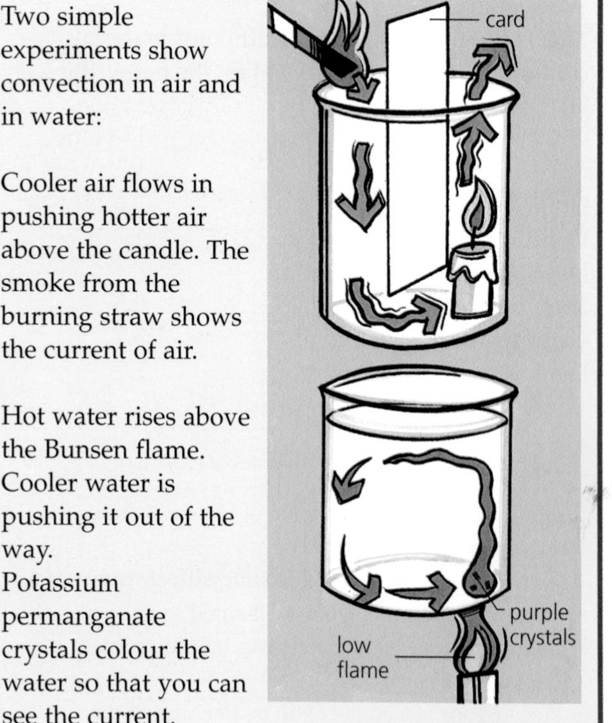

Why warm air rises

When air is heated it expands. This makes it less dense because the same mass now takes up a larger volume. Being more dense, cooler air sinks, pushing the warmer air upwards.

Weather convection

In a cloud like this, warm damp air can rise at speeds of 30 metres per second or more. As the air rises, it cools, and the moisture in it forms new cloud.

Cutting convection

This method works for eggs as well as heads. Put an insulated cover over any warm surface and the circulation of air is cut down. Also, the outside air isn't heated so much. Either way, the heat lost by convection is now reduced.

Using convection

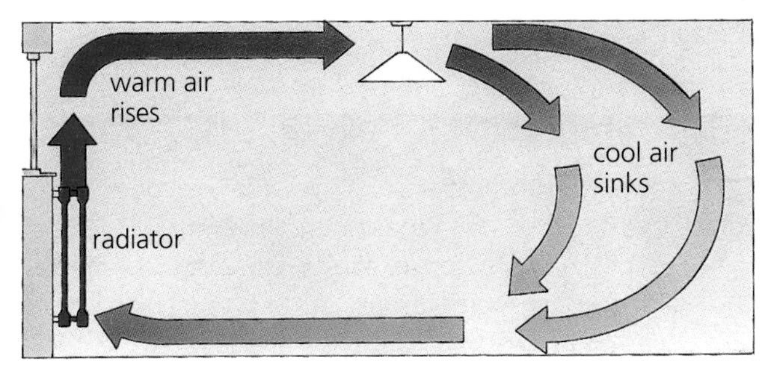

Most of the heat from a radiator is circulated by convection. Warm air rises above the radiator. It carries heat all round the room.

In a refrigerator, cold air sinks below the freezer compartment. This sets up a circulation which cools all the food in the fridge.

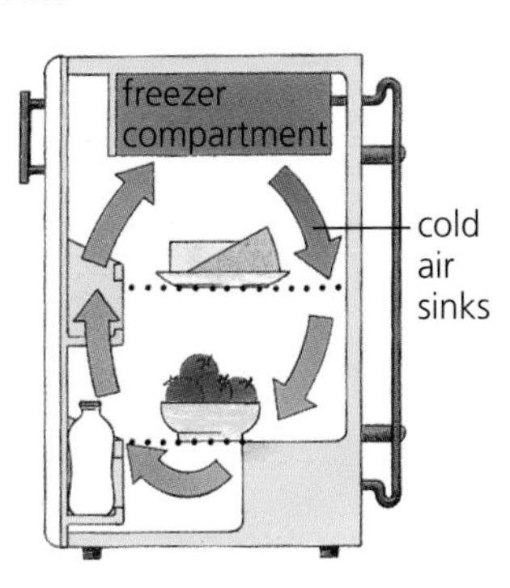

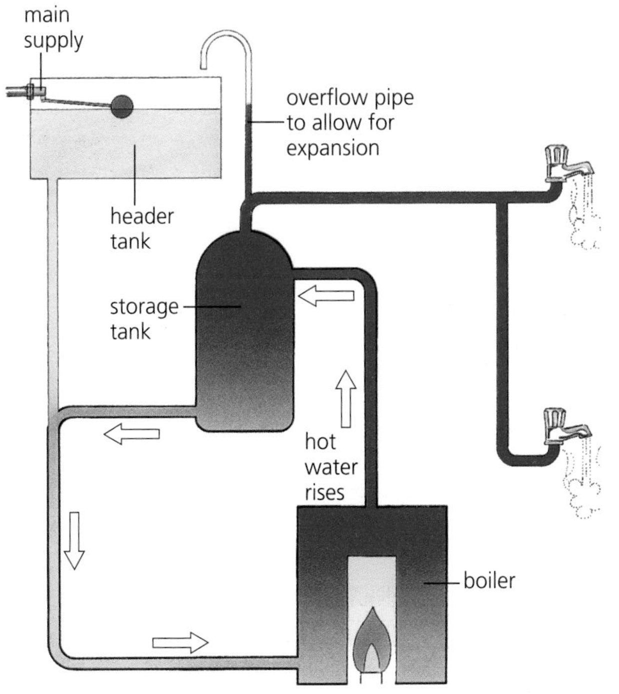

The diagram above shows a simple system for supplying taps with hot water. Water is heated in the boiler. It rises to the storage tank. Cooler water is pushing it out of the way. It too is heated. In time, a supply of hot water collects in the tank from the top down. The header tank provides the pressure to push the hot water out of the taps.

Questions

1 Explain why:

a The freezer compartment in a fridge is placed at the top.

b A fridge doesn't work properly if the food is too tightly packed inside.

c A radiator quickly warms all the air in a room, even though air is a very poor conductor of heat.

d Warm water rises when surrounded by cooler water.

2 This person feels a draught when the bonfire burns fiercely. Why?

Draw a diagram to show the flow of air.

3 Two freshly poured cups of hot tea:

One is covered, the other isn't.
This is how the temperature of each drops with time:

TIME in minutes	0	2	4	6	8	10
TEMPERATURE (covered) in °C	80	73	66	61	56	52
TEMPERATURE (uncovered) in °C	80	67	56	48	42	37

a Plot a graph of TEMPERATURE (side axis) against TIME (bottom axis) for each cup. *Use the same axes for both graphs.*

b What is the difference in temperature between the two cups after 5 minutes?

c Most people don't like drinking tea which is cooler than 45 °C. Estimate to the nearest half minute how long you could leave the uncovered drink before drinking it.

3.13 Thermal radiation

Taking it in . . .

These people are absorbing electromagnetic waves from the Sun. The waves are mostly infrared, light, and ultraviolet (see the section on electromagnetic waves). They warm up anything (or anyone) that absorbs them. They're known as 'thermal radiation' – or just 'radiation' for short.

Some surfaces are better at absorbing thermal radiation than others:

Standing in the sunshine, a black car warms up more quickly than any other. Touch the bodywork to test it for yourself.

. . . sending it out

This marathon runner is giving off radiation after the race. The more she radiates, the more body heat she loses. And that means a risk of chilling. Silvery sheets solve the problem. They're a quick and easy way of keeping everybody warm.

Some surfaces are better at sending out or **emitting** radiation than others:

A black saucepan cools down more quickly than any other. Could you design an experiment to test this for yourself?

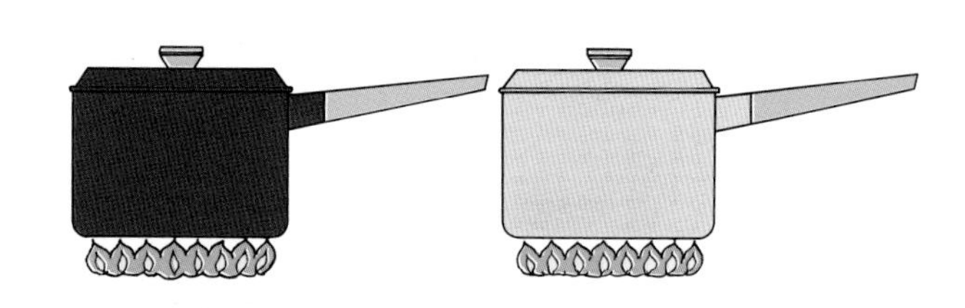

Good absorbers of thermal radiation are also good emitters.
This is how different surfaces compare:

Dull black surfaces are the best absorbers of radiation. They reflect hardly any radiation at all.

Shiny silvery surfaces are the worst absorbers of radiation. They reflect nearly all the radiation that strikes them.

absorbers		emitters
best	dull black	best
	shiny black	
	white	
worst	silvery	worst

Dull black surfaces are the best emitters of radiation.

Silvery surfaces are the worst emitters of radiation.

Keeping your food warm

Shiny aluminium foil helps keep food dishes warm when they're out on the table.

Greenhouse effects

The Sun's radiation passes easily through the glass of a greenhouse and warms the plants inside. The warmed plants also radiate energy, but some of this is reflected back by the glass. That is how a greenhouse traps the Sun's heat. Carbon dioxide in the Earth's atmosphere has a similar effect – it's called the **greenhouse effect**.

Keeping your drinks hot (or cold)

A vacuum flask like the one above can keep drinks hot (or cold) for hours. It has these features for slowing down the energy flow out (or in):

1 A stopper to prevent convection (hot air rising). The stopper is also insulated to reduce conduction.
2 A double-walled container with a gap between the walls. Air has been removed from the gap to reduce conduction.
3 Walls with silvery surfaces to reduce thermal radiation.

Questions

1

Which of these surfaces is best at:

a absorbing thermal radiation?
b emitting thermal radiation?
c reflecting thermal radiation?

2 All three kettles are the same except for their outside surfaces. All are full of boiling water.

dull black

silvery

shiny black

When the kettles are left to cool, this is what happens to their temperature:

	Temperature in °C		
	Kettle A	Kettle B	Kettle C
	100	100	100
After 5 min	85	90	80
After 10 min	73	82	65

a Which kettle has the silvery surface?
b Which kettle has the dull black surface?

3 Explain why:

a In hot countries, houses are often painted white.
b On a hot summer's day, the inside of a white car is cooler than a dark one.
c If you use a lens to focus the Sun's rays on newspaper, the print burns more easily than the white paper.

3.14 Coping with cold

This man has cold hands. But at least the core of his body is warm. And if his temperature drops beneath the normal 37 °C, then his automatic temperature-control system goes into action:

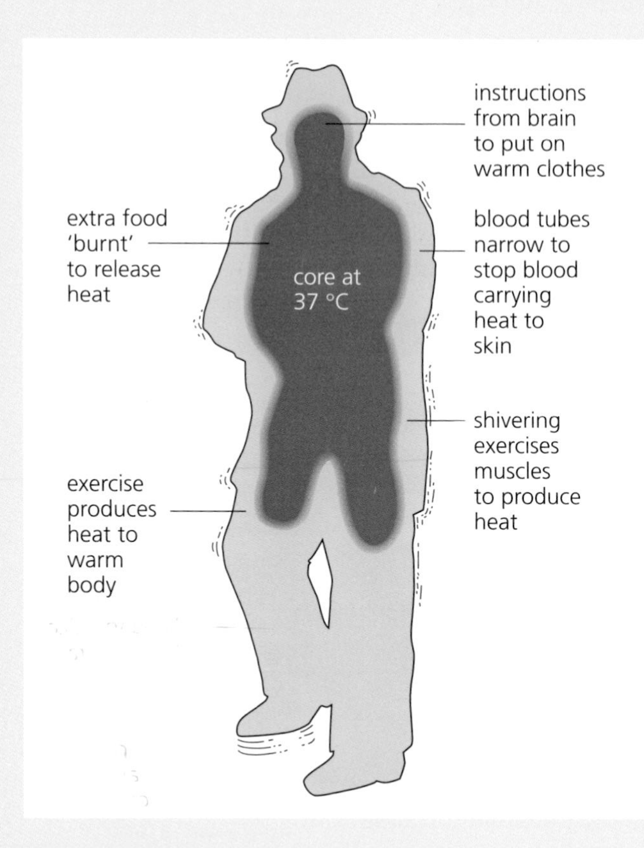

At risk

If the body loses too much heat, the core temperature starts to drop. If it drops more than 2 °C, the body stops working properly. The condition is called **hypothermia**.

Old people are especially at risk from hypothermia. Every winter, thousands of old people die because they cannot afford to heat their homes properly.

Young babies also find it difficult to cope with the cold. They don't store as much body heat as adults, so a loss of heat can have a more drastic effect. And they can't adjust to sudden heat losses because their temperature-control system isn't fully developed.

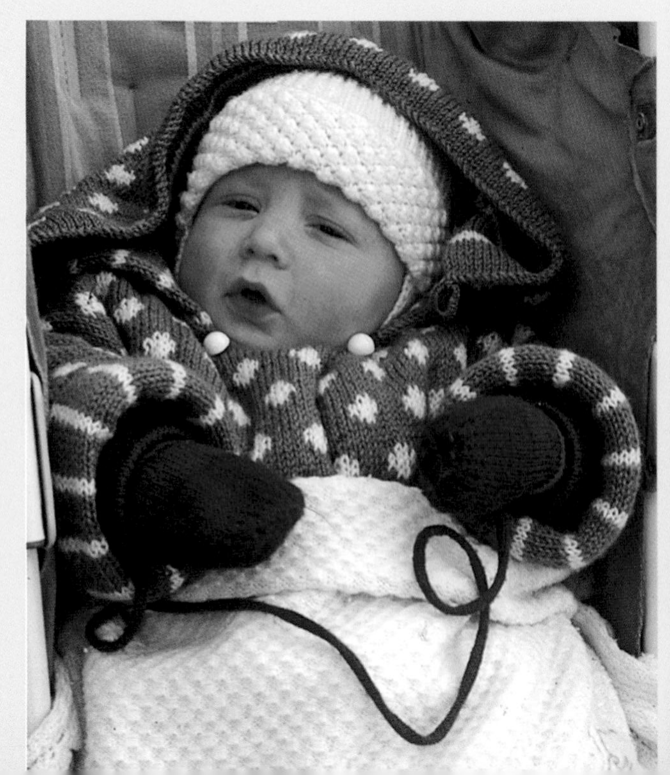

Survival on the hills

In winter and spring a mild sunny day can suddenly turn cold, wet, and windy. Down in the town, the weather is just a nuisance. But for walkers up on the hills, it can be a killer.

Water evaporating from wet clothes quickly takes heat from the body. And a sharp wind makes matters worse. A 30 m.p.h. wind has the same chilling effect as a 40 °C drop in air temperature. Accidents bring extra problems, because the risk of hypothermia ('exposure') is much greater if someone is injured and can't move.

To face the weather, hill walkers need to be properly equipped:

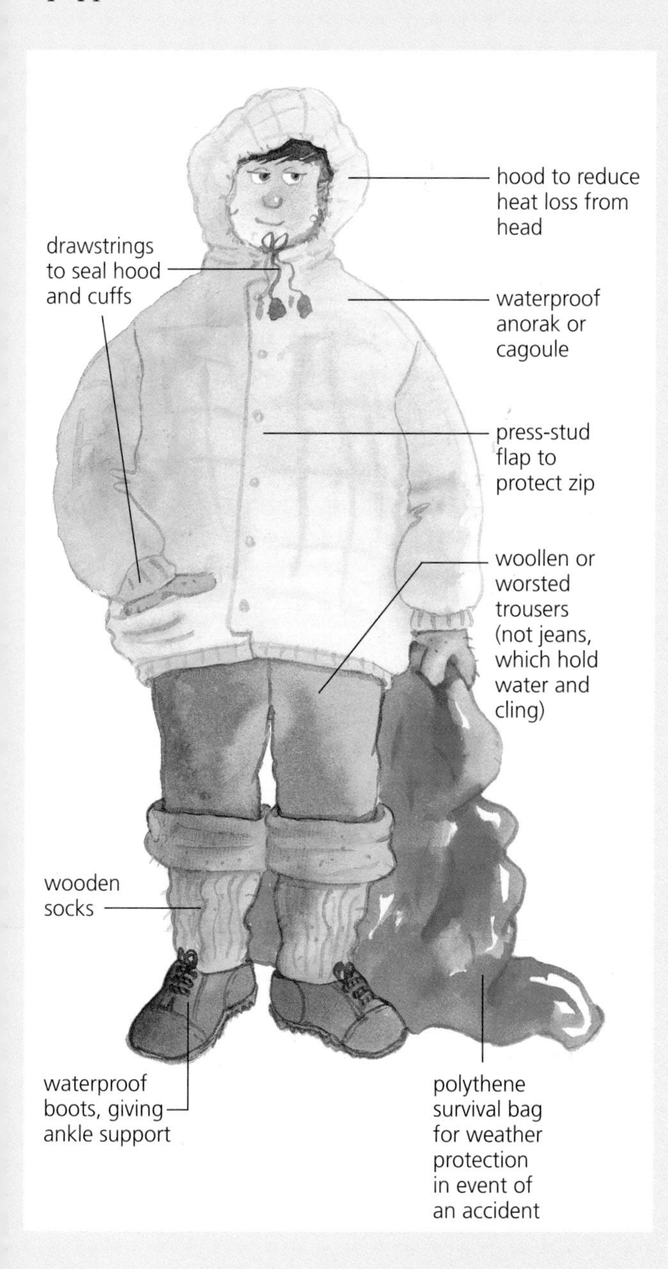

Survival at sea

Without an insulating suit this North Sea diver would be suffering from hypothermia in a matter of minutes. In a cold sea, the human body loses heat over 20 times faster than in cold air.

'Dry suits' made of neoprene provide the best insulation. More insulation comes from thousands of tiny nitrogen bubbles in the suit lining.

Can you think of reasons why:

- babies store less body heat than adults?
- old people are more at risk from hypothermia than younger people?
- hill walkers and climbers are more at risk from hypothermia if they are injured?
- a swimming-pool changing room is kept at a temperature of 25 °C, but the pool itself is kept at 30 °C?

Questions on Chapter 3

1 The diagram below shows how much heat might escape from a house if there was no insulation.

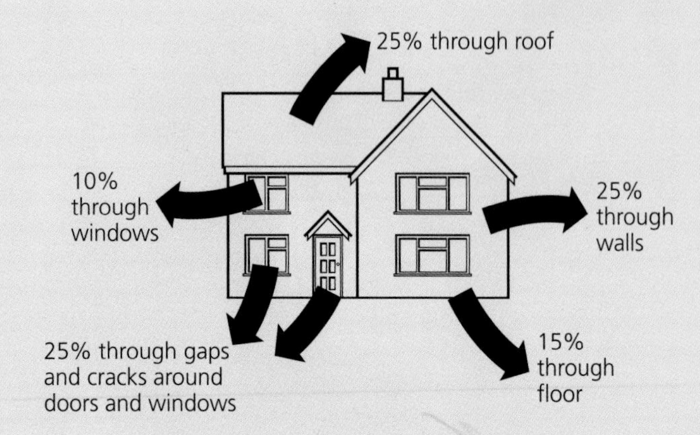

a Suggest *five* methods of reducing the loss of heat from this house.
b Why is it necessary that some hot air should escape through windows, doors, and chimneys?

2 Calculate the work done in the following situations:
a A car is pushed 30 m using a force of 800 N.
b A lawn mower is pushed across a lawn which is 20 m long. A force of 100 N is needed to push the mower.
c A box weighing 50 N is lifted from the floor onto a shelf 3 m above the ground. What kind of energy does the box gain?

3 Calculate the kinetic energy of the following:
a a stone of mass 0.1 kg travelling with a velocity of 20 m/s
b a car of mass 500 kg travelling with a velocity of 100 m/s
c a bullet of mass 0.01 kg travelling with a velocity of 500 m/s.
The bullet in **c** strikes a fixed wooden target. What happens to the kinetic energy of the bullet?

4 The diagram below shows a hydroelectric scheme. Water rushes down from the top of the lake to the power station. In the power station, the water turns a turbine which drives a generator.

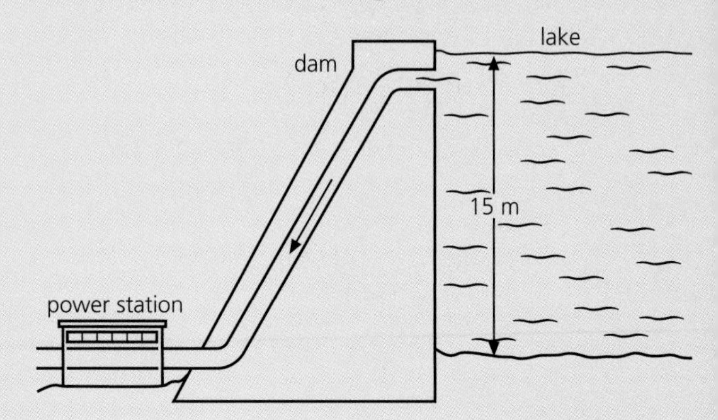

a What type of energy does the water have when it reaches the power station?
b Some of the water's energy is wasted.
i Why is energy wasted?
ii What happens to the wasted energy?

5 Some workers on a building site have set up an electric winch in order to lift a bucket filled with tiles up to the roof. If the bucket and tiles weigh 500 N:
a What is the minimum force that must be applied in order to lift the bucket of tiles off the ground?
b How much work is done in lifting the tiles 20 m from the ground to the roof?
c What energy transformations are taking place as the tiles are raised?
d If the tiles are lifted 20 m in 10 s, what is the power of the winch?
e If the winch is only 50% efficient, how much energy must be fed into the electrical motor to lift the tiles the 20 m?
f Suggest one or two reasons why the system might be less than 100% efficient.
g How can the efficiency of the system be improved?

6 At night-time when most of us are asleep the demand for electricity is quite small. The generators at the power stations, however, are still working as it is very wasteful and inefficient to turn them off. In some power stations the excess electrical energy they are manufacturing is used to

pump water uphill into dams. Then during the day the water is released and used to drive generators when demand is high.

a What weight of water can be pumped 50 m vertically if the surplus energy from a generator is 2 MJ?

b When released, how much kinetic energy will this water have after it has fallen

i 25 m?

ii 50 m?

What assumptions have you made?

c If the generator driven by the water is only 40% efficient, how much energy is lost?

d Suggest why off-peak night-time electricity is cheaper than daytime electricity.

7 In sunny countries, some houses have a solar heater on the roof. It warms up water for the house. The diagram below shows a typical arrangement.

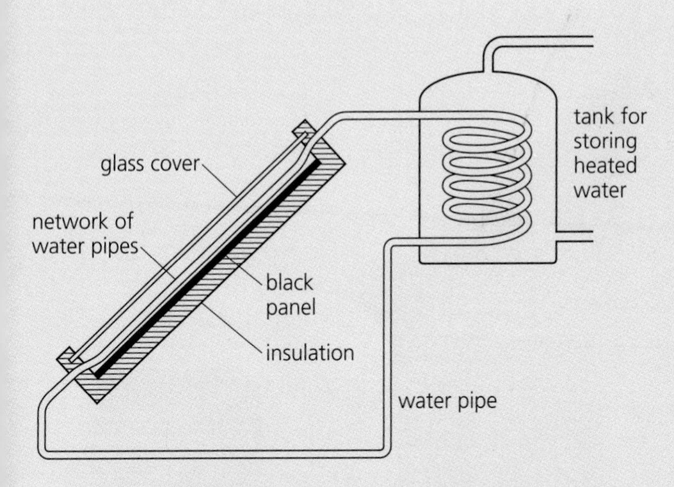

a Why is the panel in the solar heater black?

b Why is there an insulating layer behind the panel?

c How does the water in the tank get heated?

d Why does the solar panel work best if placed at an angle, rather than flat or upright?

e On average, each square metre of the solar panel above receives 1000 joules of energy from the Sun every second. Use this figure to calculate the power input (in kW) of the panel if its surface area is 2 m^2.

f The solar heater in the diagram has an efficiency of 60% (it wastes 40% of the solar energy it receives). What area of panel would be needed to deliver heat at the same rate, on average, as a 3 kW electric immersion heater?

g **i** What are the advantages of using a solar heater instead of an immersion heater?

ii What are the disadvantages?

8 The diagram below shows a hot-water storage tank. The water is heated by an electric immersion heater at the bottom.

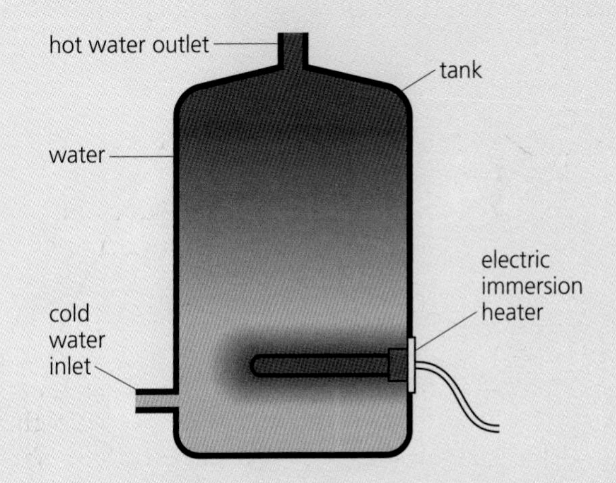

a How could heat loss from the tank be reduced? What materials would be suitable for the job?

b Why is the heater placed at the bottom of the tank rather than the top?

c The heater has a power output of 3 kW.

i What does the 'k' stand for in 'kW'?

ii How many joules of heat energy does the heater deliver in one second?

iii How many joules of heat energy does the heater deliver in 7 minutes?

9 An isolated village uses solar panels and windmills as energy sources.

a Write down one **advantage** of using these energy sources.

b Write down one **disadvantage** of using solar panels.

c Write down one **disadvantage** of using windmills.

Chapter 4

Rays and waves

This hyla tree frog from South America uses the large, inflatable sac under its throat to amplify the sound of its voice. Only the males can do this, and their calls can travel ten times further than sounds from other frogs. The sound itself is generated when air from the sac is blown past two stretched membranes in the bottom of the frog's mouth, making them vibrate. ■

4.01 Rays of light

Almost anything can give out light.

You see some things because they give off their own light: the Sun, for example.

You see other things because daylight, or other light, bounces off them. They **reflect** light into your eyes: this page, for example.

Rays and beams

In diagrams, **rays** are lines with arrows on them. They show you which way the light is going. A **beam** is drawn using several rays side by side.

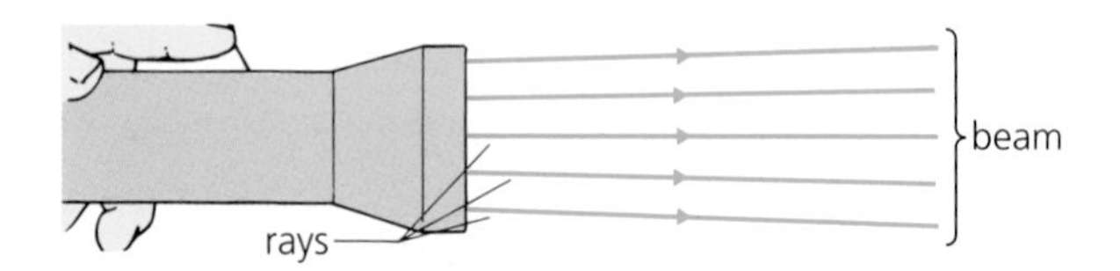

Some facts about light

Light carries energy. This calculator doesn't need a battery to keep it going. Just plenty of sunlight.

Light travels in straight lines. The edge of a laser beam shows you this. You can see the path of the beam because dust in the air glints when light reflects from it.

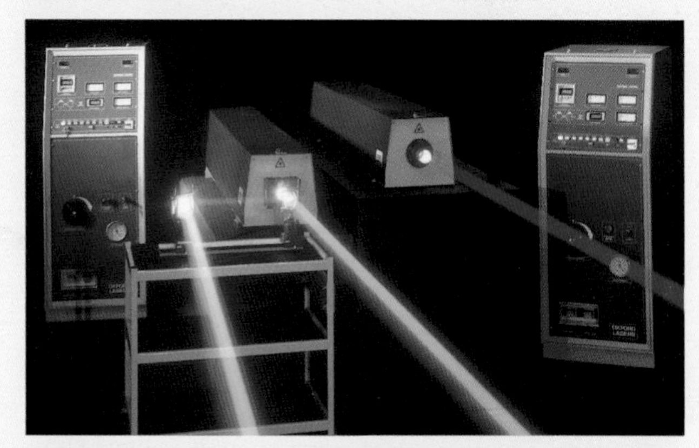

Light waves can travel through empty space. Otherwise it wouldn't be possible to see the Sun and the stars. The waves travel very fast – about 300 000 kilometres every second.

Light is made up of waves. Throw a stone into a pond and ripples spread across the surface of the water. Light travels in much the same way. But the 'ripples' are tiny electric and magnetic vibrations. And they don't need water to travel across.

Part of the family

Light is a member of a whole family of **electromagnetic waves** (there is more on this later in the book). The different types are affected differently by different materials. For example, light is transmitted by glass (it will pass through it), reflected by metal, but absorbed by soot, which is why soot looks black.

Holograms

The picture on the credit card is called a **hologram**. It looks three-dimensional. And its colour changes as you look at it from different angles. The image is actually a pattern of light waves reflecting from the surface of the card. The hologram is put on the card to make it difficult for a forger to copy.

Lasers

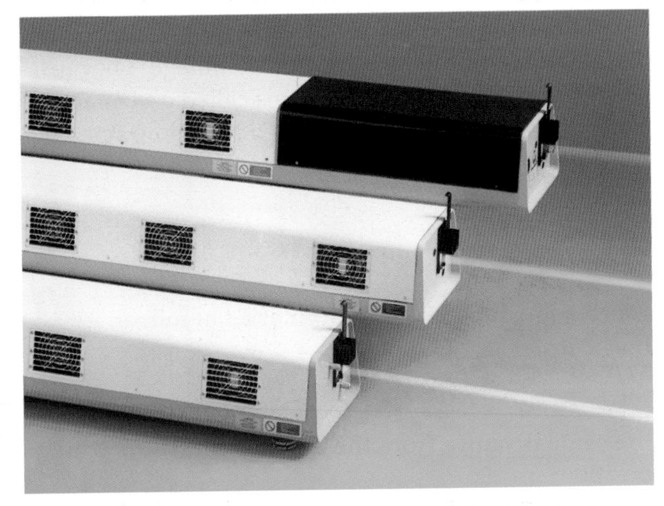

Lasers give out a very intense beam of light. The beam is extremely narrow. It is just one colour.

Surgeons use lasers in delicate operations on eyes and nerves. The fine beam gives a concentrated heat which can seal blood vessels and cut tissue very accurately.

Lasers are used in compact disc (CD) players. As the disc rotates, light from a tiny laser is reflected in pulses from it. The pulses are changed into electrical signals and then into sound. Telephone systems also use pulses of laser light to send speech long distances through **optical fibres**. Look at the index to find out more about optical fibres.

At many supermarket check-outs, the price of each item is 'read' by passing its bar-code over a laser. A detector picks up the reflected beam. The light pulses are changed into electrical signals for the till.

ISBN 0-9538777-2-8
9 780953 877720

Questions

1 Which of the following give off their own light?
A A page of a book;
B The Sun;
C Traffic lights.

2 Write down *three* uses of lasers.

3 A student isn't convinced that light is a form of energy.
He wants evidence for this. What can you suggest?

4 What is the speed of light through space?

4.02 Flat mirrors

The door isn't as smooth as the mirror. It scatters light in every direction.
Mirrors reflect light in such a way that they produce images.

Laws of reflection

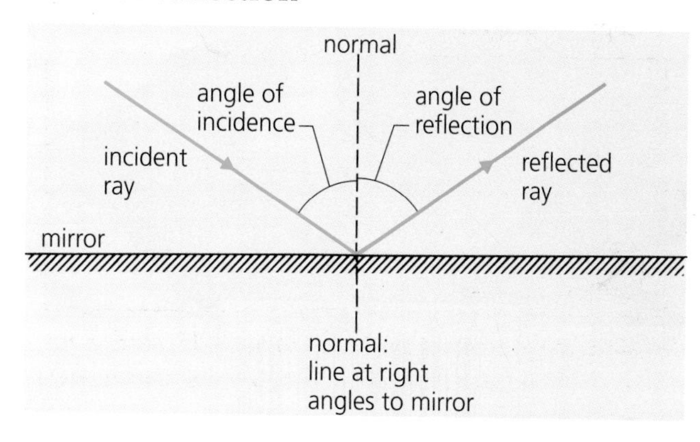

When a ray of light is reflected from a mirror, it obeys two simple rules:

1 **The angle of reflection is equal to the angle of incidence.** The ray is reflected from the mirror at the same angle as it arrives.

2 **The ray striking the mirror, the reflected ray, and the normal all lie in the same plane.** You can draw all three on one flat piece of paper.

These are the **laws of reflection**.

How a flat mirror makes an image

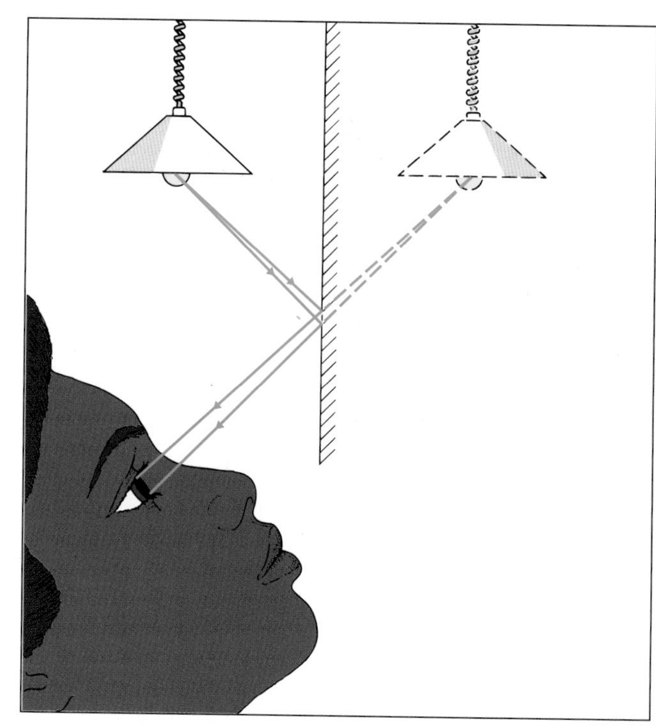

Thousands of rays could be drawn from the lamp. But to keep things simple, only two are shown. The rays are reflected into the eye. They seem to come from a position behind the mirror. This is where you would see an image of the lamp.

Rays don't actually pass through the image. They just *seem* to come from it. The image is called a **virtual image**. Unlike the image produced by a projector, it can't be put on a screen.

More rules

When something is put in front of a flat mirror, its image is:

the same size;

the same distance from the mirror and in a matching position;

laterally inverted – 'left' becomes 'right' and 'right' becomes 'left'.

Finding the image

You can find the position of an image by experiment:

1 Stand a mirror along the middle of a piece of paper. Draw a pencil line along the back of the mirror. Place a pin upright in front of the mirror. Mark its position.

2 Line up one edge of a ruler with the image of the pin in the mirror. Do this again from another position. Mark the position of the ruler edge each time.

3 Take away the mirror, pin, and ruler. Find out where the ruler lines would cross. This is the position of the image.

Periscope

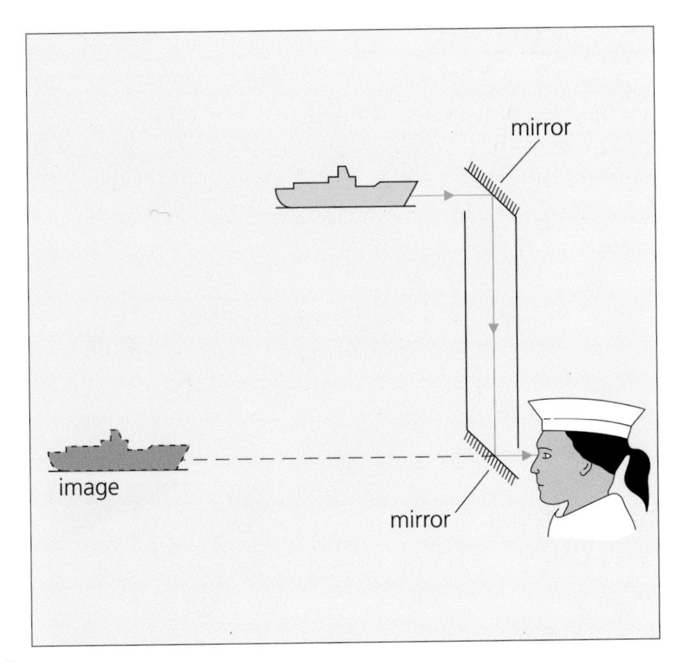

A periscope uses two mirrors to give you a higher view than normal. The image you see is the right way round because one mirror cancels out the lateral inversion of the other.

Note: some periscopes use reflecting prisms rather than mirrors. Look up prisms in the index to find out more.

Questions

1 Copy the diagram.

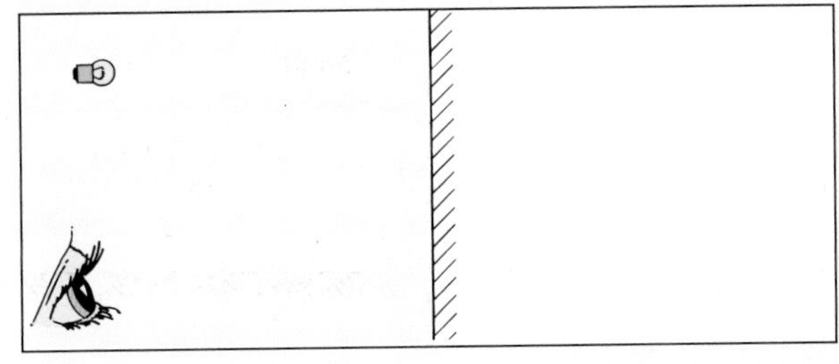

Mark the position of the image of the bulb. Draw two rays which leave the bulb, reflect from the mirror, and enter the eye.

2 This is a plan of a room.

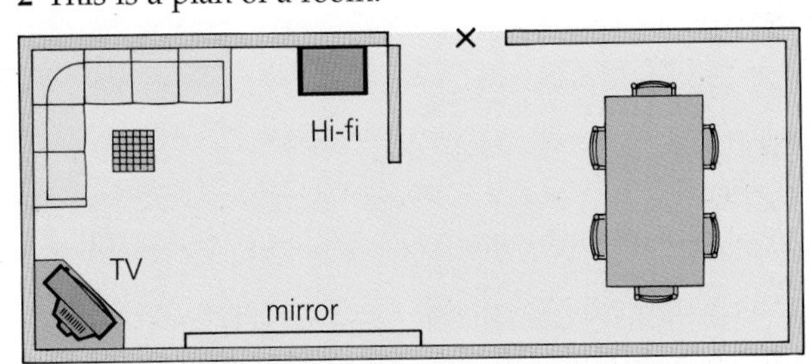

There is a mirror on the wall. If you stood in the doorway at X, would you be able to see:

a the television? b the hi-fi?

3 A girl stands 10 m in front of a flat, large mirror.

a How far away is she from her image?

b How far must she walk to be 5 m away from her image?

4.03 Bending light

It doesn't hurt!

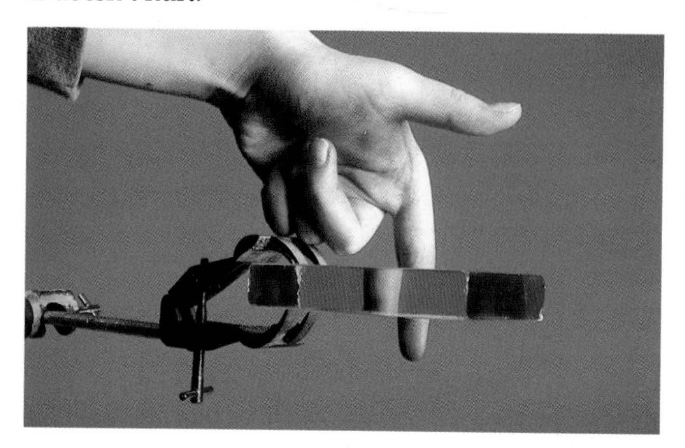

Turn this glass block, and out comes a piece of finger. Or so it seems. In fact, it is the light rays which move, not the finger.

This is how a ray of light passes through a glass block:

The ray is bent, or **refracted**, when it goes into the block. It is bent again when it leaves the block. So, the block moves the ray sideways.
The only time the ray doesn't bend is when it strikes the face of the block 'square on', at right angles.

When light goes into glass, water, or other transparent material, it bends towards the normal. In other words:

> the angle of refraction is less than the angle of incidence.

When light leaves a transparent material, it bends away from the normal.

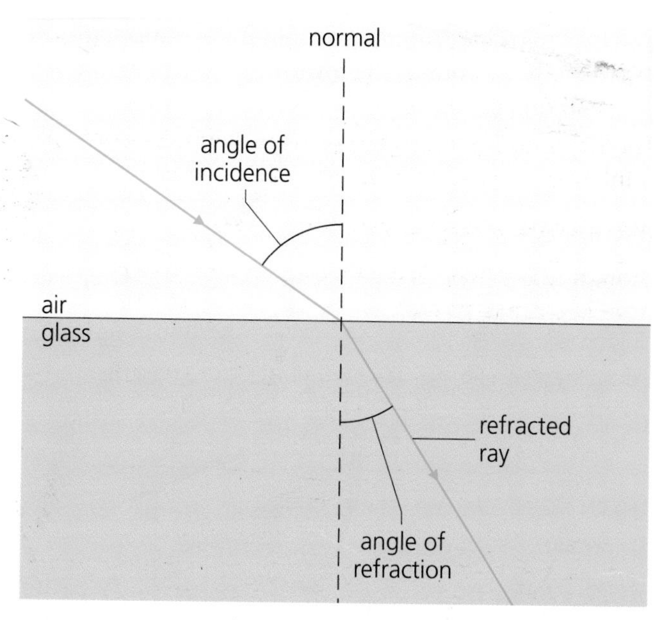

Deeper than it looks

Water never looks as deep as it really is:

Light rays from the pebble bend away from the normal when they leave the water. From above, the rays seem to come from a point which isn't so deep, and is slightly to one side. So the pebble seems closer than it actually is.
Because of this, objects seem larger underwater. When scientists or archaeologists are working on marine life or wrecks, they overestimate sizes and must measure for accuracy.

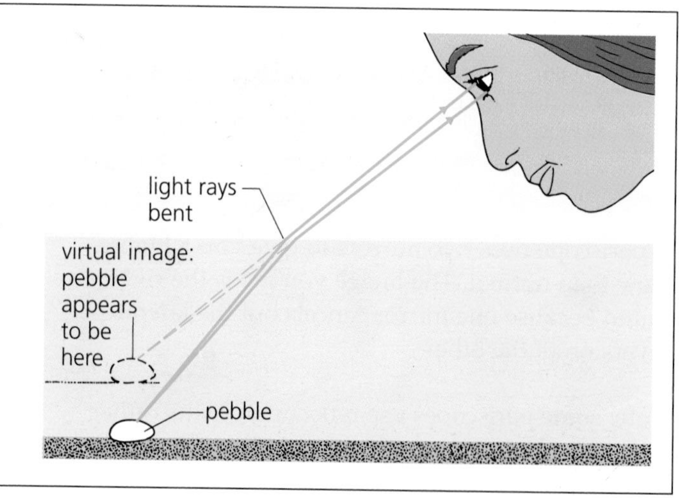

Colour

This is where colours come from:

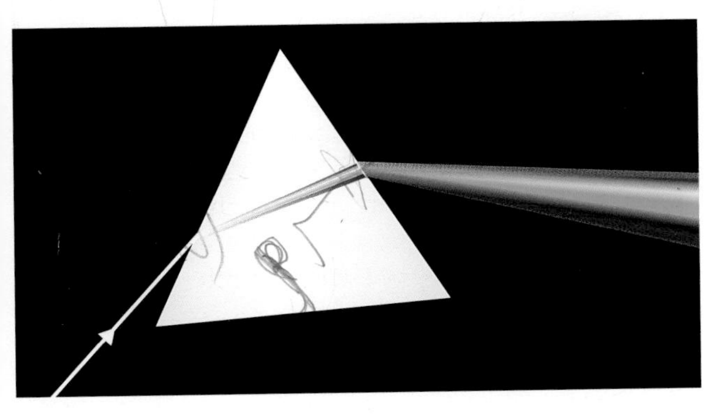

When a narrow beam of white light passes through a prism, the beam splits into all the colours of the rainbow. White isn't a single colour at all, but a mixture of colours. The colours enter the prism together but are bent different amounts by the glass. The effect is called **dispersion**.

The range of colours is called a **spectrum**. Most people think they can see six colours in the spectrum:

red, orange, yellow, green, blue, violet,

though really there is a continuous change of colour from beginning to end.

The different colours are actually light waves of different wavelengths. Red light has the longest wavelength, blue the shortest.

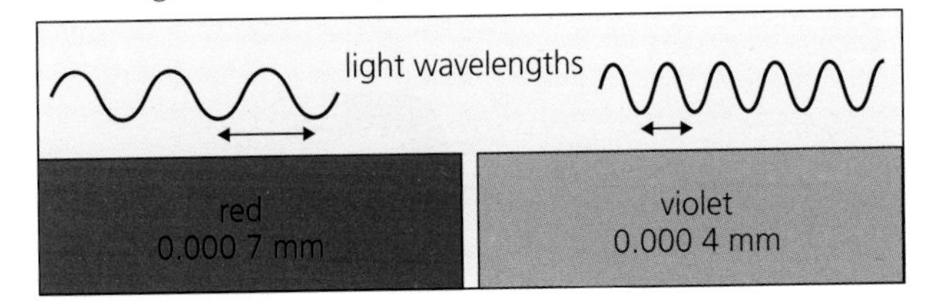

Why light bends

A fast car drives at an angle into sand.
One front wheel strikes the sand before the other.
So one side of the car is slowed down before the other.
The path of the car is bent.
Light isn't solid like a car.
But it too bends because it is slowed down.
The more it is slowed, the more it bends.

In air, light travels at about 300 000 kilometres/second. This is its speed in some other materials:

Material	Speed of light
Water	225 000 km/s
Glass	197 000 km/s
Perspex	201 000 km/s
Diamond	124 000 km/s

(These speeds vary slightly depending on the colour.)

Questions

1 Copy the diagrams below. Complete them to show what happens to each ray of light as it passes through the glass block.

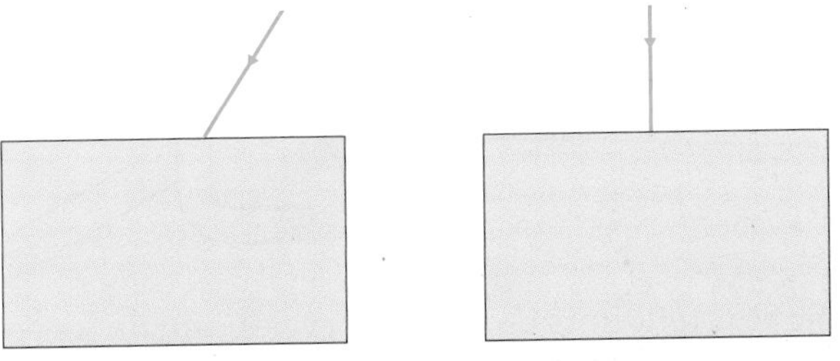

2 Here is a game for a school fête. Scatter some 20p coins over the bottom of a bowl.

To play, you take aim from the side, and throw in a 2p coin. You win if your coin covers a 20p coin.
Explain why you don't have much chance of winning if the bowl is filled with water.

3 The table on this page gives the speed of light in water, glass, Perspex, and diamond.

a Which of these materials bends light the most?

b Compare water with glass. Which of these two bends light more?

c If the blocks in question 1 were made of Perspex instead of glass, how would your drawings be different?

4 Which colour is:

a bent the most by a prism?

b bent the least by a prism?

4.04 Internal reflections

The inside surface of water, glass, or other transparent material can act like a perfect mirror.
The diagrams below show what happens to three rays leaving an underwater lamp at different angles. If light strikes the surface at a angle greater than the **critical angle**, there is no refracted ray. All the light is reflected. The effect is called **total internal reflection**.

The value of the critical angle depends on the material. Here are some examples:

	Critical angle
water	49°
acrylic plastic	42°
glass (crown)	41°
diamond	24°

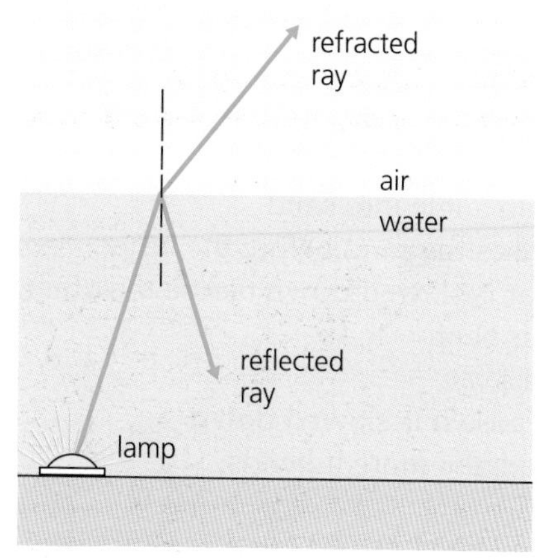

The ray splits into a refracted ray and a weaker reflected ray.

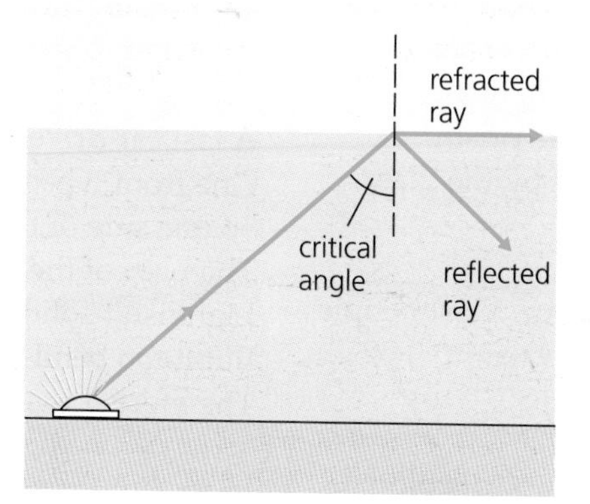

The rays splits, but the refracted ray only just leaves the surface.

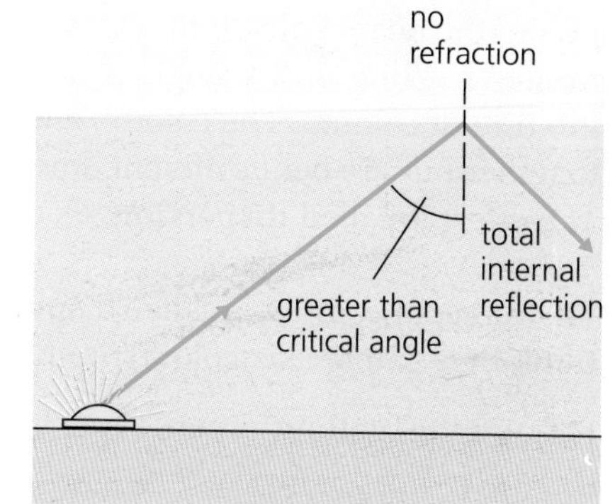

There is no refracted ray. The surface of the water acts like a perfect mirror.

Reflecting prisms

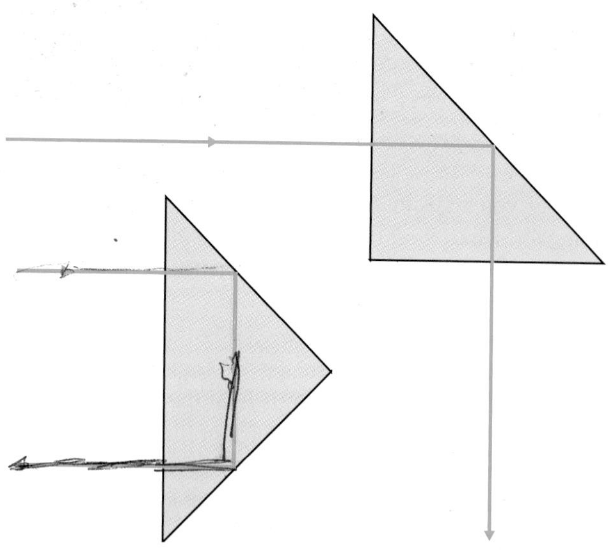

The inside faces of these **prisms** are acting like perfect mirrors because the light is striking them at 45°. That is bigger than the critical angle for glass or acrylic plastic.

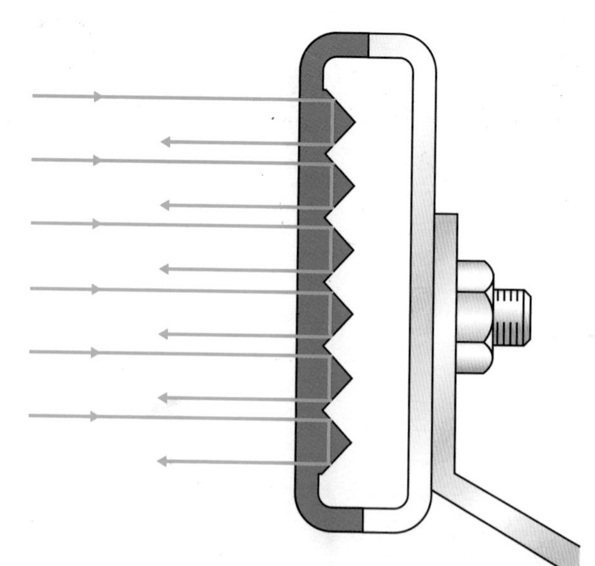

The rear reflectors on cars and cycles contain lots of tiny prisms. These use total internal reflection to send light back in the opposite direction.

Optical fibres

Optical fibres are thin, flexible rods of glass or transparent plastic. Light put in at one end comes out of the other end because of total internal reflection from the sides, as shown below.

Although some light is absorbed as it travels through the glass or plastic, light comes out of the fibre almost as bright as it went in – even if the fibre is several kilometres long.

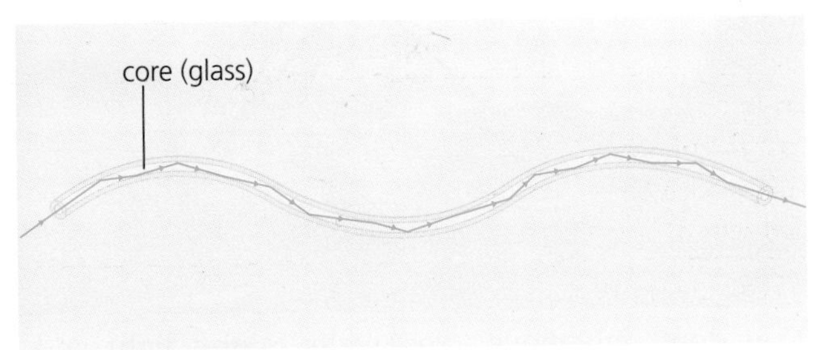

Single optical fibre In the type shown here, the core has a coating around it to protect its reflecting surface.

Bundle of optical fibres If the fibres are in matching positions at both ends, you can see a picture through them.

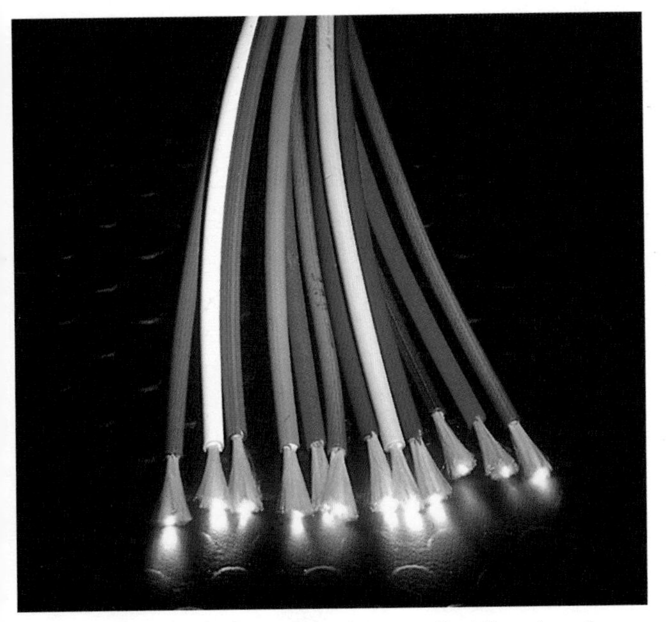

Optical fibres can carry telephone calls. The signals are coded and sent along the fibre as pulses of laser light. Fewer booster stations are needed than with electrical cables.

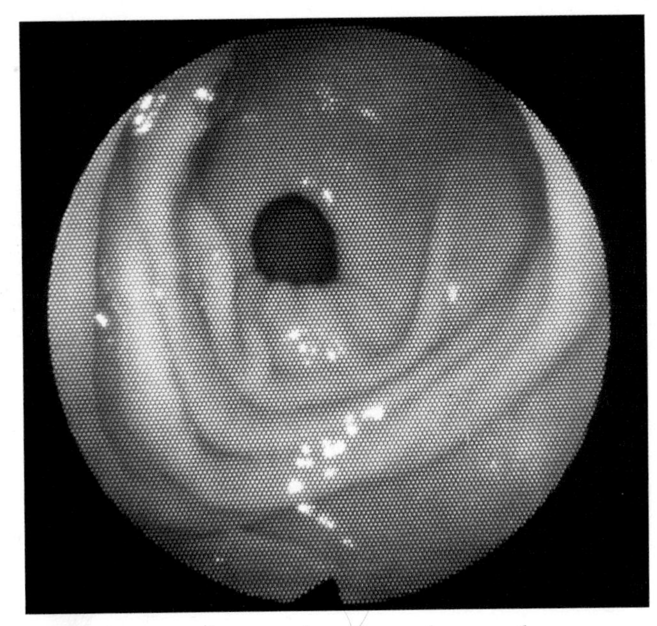

This photograph was taken through an **endoscope**, an instrument used by surgeons for looking inside the body. An endoscope contains a long, thin bundle of optical fibres.

Questions

1 Glass has a critical angle of 41°. Explain what this means.

2 a Copy and complete the diagrams on the right to show where each ray will go after it strikes the prism.

b If the prisms on the right were transparent triangular tanks filled with water, would total internal reflection still occur? If not, why not?

3 a Give two practical uses of optical fibres.

b Give another practical use of total internal reflection.

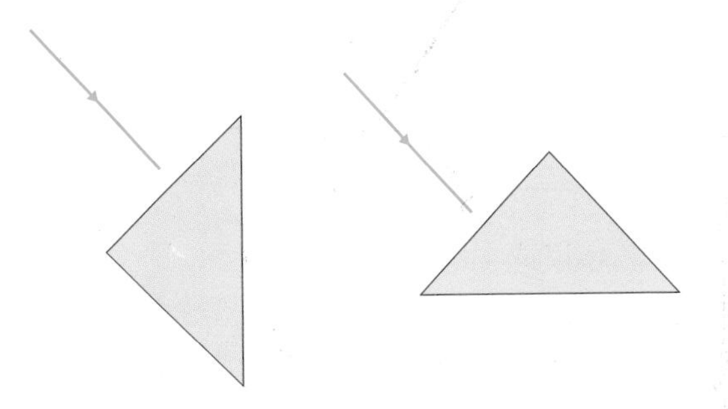

4.05 Waves

Havoc in Alaska

The picture shows the after-effects of a tsunami or 'tidal wave'. It started with a violent underwater earthquake thousands of kilometres away. This set waves racing across the ocean. Far out at sea, the waves were small. Ships moved up and down a metre or so, but no more. But as the waves approached the coast, they grew to an enormous size. Finally, taller than a house, they hit the shore. As they collapsed, they caused a forward rush of water which carried trees, boulders, and boats hundreds of metres inland.

Waves carry energy from one place to another.

They don't only move across water. Sound, light, and radio signals all travel in the form of waves.
There are two main types of wave. You can study them using a stretched 'Slinky' spring.

Transverse waves

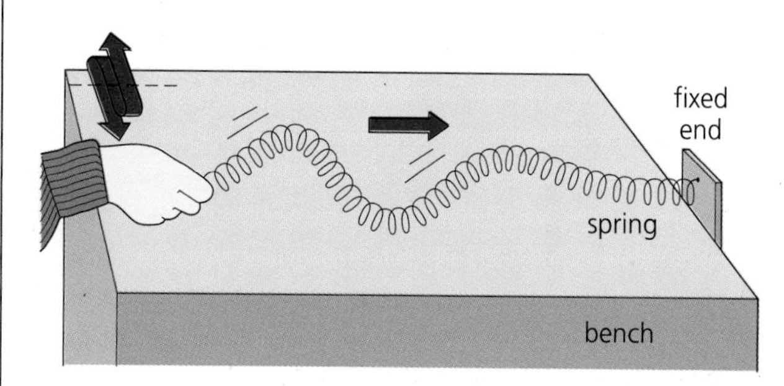

Keep moving one end of the spring from side to side and waves travel along the spring. Each coil moves from side to side but a little later than the one before. Waves like this, where the movements are sideways (or up and down), are called **transverse waves**.

Light and radio waves are transverse waves.

Longitudinal waves

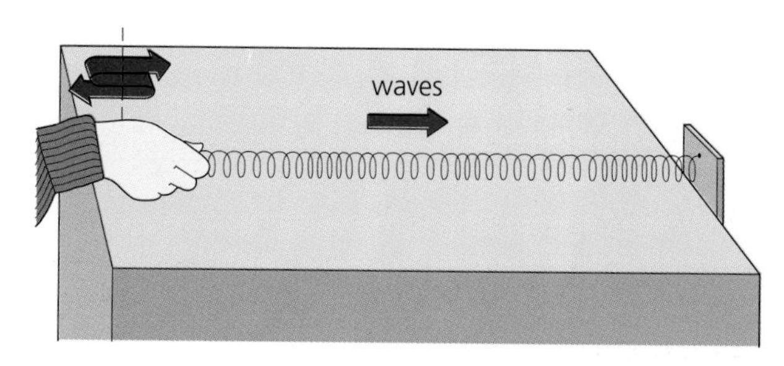

Keep moving one end of the spring backwards and forwards and waves travel along the spring. Each wave is a compression followed by a stretched-out section. Waves like this, where the movements are backwards and forwards, are called **longitudinal waves**.

Sound waves are longitudinal waves.

How to draw waves

Transverse waves can be drawn like this.

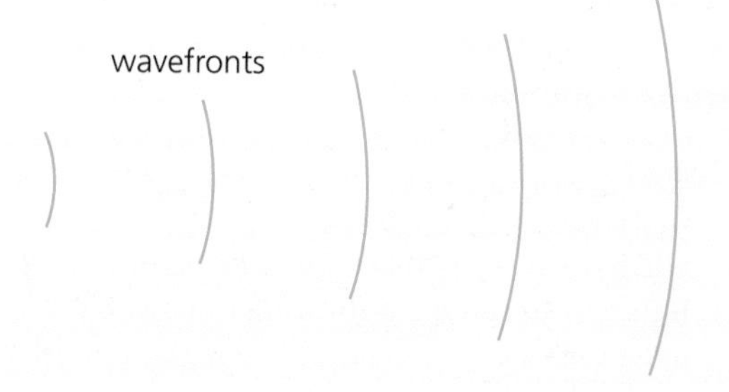

You can also draw waves using lines called wavefronts. Think of each wavefront as the top of a transverse wave, or the compression of a longitudinal wave.

Describing waves

Frequency This is the number of waves per second. It is measured in **hertz (Hz)**. If there are 100 waves every second, the frequency is 100 Hz.

Period This is the time for one complete wave to pass. If there are 100 waves every second, then each one takes 1/100 second so:

$$\text{frequency} = \frac{1}{\text{period}}$$

Amplitude This is shown in the diagram.

Wavelength This is the distance between wavefronts . . . or between any point on one wave and the same point on the next.

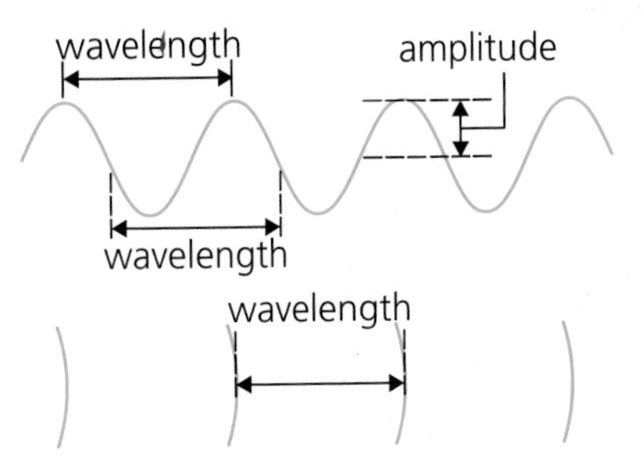

An equation for waves

Imagine waves travelling across the sea . . .

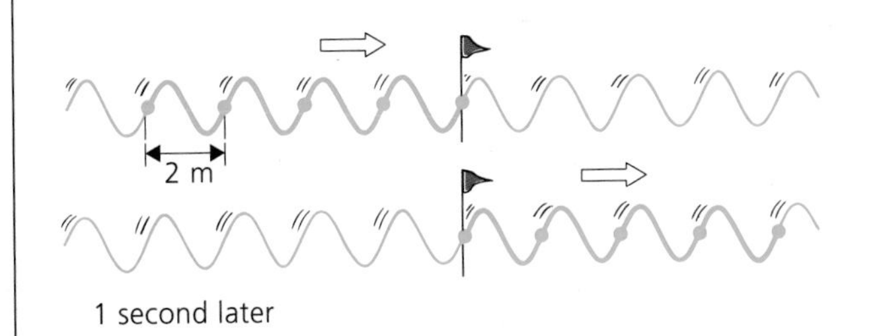

Here, 4 waves pass the flag in one second . . . so the frequency is 4 Hz.

Each wave is 2 metres long . . . so the wavelength is 2 m.

This means that:

The waves travel 8 metres in one second . . . so the speed is 8 m/s.

$$\text{speed} = \text{frequency} \times \text{wavelength}$$

This equation is true for all waves.

In this example,

8	=	4	×	2
m/s		Hz		m

Questions

1

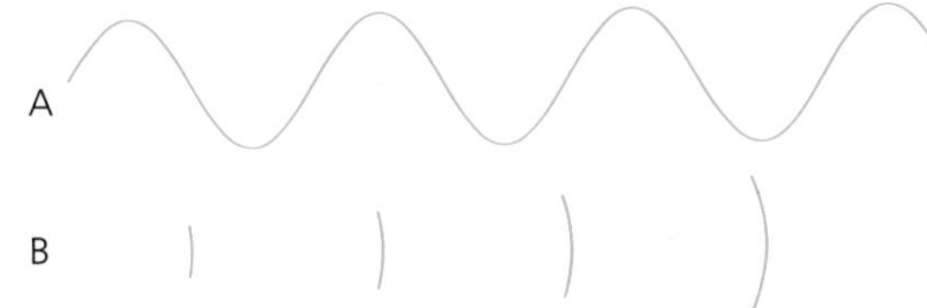

a What type of wave is A?

b Using a ruler marked in millimetres, measure:
the wavelength of A;
the amplitude of A;
the wavelength of B.

2 Three waves travel at the same speed, but they have different frequencies and wavelengths. Copy the chart, then fill in the blank spaces:

	Speed in m/s	Frequency in Hz	Wavelength in m
Wave 1		8	4
Wave 2		16	
Wave 3			1

3 These waves all travel at the same speed:

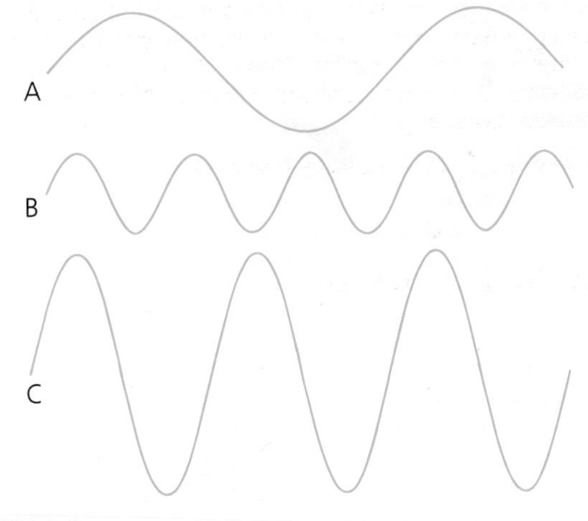

Which has:

a the highest frequency?
b the longest wavelength?
c the greatest amplitude?
d the shortest period?

4.06 Ripples of water and light

This is a **ripple tank** – for studying how waves behave. The shallow tank is filled with water. The vibrating dipper sends ripples across its surface. You place different shapes in the water to reflect or bend the wave 'beam'.

The ripples seem to behave in much the same way as a beam of light. This is one good reason for thinking that light is made up of waves.

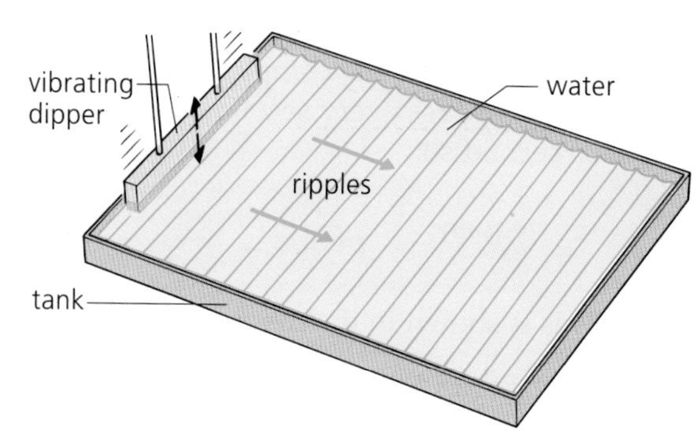

In water

Reflection

In light

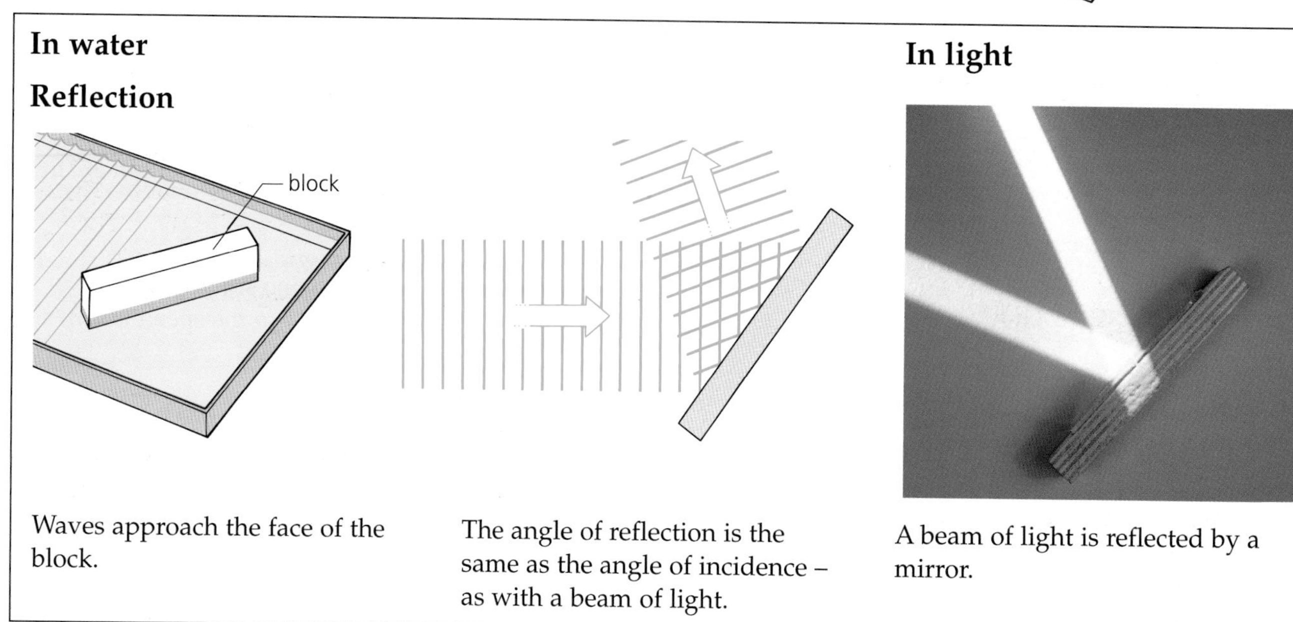

Waves approach the face of the block.

The angle of reflection is the same as the angle of incidence – as with a beam of light.

A beam of light is reflected by a mirror.

Here is another example of reflection:

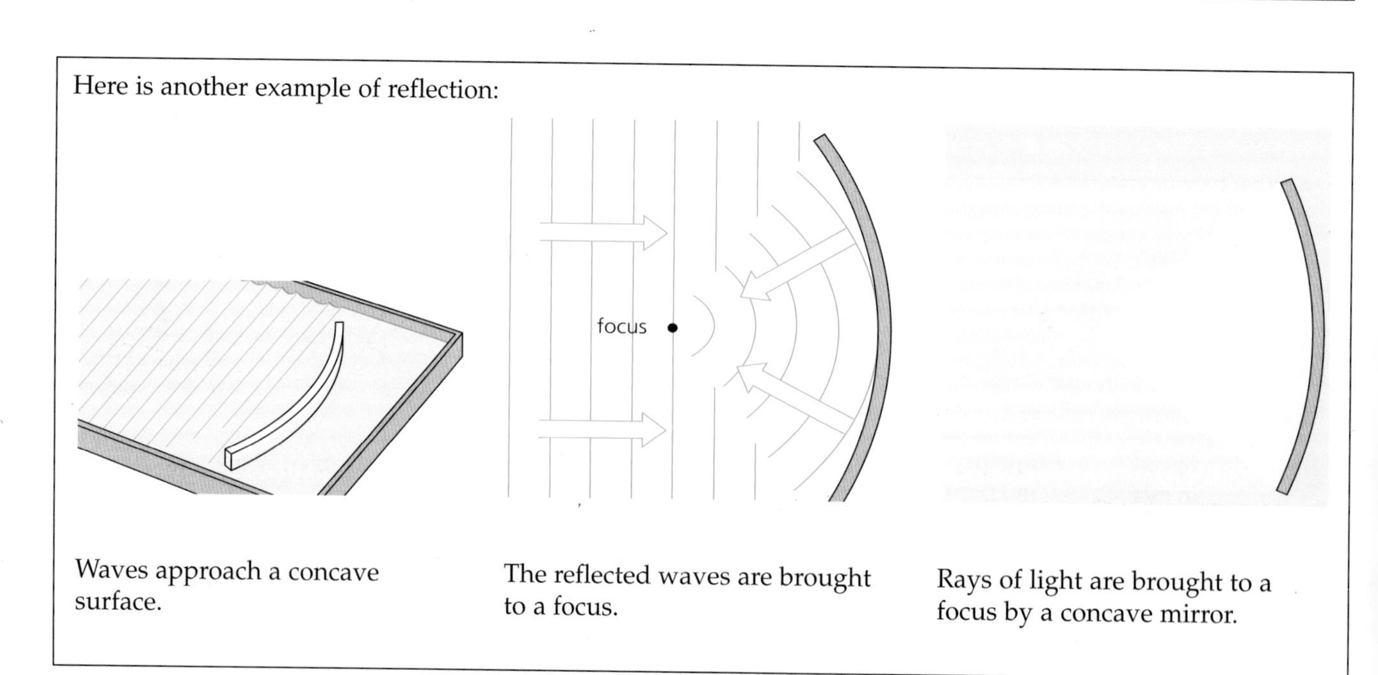

Waves approach a concave surface.

The reflected waves are brought to a focus.

Rays of light are brought to a focus by a concave mirror.

Refraction

ripples slow
in shallow water

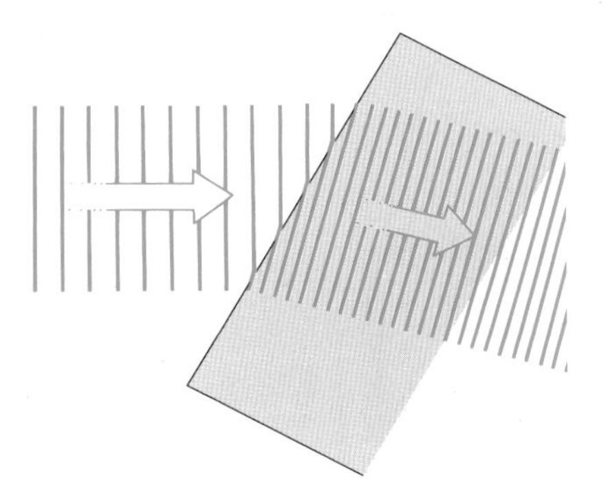

A flat piece of plastic makes the water less deep. This slows down the waves. As they slow down, they bend – like a beam of light.

A beam of light bends when it enters glass.

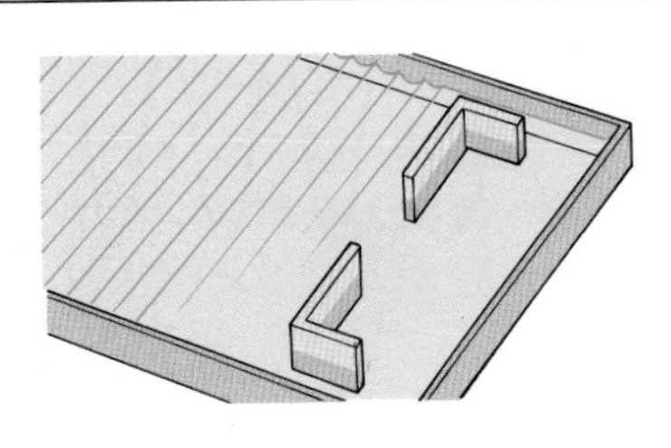

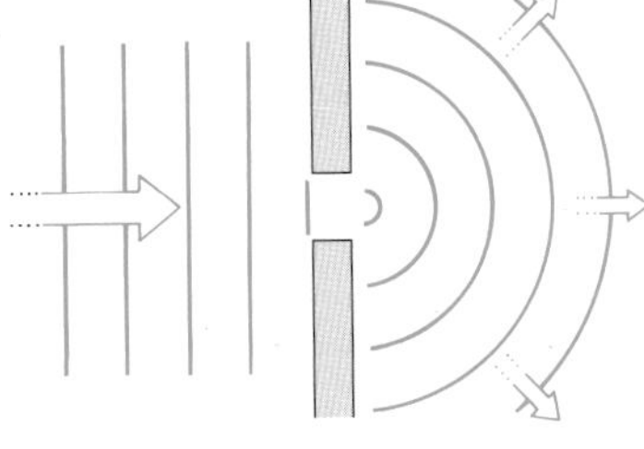

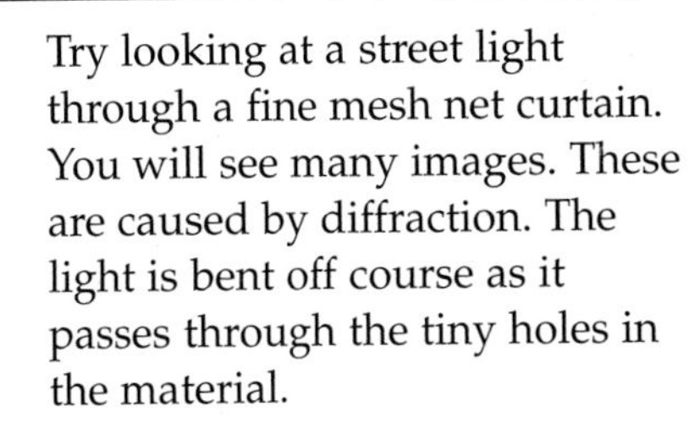

Try looking at a street light through a fine mesh net curtain. You will see many images. These are caused by diffraction. The light is bent off course as it passes through the tiny holes in the material.

Diffraction

Waves bend when they pass through a narrow gap. This is called **diffraction**. It works best if the width of the gap is about the same as the wavelength. Wide gaps don't cause much diffraction.

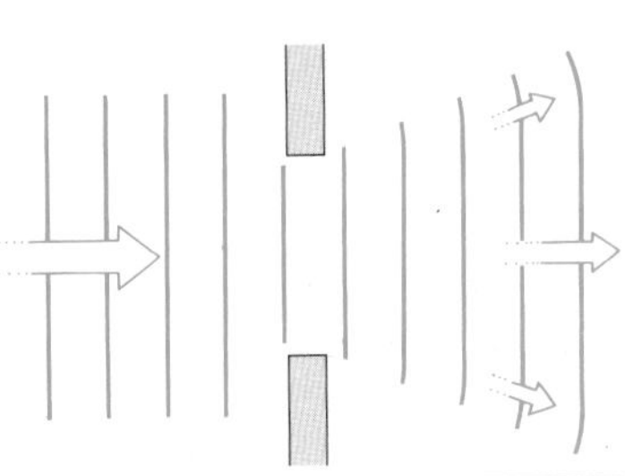

Gaps have to be extremely small to diffract light. What does this tell you about the wavelength of light waves?

Questions

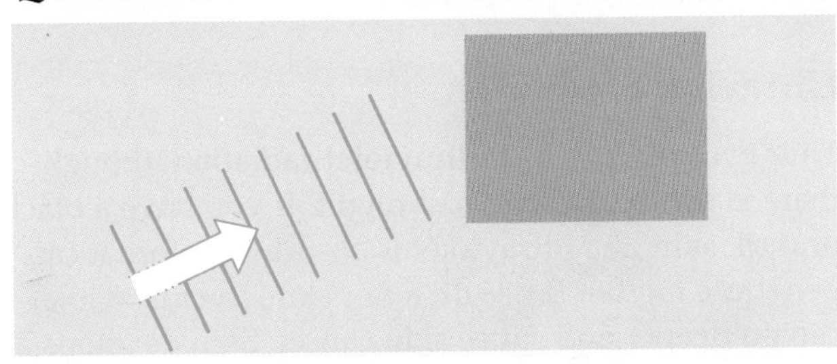

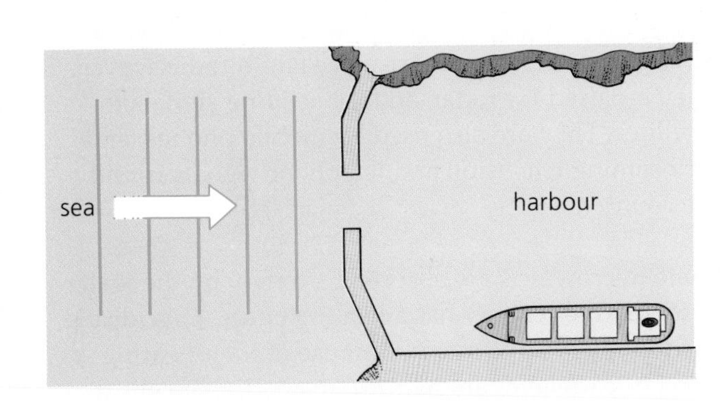

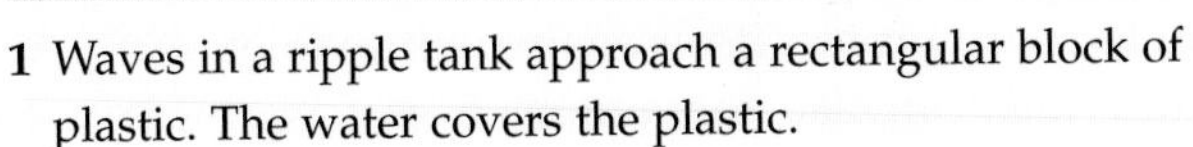

1 Waves in a ripple tank approach a rectangular block of plastic. The water covers the plastic.

a What happens to the speed of the waves when they reach the plastic? What happens to the waves?

b Copy and complete the diagram to show what happens to the waves.

c The plastic is replaced by another block which is deeper than the water. Draw a diagram to show what now happens to the waves.

2 a Copy and complete the diagram to show what happens to the waves when they pass through the harbour entrance.

b What is this called?

c What difference would there be if the harbour entrance were wider?

4.07 Electromagnetic waves

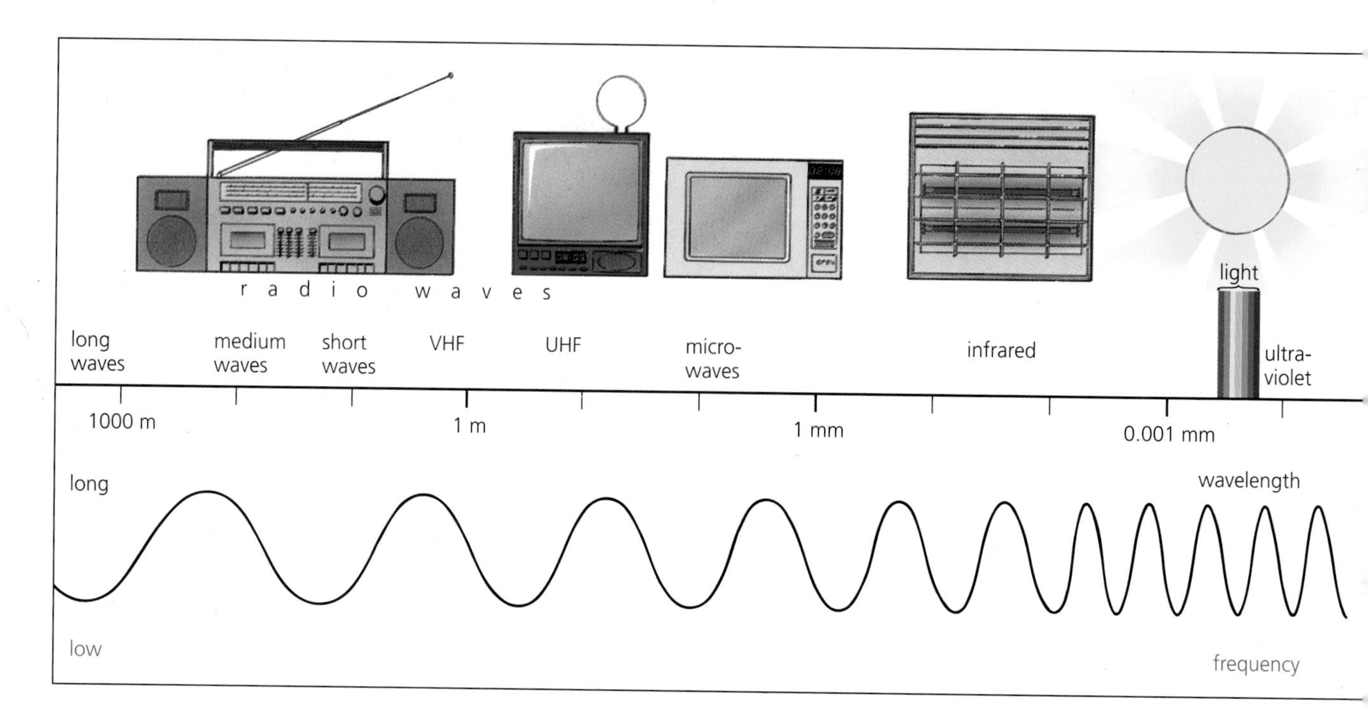

Radio waves

Radio waves can be produced by making a current vibrate in an aerial. They can't be seen or heard. But they can be sent out in a pattern which tells a TV or radio what pictures or sounds to make.

Long and medium waves are used for AM radio.

VHF waves are used for FM stereo radio.

UHF waves are used for television.

Microwaves are very short-wavelength radio waves. They are used for radar, and for sending signals to satellites. They are also used by mobile phones, and for beaming television and telephone signals round the country.

Some microwaves are absorbed strongly by the water in food. Their energy has a heating effect. This idea is used in microwave ovens. Because of their heating effect, microwaves are harmful to any living cells that absorb them.

Infrared radiation

Hot things like fires and radiators give off **infrared** radiation. You can detect it by the heating effect it has on your skin. Too much can cause burns.

As a material gets hotter, its infrared wavelengths get shorter. When it is 'red hot', some wavelengths are so short that they can be detected by the eye.

Security lamps have detectors which send out beams of infrared and pick up the reflections from anyone approaching. In telephone networks, speech and data are coded and sent along optical fibres as pulses of infrared 'light'. TV remote controllers work by transmitting infrared pulses. With infrared cameras, night photography is possible.

Ultraviolet radiation

Your eyes can't detect **ultraviolet** radiation, though there is plenty present in sunlight. If you have a black or dark skin, the ultraviolet is absorbed before it can penetrate too far. But with a fair skin, the ultraviolet can go deeper and cause skin cancer. Skin develops a tan to try to protect itself against ultraviolet. Ultraviolet can also damage the eyes.

Some chemicals glow when they absorb ultraviolet. The effect is called **fluorescence**. In fluorescent lamps, the inside of the tube is coated with a white powder that gives off light when it absorbs ultraviolet. The ultraviolet is produced by passing a current through a gas in the tube.

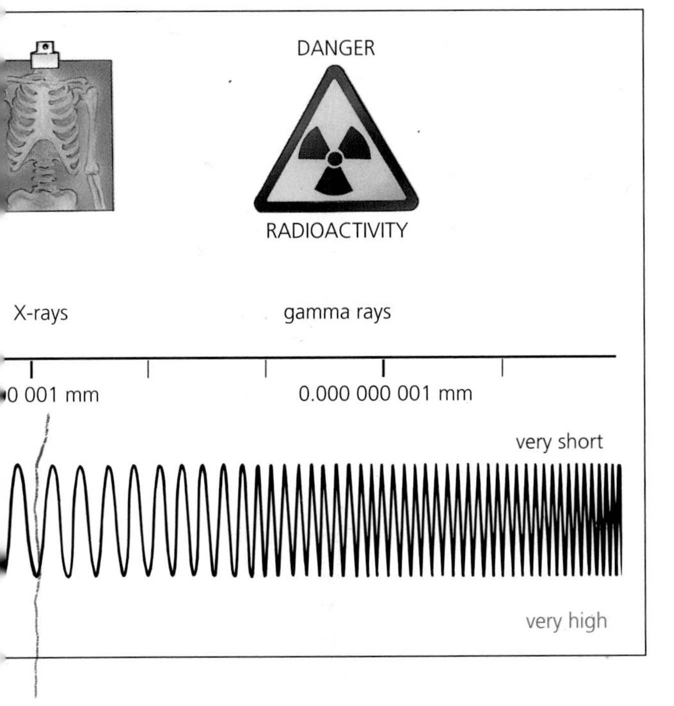

X-rays

X-rays are produced in an X-ray tube when a beam of electrons hits a metal target. Short-wavelength X-rays are very penetrating, and can pass through thick metals. Long-wavelength X-rays are less penetrating. They can pass through flesh but not bone. So, bones will show up on an X-ray photograph.

X-rays can damage living cells deep in the body, and cause cancer. So exposure times must be kept very short, and the people who use the equipment need lead shielding to protect them. However, concentrated beams of X-rays can be used to destroy cancerous cells.

Gamma rays

These are given off by radioactive materials. They are similar to X-rays, and are used for X-ray-type photography and cancer treatment. As they kill harmful bacteria, they are also used for sterilizing food and medical equipment.

Ionizing effect

Ultraviolet, X-rays, and gamma rays cause **ionization**: they strip electrons from atoms in their path. Ionization is harmful to living cells.

Light is a member of a whole family of waves called the **electromagnetic spectrum**. These waves have several things in common:

- they can travel through empty space;
- their speed through space is 300 000 km/s;
- they are transverse electric and magnetic ripples, mostly given off by atoms or electrons as they vibrate or lose energy. (Electrons are tiny charged particles from inside atoms.)

The shorter the wavelength, the higher the frequency. Higher frequencies can deliver more energy when absorbed, which makes them more dangerous.

Questions

1 When the beam from the filament passes through the glass prism, two other types of radiation can be detected, as well as light.
a Which type of radiation is at X **b** is at Y?

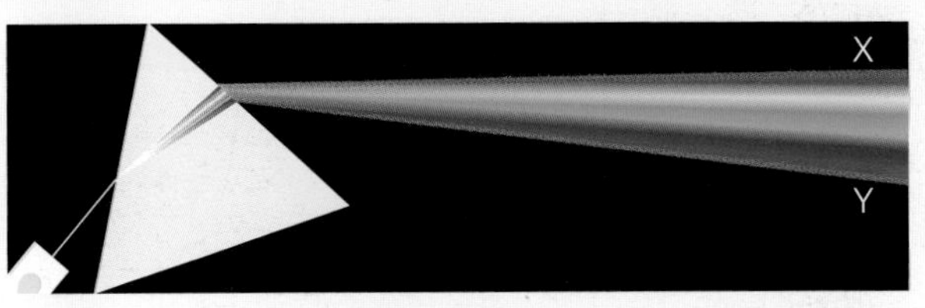

2 Give *two* properties (features) common to all electromagnetic waves.

3 Name one type of electromagnetic wave which:
a can cause fluorescence
b is used by TV remote controllers
c is used for radar
d can pass through metals
e is given off by hot materials
f can be detected by the eye
g causes ionization

4

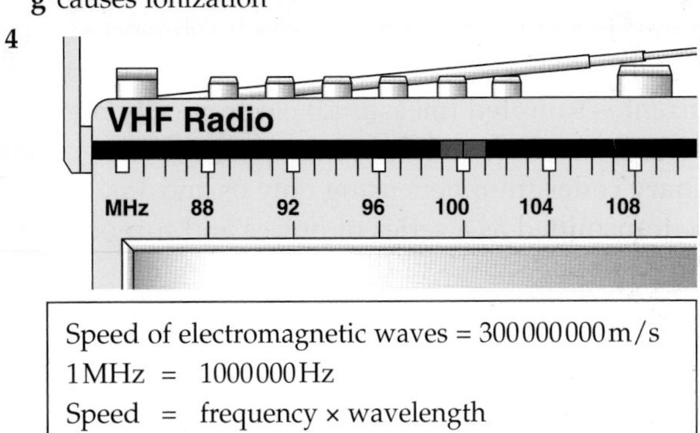

Speed of electromagnetic waves = 300 000 000 m/s
1 MHz = 1 000 000 Hz
Speed = frequency × wavelength

Use the information above to calculate the wavelength of the waves being picked up by the radio.

4.08 Sending signals

Telephone, radio, and TV are all forms of **telecommunication** – ways of transmitting (sending) information long distances. The information may be sounds, pictures, text, or data. It can be sent using wires, light, or radio waves.

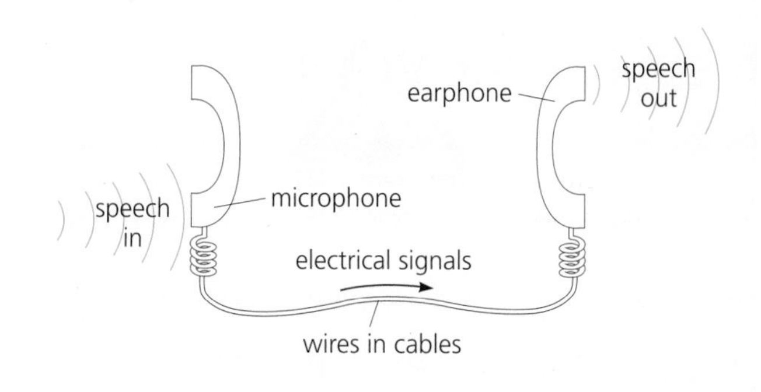

In the simple telephone system on the right, the microphone turns the incoming information (speech) into a changing current. The changes, called **signals**, pass along wires to the earphone. This turns them back into useful information (speech). In a real system, **amplifiers** are used to boost the strength of the signals.

Analogue and digital signals

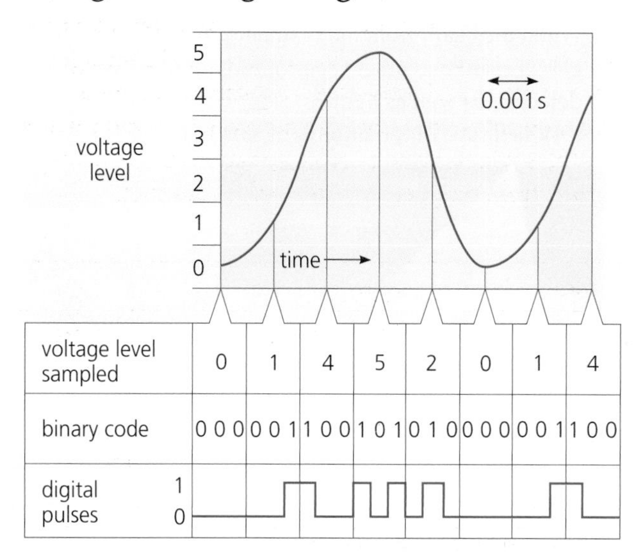

The sound waves entering a microphone make the current through it vary – as shown above. A continuous variation like this is called an **analogue signal**. The table shows how it can be converted into **digital signals** – signals represented by numbers. The current is **sampled** (measured) electronically many times per second, and the measurements changed into **binary codes** (numbers using only 0s and 1s). These are transmitted as a series of pulses and turned back into analogue signals at the receiving end.

Advantages of digital transmission

- Digital signals give better quality than analogue ones, for the following reason. Signals get weaker as they travel along. With analogue signals, some frequencies weaken more than others, and interference spoils the quality. With digital signals, these effects don't matter because the sequence of 0s and 1s still reaches the receiver.
- Digital signals can carry more sets of information every second along a cable (or radio channel) than analogue signals can.

Optical fibres carry digital signals as pulses of infrared or light. Optical fibre cables are thinner and lighter than electric cables, and can carry more signals, with less loss of power.

Using radio waves

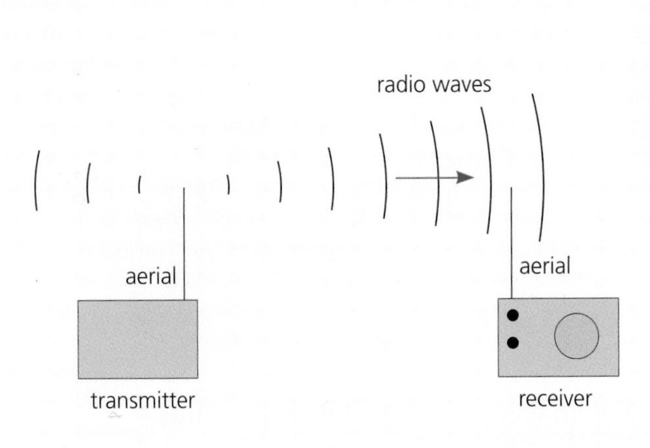

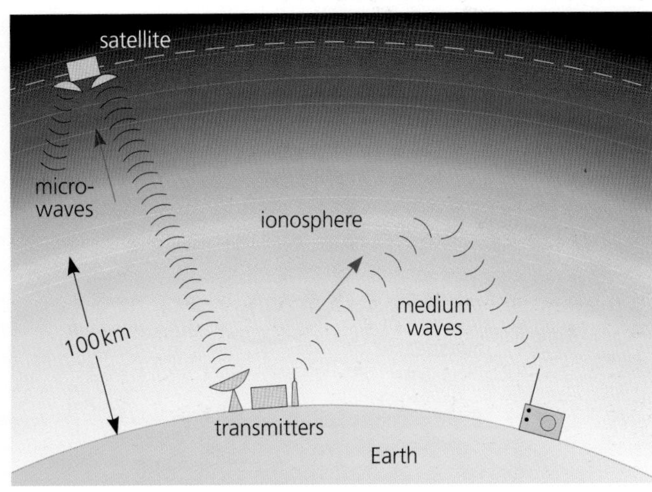

Radio waves are used for radio, TV, and mobile phones. Sent from a **transmitter**, they generate a tiny current of the same frequency in the aerial of the **receiver**. To carry the signals, a set of waves called the **carrier** must be varied in some way. With **AM** (amplitude modulation), the strength is varied. With **FM** (frequency modulation), the frequency is varied. FM is less affected by interference.

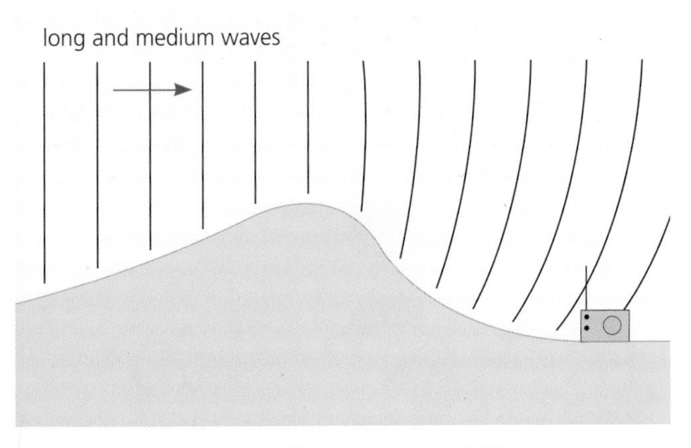

Long and medium waves diffract (bend) round hills. A radio can still pick them up in a valley.

Medium waves are reflected by the **ionosphere**, a layer of charged particles in the upper atmosphere. This increases their range. Higher frequencies, such as VHF, UHF, and microwaves, aren't reflected like this and don't bend round hills. So they need a straight route to your aerial. Microwaves can be beamed across country between dish aerials set on tall towers. Satellites can be used to relay (pass on) microwave signals from one part of the Earth to another.

Typical radio frequencies	
AM radio – long wave (200 kHz)	0.2 MHz
AM radio – medium wave	1 MHz
FM radio (VHF)	100 MHz
television (UHF)	500 MHz
mobile phone	900 MHz
television (satellite)	12 000 MHz

1 megahertz (MHz) = 1 000 000 Hz
= 1 million waves per second

Questions

1 What is the difference between an *analogue* signal and a *digital* signal?

2 What does an *amplifier* do?

3 Telephone systems sometimes make use of optical fibres.

a In what form do the signals travel along the fibre?

b Give *two* advantages of sending digital signals rather than analogue ones.

c Give *two* advantages of using an optical fibre link rather than a cable with wires in it.

4 Explain why, if you use a radio down in a valley, long-wave AM reception may be good, but VHF reception poor.

5 Explain why medium waves usually have a longer range than VHF or UHF.

6 A mobile phone uses a frequency of 900 MHz. Use the following information to calculate the wavelength of the radio waves:
speed of radio waves = 300 000 000 m/s
speed = frequency × wavelength

4.09 Sound waves

When these vibrate . . .

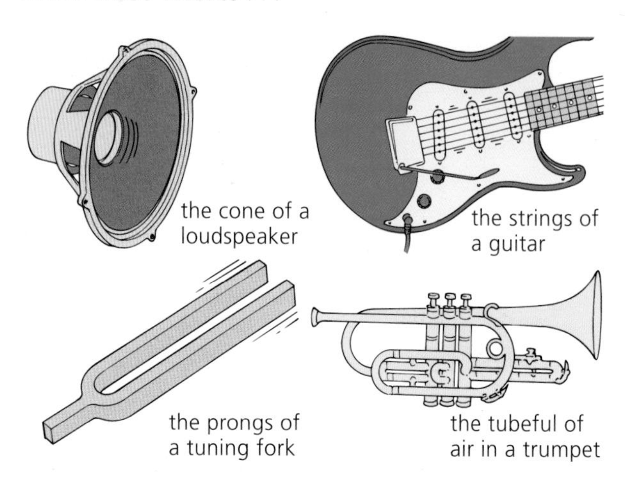

. . . they give off sound waves.

Sound waves are vibrations.
When a loudspeaker cone vibrates it moves in and out very fast. This stretches and squashes the air in front. The 'stretches' and 'squashes' travel out through the air as waves. When they reach your ears, they make your eardrums vibrate and you hear a sound.

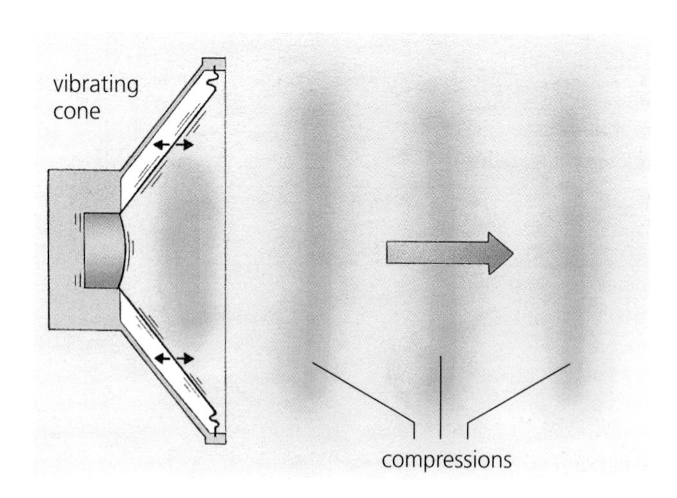

Sound waves are longitudinal waves; the vibrations are backwards and forwards.

The 'squashes' are called **compressions**; the air pressure here is higher than normal.

The 'stretches' are called **rarefactions;** the air pressure here is lower than normal.

Sound waves can travel through solids.
They can travel through doors, floors, ceilings, and brick walls.

Sound waves can travel through liquids.
You can still hear sound when you are swimming underwater.

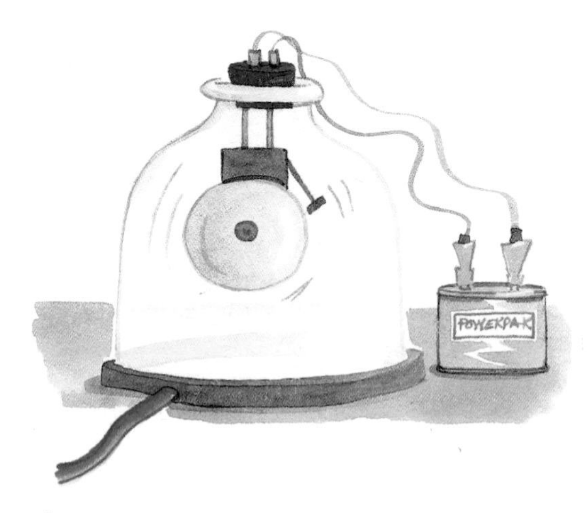

Sound waves can travel through all gases.
This flask has air in it. But you would still hear the bell ringing whatever type of gas was in the flask.

Sound waves can't travel through a vacuum (empty space).
If the air is pumped out of the flask, the sound stops, even though the bell goes on working. Sound waves can't be made if there is nothing to be squashed and stretched.

Sound waves can be reflected and refracted
See the next spread.

Sound waves can be diffracted They can bend round obstacles, which is why you hear round corners. The longer the wavelength, the greater the diffraction.

Seeing sounds

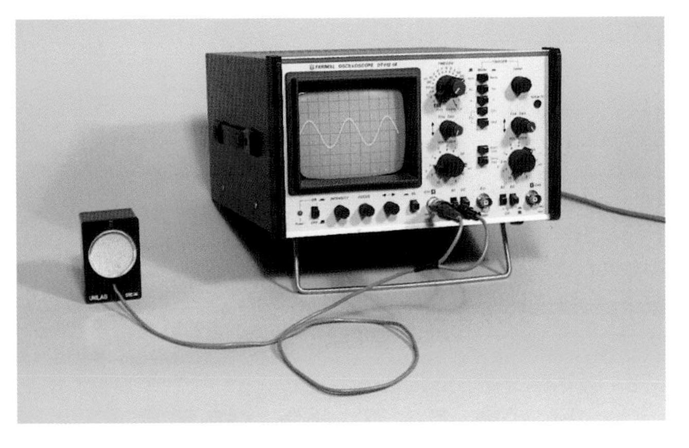

You can't see sounds. But with a microphone and an oscilloscope, you can show sounds as wave shapes on a screen. When sound waves reach the microphone, they make a tiny sheet of metal vibrate. The microphone changes the vibrations into electrical vibrations. The oscilloscope uses these to make a spot vibrate up and down on the screen. It moves the spot steadily sideways at the same time. The result is a **waveform**.

The waveform looks like a series of transverse waves. But it is really a graph of pressure against time. It shows how the air pressure near the microphone rises and falls as sound waves pass.

Recorded sounds

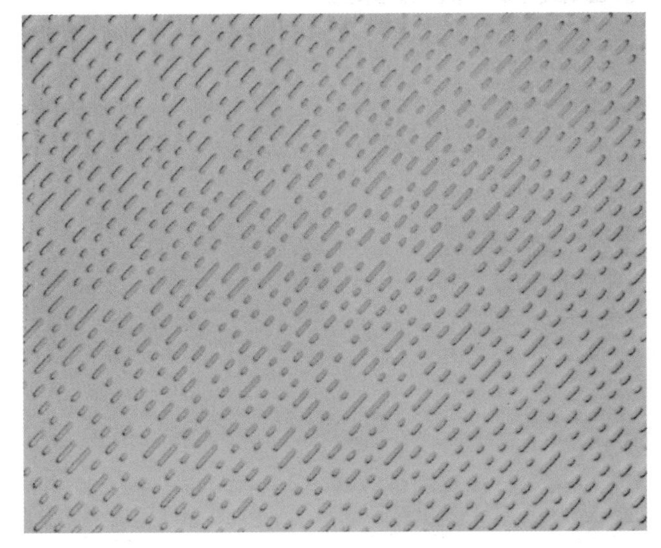

The playing surface of a **compact disc** (**CD**) is covered with millions of tiny steps, arranged in a track which spirals outwards from the centre. When the disc rotates, a tiny beam of laser light is reflected from the steps and the gaps between. As a result, a series of light pulses is picked up by a detector and changed into electrical signals for processing. The processed signals represent numbers. If you plotted them, the graph would be the waveform of the recorded sound. A CD player doesn't plot graphs! But it does process the number signals to give electrical signals which will make a loudspeaker cone vibrate.

Recording using numbers is called **digital** recording.

Questions

1 Someone blows a whistle near a microphone. This is the waveform produced on the screen of an oscilloscope.

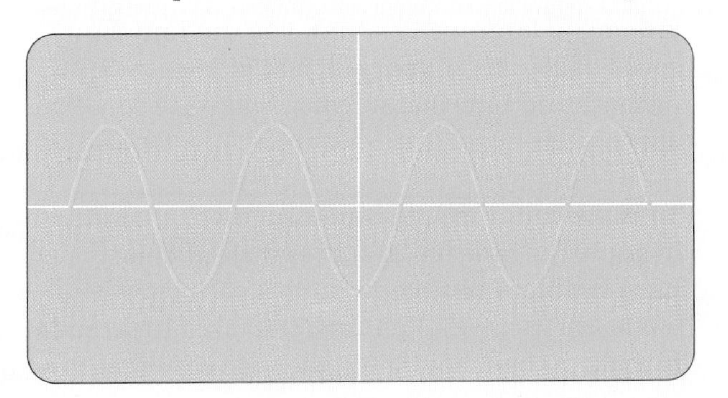

a Use a ruler marked in millimetres to measure the amplitude of the waveform.

b Redraw the waveform so that it has an amplitude of 15 mm. Would the whistle that produced this be louder than the one before?

2 Copy the sentences and fill in the blanks:

a Sounds are caused by ___.

b Sound waves can't travel through a ___.

c Sound waves are ___ waves.

d When sound waves pass, the ___ of the air rises and falls rapidly.

3 Using things you might find around the house, how could you show someone that sound can pass through solid materials?

4.10 Speed of sound

When lightning strikes, you see the flash and then the crash comes later. Much later if you're lucky.

Sound is very much slower than light. So you always hear things after you've seen them. Over short distances, you don't notice the difference. But with distant lightning, there can be a delay of several seconds. The longer the delay, the further away the lightning – it's about 3 seconds for every kilometre (half a mile).

In air, the speed of sound is about 330 metres/second. That's about four times faster than a racing car, but slower than Concorde.

The speed of sound depends on the temperature of the air. Sound waves travel faster through hot air than through cold air. This means, for example, that sound changes speed when it passes from warmer into cooler air, or vice versa. As with other types of wave, the change in speed can cause refraction – a change in direction of travel.

The speed of sound is different through different materials. Sound waves travel faster through liquids than through gases. They travel fastest of all through solids.

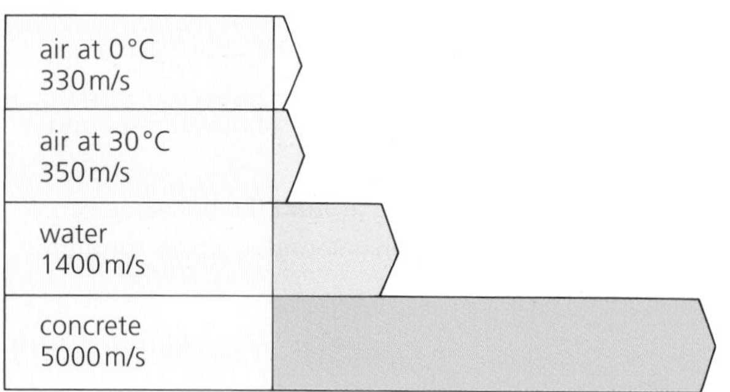

Echoes

Hard surfaces like walls reflect sound waves. When you hear an **echo**, you are hearing a reflected sound a short time after the original sound.

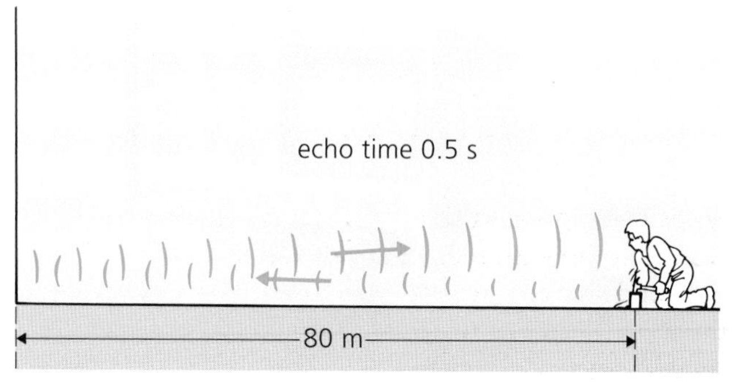

This girl is 80 metres from a large brick wall. She is hammering a block of wood.
Every time she hits the block, she hears an echo 0.5 seconds later. This is the **echo time**.

She could use this information to calculate the speed of sound:

$$\text{speed} = \frac{\text{distance travelled}}{\text{time taken}}$$

so

$$\text{speed of sound} = \frac{\text{distance to wall and back}}{\text{echo time}} = \frac{2 \times 80}{0.5} = \frac{160}{0.5} = 320\,\text{m/s}$$

Do it yourself

If there's a large wall around, you can find the speed of sound for yourself. Just fit your own distance and time measurements into the equation above.

To make your time measurement more accurate, measure the time for 20 echoes instead of just one. Bang the block repeatedly so that each blow is made just as an echo returns. If it takes 10 seconds to make 20 hammer blows, then the echo time is 10 ÷ 20 seconds or 0.5 seconds.

Using echoes

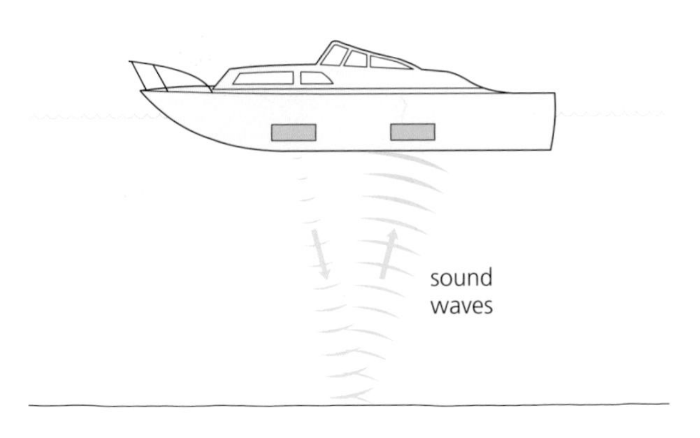

Ships use **echo sounders** to measure the depth of water underneath them. An echo sounder sends bursts of sound waves towards the seabed. Then it measures the time taken for the echoes to return. The longer the time, the deeper the water.

For example:

If – a burst of sound takes 0.1 seconds to reach the seabed and return,

and – the speed of sound in water is 1400 m/s,

then – distance travelled = speed × time

= 1400 × 0.1 m

= 140 m

But – the sound has to travel down *and* back,

so – the depth of water is 70 m.

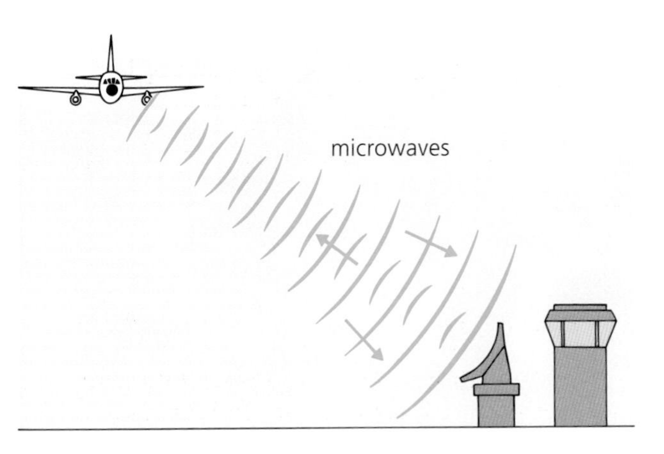

Radar works rather like an echo sounder. Except that microwaves are sent out rather than sound waves. The microwaves are reflected by aircraft. The longer they take to return, the further away the aircraft.

Losing echoes

Echoes can be a nuisance. In empty rooms, cinemas, and concert halls, reflected sounds can take so long to die away that it is sometimes difficult to hear anything clearly. Carpets, curtains, and soft chairs help to solve the problem. Modern concert halls are designed so that sounds are neither muffled nor echoing around.

Questions

		distance travelled in m	time taken in s
	rocket	900	3.0
	aircraft	1000	2.0
	bullet	100	0.5
	meteoroid	3000	0.1

1 If the speed of sound in air is 330 m/s, which of the above are travelling faster than sound?

2 If the speed of sound in air is 330 m/s, how far does sound travel in:

a 1 second? **b** 2 seconds? **c** 10 seconds? **d** 0.1 seconds?

3 Jeff thinks that his cassette player sounds clearer in the bedroom than it does in the kitchen. Is he imagining things? Or could he be right? Explain.

4 The echo sounder in a ship sends a burst of sound waves towards the seabed. 0.2 seconds later, reflected waves are picked up by the ship.

a How long did it take the waves to reach the seabed?

b If the speed of sound in water is 1400 m/s, how far is it to the seabed?

4.11 Noise and vibration

Noise levels

Unwanted sound is called **noise**. Scientists check noise levels using meters marked in **decibels (dB)**. The table on the right gives some typical readings.

Strictly speaking, loud music isn't noise – unless you don't want to hear it. But if you listen to it for hours on end, it can damage your ears. In extreme cases, it can lead to deafness.

	Noise level in dB
Personal stereo, played loud	150
Damage to ears	140
Rock concert	110
Some ear discomfort	90
Telephone ringing	70
Normal speech	60
Whispering	40

What noise?

This worker is protected from noise by health and safety regulations. For jobs like this, her company must provide her with ear protectors.

Antinoise

In some aircraft, the noise level in the passenger cabin is reduced using 'antinoise'. On an oscilloscope screen, antinoise looks the same as the original noise except that its peaks match the noise's troughs, and vice versa. When you hear noise and its antinoise together, one cancels out the other. To create the antinoise, the sound of the aircraft's engines is picked up by microphones, processed electronically, and put out as antinoise from loudspeakers hidden around the cabin.

Vibration damage

Noise is caused by vibrations, and vibrations can have other effects as well:

Old brickwork is easily damaged by the vibrations from heavy traffic.

NVH...

...stands for 'noise, vibration, and harshness', and car designers want to get rid of it. Inside a car, you are sitting in a metal box which can magnify noise and vibration from the engine and road.
Using computer modelling, designers can now predict how different car parts will produce or transmit vibrations. With careful design of engine mounts, suspension parts, and body panels, the level of NVH can be greatly reduced.

- Can you think of any evidence that noise travels through solid materials as well as through air?
- If you want to play your stereo loudly without annoying the neighbours, can you suggest ways of reducing the amount of noise reaching them?
- Most cinemas have several films on show in the same building. See if you can find out how the noise from one studio is prevented from reaching another.

Damaging vibrations can be put to work to crack concrete.

Escaping noise?

This 'dead room' has a special lining on its walls which absorbs over 99% of the sound energy striking it. Here, a tractor has been placed in the room so that noise levels from its engine can be measured accurately. If you stood in the room by yourself you would hear the food churning in your stomach and the blood pumping through your veins. Perhaps a little noise isn't such a bad thing after all!

4.12 High and low, loud and quiet

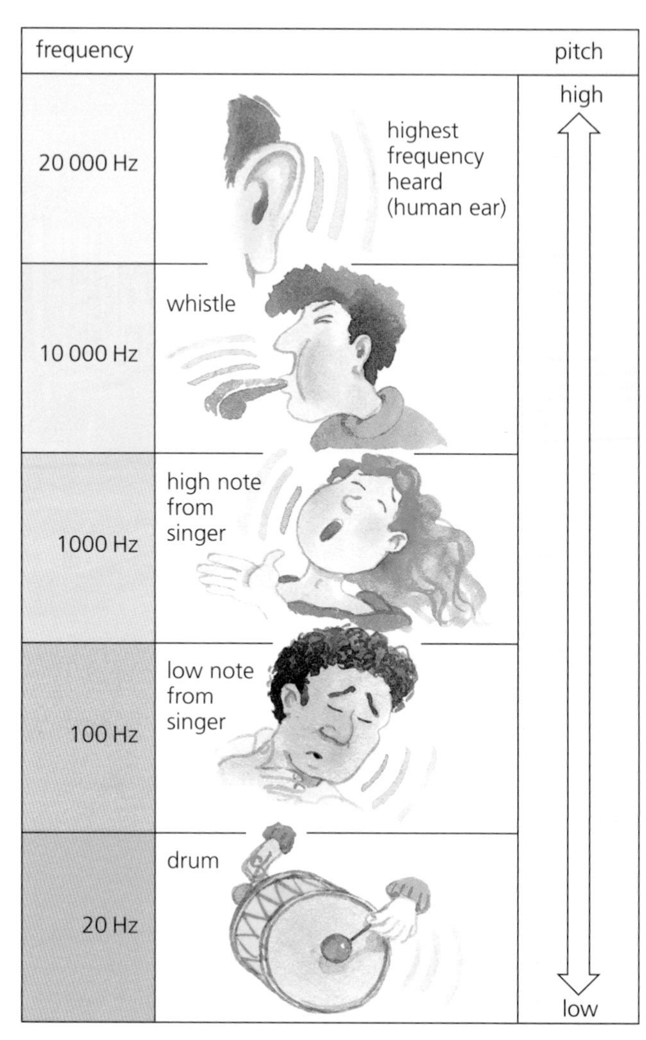

Frequency and pitch

The **frequency** of a sound is measured in **hertz (Hz)**. If a loudspeaker cone vibrates 100 times per second, it gives out 100 sound waves per second, and the frequency is 100 Hz.

Different frequencies sound different to the ear. You hear *high* frequencies as *high* notes: they have a **high pitch**.

You hear *low* frequencies as *low* notes: they have a **low pitch**. So:

The higher the frequency of a sound, the higher its pitch.

The human ear can detect frequencies ranging from about 20 Hz up to 20 000 Hz, although the upper limit gets less with age.

On the right, you can see what different frequencies look like on the screen of an oscilloscope. With the higher frequency, there are more waves on the screen: the waves are closer together.

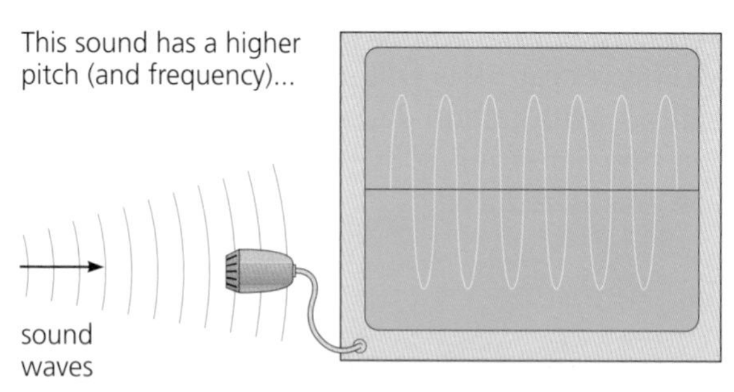

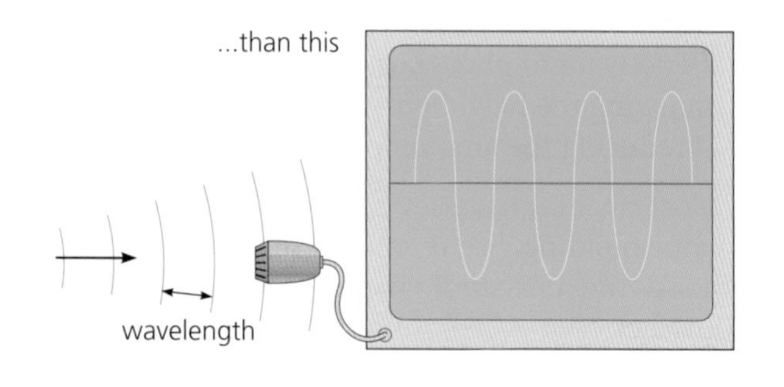

Amplitude and loudness

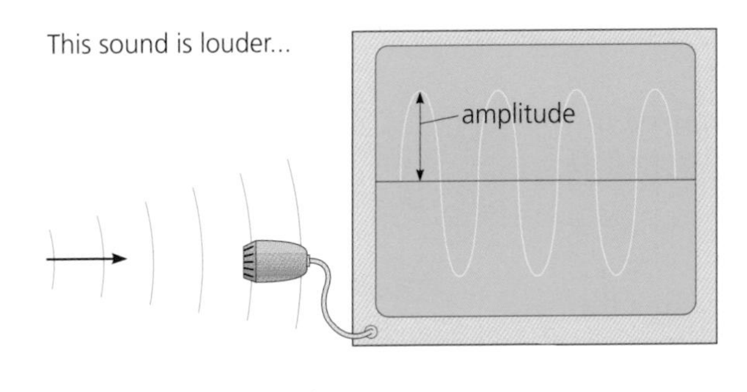

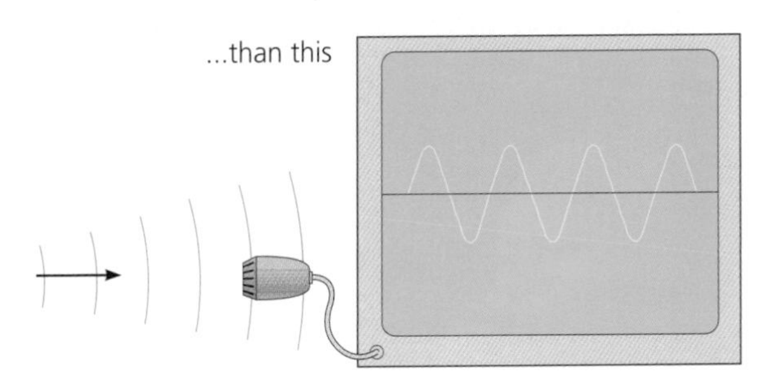

Low *and* loud.

The sounds shown on the oscilloscope screens above have the same frequency. But one is *louder* than the other. The vibrations in the air are bigger and the **amplitude** of the waveform is greater. So:

The greater the amplitude, the louder the sound.

The wave equation

This equation applies to sound waves, just like other waves:

speed = frequency × wavelength
in m/s   in Hz   in m

Here are some examples of the link between speed, frequency, and wavelength:

speed of sound	frequency	wavelength
330 m/s	110 Hz	3.0 m
330 m/s	330 Hz	1.0 m
330 m/s	3300 Hz	0.1 m

From the above examples, you can see that the following applies:

The higher the frequency, the shorter the wavelength.

Questions

1 *Sound A: 400 Hz   Sound B: 200 Hz*
Sounds A and B are played equally loudly.
a For someone listening to the two sounds, how would B compare with A?
b Which sound has the longer wavelength?

2 A microphone picks up three different sounds, X, Y, and Z, one after another. Here are their waveforms on the screen of an oscilloscope:

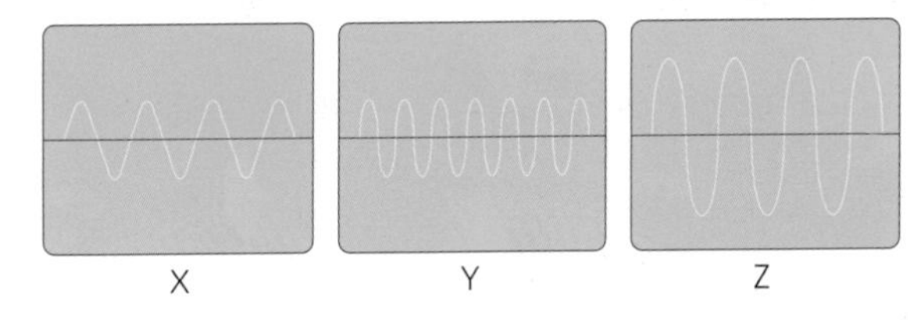

a Which sound has the greatest amplitude?
b Which sound is the loudest?
c Which sound has the highest frequency?
d Which sound has the highest pitch?

3 Use the wave equation on this page to work out the following (assume that the speed of sound in air is 330 m/s):
a The wavelength of a sound whose frequency is 660 Hz.
b The frequency of a sound whose wavelength is 2 m.

4.13 The sounds of music

Within the range of human hearing, sounds can be varied and mixed to produce the complicated patterns which we call music.

Changing note

The higher the frequency of the sound waves, the higher the pitch of the note you hear.

If you play in a steel band you use tuned oil drums called pans. The end of each pan is skilfully shaped so that different sections produce different notes when hit.

On a trombone, you can raise the pitch of a note by shortening the length of tubing that the sound waves travels along. You can also change pitch by controlling how your lips vibrate when you blow.

On a guitar, you raise the pitch of a note by pressing the string against a fret to shorten the length that can vibrate. During tuning, you tighten or slacken the string to adjust the pitch.

On a saxophone, you raise the pitch of a note by uncovering more and more holes along the barrel. You do this by pressing on levers called keys with your fingers.

Octaves

Musical scales are based on **octaves**. If two notes are an octave apart, one has *double* the frequency of the other.

The keyboard below is tuned to 'scientific pitch'. Bands and orchestras tune to slightly different frequencies from those shown here.

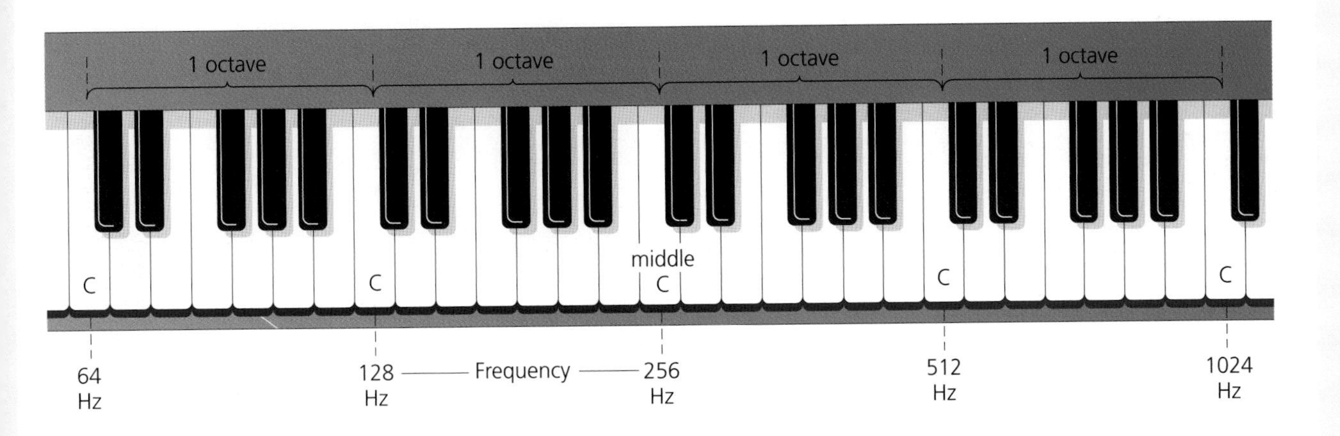

The same but different

If you play Middle C on a guitar it doesn't sound quite the same as Middle C on a piano. The two sounds have a different **quality** or **timbre**. Each has a strong **fundamental frequency**, giving Middle C. But other, weaker frequencies, called **overtones**, are mixed in. These differ from one type of instrument to another.

An electronic keyboard or synthesizer, as on the right, has a built-in computer which can mix different frequencies to produce the sound of a guitar, piano, or any other instrument. To sound right, each note must begin and end correctly. For example, the 'plonk' of a piano starts suddenly and then fades away: it has a short **attack** and a longer **decay**. To sound like the real instrument, a synthesizer must produce this effect as well.

A synthesizer: any sound you like.

Chords

Chords are groups of notes which blend well when heard together. For example, the notes C, E, and G form a chord. The blending occurs because there is a simple ratio between their frequencies:
The frequency of E is 5/4 times that of C.
The frequency of G is 3/2 times that of C.
Complicated ratios don't mix so well. If you play C and D together, they are discordant – they clash.

By using information from this spread or elsewhere, can you explain the following?

- A guitar string produces a higher note if you tighten it.
- A guitar doesn't sound like a saxophone, even if both play the same note.
- An electronic synthesizer can reproduce the sound of almost any musical instrument.

4.14 Ultrasound

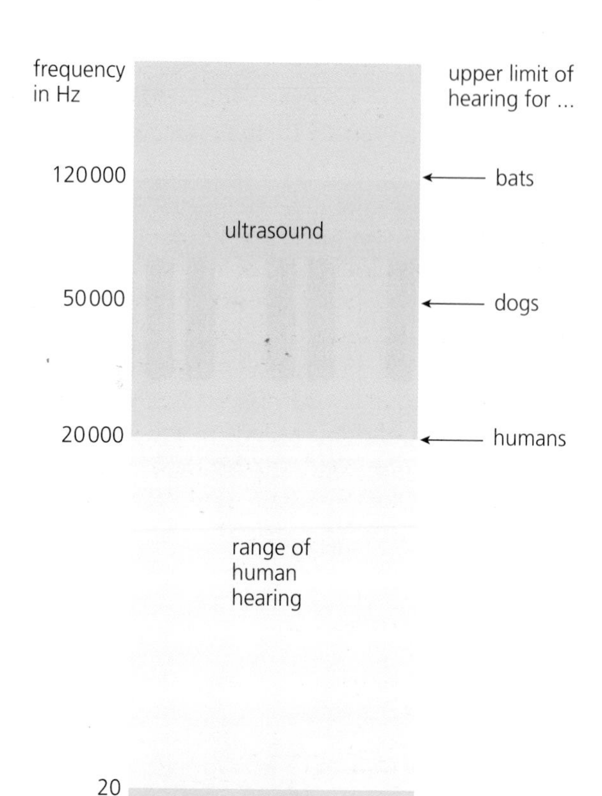

This bat uses ultrasound to find insects and other things in front of it. It send out ultrasound pulses and use its specially-shaped ears to pick up the reflections.

The human ear can detect sounds up to a frequency of about 20000 Hz. Sounds above the range of human hearing are called **ultrasonic sounds**, or **ultrasound**. To produce ultrasound, oscillations from electronic circuits can be used to make a crystal vibrate at high frequency. Here are some of its uses:

Cleaning and breaking

Using ultrasound, delicate machinery can be cleaned without dismantling it. The machinery is put in a tank of liquid, then the vibrations of high-power ultrasound are used to dislodge the dirt and grease.

In hospitals, concentrated beams of ultrasound can be used to break up kidney stones and gall stones without patients needing surgery.

Echo sounding

Ships use **echo sounders** to measure the depth of water beneath them. An echo sounder sends pulses of ultrasound towards the seabed, then measures the time taken for each echo (reflected sound) to return. The longer the time, the deeper the water. For more about this, look up echoes in the index.

Metal testing

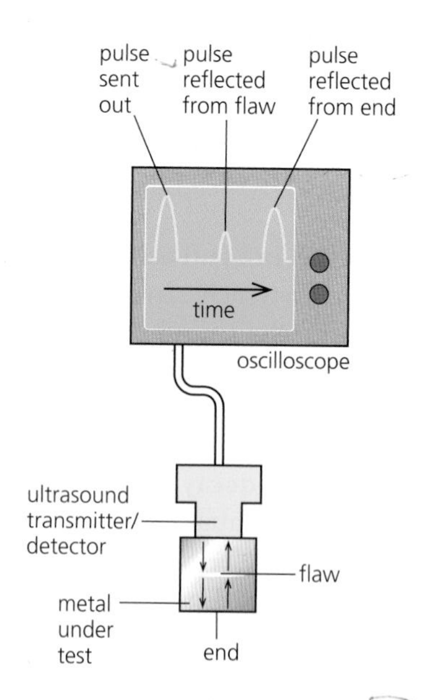

Flaws in metals can be detected using the echo-sounding idea. Above, a pulse of ultrasound is sent through the metal. Because there is a flaw (tiny gap) in the metal, *two* pulses are reflected back to the detector – one from the flaw and the other from the far end of the metal. The pulses can be displayed using an oscilloscope.

Scanning the womb

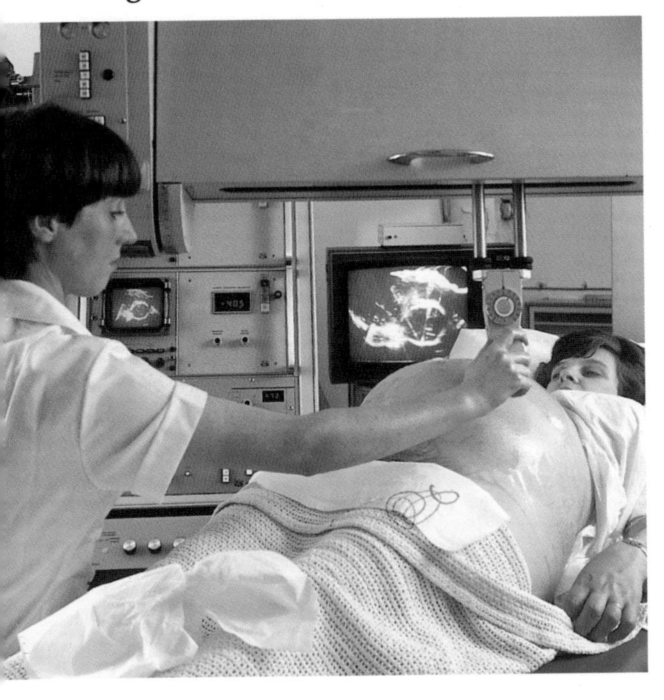

The pregnant mother above is having her womb scanned by ultrasound. A transmitter sends pulses of ultrasound into the mother's body. The transmitter also acts as a detector and picks up pulses reflected from the baby and different layers inside the body. The signals are processed by a computer, which puts an image on the screen.

Using ultrasound to 'see' inside the womb is much safer than using X-rays because X-rays can cause cell damage in a growing baby. Also, an ultrasound scan can show up different layers of soft tissue, which an ordinary X-ray photo cannot.

Ultrasound can also be used to monitor the baby's heartbeat. The movement of the heart changes the frequency of reflected ultrasound – just as the motion of an ambulance changes the frequency of the sound you hear from its siren when it rushes past. Using a special stethoscope, a doctor or nurse can detect the frequency change caused by the heartbeat.

Quality control

In production processes, when things are being made, it is important to check that the size and quality are up to standard. This is called **quality control**.
Below, you can see one method of automatic quality control, used in the production of rolled steel. An ultrasound detector is sending out signals to control the gap between the two rollers. Its job is to make sure that the steel is not rolled too thickly or too thinly. If the thickness varies, the strength of the ultrasound reaching the detector changes.

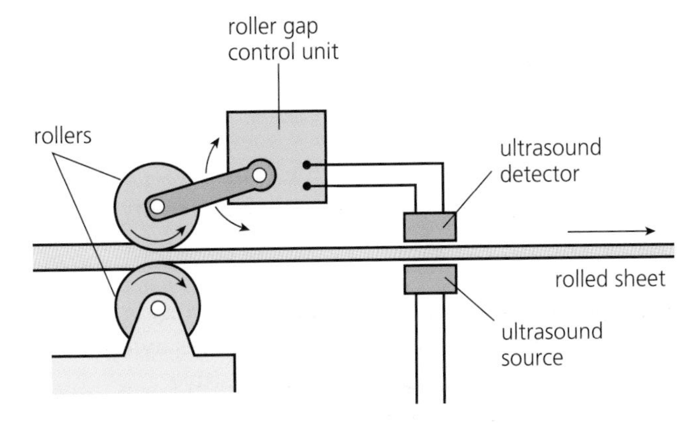

Questions

1 What is *ultrasound*?
2 a What is an *echo sounder* used for?
  b How does an echo sounder work?
3 In hospitals, doctors can use ultrasound to 'see' into a pregnant mother's womb.
  a Why do doctors prefer to use ultrasound for this, rather than X-rays?
  b Give one other use of ultrasound in hospitals.
4 Give *two* uses of ultrasound in industry.
5 Look at the diagram on the opposite page, showing a piece of metal being testing for flaws.
  Describe (or draw a diagram to show) how the trace on the oscilloscope would be different in each of the following cases.
  a The position of the flaw is closer to the top end of the metal.
  b The flaw is in the same position, but the metal is of a different type, so that the speed of sound is higher.
6 Look at the diagram above, showing a steel-rolling process.
  a If the thickness of the rolled sheet increases, how will this affect the ultrasound received by the detector?
  b What will the signals from the detector make the control unit do?
  c What will happen if the steel is rolled too thinly?

4.15 Seismic waves

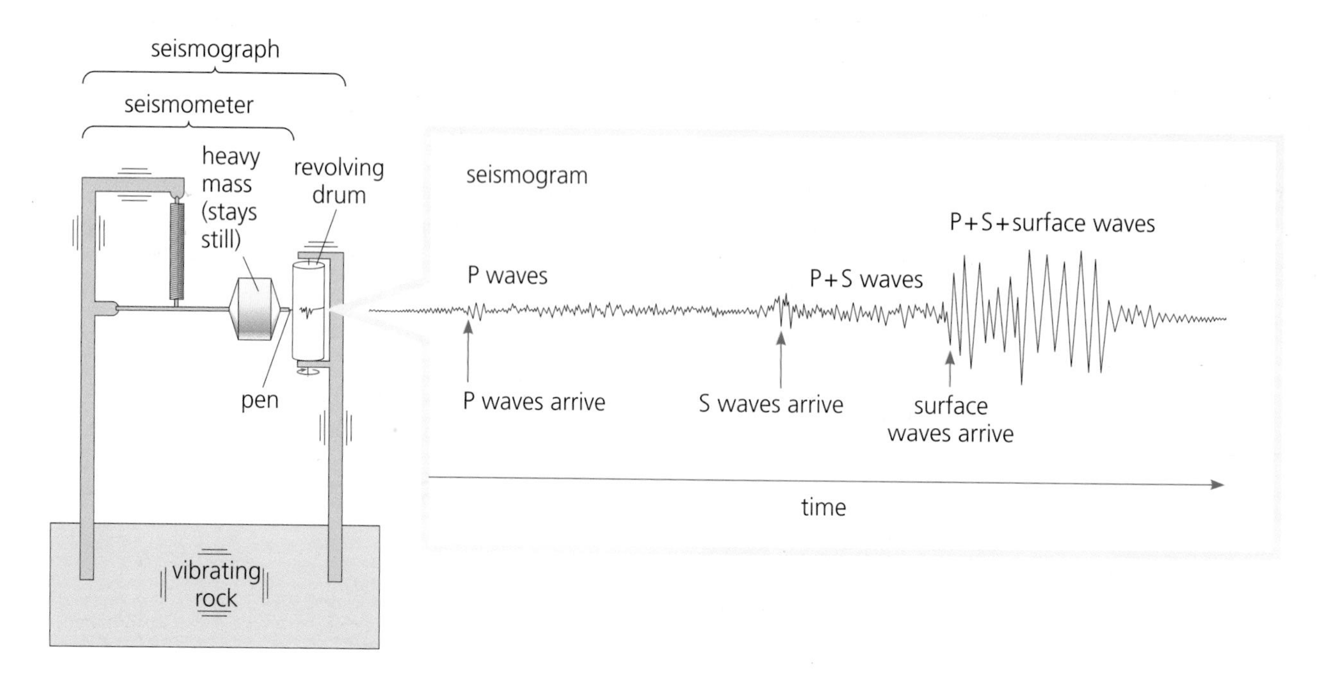

Earthquakes are caused by sudden rock movements underground. The vibrations send **seismic waves** (shockwaves) through the Earth.

Seismic waves get weaker as they travel through the ground. However, thousands of kilometres away, they can be detected and recorded by a sensitive instrument called a **seismograph**. Small vibrations in the ground are magnified so that a pen moves up and down. The pen draws a graph on a slowly revolving drum, as shown above.

The recordings show that there are different types of seismic waves. These leave the **focus** (site) of the earthquake together, but travel at different speeds and arrive at different times.

P waves (primary waves) are longitudinal waves. They are the fastest and arrive first. They travel through solids and liquids deep in the Earth at speeds of several kilometres per second.

S waves (secondary waves) are transverse waves. They arrive after the P waves because they are slower. They can pass through solids deep in the Earth, but not through liquids such as molten (melted) rock.

Surface waves are the slowest and arrive last. They travel round the Earth's surface. In the earthquake zone itself, they are the most destructive. They can cause huge fissures (cracks) to appear and then close seconds later.

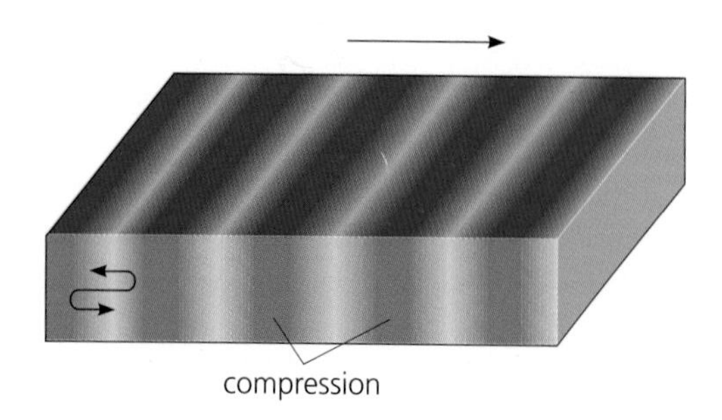

P waves (Primary waves) are longitudinal or 'Push – pull' waves. The rock vibrates backwards and forwards.

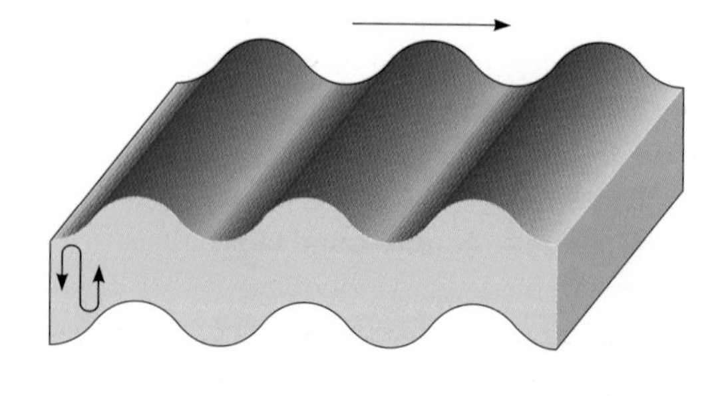

S waves (Secondary waves) are transverse or 'Shake' waves. The rock vibrates up and down.

Inside the Earth: seismic clues

P and S waves travel faster in denser rock. A gradual change in density causes a gradual change in speed and makes the waves follow a curved path. The bending is an example of **refraction**. A sudden change in density causes a sudden change in direction, and also some reflection.

By measuring the travel times of P and S waves arriving at different seismic recording stations around the Earth, scientists can work out the paths of the waves through the Earth. The results give clues about the Earth's inner structure and density. There are some examples on the right.

- Some P and S waves are reflected at a boundary 7–70 km beneath the Earth's surface. This suggests that the Earth has an outer **crust**, with a layer of denser rocks (the **mantle**) beneath.
- The curving of the P and S waves through the Earth suggests that the density of the rocks increases with depth.
- S waves are blocked by the central part of the Earth. As S waves cannot pass through liquids, this suggests that the Earth has a central **core** whose outer part must be liquid.
- There is a 'shadow zone' where no waves are detected. This suggests that the core must be refracting P waves inwards.

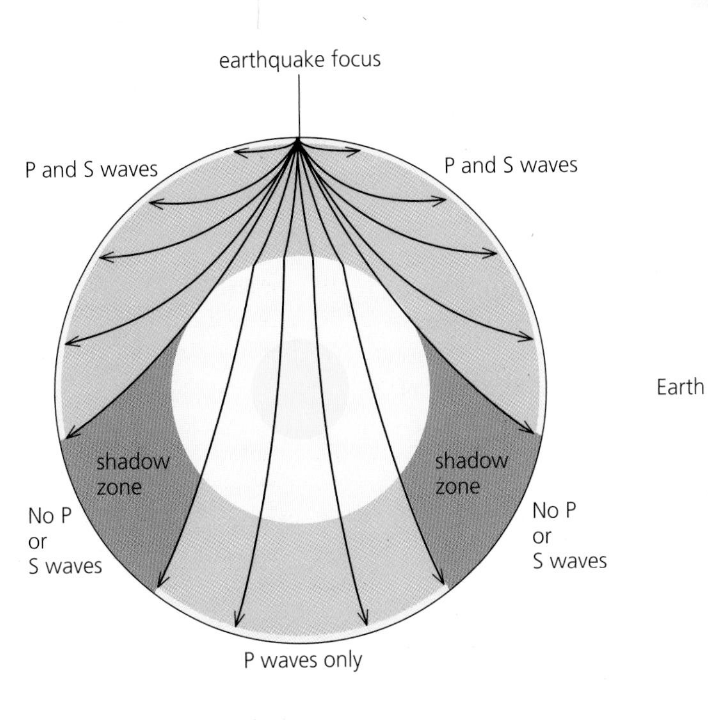

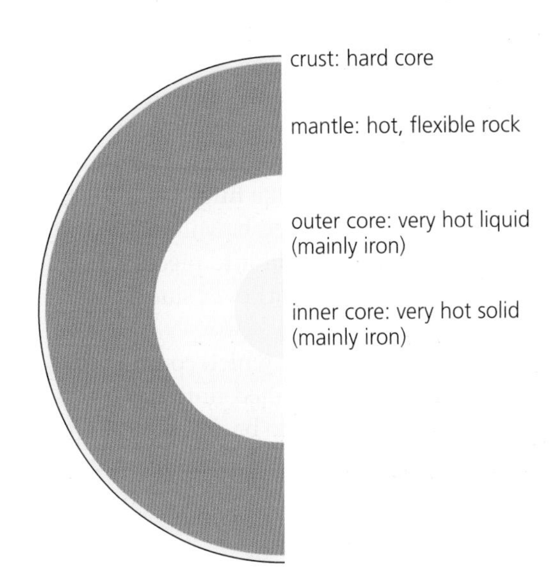

Questions

1 *P waves* and *S waves* can travel through the Earth.

a Which type is faster? How you can tell this from the seismogram on the opposite page?

b Which type is transverse?

2 Why do seismic waves bend when they travel through the Earth?

3 The graph on the right shows the speeds of P and S waves at different depths down to the Earth's centre.

a Which line is for the P waves? How can you tell?

b At what depth is the boundary between the mantle and the outer core?

c How can you tell that the outer core is liquid?

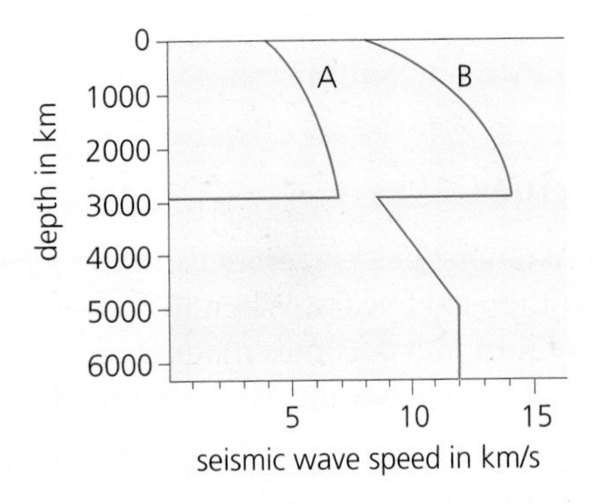

4.16 Moving continents I

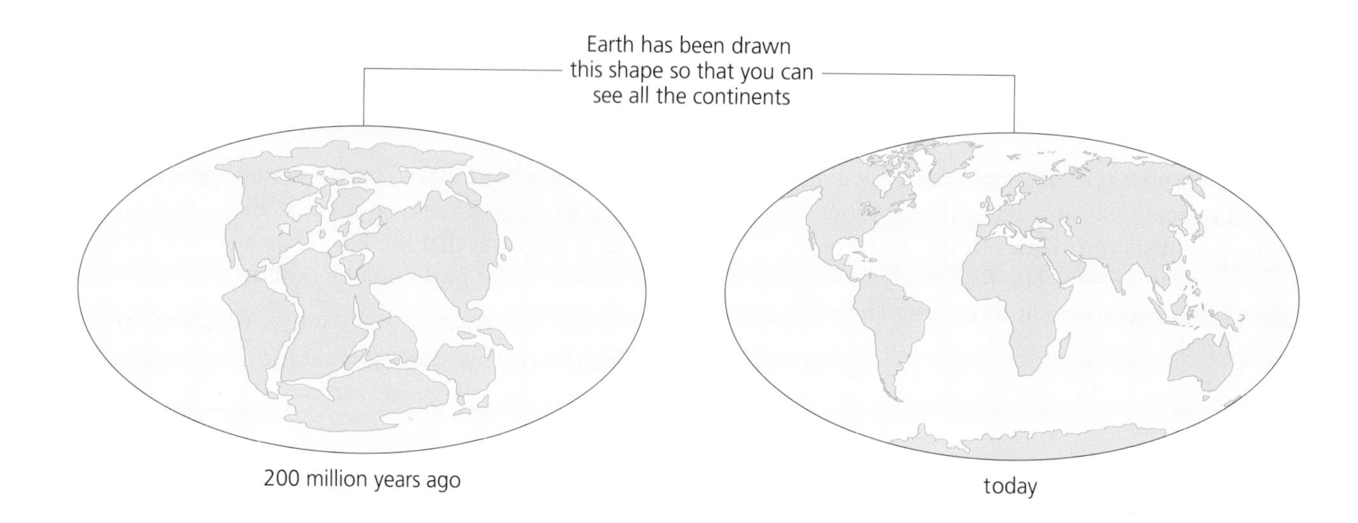

In 1915, Alfred Wegener pointed out that the shapes of the continents could fit together like the pieces of a jigsaw. In his theory of **continental drift**, he suggested that the continents are like huge rafts which 'float' on the denser material beneath. Millions of years ago, a huge supercontinent split into pieces. These have slowly been drifting apart ever since.

With no obvious way in which continents could move, Wegener's idea was rejected until the 1960s, when the first pieces of evidence to back it were found. Here are two examples (see also the diagram on the right).

Patterns of rocks and fossils These match on different continents: for example, along the Atlantic coasts of Africa and South America.

Sea-floor spreading Molten (melted) rock is oozing out of volcanic cracks in a ridge along the bottom of the Atlantic Ocean. It is cooling, and solidifying to form new crust. As it does so, the Atlantic is slowly getting wider – by a few centimetres a year.

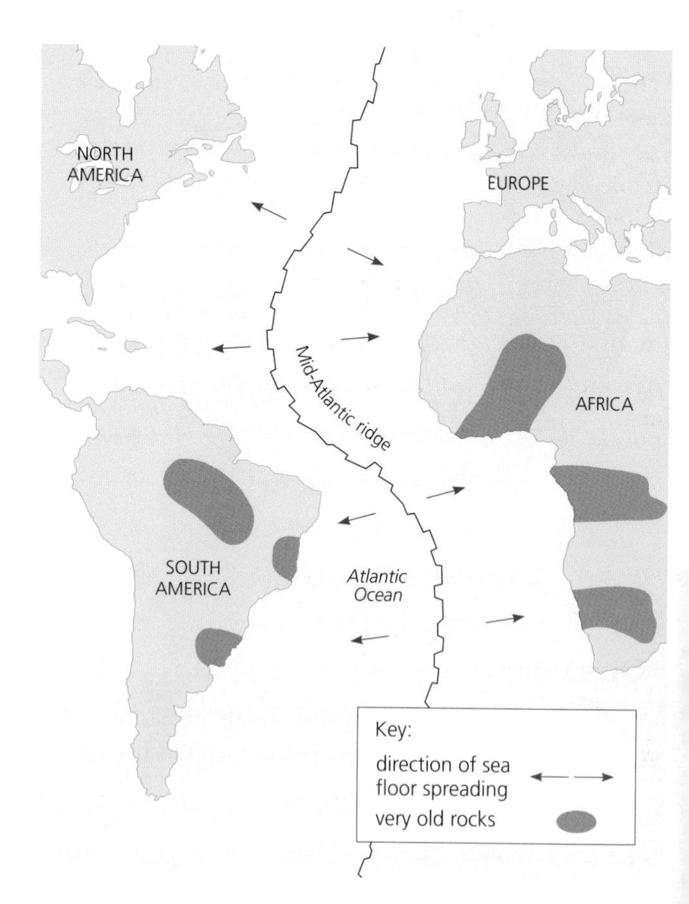

Magnetic clues

The Earth's magnetic field reverses direction every few hundred thousand years. When molten rock solidifies, any iron in it becomes magnetized by the field. Moving out from the Mid-Atlantic Ridge, the rocks show a pattern of repeated field reversals – evidence that the oldest rocks are furthest out, and sea-floor spreading has occurred.

Tectonic plates

The Earth's crust and upper mantle is called the **lithosphere**. Scientists think that the it is divided up into large pieces, called **tectonic plates** – or just 'plates' for short. These are slowly moving over the denser, more flexible material beneath them.

Earthquakes and volcanoes

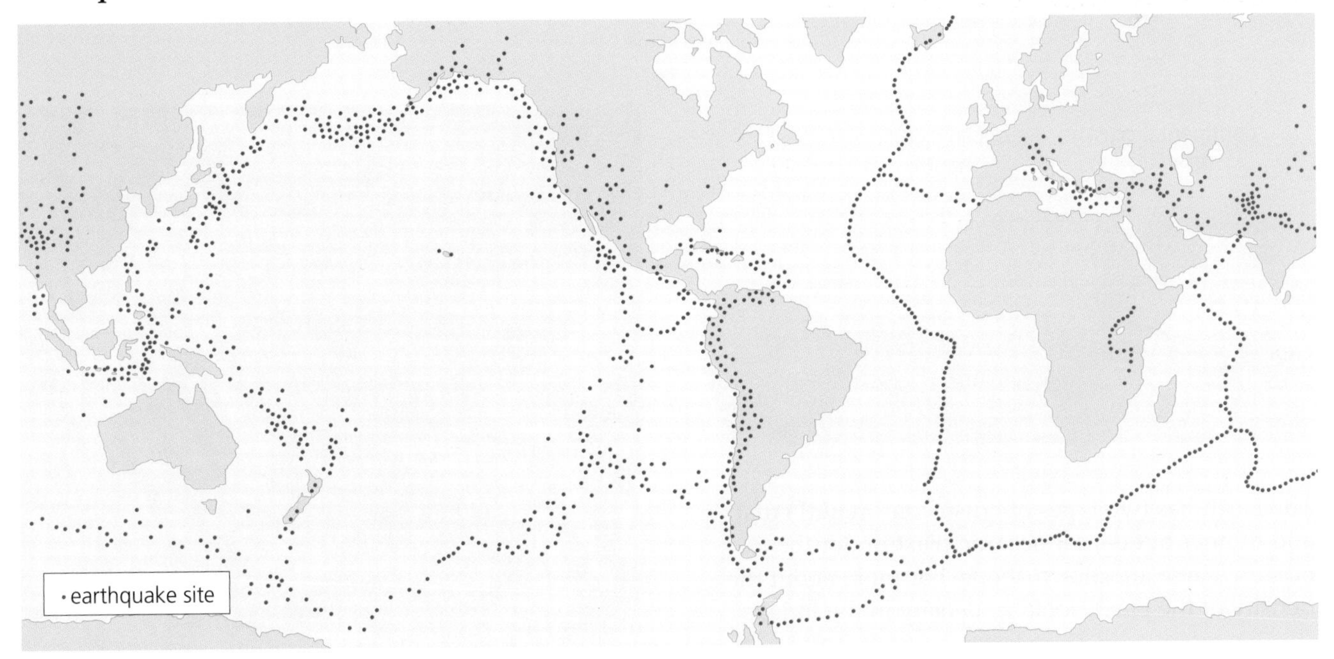

Where plates slide or push against against each other, there may be earthquakes. On the map above, each dot shows where an earthquake has happened in the last 20 years. Together, the dots show where the different plates meet.

Most volcanoes are near plate edges, where the crust is cracked and weak. It is here that the friction of plates rubbing together can produce heat. Hot rock in the mantle turns liquid. The molten (melted) rock is called **magma**. It is pushed out from volcanoes as **lava**:

Why plates move

Most of the rock in the mantle is hot but not molten. However, it is flexible enough to flow very slowly, and it does so because of the effect of heat. The heat comes from radioactive materials which are naturally present in the Earth, and it causes **convection currents** in the mantle. (A convection current is any circulating flow of material caused by heat. For example, the hotplate on a cooker causes convection currents in the water in a saucepan.)

Questions

1 In 1915, Alfred Wegener suggested that, millions of years ago, the continents may all have been part of one huge supercontinent. What observation did he make that gave him this idea?

2 Give two pieces of evidence to support the idea that the continents have moved apart.

3 What are tectonic plates?

4 The map at the top of the page shows the sites of earthquakes over the last 20 years.

- **a** Why do earthquakes tend to happen along the lines shown, rather than all over the Earth?
- **b** Why are most volcanoes found close to the lines marked by the red dots?

5 What causes the slow movements of plates?

4.17 Moving continents II

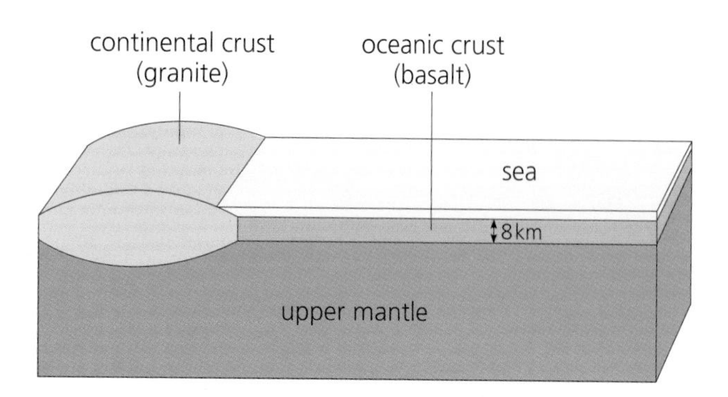

The Earth has two types of crust: **continental crust**, and thinner but denser **oceanic crust** under the oceans. These are shown above. For more about the density of the Earth, look up density in the index.

In places, the crust is cracked and folded (see the example on the right). At one time, scientists thought that features like this were caused by shrinkage in the crust when the young, hot Earth cooled down. Now their explanations are based on plate movements.

These folds were caused by plate movements.

Plates meet at boundaries:

Constructive boundaries These are mainly under oceans – for example, the Mid-Atlantic Ridge is a constructive boundary. Plates move apart and get bigger as magma (molten rock) oozes up through cracks and then cools to form new oceanic crust.

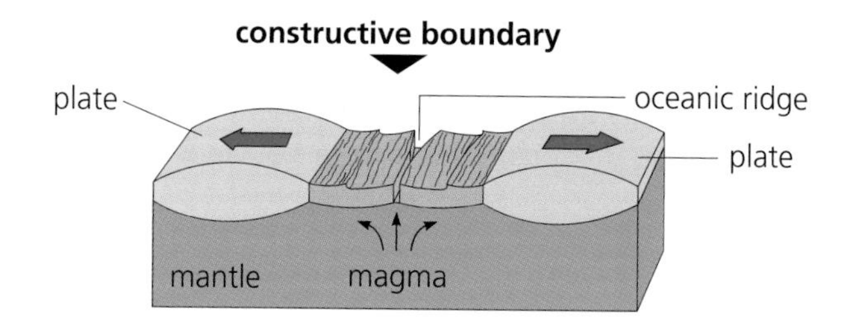

Destructive boundaries Plates move together so that one is **subducted** (carried down) under the other. Heat from the friction may melt the rock, causing volcanoes where magma is pushed out of the ground as lava. As the plates collide, layers of rock are crumpled into **folds**, forming mountains. Movements like this produced the Andes and its volcanoes in South America.

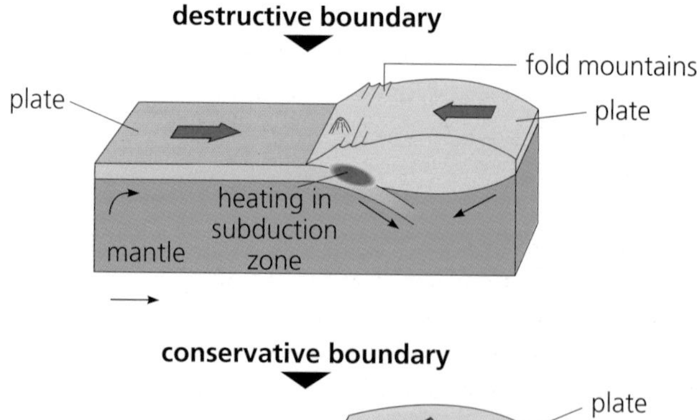

Conservative boundaries Plates slide past each other, so their shape is 'conserved'– it does not change. Sometimes, the plates catch on each other. When they jerk free, there may be big earthquakes. This is the cause of the earthquakes that occur along the coast of California, USA.

conservative boundary

plate

plate

mantle

New rocks from old

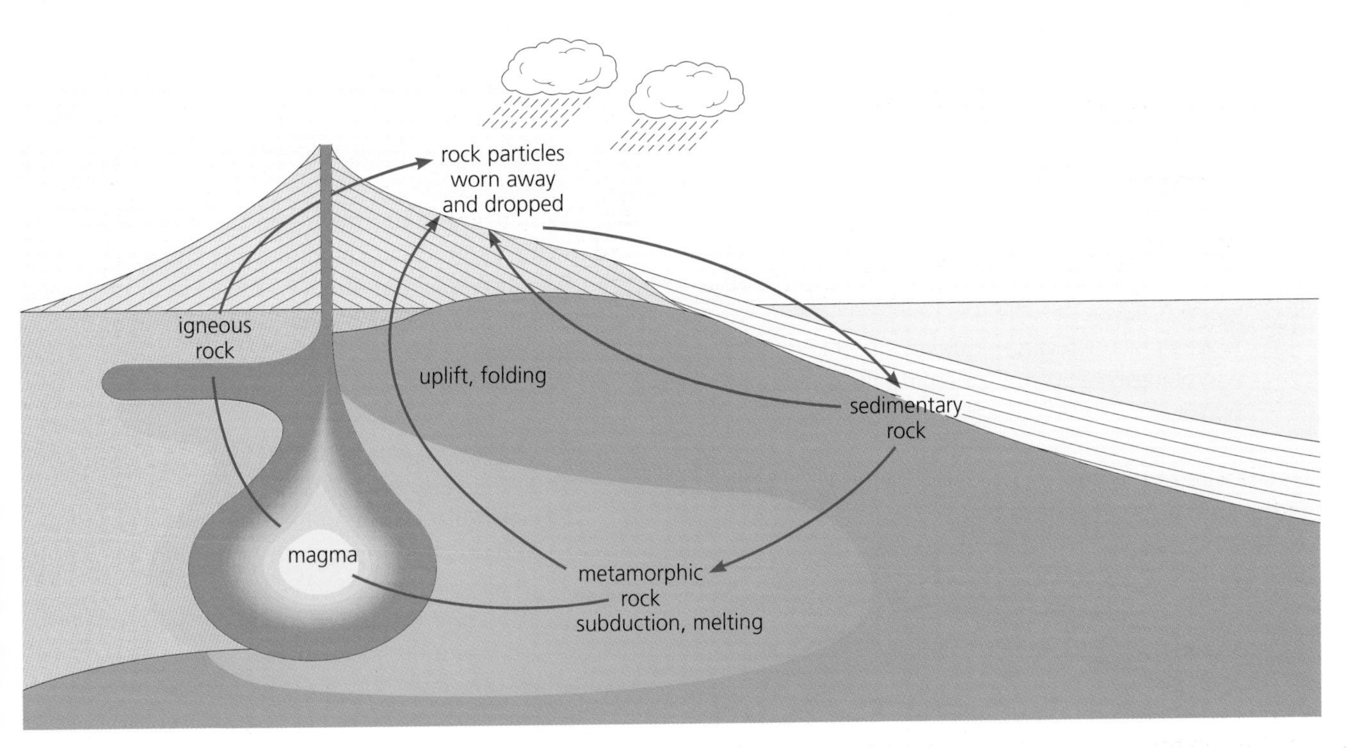

Over millions of years, rocks in the crust can be subducted, melt to form magma, be uplifted, and then solidify to form new rock. The recycling of old rock to form new is called the **rock cycle**.

There are three main types of rocks in the Earth's crust:

Igneous rocks, such as granite and basalt, are made of tiny crystals. They are formed when magma cools and solidifies.

If magma cools *quickly*, the crystals are *small*. This happens, for example, when lava comes out of a volcano and cools. If magma cools *slowly*, the crystals have time to grow, and are *large*. This can happens to magma deep in the crust.

Sedimentary rocks, such as sandstone and limestone, are formed from layers of sediment dropped by water or wind. In many cases, the sediment is bits worn away from old rock. As more sediment collects above it, it gets compressed, and sets like concrete.

Metamorphic rocks Deep underground, igneous and sedimentary rocks can be recrystallized by heat or pressure or both. They become metamorphic ('changed') rock which is usually harder than the original. Examples include marble and slate.

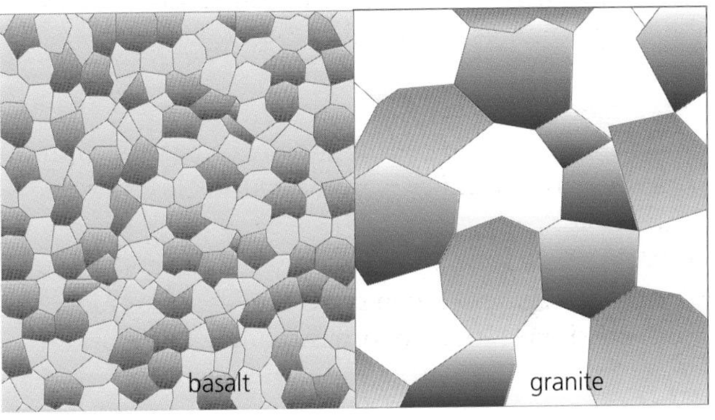

This rock cooled more quickly... ...than this.

Questions

1 What is *magma*?
2 Here are two ways in which plates may move:
towards each other *away from each other*
a Which of the above produces fold mountains?
b Which produces a subduction zone?
c In what other way can plates move?
3 Why may volcanoes form above a subduction zone?
4 Why are metamorphic rocks likely to be found near a subduction zone?
5 Igneous rock is formed when magma cools and solidifies. How could you tell whether the magma had cooled quickly or slowly?

Questions on Chapter 4

1 Surface water waves are transverse waves. Sound waves are longitudinal waves.

a Describe in detail and with diagrams the difference between a transverse wave and a longitudinal wave.

b A sound wave has a frequency of 250 Hz and a wavelength of 1.3 m. Calculate the speed of this wave.

c A water wave has a frequency of 30 Hz and a wavelength of 10 cm. Calculate the speed of this wave.

2 The diagram below shows a ray of light travelling through an optical fibre.

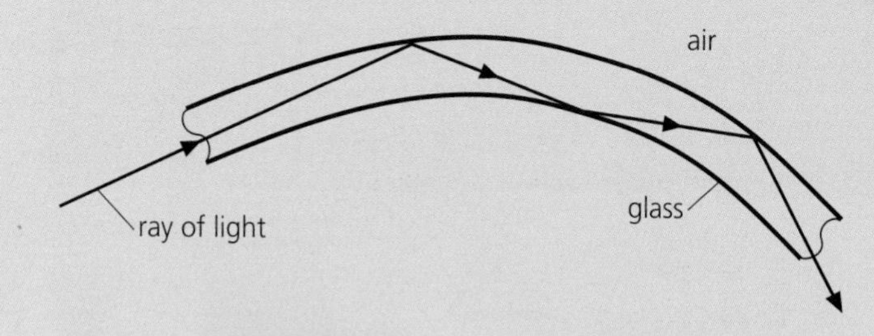

Explain what happens to the ray of light each time it strikes the boundary between the glass and the air.

3 A microphone is connected to an oscilloscope (CRO). When three different sounds, A, B, and C, are made in front of the microphone, these are the waveforms seen on the screen:

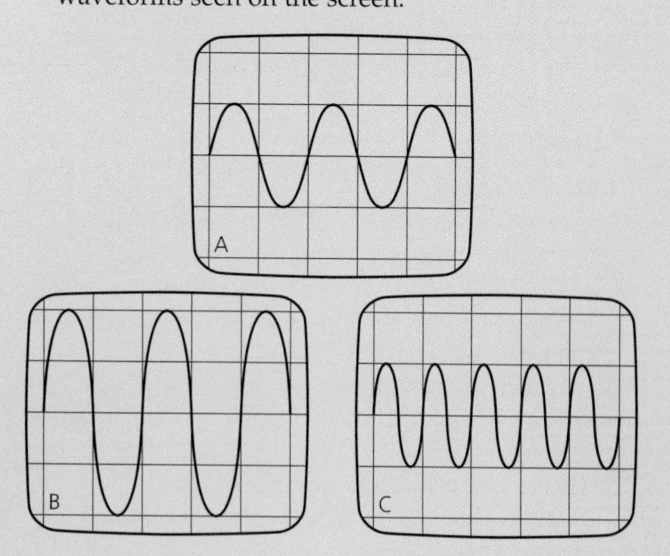

a Comparing sounds A and B, how would they sound different?

b Comparing sounds A and C, how would they sound different?

c Which sound has the highest amplitude?

d Which sound has the highest frequency?

e Sound A has a frequency of 220 Hz. If the speed of sound is 330 m/s, what is the wavelength of sound A?

f What is the frequency of sound C?

4 a Sound X: frequency 10 000 Hz.
Sound Y: frequency 30 000 Hz.
Upper limit of human hearing: 20 000 Hz.

i What is the upper limit of human hearing in kHz?

ii Which of the above sounds is an example of ultrasound?

b Ultrasound can travel through some human tissues and can be reflected by different layers inside the body.

i Describe one example of how ultrasound is used in hospitals.

ii For producing medical images, why do doctors prefer to use ultrasound if they can, rather than X-rays?

iii Describe one example of the industrial use of ultrasound.

5 Copy this table of the electromagnetic spectrum and fill in the blank spaces.

Type of wave		
X-rays		
	300 000 m/s	
microwaves		microwave oven

a What property of these waves increases as we move from left to right in this table?

b What property of these waves increases as we move from right to left in this table?

c Name five properties or characteristics that these waves have in common.

d i Name **two** parts of the electromagnetic spectrum which can be used for communication.

ii Name **two** parts of the electromagnetic spectrum which can cause cancer in people.

iii Name **two** parts of the electromagnetic spectrum which can be used to heat up food.

6 When there is an earthquake, two types of seismic waves travel through the Earth.
P waves are longitudinal waves.
S waves are transverse waves.

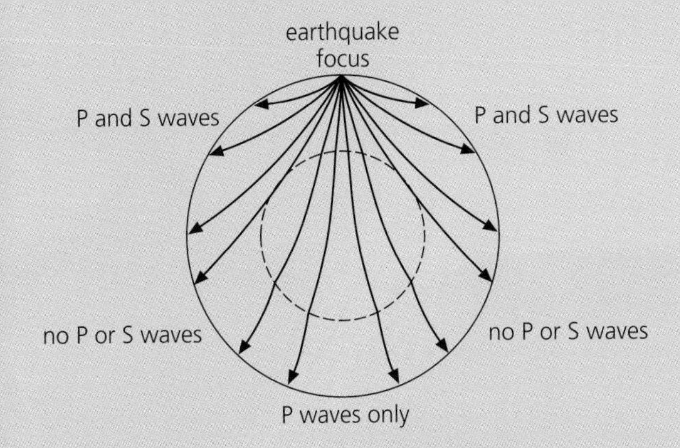

a What is the difference between *longitudinal* waves and *transverse* waves? Give one example of each type, other than seismic waves.

b Why do seismic waves travel through the Earth in curved paths?

c Why are no S waves detected on the opposite side of the Earth from the earthquake focus?

d Explain how, by comparing signals from several monitoring stations, it is possible to work out where an earthquake has taken place.

7 The diagram below shows a ray of light entering a glass block.

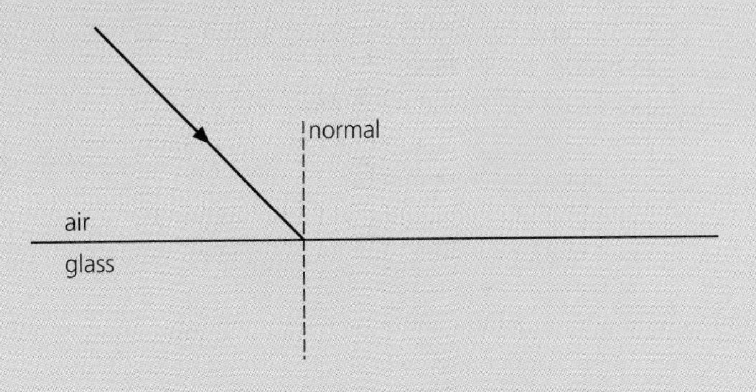

a Copy the diagram and draw in the path of the ray through the glass block.

b What happens to the ray as it enters and leaves the block?

c Explain why the ray behaves in this way.

d Draw a diagram to show what happens to a ray of light if it strikes the surface of the glass block at 90°.

8 a Draw a diagram of a wave. Label both its amplitude and its wavelength.

b Your diagram represents a sound wave. What would you hear if:

i the wavelength got shorter?

ii the amplitude got larger?

iii the shape of the wave changed?

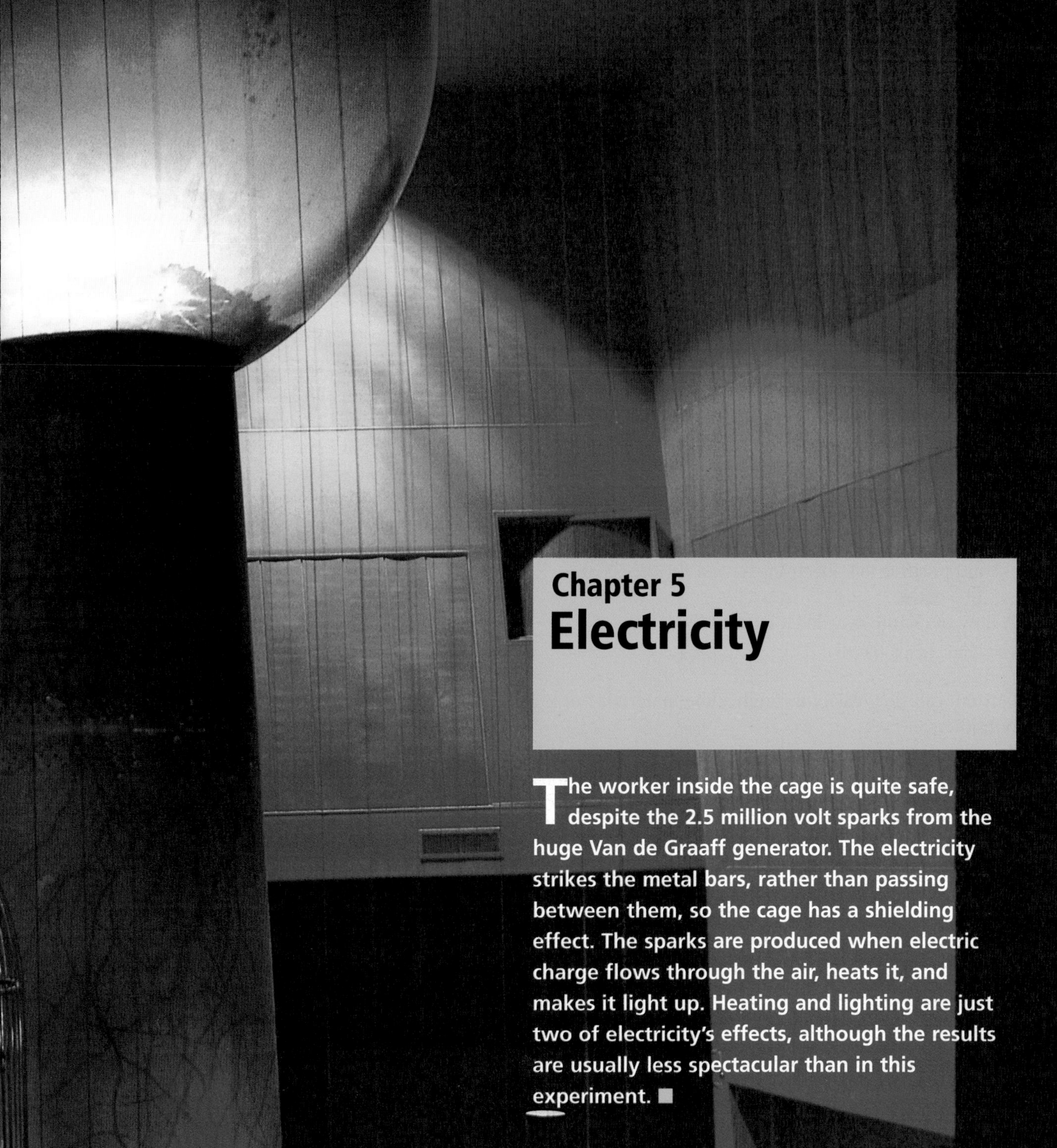

Chapter 5
Electricity

The worker inside the cage is quite safe, despite the 2.5 million volt sparks from the huge Van de Graaff generator. The electricity strikes the metal bars, rather than passing between them, so the cage has a shielding effect. The sparks are produced when electric charge flows through the air, heats it, and makes it light up. Heating and lighting are just two of electricity's effects, although the results are usually less spectacular than in this experiment. ■

5.01 Electricity in action

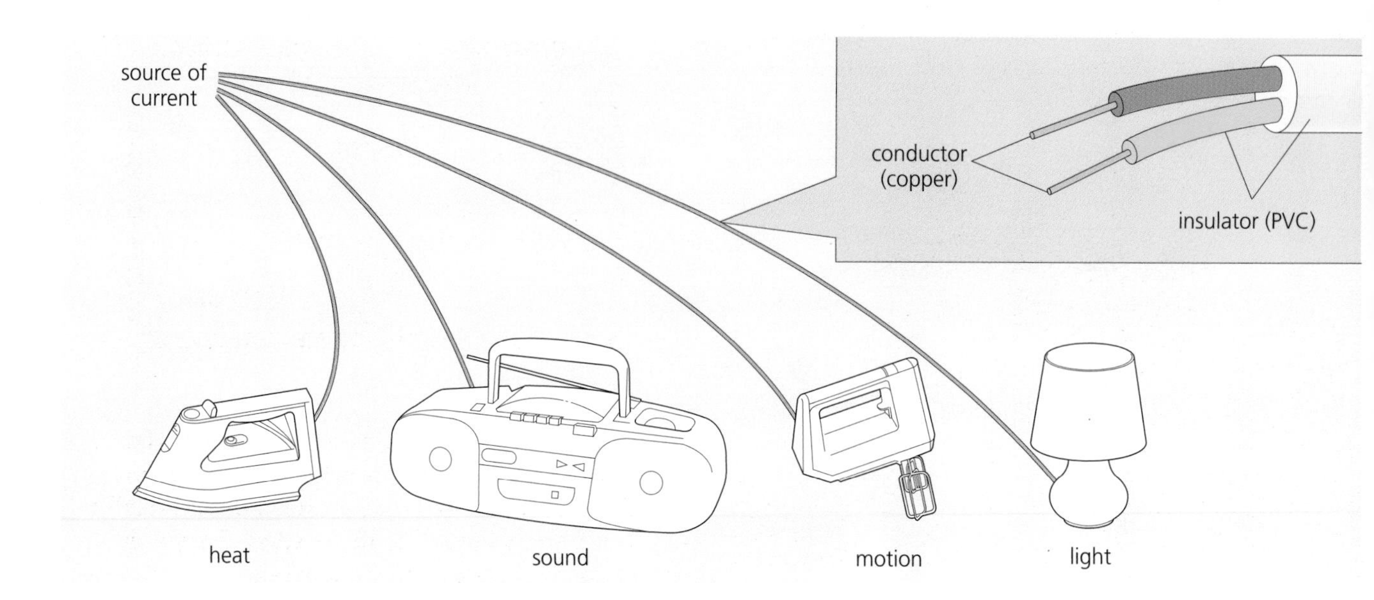

Electricity is a convenient way of delivering energy. Above, you can see some of the ways of using that energy.

When you switch something on, the 'electricity' in the wires is a flow of tiny particles called **electrons**. These are so small that they can pass between the atoms of the wires. Electrons each carry a tiny electric **charge**.

There are two types of electric charge, called negative (–) and positive (+). Electrons have a *negative* charge.

A flow of charge is called a **current**. So a flow of electrons is a current.

Current can flow easily through some materials but not others:

Why metals are good conductors

Everything is made of atoms, and all atoms contain electrons. In insulators, the electrons are tightly held to their atoms. But in metals, some are only loosely held and are free to move through the material. That is why metals are good conductors.

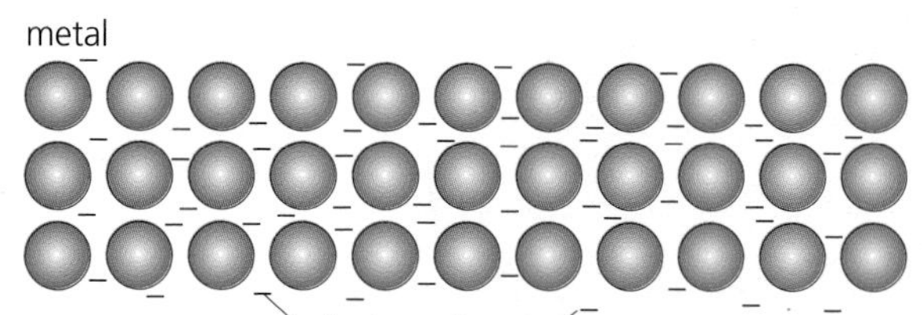

Conductors	Semiconductors	Insulators
Materials that let a current flow through. For example: *Good*: metals, especially silver, copper, aluminium; carbon *Poor*: water, human body, earth Good electrical conductors are also good thermal (heat) conductors.	'In between' materials: they are poor conductors when cold, but much better conductors when warm. For example: silicon germanium	Materials that hardly conduct at all. For example: plastics e.g. PVC polythene Perspex glass rubber air (dry)

Sources of current

Our main sources of current are electric **cells**, **batteries**, and **generators**. Cells and batteries push out current when chemicals inside them react. A battery really means a collection of cells. However, the word is commonly used for just one cell.

The large battery above is a car battery. It contains six cells, all in the same case.

Generators push out current when a shaft is turned. Mains current comes from huge generators in power stations. The generators are often turned by turbines driven round by jets of high-pressure steam from a boiler.

The bulbs on this carnival float get their current from a generator turned by a diesel engine.

Static electricity

If charge collects on the surface of an insulator, it tends to stay there because it can't flow away. This is often called **static electricity**, or **electrostatic charge**. Look it up in the index to see where you can find out more about it.

A complete circuit

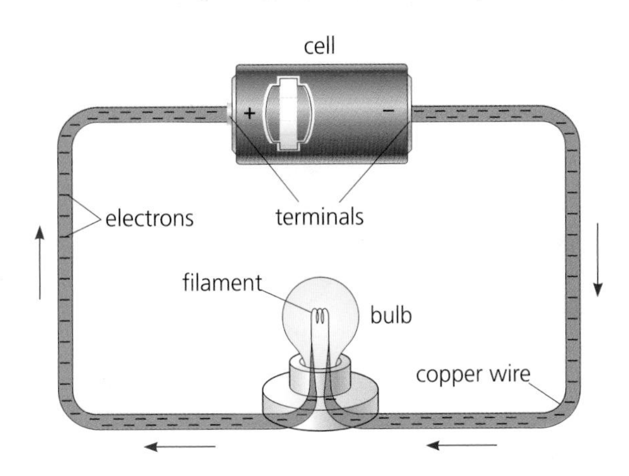

Above, a bulb is connected by wires to a cell. The conducting loop through the cell, wires, and bulb is called a **circuit**. Electrons are pushed out of the cell's negative terminal round to the positive. They only keep flowing if the circuit is unbroken.

Questions

1 What word means a flow of charge?

2 Name a material that could be used for:
 a the wire inside an electric cable;
 b the insulation round the outside of the cable.

3 Name a device that delivers a current:
 a when chemicals react inside it.
 b when a shaft is turned.

4 Write down two things that:
 a get their current from generators.
 b use current to produce motion.
 c use current to produce heat.

5 Why are metals the best conductors?

6 The chart below gives information about a portable stereo system and the cells it needs.
 a How long will the stereo run on one set of cells?
 b What is the cost of running the stereo for an hour?

Number of cells needed	6
Cost of each cell	50p
Energy stored in each cell	10 000 joules
Energy used by stereo system in 1 hour	20 000 joules

5.02 Circuits and currents

The hairdryer and cable are part of a huge circuit which passes right out of the house.
The circuits on this spread are much smaller. But the principles are just the same.

Current

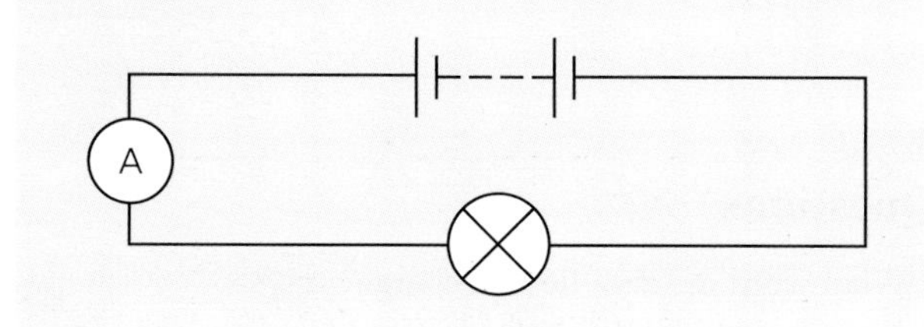

The above circuit contains a bulb, wire, meter, and battery – all drawn using electrical symbols.

The meter is measuring the current.
It is called an **ammeter**.

The unit of current is the **ampere** (**A**).

A current of 1 ampere means that about 6 million million million electrons are flowing round the circuit every second (although the ampere isn't defined in this way).

Typical current sizes	
Current through . . .	
. . . a small torch bulb	0.2 A
. . . a hairdryer	3 A
. . . a car headlight bulb	4 A
. . . an electric kettle	10 A

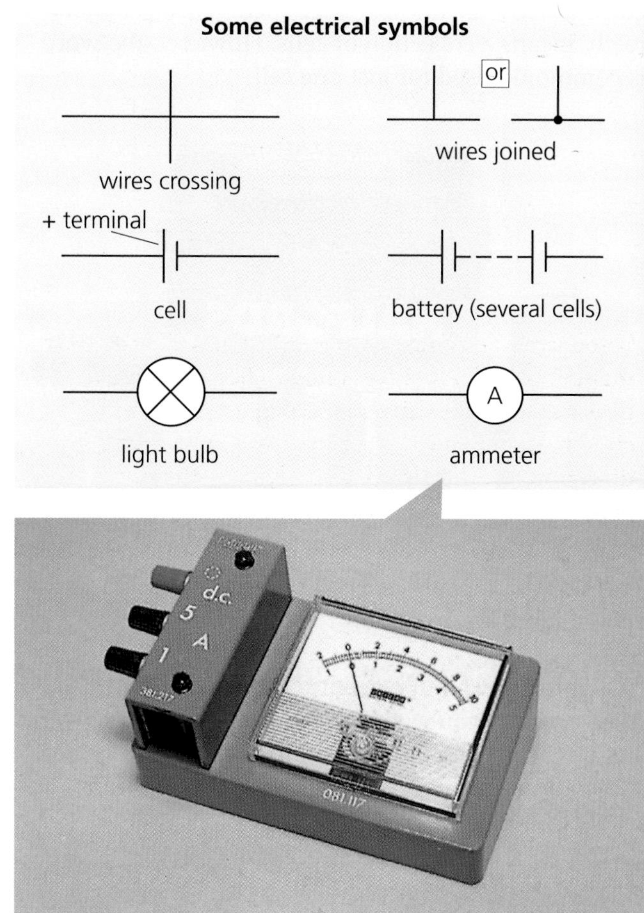

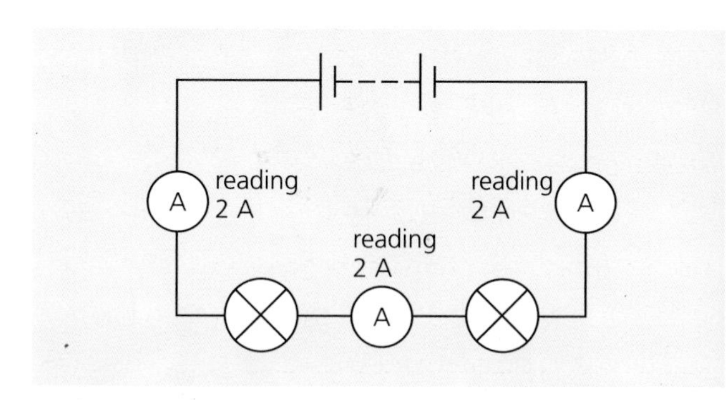

This circuit has three ammeters and two bulbs in it. When electrons leave the battery, they flow through each of the ammeters in turn. So the readings are all the same.

In a simple circuit, the current through every part is the same.

Putting ammeters in the circuit doesn't affect the current. As far as the circuit is concerned, the ammeters are just like pieces of connecting wire.

Which way?

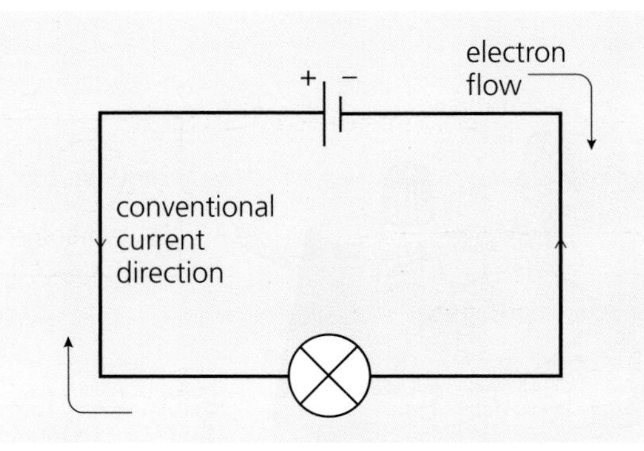

Some circuit diagrams have arrowheads marked on them. These don't show a flow. They just give the direction from positive (+) to negative (–) round the circuit. This is called the **conventional current direction**. The electrons actually flow the opposite way.

Current and charge

If a current is flowing, then electric charge is passing round a circuit.
Amounts of charge are measured in **coulombs**:

If a current of	flows for	then the charge passing is
1 ampere	1 second	1 coulomb
2 amperes	1 second	2 coulombs
2 amperes	3 seconds	6 coulombs
	. . . and so on.	

You can use an equation to calculate charge:

charge (coulombs)	=	current (amperes)	×	time (seconds)

Use it to check the examples above.

If you think of a current as a flow of charge, then:

This current	*Means this* flow of charge
1 ampere	1 coulomb every second
2 amperes	2 coulombs every second
	. . .and so on.

Questions

1 What is the reading on each of these ammeters?

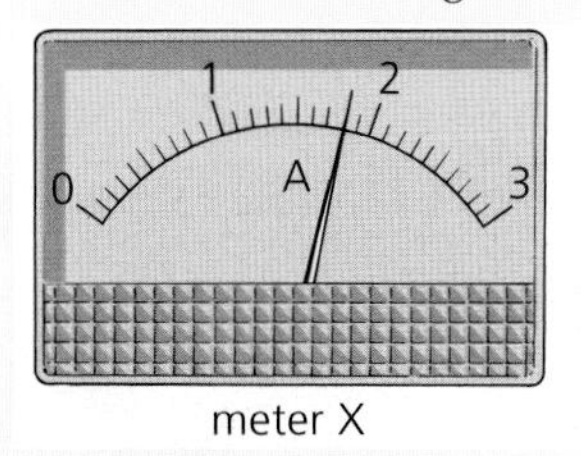

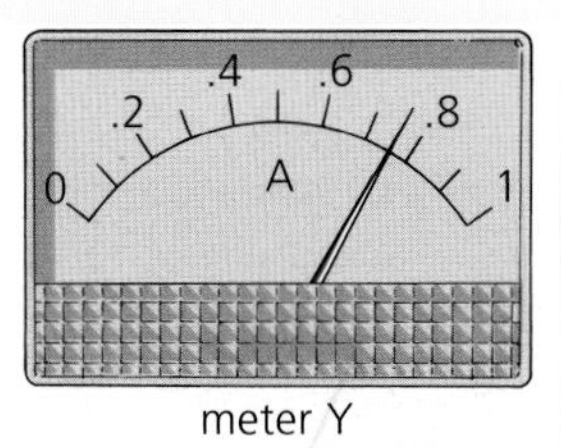

2 Copy the diagram below.

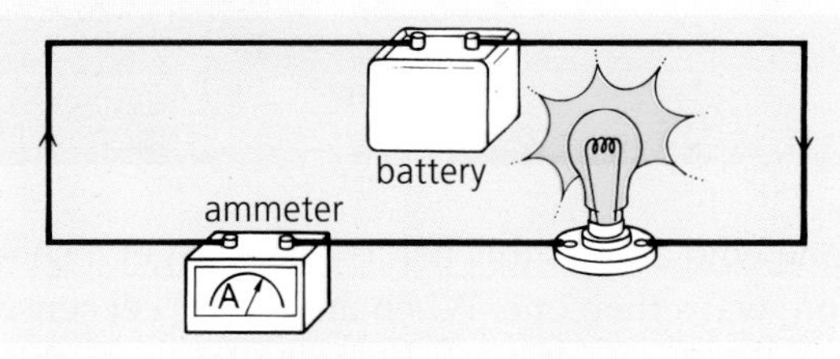

a What do the arrows on this diagram show?
b Mark in the positive and negative terminals of the battery.
Mark in the direction of electron flow, using an arrow alongside the wire.
c Redraw the diagram using the correct electrical symbols.

3 The current through this bulb is 3 A.

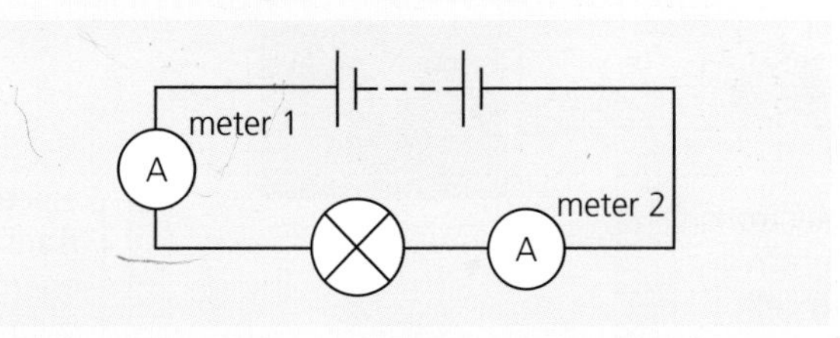

a What is the current through the battery?
b What is the current through meter 1?
c What is the current through meter 2?

4

Appliance	**Time switched on in s**	**Current in A**
Electric drill	20	2
Food mixer		1
Hairdryer	8	

The electrical appliances in the chart were all switched on for different times.
a How much charge was taken by the electric drill?
b If the food mixer took the same charge as the electric drill, how long was it switched on for?
c If the hairdryer took the same charge as the other two, what current was flowing through it?

5.03 Voltage

Anyone who attacks this fish is likely to get a shock – in more ways than one. When an electric eel senses danger, it turns itself into a living battery – pushing out electrons with nearly double the energy of those from a mains socket.

Energy from a battery

When electrons are pushed out of a battery, they carry energy with them.

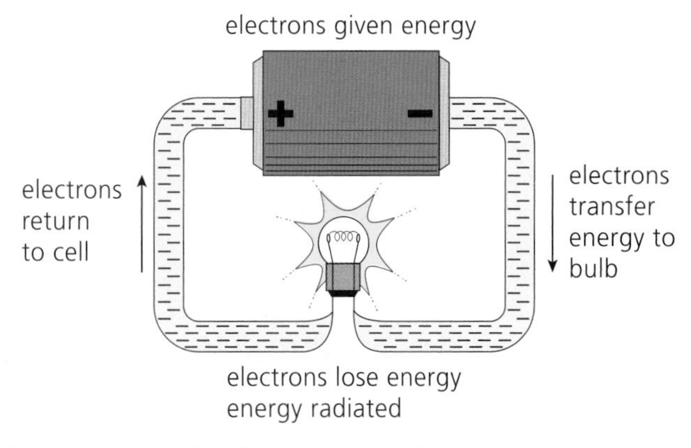

In the circuit, the electrons use all their energy passing through the bulb. The energy is changed into heat and light. When the electrons reach the battery again, all their energy has gone.

Battery voltage

Some batteries give electrons more energy than others. The higher the **voltage**, the more energy is given to each electron.

Voltage is also known as **potential difference (p.d.)**. The unit of p.d. is the **volt (V)**.
Voltage is measured by connecting an instrument called a **voltmeter** across the battery terminals.
The voltage produced inside a battery is called the **electromotive force (e.m.f.)** of the battery.

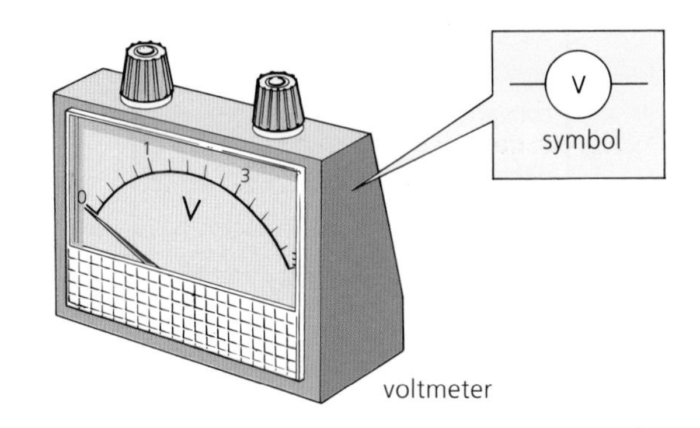

Voltages round a circuit

Below are three bulbs connected to a 12 volt battery. The battery gives the electrons energy.

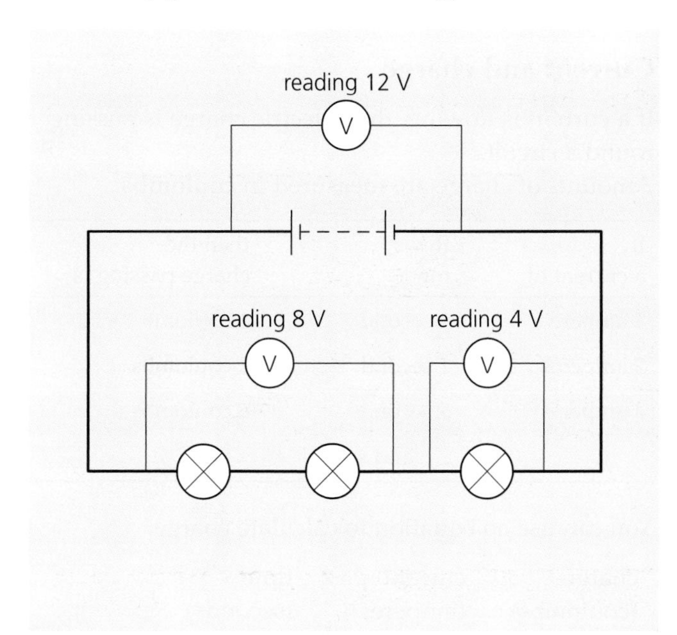

The electrons use some of their energy in the first bulb, some in the second, and the rest in the third. Connect a voltmeter across any of the bulbs and it shows a reading. The higher the voltage, the more energy each electron uses as it passes through that part of the circuit.

Between them, the bulbs give out all the energy supplied by the battery:

The voltages across the bulbs add up to equal the battery voltage.

Connecting a voltmeter has almost no effect on the current flowing in the circuit. As far as the circuit is concerned, the voltmeter might as well not be there.

Cells in series

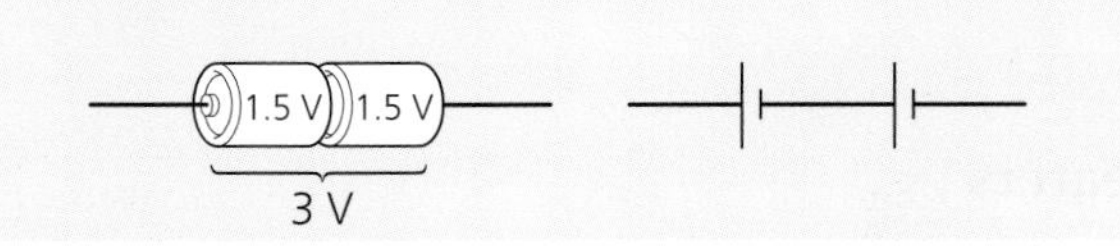

These cells are connected in **series**.
They give twice the voltage of a single cell.

Voltage, charge, and energy

There is an exact link between voltage, charge, and energy:

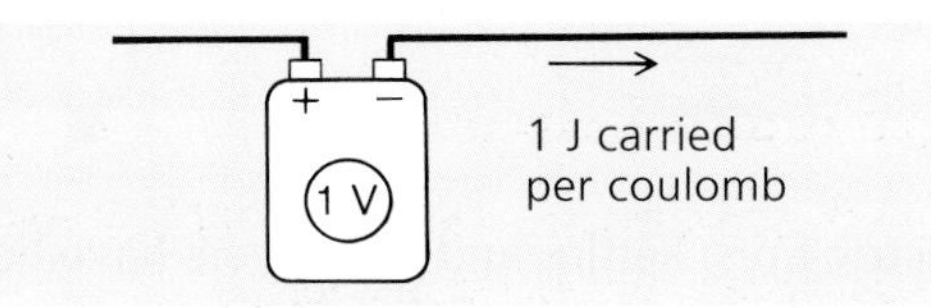

Voltage across cell: 1 volt.

This cell gives 1 joule (J) of energy to every coulomb (C) of charge it pushes out.

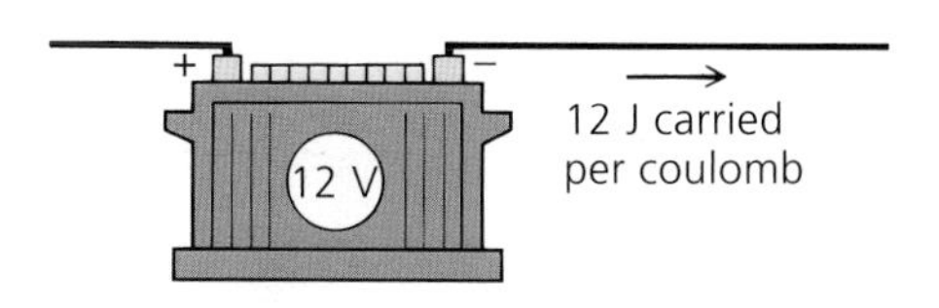

Voltage across battery: 12 volts.

This battery gives 12 joules of energy to every coulomb of charge it pushes out.

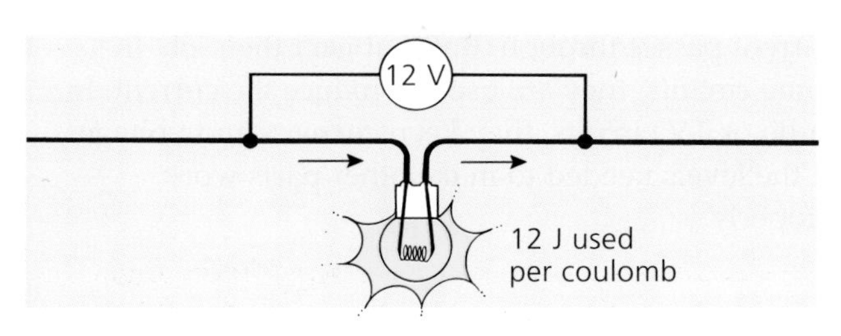

Voltage across bulb: 12 volts.

12 joules of energy are used by every coulomb of charge passing through.

The above examples can be summed up by the following equation:

energy* in J	=	voltage in V	×	charge in C

*this is the energy given or lost. It may also be called the energy transformed (or transferred).

Questions

1 In which section of this circuit do the electrons have:
  a most energy;
  b least energy?

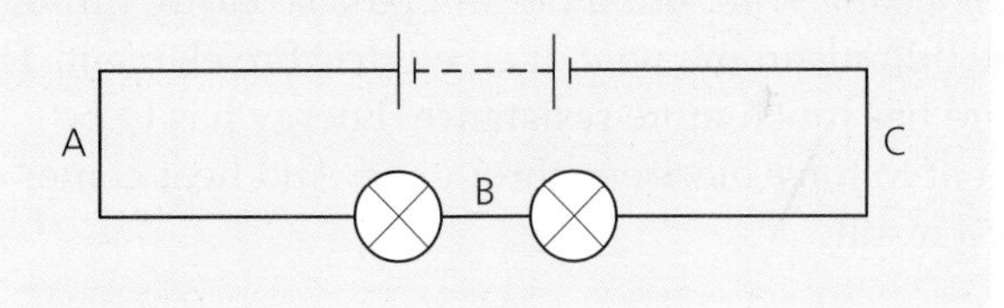

What happens to the energy they lose?

2 What is the voltage across each arrangement of cells?

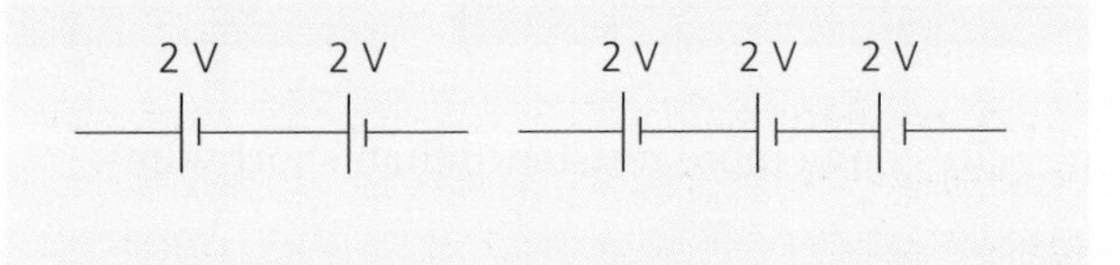

3 **a** What is the reading on the voltmeter across bulb B?

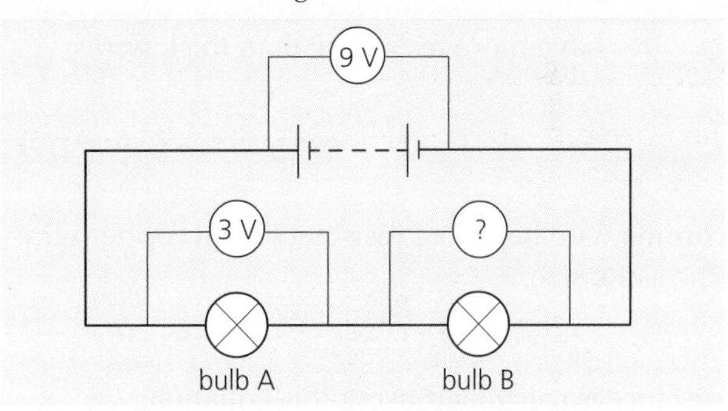

  b How much energy does the battery give each coulomb of charge it pushes out?
  c How much energy is lost by each coulomb of charge as it passes through bulb A?

4 To answer this question, you may need to look up information on another spread.

	A Battery of dry cells	B Car battery	C Watch battery
Voltage in V	15	12	1.5
Maximum current in A	6	100	0.01

  a Which battery can push out the most electrons every second?
  b Which battery pushes out electrons with most energy?
  c How much charge can the car battery push out in 10 seconds?
  d How much energy can the car battery deliver in 10 seconds?

5.04 Resistance

Current passes easily through a piece of copper connecting wire. But it doesn't pass so easily through the thin nichrome wire of an electric fire element. This wire has much more **resistance**. Energy has to be spent to force electrons through it. And heat comes off as a result.

All conductors have some resistance. But:

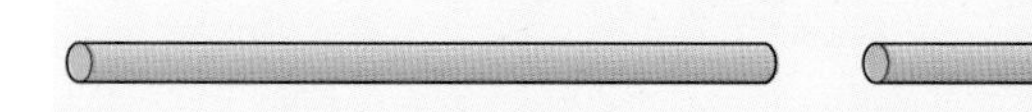

long wires have more resistance than short wires;

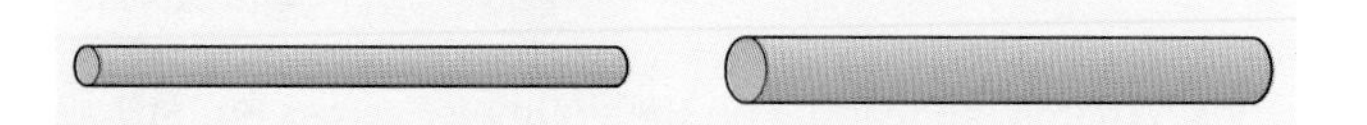

thin wires have more resistance than thick wires;

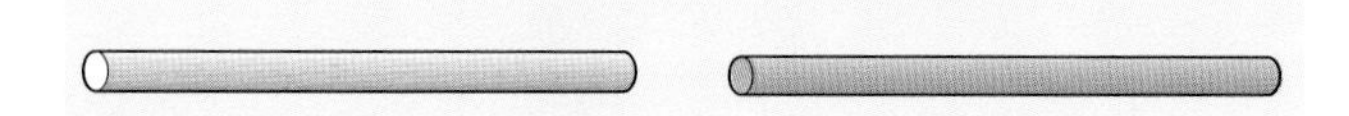

nichrome wire has more resistance than copper wire of the same size.

Resistance is calculated using this equation:

$$\text{resistance} = \frac{\text{voltage}}{\text{current}}$$

The unit of resistance is the **ohm** (Ω).

For example:

If there is a voltage of 12 volts across this piece of nichrome, then a current of 4 amperes flows through.
So:

$$\text{resistance} = \frac{12}{4}\text{ ohms} = 3\text{ ohms}$$

If there is a voltage of 12 volts across this piece of nichrome, then a current of 2 amperes flows through.
So:

$$\text{resistance} = \frac{12}{2}\text{ ohms} = 6\text{ ohms}$$

The *higher* the resistance, the *less* the current flows for each volt across the wire.

Heaters . . .

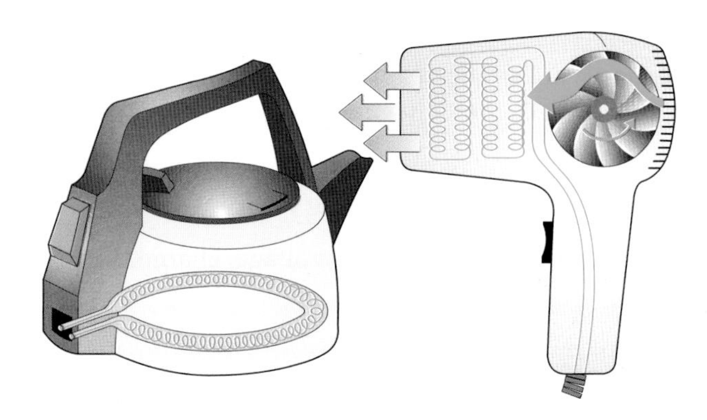

Like electric fires, kettles and hairdryers have heating elements made from coils of thin nichrome wire. The wire gives off heat when a current passes through.

. . . and resistors

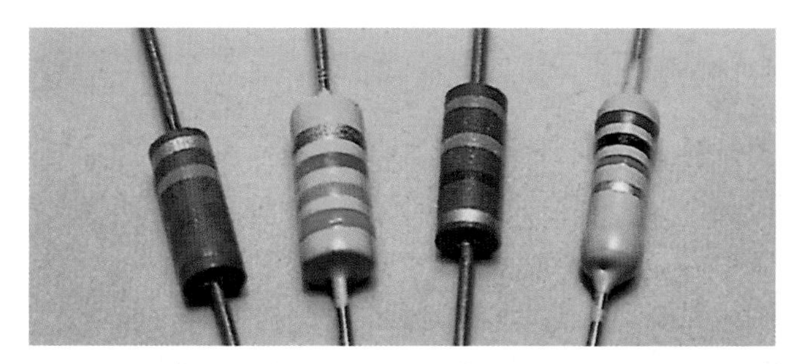

These are **resistors**. They also give off heat when a current passes through. But that isn't their job. In some circuits, they are used to reduce the current. In radio or TV circuits, they keep currents and voltages at the levels needed to make other parts work properly.

In a **variable resistor** there is a sliding contact which moves along a coil of nichrome wire. By moving the contact, you can change the resistance.
Variable resistors like this are used as volume controls in TVs and radios, and also in computer joysticks.

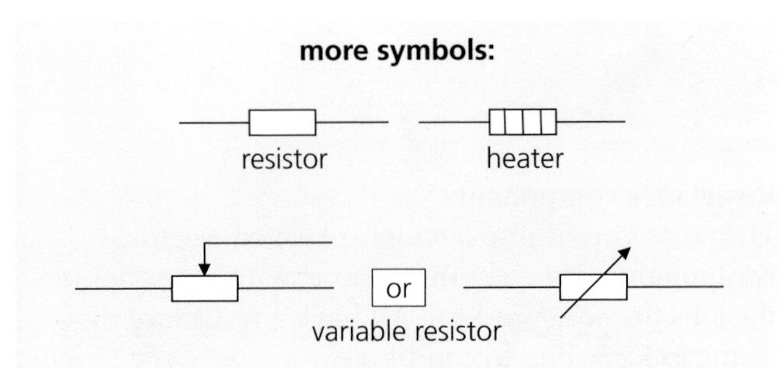

Measuring resistance – Ohm's law

This is an experiment to measure the resistance of a length of nichrome wire when different currents are flowing through it:

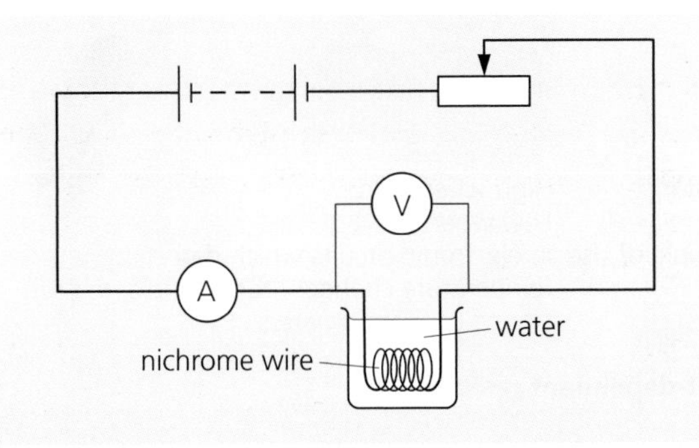

The voltmeter measures the voltage across the wire. The ammeter measures the current flowing through. The water keeps the wire at a steady temperature. To change the voltage across the wire, you move the sliding contact on the variable resistor. This gives the wire a different share of the battery voltage. You increase the voltage in stages, and measure the current each time. For example:

Voltage across wire in V	Current through wire in A	Voltage ÷ current in Ω
3.0	1.0	3
6.0	2.0	3
9.0	3.0	3
12.0	4.0	3
		= resistance

Here, the voltage and current are in *proportion*. The resistance has the same value every time. Like all other metals the nichrome obeys **Ohm's law**:

The resistance of a metal conductor is the same, whatever current is flowing – provided the temperature doesn't change.

The effect of temperature

If a metal is warmed, its resistance goes up – although not usually by very much. For example, the resistance of a piece of nichrome increases by only about 1% for a 100 °C rise in temperature. However, a very large temperature change can have a noticeable effect on resistance:

When this bulb is switched on, the tungsten filament heats up to 3000 °C. At this temperature, its resistance is about double that when cold.

Questions

1 When a kettle is plugged into the 230 V mains, a current of 10 A flows through its element. What is the resistance of the element?

2 A piece of nichrome wire is kept at a steady temperature. Different voltages are applied across the wire, and the current measured each time. Copy the table, and fill in the missing values.

Voltage in V	Current in A	Resistance in Ω
8	2	?
4	?	?
2	?	?

3 A headlamp bulb has a filament made of tungsten metal. This is how the current through the bulb rises when the voltage across it is increased:

Voltage in V	2	4	6	8	10	12
Current in A	1.8	2.8	3.5	4.1	4.6	5.0

Plot a graph of *current* (side axis) against *voltage* (bottom axis). Use your graph to find:

a the current flowing when the voltage is 9 V;
b the resistance of the bulb when the current is 2 A;
c the resistance of the bulb when the current is 4 A;
d the highest resistance of the bulb.
e Mark on your graph the point where the temperature is highest.

5.05 More about resistance

Controlling current

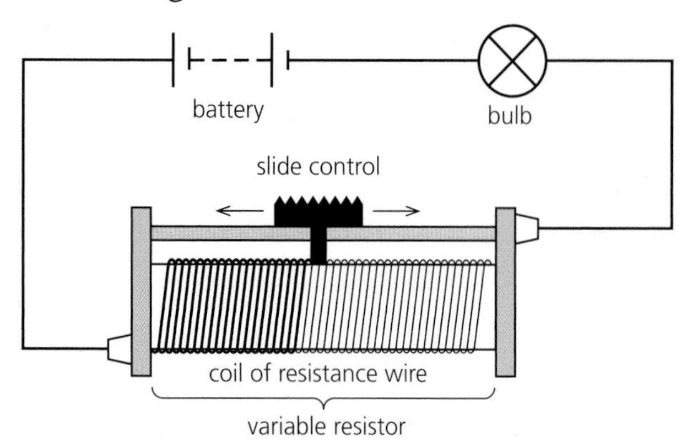

Above, a variable resistor is being used to control the brightness of a bulb. If you move the slide control to the right, you increase the length of resistance wire in the circuit. This reduces the current and dims the bulb. There is one problem with this type of dimming circuit. As the length of nichrome wire is shortened and the current rises, the wire gets hot, and can give off more heat than the bulb. Modern dimmer switches like the one below have a neat way of overcoming this problem:

In this dimmer switch, the variable resistor only takes a small current. Its job is to control an electronic circuit that switches the power on, off, on, off ... very fast, so that the bulb never has time to come up to full brightness. The slight flickering is too fast to notice. When you turn down the control, the 'offs' get longer and the 'ons' shorter, so the bulb gets dimmer. Speed controllers for electric motors work in the same way.

Resistance components

The parts you fit into circuits are called electrical **components**. Here are three more, with examples of the jobs they are used for. All have a resistance that changes according to conditions.

Thermistor

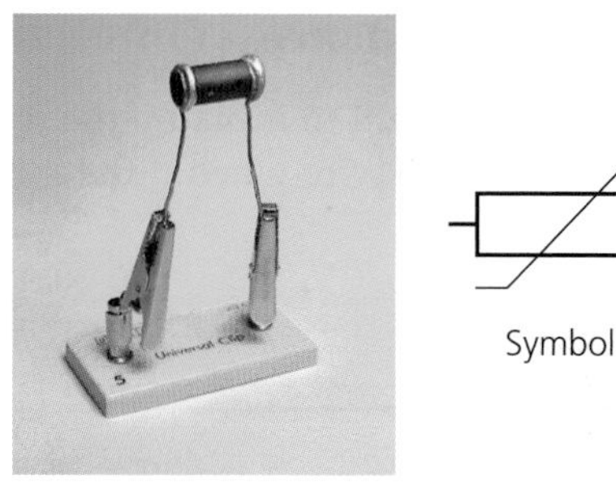

Resistance	High when cold Low when hot
Example of use	In electronic circuits which detect temperature change – for example, in fire alarms or thermometers.

Light-dependent resistor

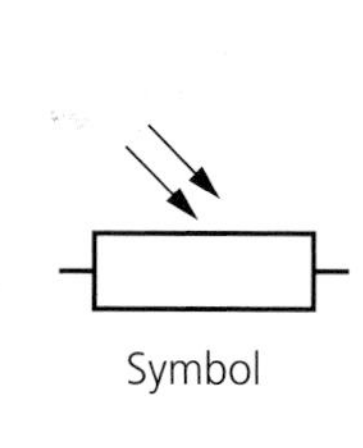

Resistance	High in the dark Low in the light
Example of use	In electronic circuits which switch on lights automatically.

Diode

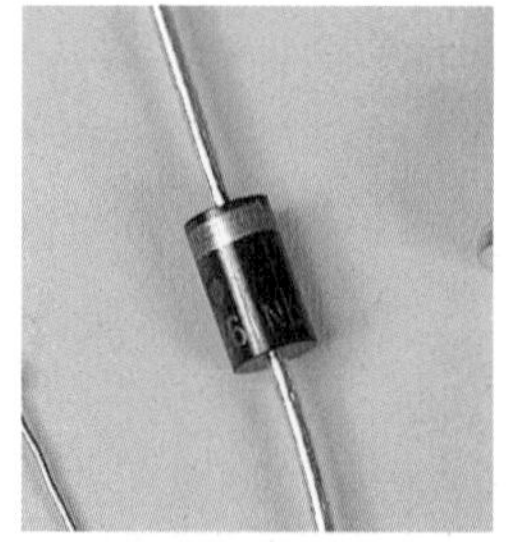

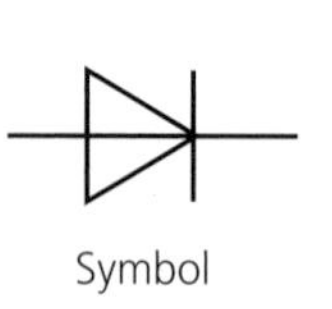

Resistance	Very high in one direction Very low in opposite direction
Example of use	Lets current flow in one direction only. Used in power adaptors and electronic equipment.

Current–voltage graphs

In the previous spread, there is a circuit for finding how the current through some nichrome wire depends on the voltage across it. Similar circuits can be used for other components.

Here are three examples of the graphs produced. In each case, the resistance (in ohms) at any point on the graph line can be found by dividing the voltage (in V) by the current (in A).

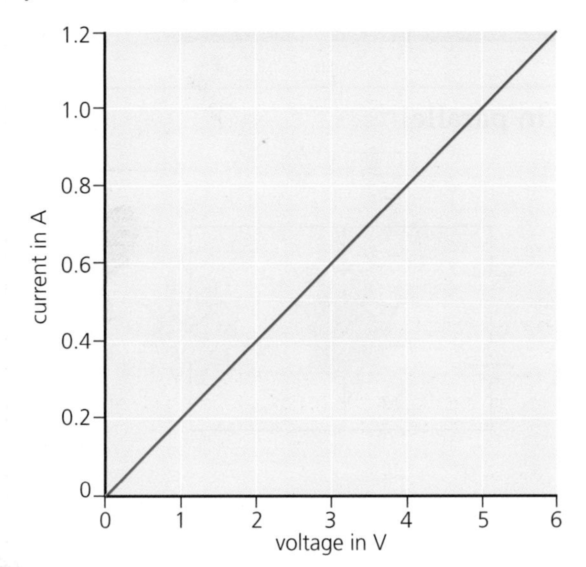

Metal resistor at a steady temperature (for example, nichrome wire) The graph is a straight line through the origin. Mathematically speaking, the current is proportional to the voltage. Voltage ÷ current is the same at all points, so the resistance doesn't change.

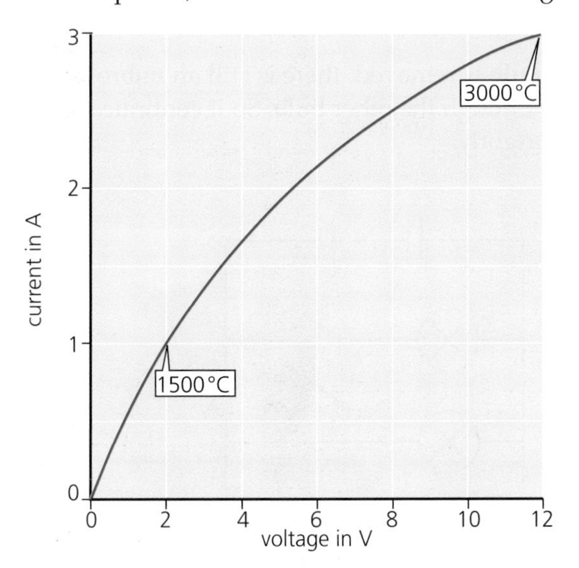

Tungsten filament (in a bulb) As the current increases, the temperature rises and the resistance goes up. Voltage ÷ current is not the same at all points. The current is not proportional to the voltage.

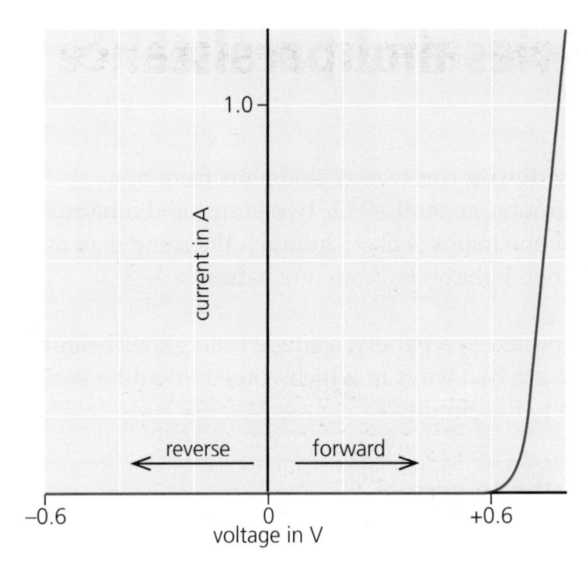

Diode The current is not proportional to the voltage. And if the voltage is reversed (by connecting the diode into the test circuit the other way round), the current is almost zero. In effect, the diode 'blocks' current in the reverse direction.

Questions

1 In the first diagram on the opposite page, a variable resistor is controlling the brightness of a bulb. What happens if the slide control is moved to the left? Give a reason for your answer.

2 What component has:

a a high resistance in the dark but a low resistance in the light?

b a very low resistance in one direction, but an extremely high resistance in the other?

c a resistance that falls when the temperature rises?

3

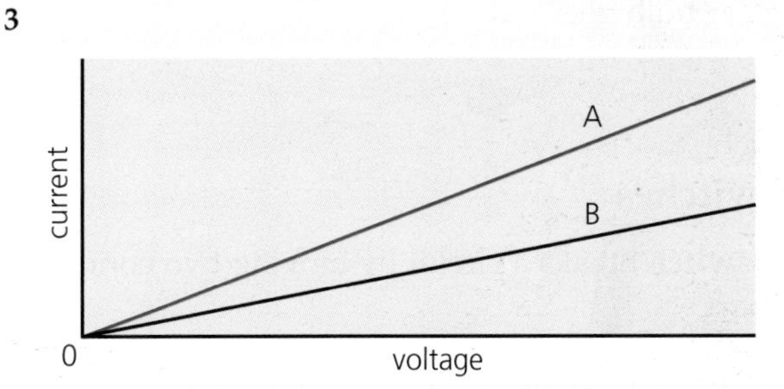

Graph lines A and B are for two different conductors. Which has the higher resistance?

4 Look at the graph for the tungsten filament. Calculate the resistance of the filament

a at 1500 °C **b** at 3000 °C.

5 Look at the graph for the diode. Does the diode have its highest resistance in the *forward* direction or the *reverse*? Explain your answer.

5.06 Series and parallel

How do you run twenty dodgems from one fairground generator? Or two lamps and a hairdryer from one mains socket? In much the same way as you run two light bulbs from one battery.

Connected to a battery, a single bulb glows brightly. Here are two ways in which you could add a second bulb to the circuit:

Bulbs in series

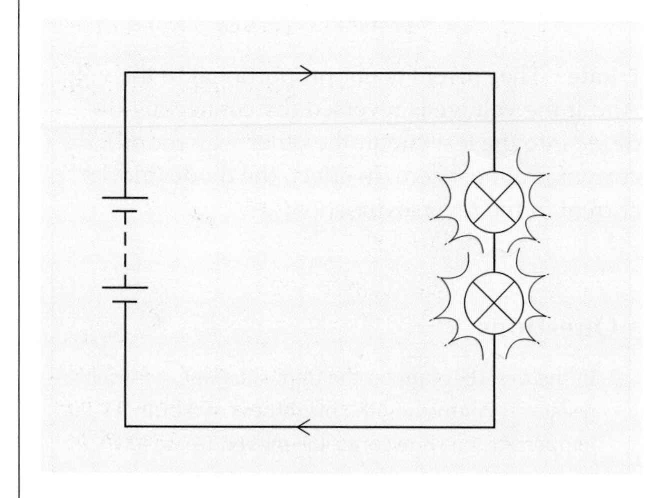

These bulbs are connected in **series**.
They have to share the battery voltage. So each glows dimly.

If one bulb is removed, the circuit is broken. The other bulb goes out.

Bulbs in parallel

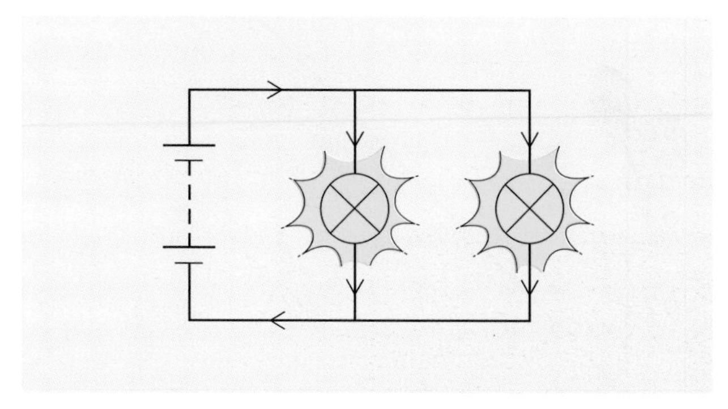

These bulbs are connected in **parallel**.
Each has direct connections to the battery.
Each gets the full battery voltage. So each glows brightly. But together, the bulbs take twice as much current as a single bulb. Energy is taken from the battery at a faster rate, so the battery goes 'flat' more quickly.

If one bulb is removed, there is still an unbroken circuit through the other bulb. So it continues to glow brightly.

Switches

A **switch** breaks a circuit by moving two contacts apart.
In this circuit, each bulb is controlled by a switch.
To find out which:

trace a route with your finger from one side of the battery, through a bulb, to the other side.
Your finger will pass over a switch.
This is the switch that turns the bulb on and off.

Two of the bulbs are controlled by the same switch. Can you tell which?

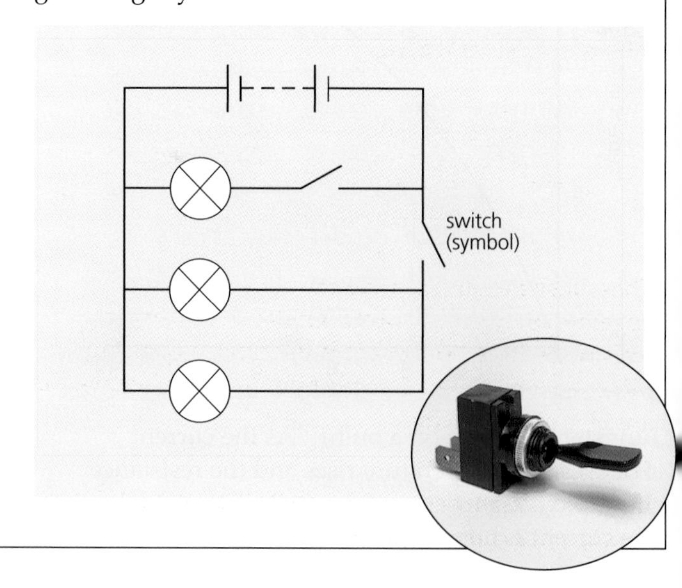

Resistors in series

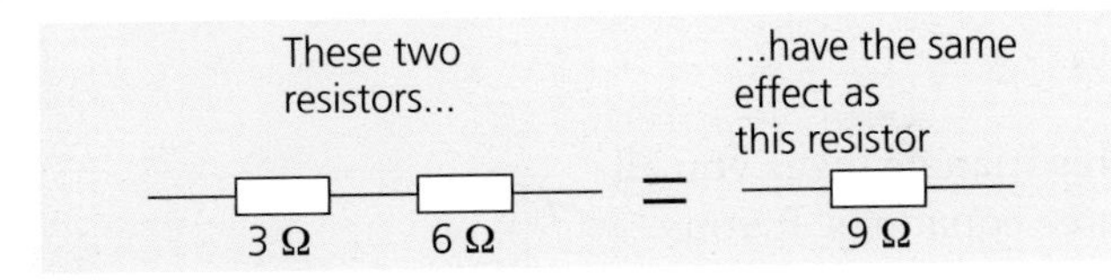

These resistors are in series.
Together, they give a higher resistance than either resistor by itself. The effect is the same as joining two short lengths of nichrome wire together to make a longer length.

To find the combined resistance, just add up the resistance values:

combined resistance = first resistance + second resistance

The rule works for three or more resistances as well.

If one bulb breaks they all go off. What does this tell you about the way that these lights are connected?

Resistors in parallel

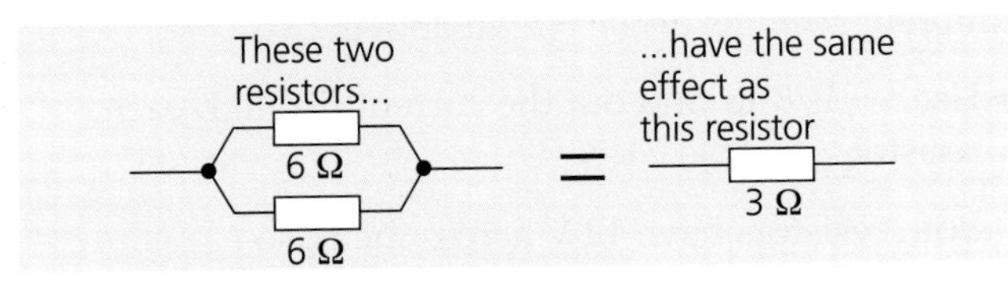

These resistors are in parallel.
Together, they give a lower resistance than either resistor by itself. The effect is the same as putting two pieces of nichrome wire side by side. They behave like a wider piece of wire.

For example:
If the two resistances are the *same*, the combined resistance is *half* a single resistance.

More symbols

To show whether switches are on or off, these symbols are sometimes used:

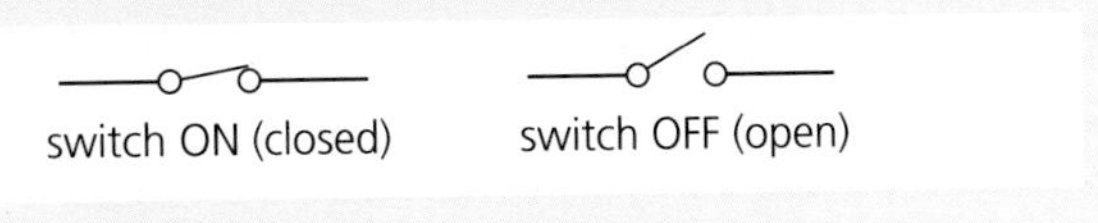

Questions

1 Some bulbs are to be powered by the same battery. Give *two* advantages of connecting the bulbs in parallel rather than in series.

2

	Power source	Bulbs connected	Voltage across each bulb	Effect of removing one bulb
A	230 V bulbs	3 ceiling bulbs	230 V	others stay ON
B	230 V mains	20 Christmas tree bulbs	11.5 V	?
C	12 V battery	2 headlamp bulbs	12 V	?

The chart above gives information about three sets of bulbs, A, B, and C. In each case, say whether the bulbs are in series or in parallel. Then copy and complete the last column.

3

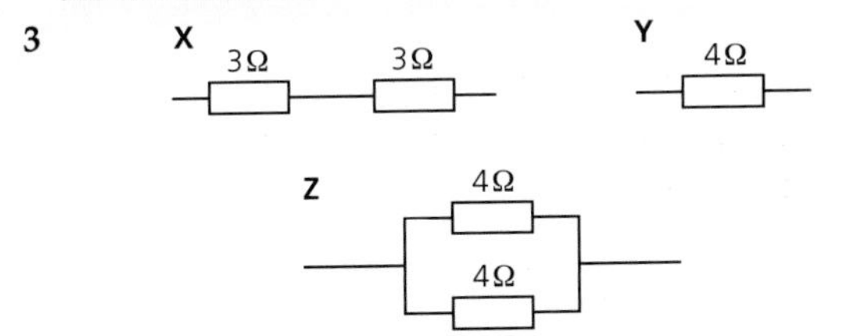

Which resistor arrangement **X**, **Y**, or **Z** has

a most resistance? **b** least resistance?

4

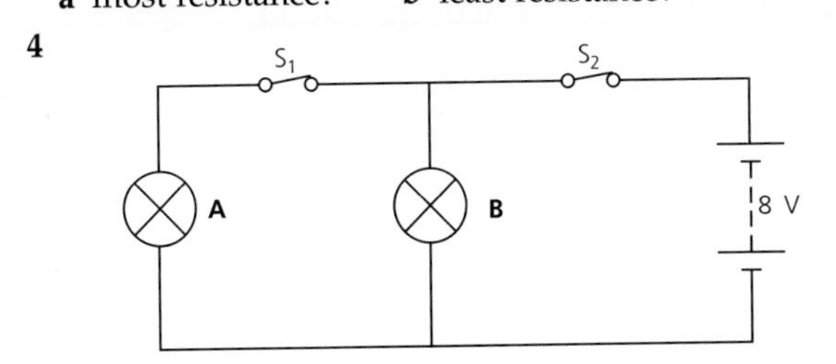

In the circuit above, will each of the bulbs **A** and **B** be ON or OFF if:

a switch S_1 only is opened?

b switch S_2 only is opened?

If both switches are closed:

c what is the voltage across bulb A?

d what is the voltage across bulb B?

5.07 Solving circuits

Useful equations

This equation: resistance = $\frac{\text{voltage}}{\text{current}}$

can be written using symbols: $R = \frac{V}{I}$

where	R is the resistance	in ohms
	V is the voltage	in volts
and	I is the current	in amperes

You can rearrange the equation in two ways:

$$I = \frac{V}{R} \text{ and } V = I \times R$$

These are useful if you know the resistance, but you need to find the current or voltage.

This triangle gives you all three equations. If you want the equation for I, just cover up I, and so on . . .

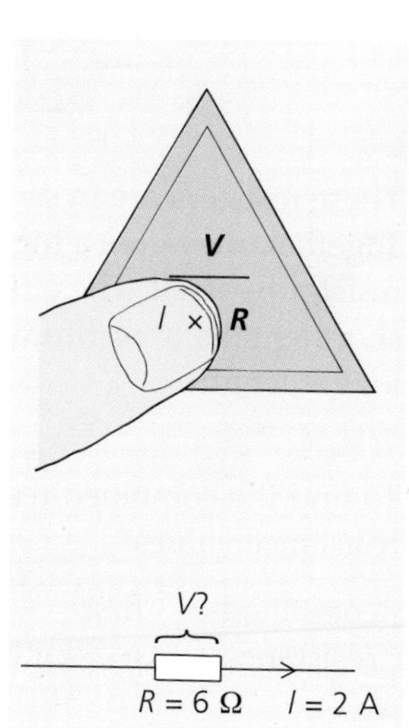

For example:

A current of 2 A flows through a 6 Ω resistor. To find the voltage across the resistor:

Select the equation for V and fill in the values of I and R:

$$V = I \times R$$
$$= 2 \times 6$$
$$= 12\,V$$

When resistors are in series . . .

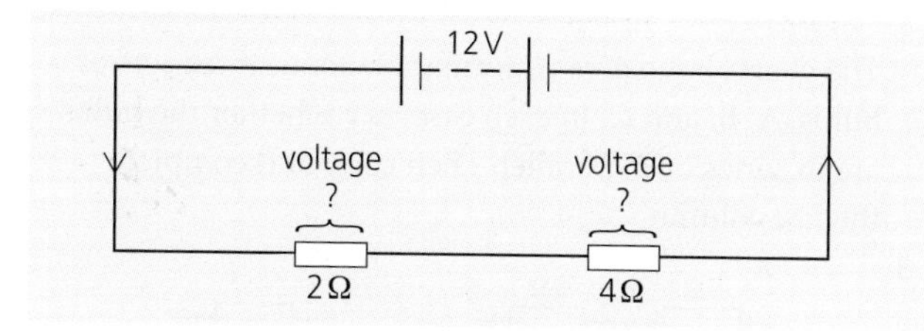

. . . the current is the same through each.

But the voltage is shared.

Problem To find out the voltage across each resistor in the circuit above:

- Find the total resistance in the circuit:

  resistance = 2 Ω + 4 Ω = 6 Ω

- Use $I = V/R$ to find the current in the circuit:

  current = 12 ÷ 6 = 2 A

- Now you know the current, use $V = I \times R$ to find the voltage across each resistor:

  voltage across 2 Ω resistor = 2 × 2 = 4 V

  voltage across 4 Ω resistor = 2 × 4 = 8 V

- Check your answers:
  The voltages across the resistors should add up to equal the battery voltage (12 V). Do they?

When resistors are in parallel . . .

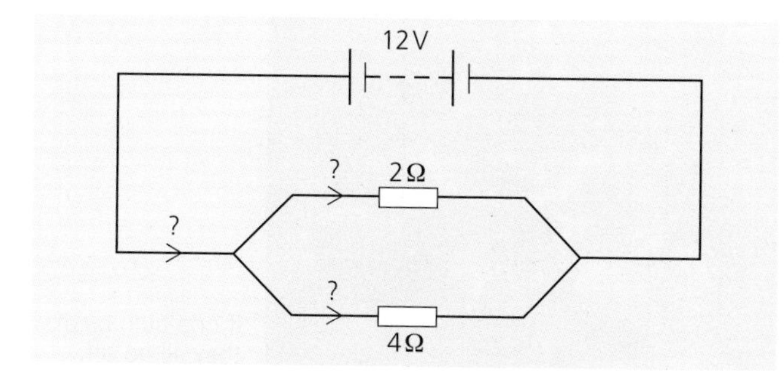

. . . the voltage is the same across each.

But the current is shared.

Problem To find the currents flowing in the different sections of the circuit above:

- Use $I = V/R$ to find out the current through each resistor:

  Both resistors have 12 V across them, so

  current through 2 Ω resistor = 12 ÷ 2 = 6 A

  current through 4 Ω resistor = 12 ÷ 4 = 3 A

- Add the currents together to find the current in the main circuit:

  current in main circuit = 6 A + 3 A = 9 A

Simpler than it looks . . .

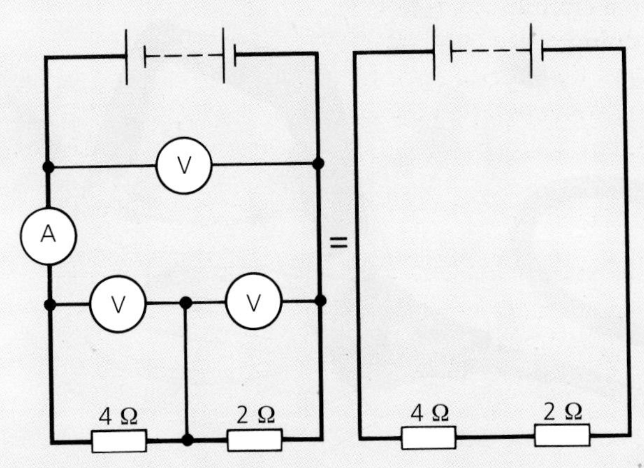

The meters don't affect the circuit. This circuit behaves . . .

. . . like this one.

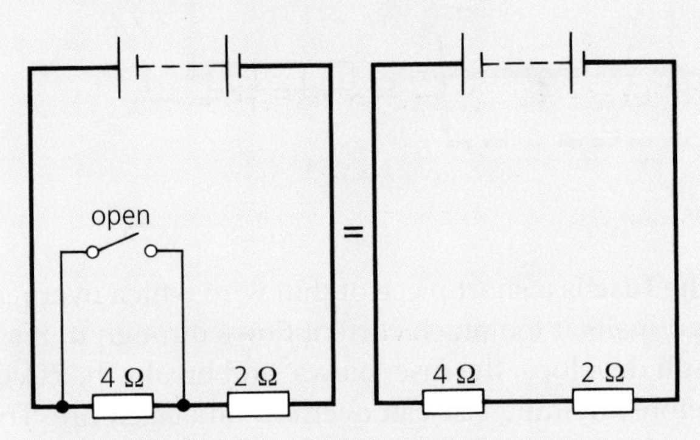

If the switch is open, this circuit behaves . . .

. . . like this one.

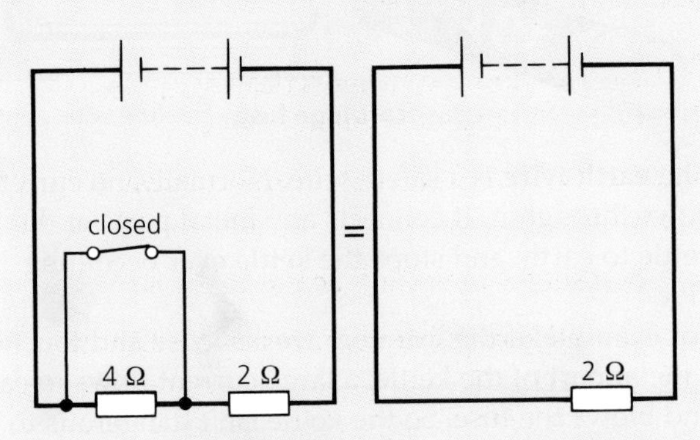

But, if the switch is closed, all the current takes the 'short circuit' route through the switch. It's just as if the 4 Ω resistor wasn't there.

Questions

1 In each of the following, the *resistance*, *voltage*, or *current* needs to be calculated. Find the missing value:

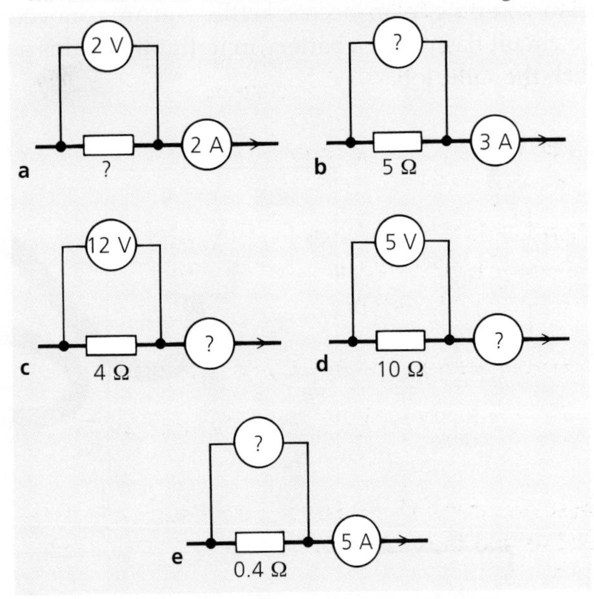

2

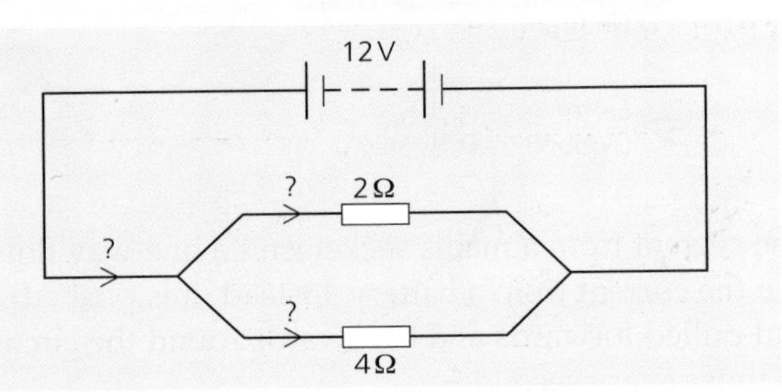

a In the circuit above, what is the current through the 4 Ω resistor?

b What is the current through the 2 Ω resistor?

c What current flows from the battery?

d Redraw the circuit, replacing the two parallel resistors with a single resistor.
If the current from the battery is the same as before, what is the resistance of this resistor?

3

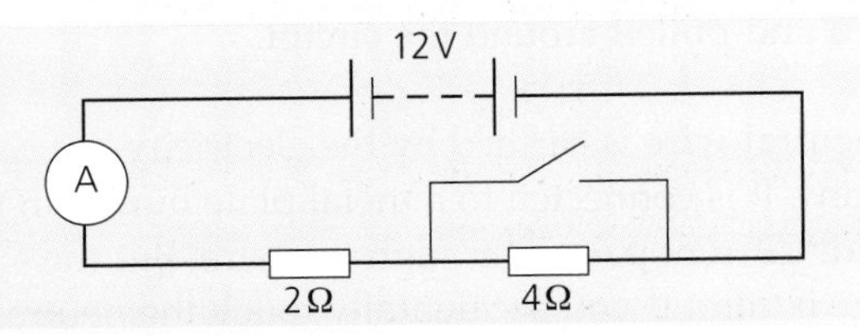

In the circuit above, what is the reading on the ammeter when the switch is:

a open?

b closed?

5.08 Mains electricity

When you plug in an electric kettle, you are connecting it into a circuit. The circuit hasn't got a battery in it. But the mains supply is doing much the same job.

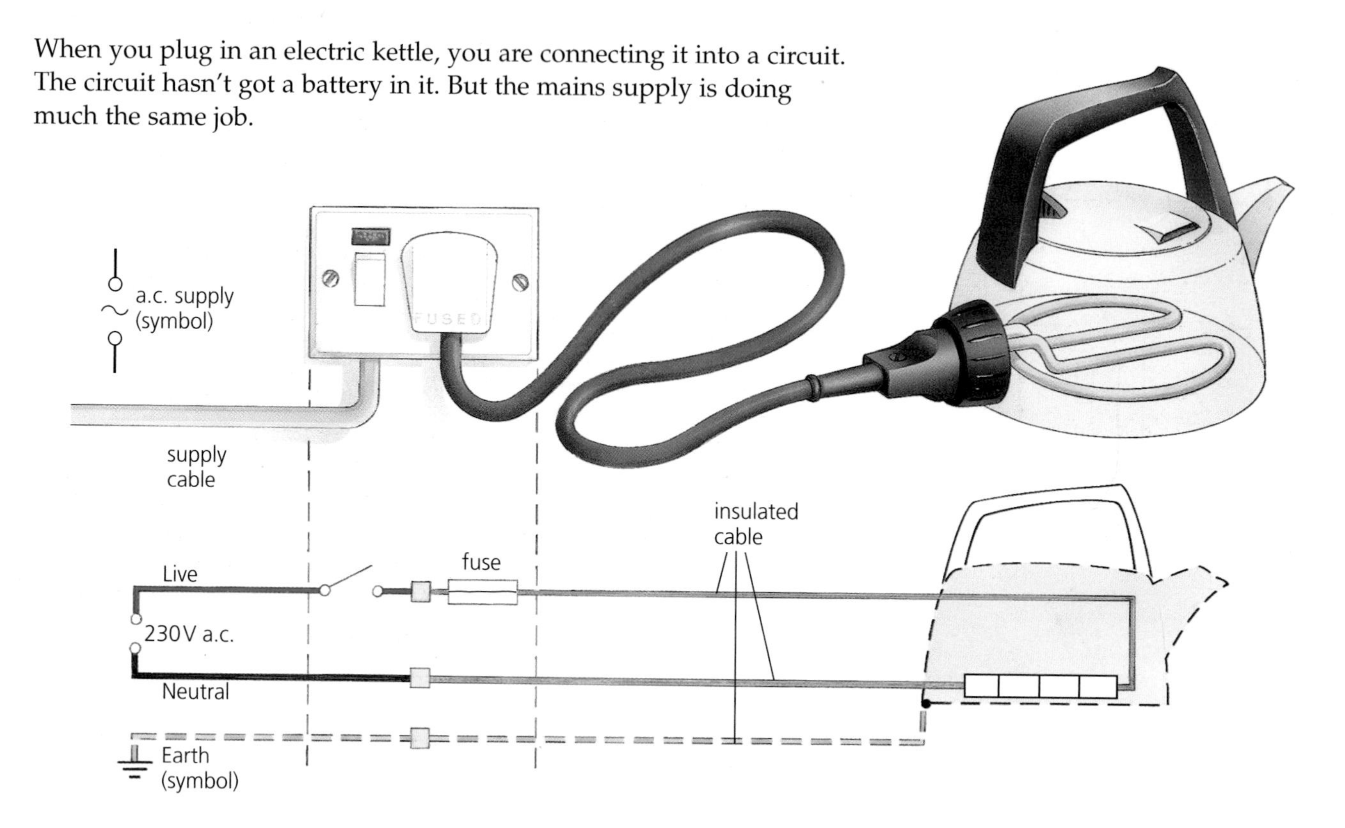

The current from a mains socket isn't a one-way flow like the current from a battery. Instead, it is pushed and pulled forwards and backwards round the circuit 50 times every second.
The current is known as **alternating current** or **a.c.**
The **mains frequency** is 50 Hz.
Power stations supply a.c. because it is easier to generate than one-way **direct current (d.c.)**.
In Britain, the supply voltage is 230 V.

The connecting wires to the kettle are insulated. They are all contained in a single cable or 'flex'.
The live wire goes alternately – and + as electrons are pushed and pulled around the circuit.

The neutral wire is earthed by the electricity company. It is connected to a metal plate buried in the ground. Current passes through the wire. But the voltage is zero. If you accidentally touch the neutral wire, you should not get a shock.

The switch on the mains socket is fitted in the live wire. This is to make sure that none of the wire in the flex is live when the switch is turned off.

The fuse is a short piece of thin wire which overheats and melts if too much current flows through it. If a fault develops, the fuse 'blows' and breaks the circuit before anything else can overheat and catch fire. The fuse is inside a small cartridge in the plug. Like the switch, it is placed in the live wire.

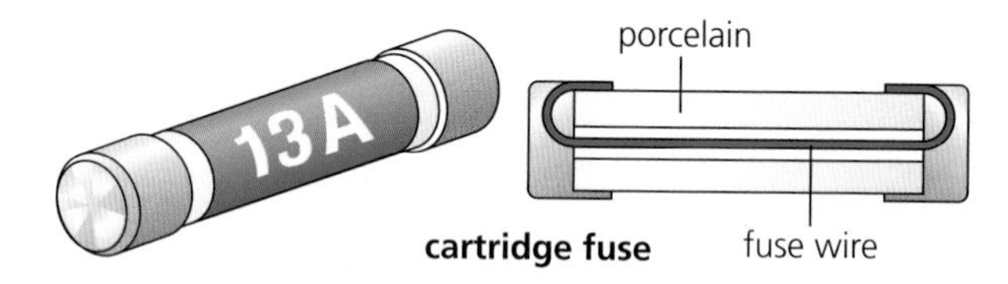

cartridge fuse

The earth wire is a safety wire. Normally, no current flows through it. It connects any metal parts of the kettle to earth, and stops the kettle ever becoming 'live'.
For example: if the live wire works loose and touches a metal part of the kettle, a large current flows to earth and blows the fuse. So the kettle isn't dangerous to touch.

Your hairdryer or radio probably doesn't have an earth wire connected to it. This is because it has an insulating plastic case, and not a metal one. As the cable is also insulated, there is **double insulation**.

Three-pin plugs

Plugs are a simple and safe way of connecting things to a mains circuit. In Britain, the square-pin fused plug is the most commonly used type.

When wiring a plug, check that:

- the wires are connected to the correct terminals:

brown	to **Live**
blue	to **Neutral**
yellow and **green**	to **Earth**

- there are no loose strands of wire.
- the cable is held firmly by the grip.
- a fuse of the correct value is fitted.

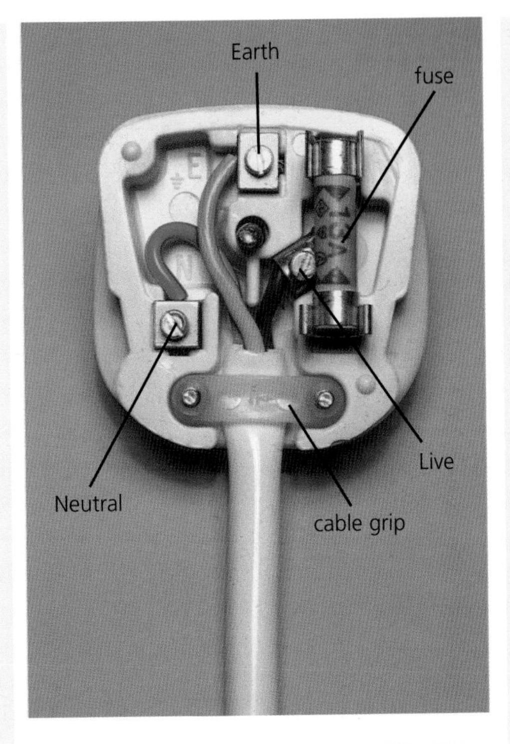

If a fuse blows:

- Switch off at the socket and pull out the plug.
- Don't fit a new fuse until the fault has been put right.

Choosing a fuse

Plugs are normally fitted with 3 A or 13 A fuses. The value tells you the current needed to 'blow' the fuse.

If a TV takes a current of 0.5 A, its plug should be fitted with a 3 A fuse.

If a kettle takes a current of 10 A, its plug should be fitted with a 13 A fuse.

The fuse value should always be more than the actual current, but as close to it as possible. The TV will still work with a 13 A fuse fitted. But it might not be safe. If something goes wrong, the circuits could overheat and catch fire without the fuse blowing.

Questions

1 LIVE NEUTRAL EARTH
Which of these wires:
a has a brown covering?
b is a safety wire?
c goes alternately + and –?
d has a blue covering?
e has a yellow and green covering?
f forms part of the circuit, but has no voltage on it?

2 Copy and complete the table to show whether a 3 A or 13 A fuse should be fitted to the plug connected to each appliance. The first is done for you.

Appliance	Current taken in A	Fuse value in A
Radio	0.1	3
Hairdryer	4	
Refrigerator	0.5	
Cassette player	0.2	
Fan heater	12	
Food mixer	2	

3 This circuit has been wrongly wired.

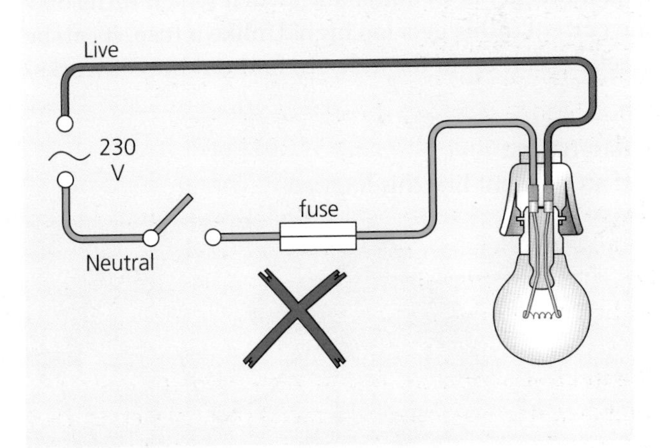

If the bulb is taken out of its socket, the circuit isn't safe. Explain why not. Redraw the circuit, showing the correct wiring.
If your circuit were used to supply current to a metal fan heater, an earth wire should be fitted. Why should this be done?

5.09 More about the mains

Connecting in parallel

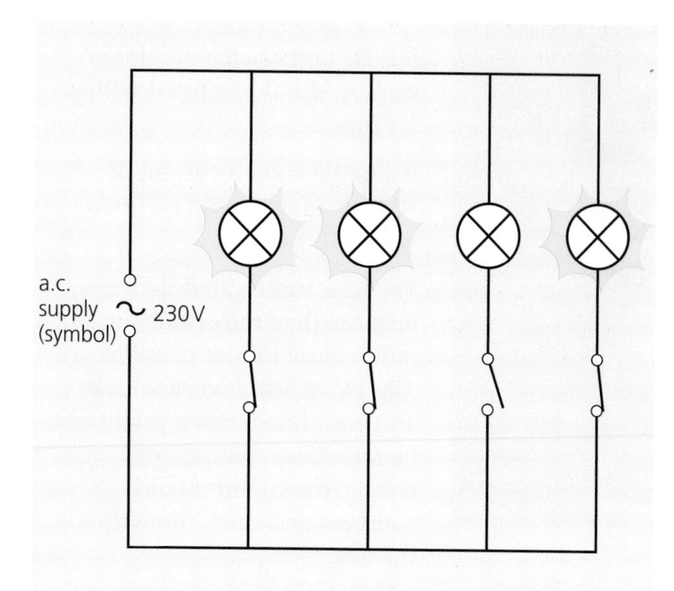

When bulbs are connected in parallel, as above, each gets the full supply voltage and each can be switched on and off independently.

In a house, the electricity supplier's cable branches into several parallel circuits for the lights, cooker, and mains sockets. In the **consumer unit** ('fuse box'), each circuit passes through a fuse or **circuit breaker**. A circuit breaker is an automatic switch which turns off the current if this gets too high. Unlike a fuse, it can be reset. Look it up in the index to find out how it works.

Two-way switches

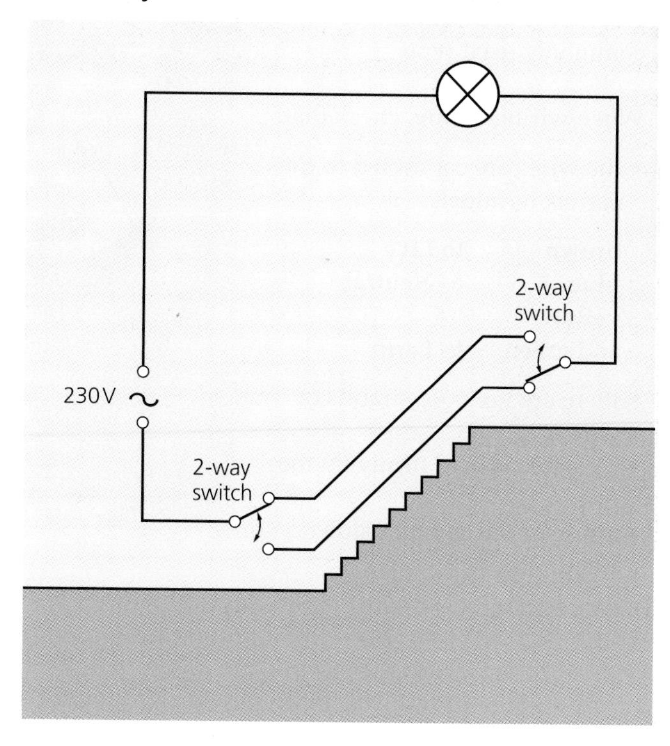

In most houses, you can turn the landing light on or off using upstairs or downstairs switches. These have two contacts instead of one. They are **two-way switches**. If both switches are up or down, then a current flows through the bulb. But if one is up and the other is down, the circuit is broken. Each switch reverses the effect of the other.

Safety first

If an accident like this happens ...

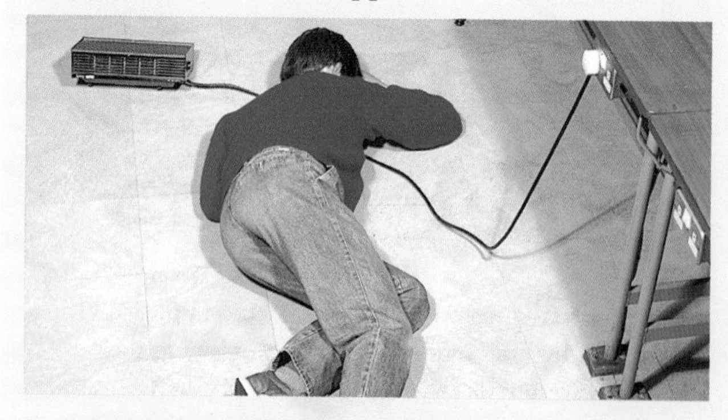

... you must do the following before giving help:

- switch off at the socket;
- pull out the plug.

To prevent accidents ...

When using extension cables to lawnmowers and drills, fit a residual current circuit breaker (RCCB). This compares the currents in the live and neutral wires. If these are not the same, then current must be flowing to earth – perhaps through your body because you are touching a cut wire. The RCCB switches off the current before any harm can be done.

More about a.c. and d.c.

Alternating current (a.c.) is easier to generate than one-way direct current (d.c.) of the type that flows from a battery.
You can see the difference between a.c. and d.c. using an **oscilloscope**. This can plot a graph very rapidly, over and over again, showing how the voltage of a supply varies with time:

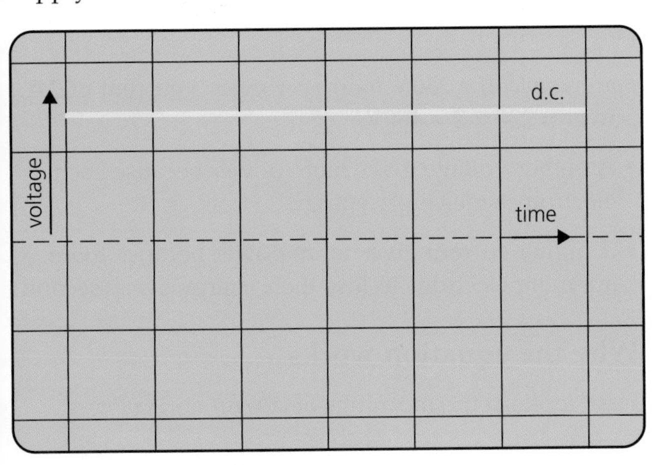

This d.c. voltage is steady, and always in the same direction.

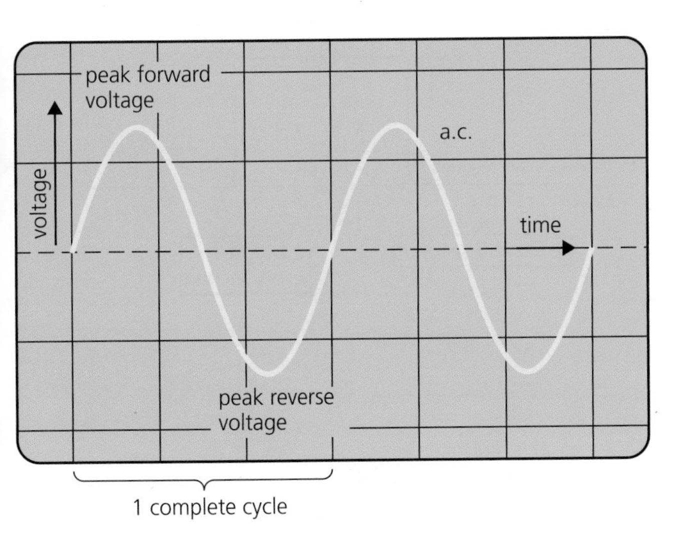

An a.c. voltage rises to a peak (maximum), falls to zero, changes direction...and so on, many times every second.

In the UK, the **mains frequency** is 50 **hertz** (**Hz**). This means that there are 50 complete backwards-and-forwards cycles every second.

In the USA, mains frequency is 60 Hz: in other words, 60 cycles every second. This means that each cycle is shorter than with a 50 Hz supply, so the peaks you see on an oscilloscope screen are closer together.

Mains voltage

In Europe, **mains voltage** is given as 230 V. That may be a bit puzzling because, with a.c., the voltage is rising and falling all the time! However, 230 V is a special type of average. It is equal to the steady d.c. voltage which would produce the same heating effect in, for example, a kettle, iron, or toaster.

Questions

1 In a house, why are the bulbs and other mains appliances connected in parallel?

2 What would you find in a *consumer unit*?

3 **a** What does a circuit breaker do?

b What advantage does a circuit breaker have over a fuse?

4

Copy and complete the diagram above to show how the bulb can be controlled by either of the switches.

5 What is the difference between a.c. and d.c?

6 In the UK, mains frequency is 50 Hz. Explain what this means.

7 If an accident occurs, and someone is electrocuted, what should you do before giving any assistance?

8 Below, the outputs of three a.c. supplies, X, Y, and Z, are displayed on an oscilloscope screen.

a Which supply has the highest peak voltage?

b Which supply has the highest frequency?

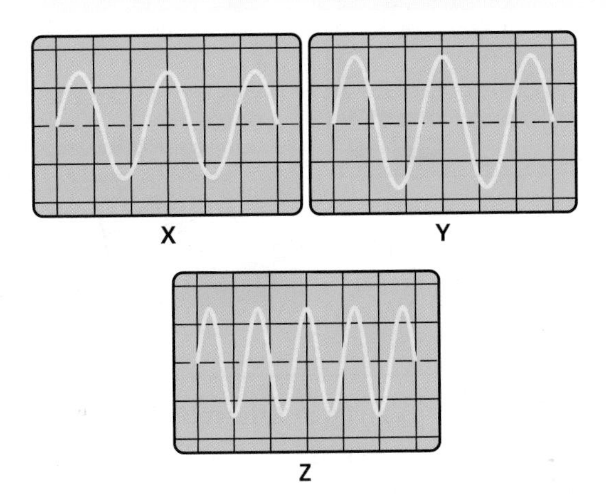

5.10 Electrical power

These both change electrical energy into sound energy.
But hers has more **power** than his.
It changes more energy every second.

Power is measured in joules per second, or watts (W).

A power of 1 watt means that 1 joule of energy is being changed every second.

Typical powers

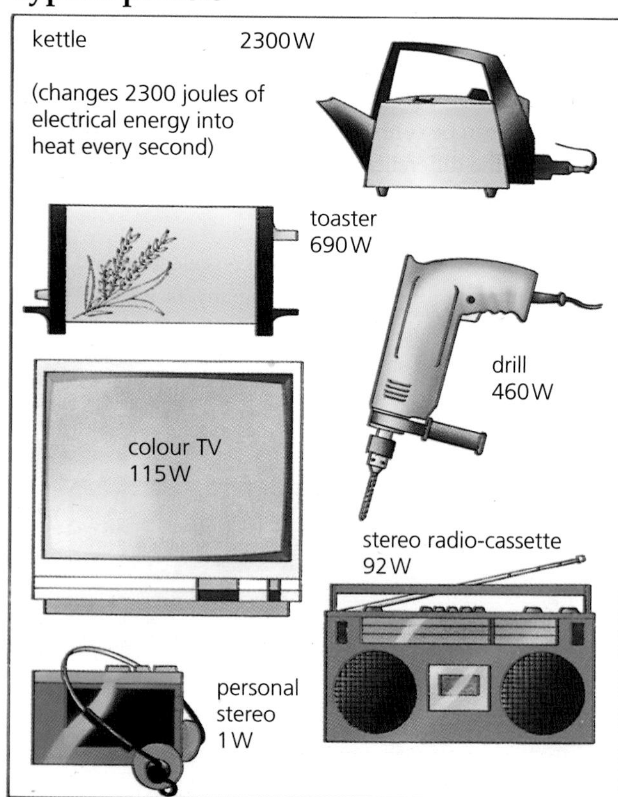

Power is sometimes given in **kilowatts:**

1 kilowatt (kW) = 1000 watts

The kettle has a power of 2.3kW.

An equation for electrical power

You can calculate electrical power using the equation:

power =	voltage	×	current
(watts)	(volts)		(amperes)

For example: If a 230V hairdryer takes a current of 2A, power = 230 × 2 = 460W.

- A higher voltage gives more power because each electron carries more energy.
- A higher current gives more power because there are more electrons to lose their energy every second.

Why the equation works

First, look up the meanings of *current* and *voltage*.

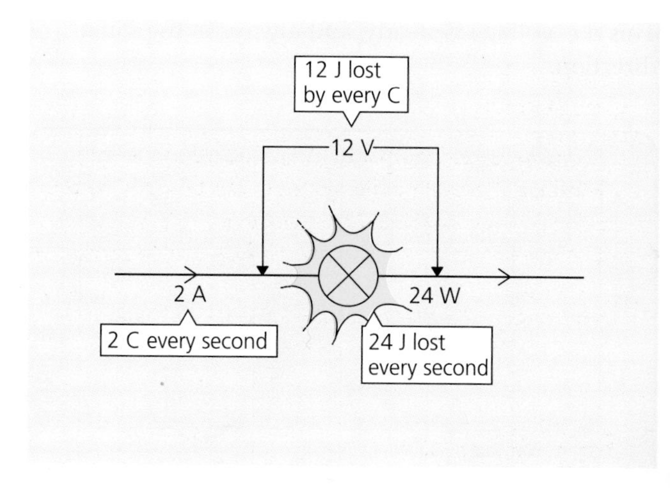

This bulb has a current of 2A flowing through it.
It has a voltage of 12V across it:

So,
2 coulombs of charge are passing through the bulb every second;
each coulomb loses 12 joules of energy as it passes through.

This means that 12 × 2 joules of energy are changed every second.
So, the power is 24 joules per second, or 24 watts.

To get this answer, you have to multiply the voltage by the current.

More equations

The power equation can be written using symbols:

$$P = V \times I$$

You can rearrange the equation in two ways:

$$V = \frac{P}{I} \quad \text{and} \quad I = \frac{P}{V}$$

These are useful if you know the power but need to find the voltage or current.

More about fuses

A kettle has more power than a TV.
It takes more current from the mains.
It needs a higher value fuse in its plug.

On the right, you can see how to work out whether a 2300 W kettle, and then a 115 W TV, needs a 3 A or a 13 A fuse. Remember: the fuse value must be more than the actual current through an appliance, but as close to it as possible.

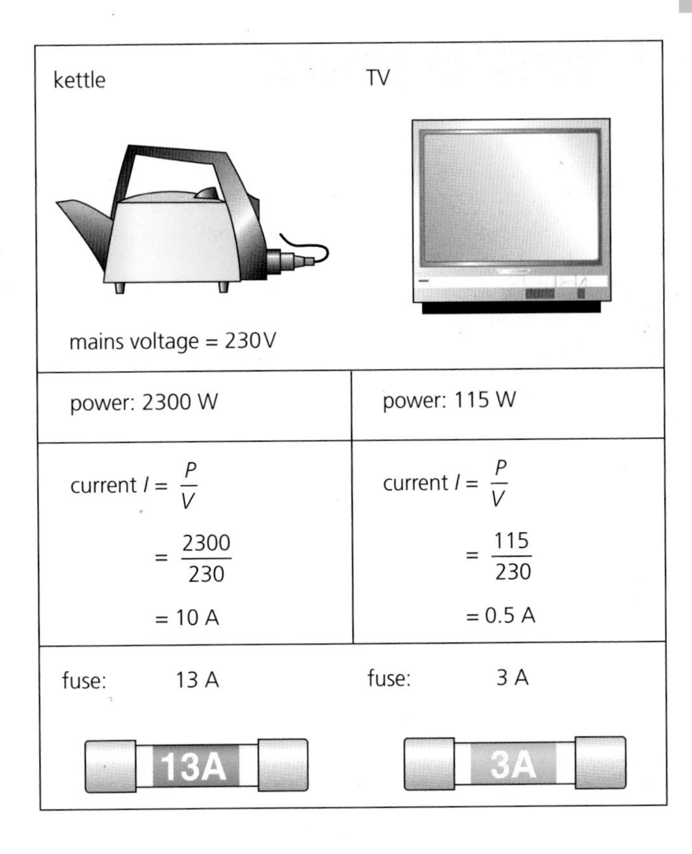

Questions

1 Someone is setting up a lighting display in a shop window. The cable to the window can take a maximum current of 5 A. If the mains voltage is 230 V:

a What is the maximum power which can be carried by the cable?

b How many 100 W light bulbs can be run from the cable?

2

Mains voltage 230 V

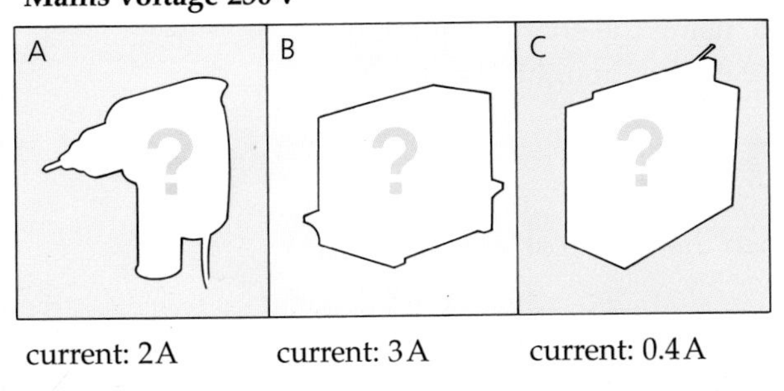

current: 2A | current: 3A | current: 0.4A

You will find these three appliances in the chart on the opposite page. Calculate the power of each one. Then work out what they are.

3

Mains voltage 230 V

A	460 watt	vacuum cleaner
B	920 watt	iron
C	1150 watt	fan heater
D	23 watt	radio
E	46 watt	video recorder

a What is the power of each appliance in kilowatts?

b What current is taken by each appliance?

c What fuse (3 A or 13 A) should be fitted to each plug?

4

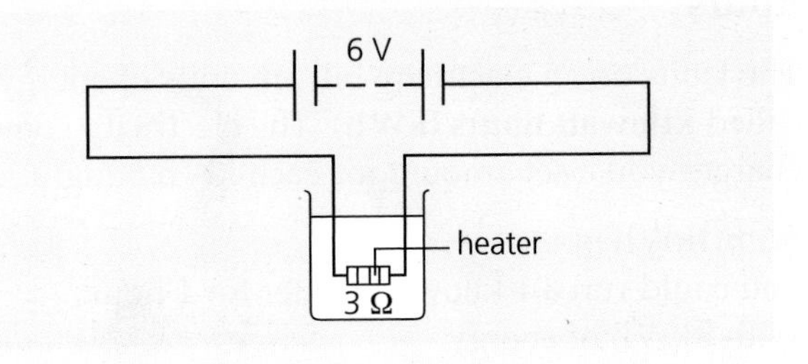

A small heater is being used to warm some water.

a What is the current through the heater?

b What is the power of the heater?

A different battery is put in the circuit. This has *twice* the voltage of the old one.

c What is the current through the heater?

d What is the power of the heater?

5.11 Buying electricity

CENTRAL ELECTRICITY VAT Registration No. 338 7449 45

UNITS USED	PRICE PER UNIT p	£
1225	10.00	122.50
STANDING CHARGE		12.00
	TOTAL	134.50

Electricity is a very convenient way of delivering energy. In the home, that energy is delivered in different forms, using cookers, microwave ovens, infrared heaters, convector heaters, TVs, radios, food mixers, and many other appliances.

Electrical energy costs money. And it can be expensive. The energy needed to keep a portable stereo running continuously for 24 hours costs:

about 2p, on the electricity bill	about £20, buying batteries

Working out the energy . . . in joules

A heater with a power of 1 watt (W) changes 1 joule (J) of electrical energy into heat energy every second.

So:

With 1 joule of energy,
you could run a 1 watt heater for 1 second.

With 6 joules of energy,
you could run a 2 watt heater for 3 seconds,
or a 6 watt heater for 1 second.

To calculate energy in joules, use the equation:

$$\text{energy (joules)} = \text{power (watts)} \times \text{time (seconds)}$$

Working out the energy . . . in kilowatt hours

The Units on an electricity bill are units of energy called **kilowatt hours (kWh)**. The electricity company charges you a set amount for each kWh bought.

With 1kWh of energy,
you could run a 1 kilowatt heater for 1 hour.
With 8kWh of energy,
you could run a 1 kilowatt heater for 8 hours,
or a 2 kilowatt heater for 4 hours.

To calculate energy in kilowatt hours, use the equation:

$$\text{energy (kWh)} = \text{power (kilowatts)} \times \text{time (hours)}$$

The cost of drying your hair

If a 1 kW hairdryer is switched on for 15 minutes,
the power = 1kW
the time = 0.25 hours

So, using the energy equation,
the energy bought $= 1 \times 0.25$
$= 0.25$ kWh

If each kWh or Unit costs 10p,
then the total cost $= 0.25 \times 10$
$= 2.5$p

If each kilowatt hour of energy costs 10p then it will cost about ...
A 5p to watch TV all evening.
B 15p to bake a cake.
C 30p to wash one load of clothes.
D 240p to leave a fan heater running all day.

Reading the meter

The 'electricity meter' in a house is an energy meter. Its tells you the total energy supplied in Units (kWh) since the meter reading was zero.

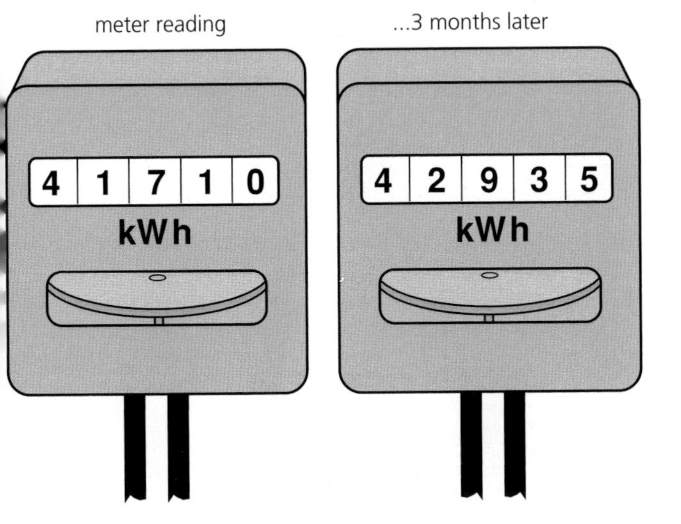

Above, you can see the readings on someone's meter at the beginning and end of a quarter (three month period). To calculate the energy supplied during the quarter, you need to find the difference between the two readings:

energy supplied = 42935 – 41710 = 1225 Units

If each Unit costs 10p:
cost of energy supplied = 1225 × 10 = 12250p
= £122.50

There may also be a quarterly standing charge to add to this amount. However, not all electricity supply companies have a standing charge.

Another energy equation

If you combine this equation...

power (watts) = voltage (volts) × current (amperes)

with this equation...

energy (joules) = power (watts) × time (seconds)

you get this equation...

energy (joules) = voltage (volts) × current (amperes) × time (seconds)

For example: If a 12V heater takes a current of 3A for 10 seconds:
energy supplied = 12 × 3 × 10 = 360 joules

Questions

1

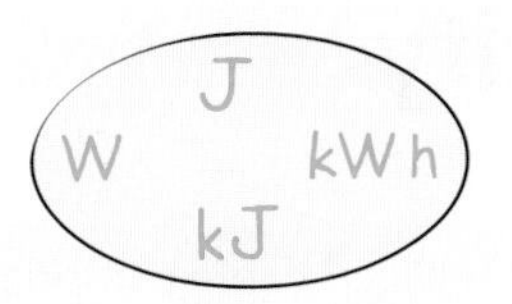

Which of these are units of energy?

2

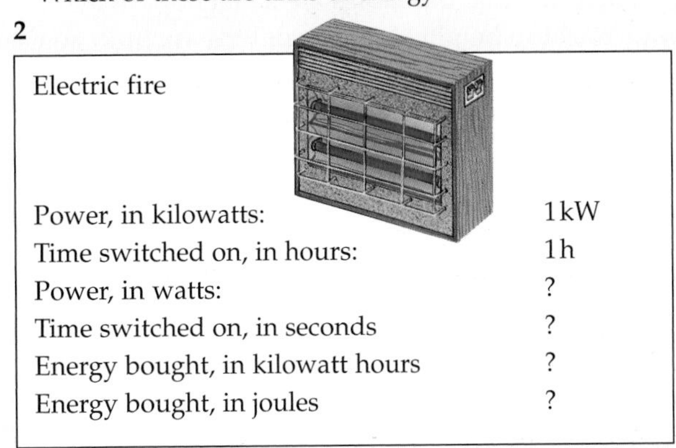

Electric fire	
Power, in kilowatts:	1kW
Time switched on, in hours:	1h
Power, in watts:	?
Time switched on, in seconds	?
Energy bought, in kilowatt hours	?
Energy bought, in joules	?

a Copy the table and fill in the missing values.
b If you can buy 1 kW h of energy for 10p, how many joules of energy can you buy for 10p?

3 In the chart on the opposite page, how much energy is bought in each case (A to D)? Give your answers in kWh.

4

Appliance	Power	Time
Mains radio	10W	16 hours
Electric blanket	100W	8 hours

Donna likes to leave her radio on all day. Her father keeps his electric blanket switched on all night. Each thinks that the other is wasting electricity. But who is adding most to the bill? Use the information in the chart to find out.

5 If each kW h of energy costs 10p, what is the cost of:
a Leaving a 2kW fire on for 5 hours?
b Leaving a 100W lamp on for 10 hours?
c Using an 800W microwave oven for 15 minutes?

6 Someone's electricity meter reads 36594.
Three months later it reads 37434.
What will the quarterly electricity bill be, assuming that energy costs 10p per Unit and there is no standing charge?

7 How much energy is supplied to a 6V bulb if it is switched on for one minute and takes a current of 2A?

5.12 Danger! Electricity

A 132 000 volt overhead cable can push more than enough current through someone to kill them. To prevent accidents, the cables are suspended way above roof-top height. And the pylons are built so that people can't climb them. However, accidents have occurred when kite lines have touched cables.

A deadly playground

Every year, over 50 children are killed or seriously injured while playing on railway lines. With more and more track being electrified, the problem is getting worse. Contact with the live rail doesn't always kill. But it can cause serious burns as current flows through arms or legs to the ground.

Lightning doesn't always kill. But it too can cause serious burns. You are most at risk on open ground, or near an isolated tree or buildings. But the chances of being struck are still very small – much less than a big win on the football pools or lottery, for example.

This is only a 12 volt battery. So most people don't expect it to be dangerous. But if a spanner is accidentally connected across the wires from the battery, the surge of current could be enough to burn you or start a fire. Wise mechanics disconnect the battery before starting work.

Fire hazards

In the home people are more at risk from electrical fires than they are from electric shocks. Here are some of the causes:

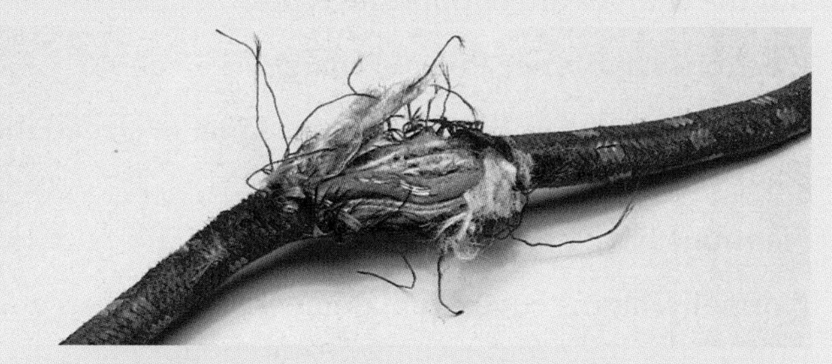

In old, frayed wiring, broken strands of wire can mean that a cable has a high resistance at one point. So heat is given off when current flows through. It may be enough to melt the insulation and cause a fire.

Dirty plug pins give a high resistance where they connect with the socket. When a current flows through, the plug may overheat.

The picture above shows too many appliances connected to one socket. If all the appliances are switched on at once, the supply cable may become overloaded.

If used for high currents, long, coil-up extension cables can be a fire hazard. The current produces heat which, in a tightly coiled cable, cannot escape properly.

Other hazards

Mains sockets need to be used with care. They can be hazardous if metal objects are poked into them. They are also dangerous if water collects inside them, because water will conduct electricity.

The TV is probably the most dangerous piece of equipment in the house. When a TV set is working, the voltages inside can reach 25 000 V or more. And parts inside are still live even when the set is switched off.

For safety's sake:

NEVER take the back off.

Switch off the TV at night or when you go out, and don't leave it on stand-by. This also helps to save energy and keeps the electricity bill down.

Can you explain why, for safety, you should disconnect the battery before working on a car engine?

Can you explain why you should NOT:

- fly kites near overhead cables?
- connect too many appliances to one socket?
- leave a television set plugged in overnight?

Try to find out why:

- bathroom lights have to be switched on and off by a pull-cord;
- extension leads shouldn't be coiled up tightly when in use;
- electric drills and food mixers are 'double insulated'.

5.13 Electric charge

It makes cling film stick to your hands, and dust stick to a TV screen. It causes crackles and sparks when you comb your hair and it can even make your hair stand on end. It is often called **static electricity**, or **electrostatic charge**.

Where charge comes from

Cling film, combs, hair, and all other materials are made from tiny particles called **atoms**. Atoms are extremely small – billions would fit on a pinhead. In many materials, the atoms are in small groups called **molecules.**

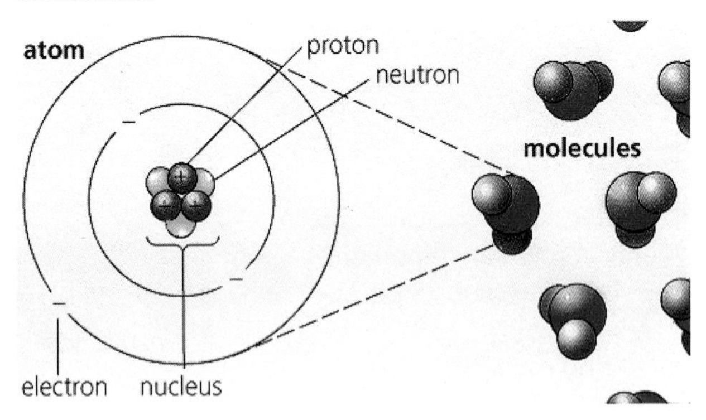

Atoms all have electric charges inside them.
In the centre of each atom there is a **nucleus**. This is made up of **protons** and **neutrons**. Even tinier particles orbit round this nucleus. These are **electrons**.

Protons and electrons both carry an electric charge.

But the charges are of opposite types:

Electrons have a negative (–) charge.

Protons have a positive (+) charge, equal in size to the charge on the electron.

Neutrons have no charge.

Normally, atoms have equal numbers of electrons and protons. So the – and + charges cancel out.

Charging by rubbing

If two materials are rubbed together, electrons may be transferred from one to the other. This upsets the balance between + and –. If the materials are insulators, the electrons tend to stay where they are, and not flow away.

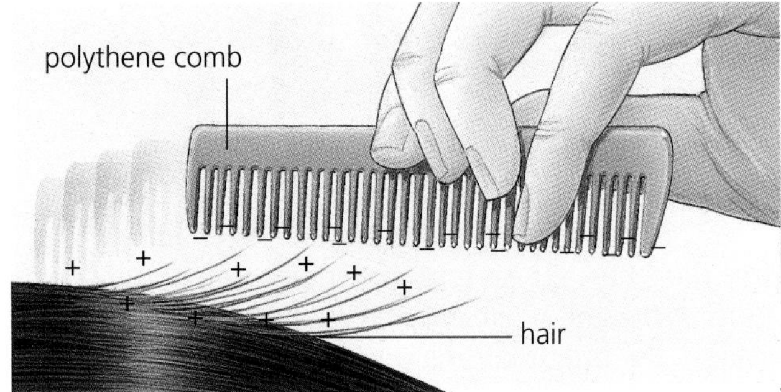

A polythene comb is pulled through hair. The polythene pulls electrons from atoms in the hair. This leaves the polythene with more electrons than normal, and the hair with less.
The hair becomes *positively* charged.

The polythene becomes *negatively* charged.

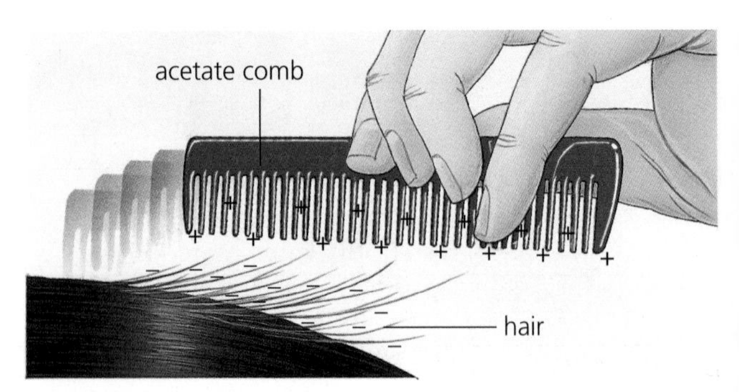

An acetate comb is pulled through hair. This time, the hair pulls electrons from the acetate.
The hair becomes *negatively* charged.

The acetate becomes *positively* charged.

Forces between charges

Like charges repel

Hold two strips of cling film together at one end. Charge them up by pulling them between your fingers.
Both strips have the same type of charge on them. They try to push each other apart.

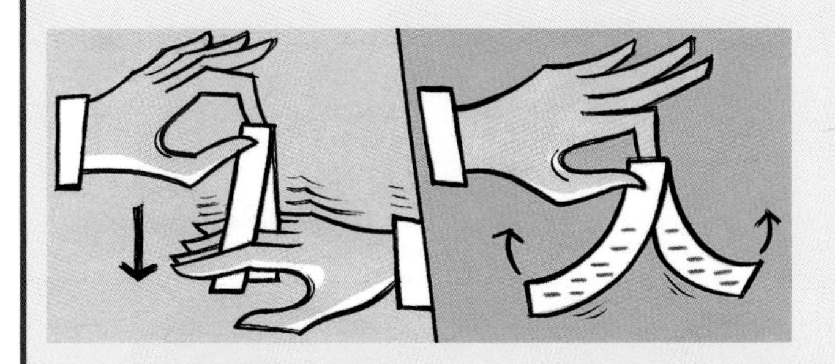

Unlike charges attract

Pull a piece of cling film across your hand. Both become charged up. But the charges are opposite. The clingfilm is attracted to your hand.

Charge attraction

A positively charged comb is put just above a small piece of kitchen foil. Electrons in the foil are pulled upwards. This makes the top end of the foil negative. But it leaves the bottom end short of electrons, and therefore positive.

The comb attracts the negative end of the foil strongly, because it is close. It repels the positive end . . . but less strongly because it is further away. The attraction wins. The foil is pulled to the comb.

This is an example of something charged (a comb) attracting something uncharged (foil). The charges which appear on the foil are called **induced** charges.

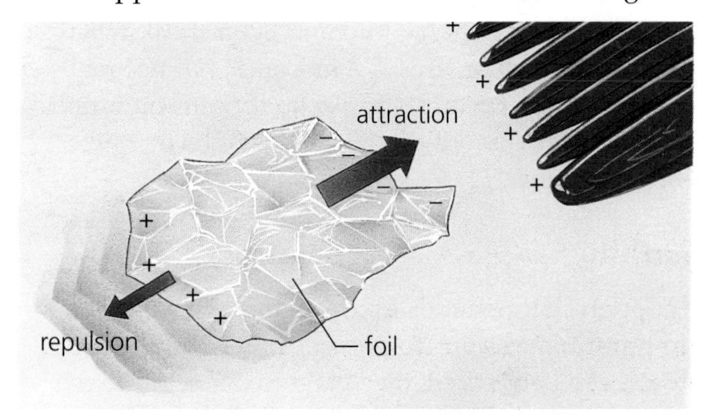

Questions

1 Say whether the things below will attract each other, repel each other, or do neither:

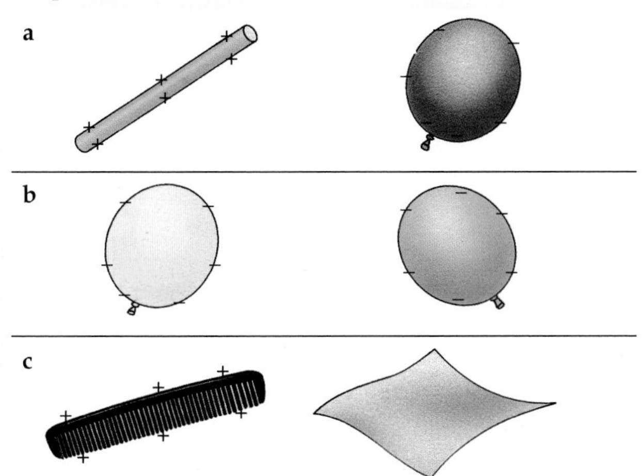

2 A balloon becomes negatively charged when rubbed against someone's sleeve.

Explain:

a how it becomes charged;

b why it will then stick to a wall.

5.14 More about charge

If you slide across the seat when you get out of a car, you may become charged up and get a shock when you touch the door. This is a nuisance, but not really dangerous. However, static electricity can sometimes be dangerous – and it can also be useful. Here are some examples:

Earthing

If enough charge builds up on something, sparks may jump through the air. To prevent charge building up, objects can be **earthed**: they can be connected to the ground by a conducting material so that the unwanted charge flows away.

An aircraft and its tanker must be earthed during refuelling, otherwise charge might build up as the fuel 'rubs' along the pipe. One spark could be enough to ignite the fuel vapour.

Inkjet printers

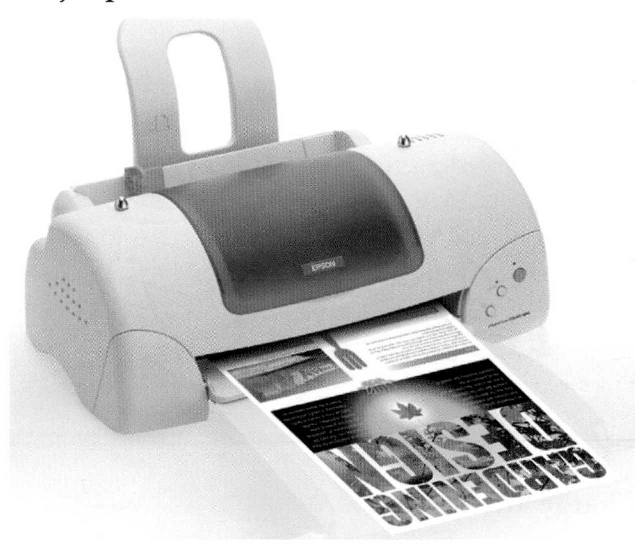

An inkjet printer works by squirting tiny droplets of ink at the paper. Each produces a dot. By printing lots of dots, whole letters can be formed. Some industrial printers use the principle shown below (although most home and office inkjet printers control where the ink goes in a different way):

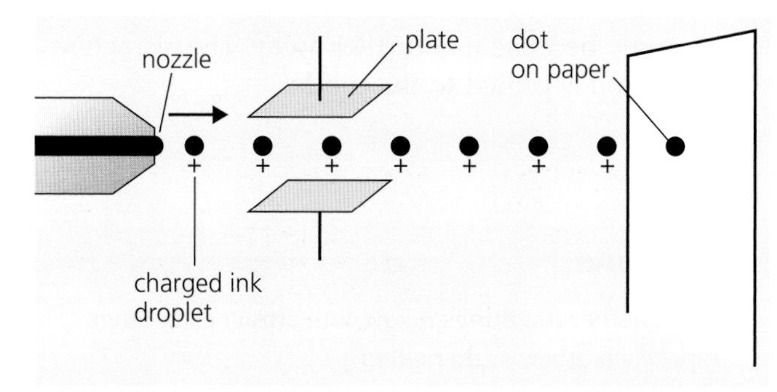

Ink droplets are charged up as they are forced out of a narrow nozzle. They pass between two metal plates.

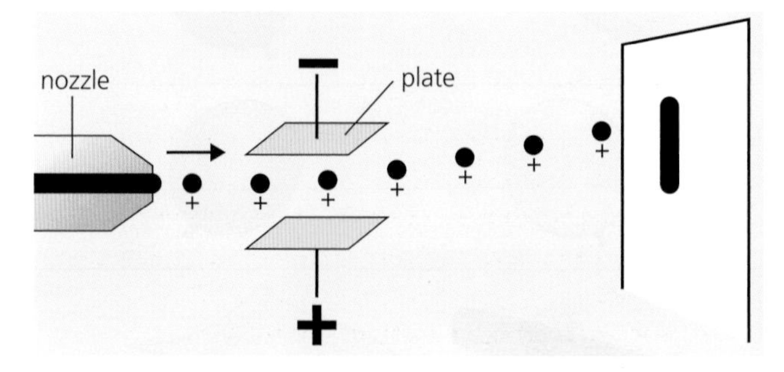

If a voltage is put across the plates, the charged droplets are attracted to one plate and repelled by the other. So they are deflected...upwards in this case.

Dealing with ash

The diagram on the right shows an **electrostatic precipitator** of the type fitted to the chimneys of some power stations and factories. It reduces pollution by removing tiny bits of ash from the waste gases. It works like this:

As the ash and waste gases pass through the chamber, the ash is given a negative charge by the wires. The charged ash is attracted to the positive plates and sticks to them. When shaken from the plates, it is collected in the tray at the bottom.

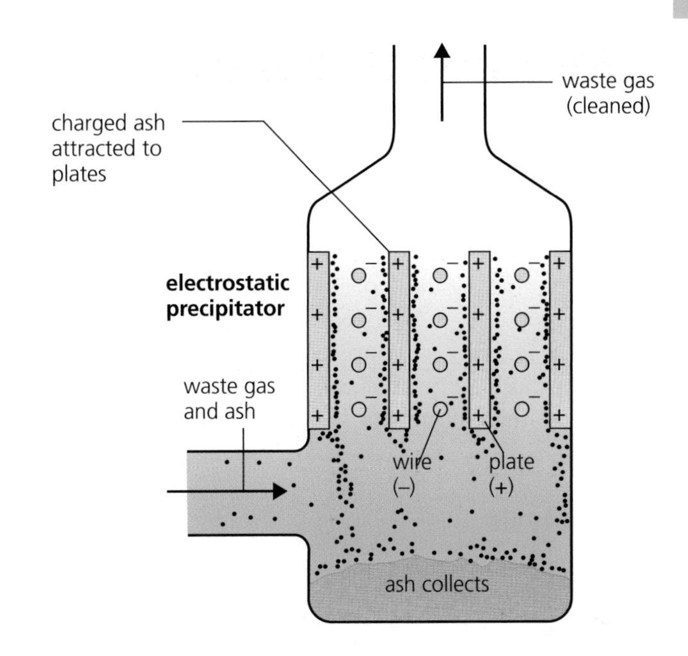

Photocopiers

Photocopiers use static electricity. Below. you can see the main stages in making a photocopy of a page with a large 'H' on it:

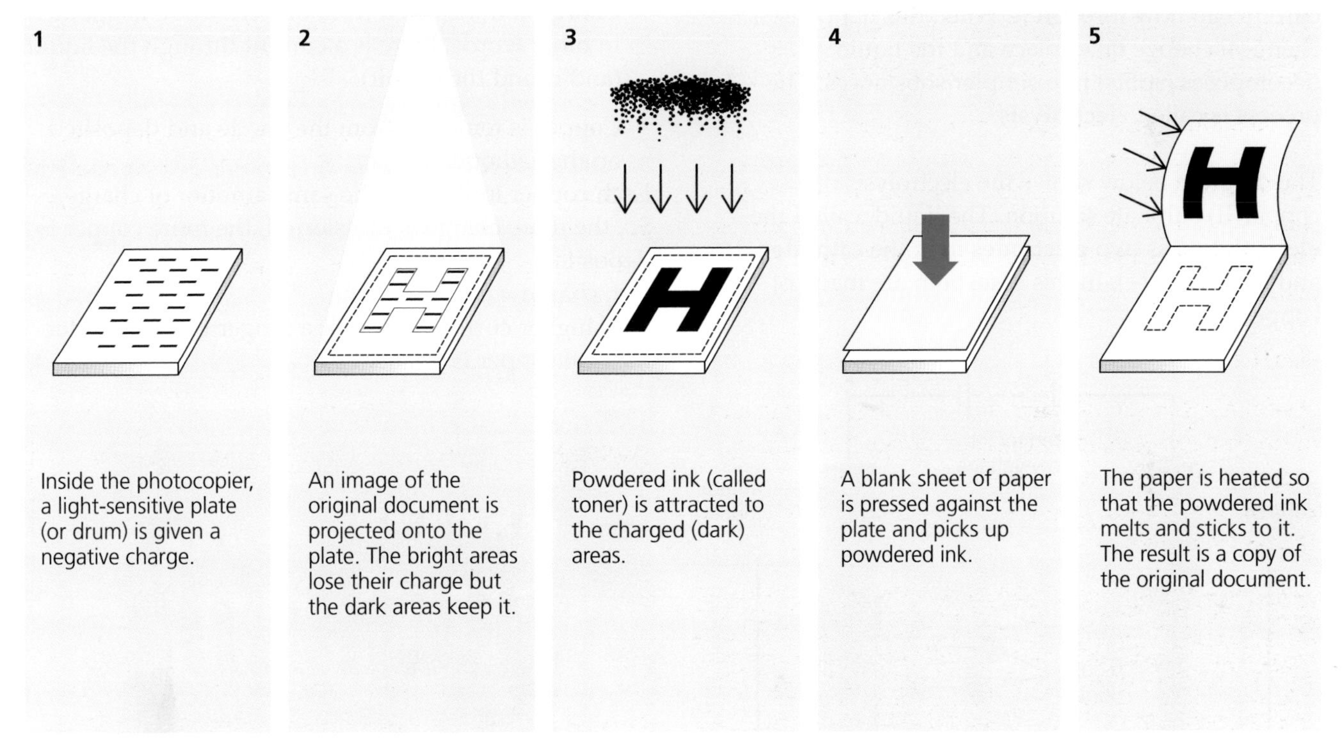

Questions

1 The build-up of static electricity can be dangerous.
  a Give one example of this.
  b Describe how the problem can be overcome.

2 a In the diagram on the right, what will happen to the droplets as they pass between the plates?
  b What piece of equipment makes use of the idea shown?
  c What difference would it make if the droplets were negatively charged instead of positive?

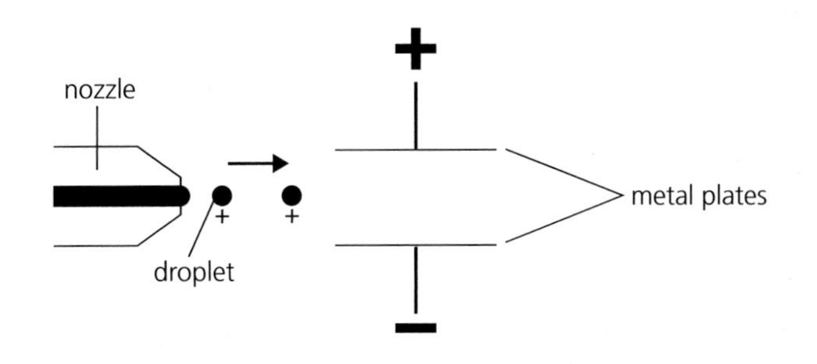

5.15 Ions on the move

Liquids and gases can conduct a current if they contain **ions**. Ions are charged atoms or groups of atoms. In other words, they are atoms or groups of atoms that have gained or lost electrons.

A current is a flow of charge. If a voltage makes ions move through a liquid or gas, there is a flow of charge, so there is current.

Electrons have a negative (–) charge so...

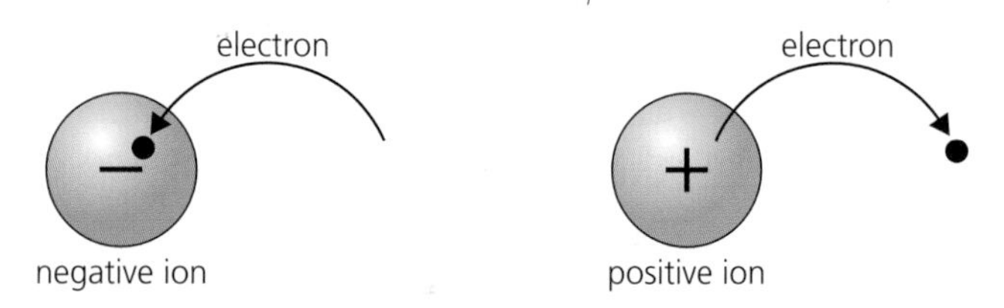

...if an atom gains an electron, it becomes a negative ion.

...if an atom loses an electron, it becomes a positive ion.

Electrolysis

Some substances dissolve in water, forming a mixture called a **solution**. Copper(II) sulphate is an example. Copper(II) sulphate solution contains ions. So a current can flow through it. When this happens, a chemical change takes place and the liquid decomposes (splits) into simpler substances. The process is called **electrolysis**.

The diagram below shows the electrolysis of copper(II) sulphate solution. The liquid, called the **electrolyte**, has two **electrodes** in it: the **cathode** (–) and the **anode** (+). In this case, both are made of copper.

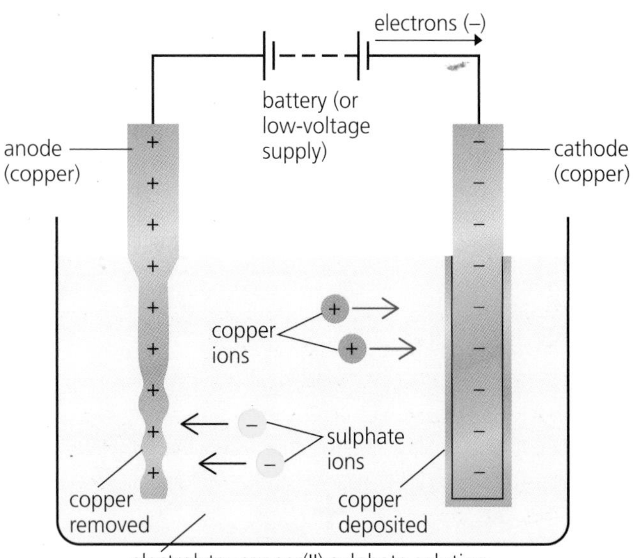

In the liquid, copper(II) sulphate splits to form positive copper ions and negative sulphate ions. The copper ions (+) are attracted to the cathode (–), where they collect electrons, become uncharged, and build up as a layer of copper. At the same time, copper from the anode dissolves in the electrolyte to replace the copper ions.

Overall, there are two effects:

- Charge is transferred from one electrode to another. In other words, there is a current through the liquid (and round the circuit).
- Copper is removed from the anode and deposited on the cathode.

Each copper ion carries the same amount of charge. So, the more charge is transferred, the more copper is deposited.
But: charge = current × time
So if higher current flows for a longer time, a greater mass of copper is deposited.

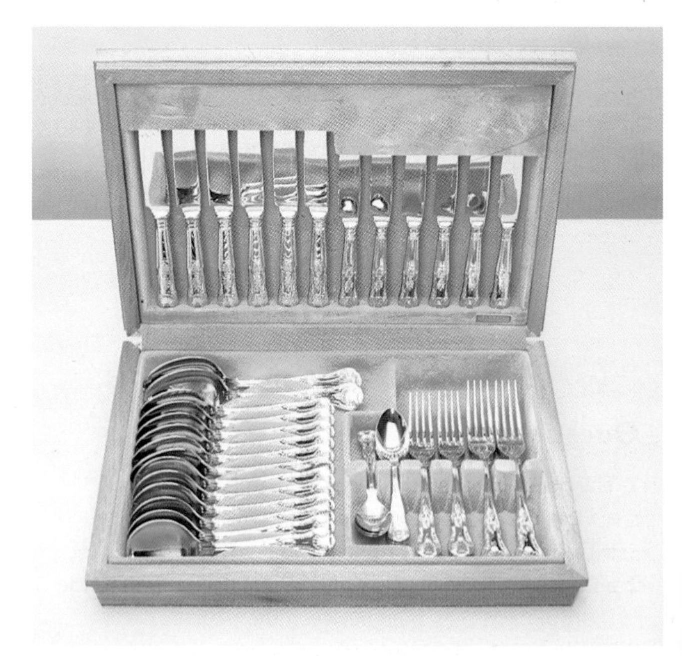

Depositing a metal by electrolysis is called **electroplating**. The cutlery above was electroplated with silver. Food cans are made from steel electroplated with tin (which is safe for food).

Ions in the air

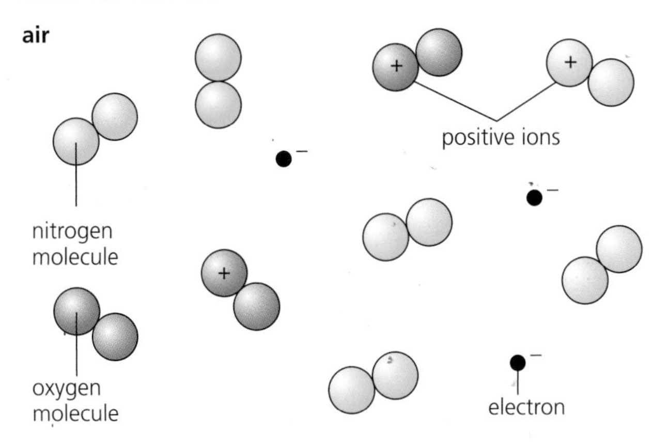

Air is mainly a mixture of nitrogen and oxygen molecules. Most are uncharged, but not all. For example, flames, radiation from space, and radiation from radioactive materials in rocks can all **ionize** air. Without ions, air is an insulator. With ions, it becomes a conductor.

Conduction through ionized air

A small Van de Graaff generator like the one below can produce voltages of 100 000 V or more. Tiny amounts of charge are 'sprayed' onto the rubber belt, carried upwards, and transferred to the dome. As more and more charge collects on the dome, the voltage gets higher and higher.

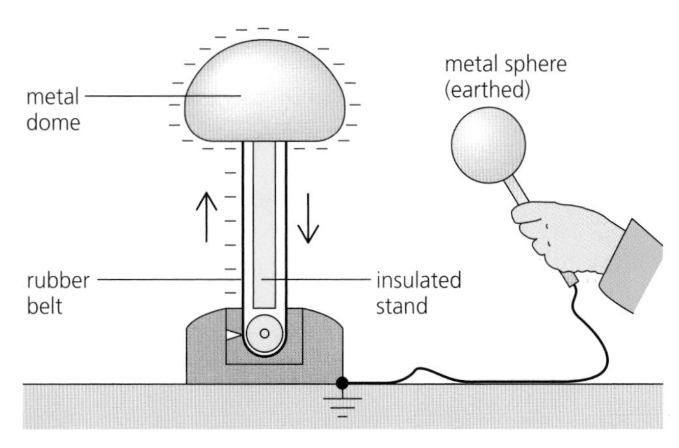

The voltage doesn't keep rising. Some of the charge on the dome leaks away through the air. And if an earthed metal sphere is brought close to the dome, there is a lightning-like spark across the gap. This is why it happens:

With a high enough voltage across the air, ions and electrons collide with molecules strongly enough to ionize them. The new ions cause more ions... and so on. The result is a sudden pulse of current which lights up the air in a spark.

Lightning happens when charge builds up on one part of a cloud, then rapidly flows as a spark to another cloud or the ground. The process is complicated, but a simple explanation for the charge build-up is that ice particles 'rub' against the air as they are sucked up through the cloud.

Questions

1 What are *ions*?

2 In the diagram on the left:

- **a** What happens to the voltage between the dome and the sphere as more and more charge collects on the dome?
- **b** Why does a spark eventually jump across the gap between the dome and the sphere?

3 Give one practical use of electrolysis.

4 Copy the diagram below. Then do the following:

- **a** Label the *cathode*, the *anode*, and the *electrolyte*.
- **b** Draw in and label the direction of electron flow through the wires.
- **c** Label each ion with a + or –.

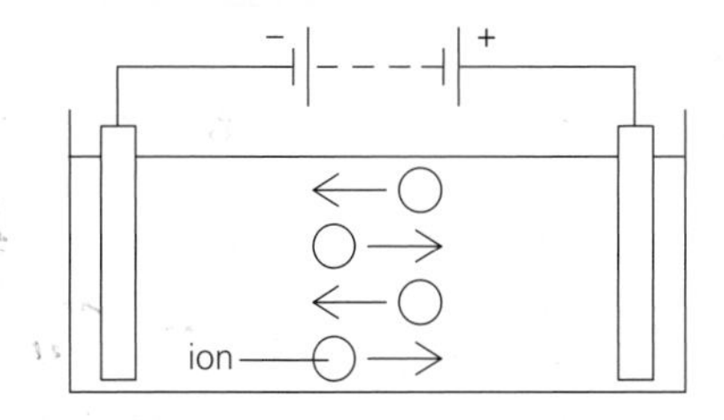

Questions on Chapter 5

1 A pupil investigates the relationship between the voltage across a lamp and the current flowing through it. She uses the circuit shown below.

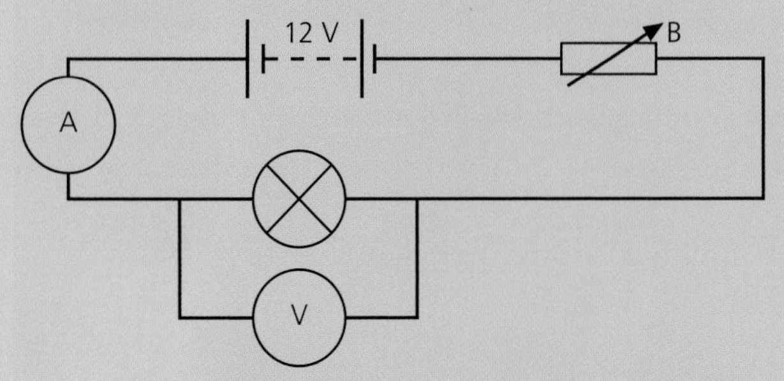

a What is A?
b What is B?
c What is V?
d Explain in your own words how the pupil should carry out the experiment.

The pupil records the results and then plots a graph.

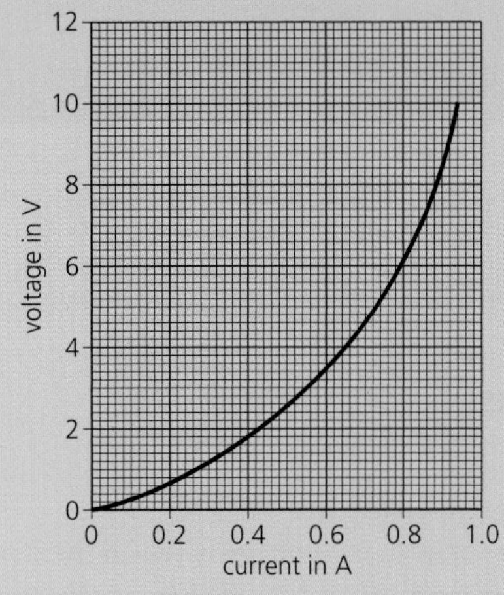

e What is the value of the current that flows when a voltage of 6.0 V is applied across the lamp?
f What is the resistance of the lamp when a voltage of 6.0 V is applied across it?
g What is happening to the resistance of the lamp as the voltage across it increases?

2 A low-energy light bulb has a power rating of only 20 W, but produces the same amount of light as an ordinary 100 W bulb. Both bulbs are to be switched on for 1000 hours.

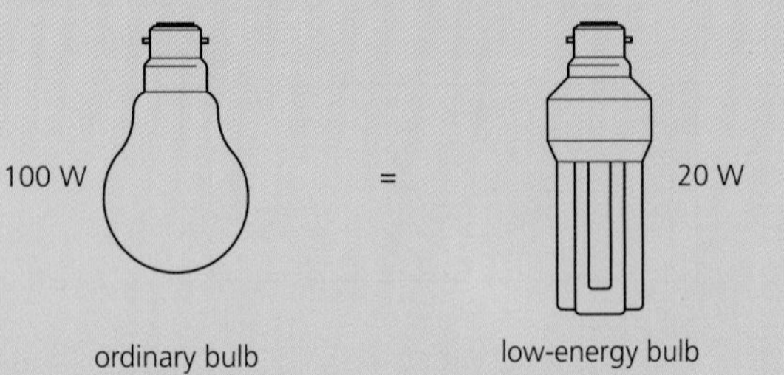

a What is the power of each bulb in kW?
b How much energy (in kW h) will the low-energy bulb use in 1000 hours?
c How much energy (in kW h) will the ordinary energy light bulb use in 1000 hours?
d If electricity costs 10p per unit (kW h), how much money will be saved on electricity bills over a 1000-hour period by using the low-energy bulb instead of the ordinary bulb?
e The ordinary bulb uses more energy than the low-energy one for the same amount of light. What happens to the extra energy supplied?

3 In the circuit below, a 6 V battery has been connected to a 3 Ω resistor:

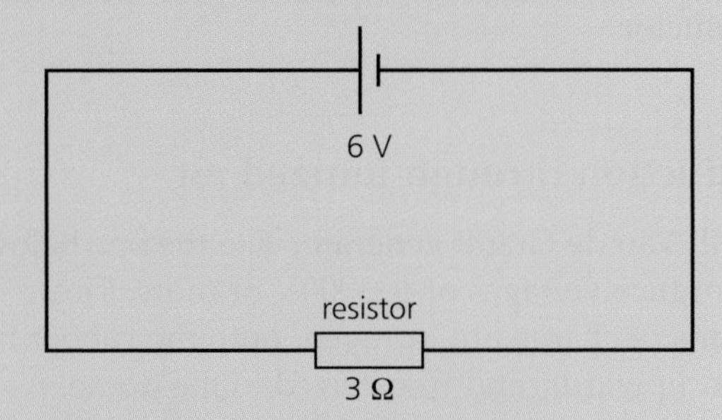

a What is the current in the circuit?
b What is the power output of the battery?
c How much energy, in joules, does the battery give to each coulomb of charge pushed out?
d How much charge, in coulombs, flows through the resistor every second?

4 The fan heater below runs on the 230 V mains. It has two heating elements, each taking a current of 4 A, and a fan taking a current of 0.5 A.

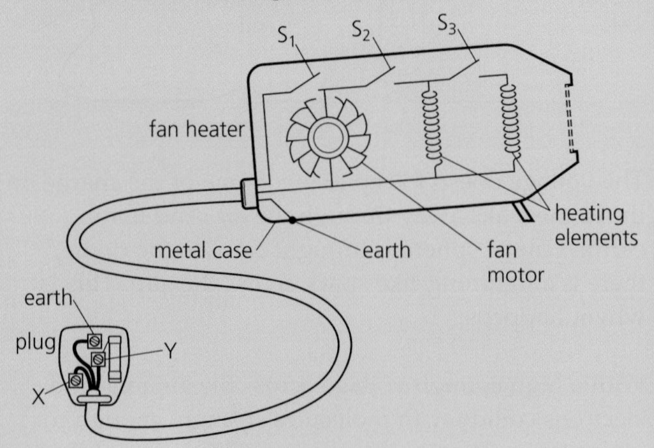

a Which switches should be closed if you want:
i the fan only, for cool air?
ii the fan and one element?

b If the fan heater is on full power, how much current flows from the mains?
c What fuse should be fitted in the plug, 3 A or 13 A?
d Which terminal in the plug is live?
e Why is the earth connection needed?
f What colour cable should be connected to terminal X?
g What colour cable should be connected to terminal Y?
h Give reasons for each of the following:
i If an appliance takes a current of 2 A, you should not fit a 13 A fuse in its plug.
ii Some appliances, such as radios and hairdryers, do not need an earth wire.

5 Use your ideas about electrons to explain each of the following:
a Electrons are pushed out of the negative (–) terminal of a battery, not the positive (+).
b If you rub a polythene rod with a piece of cloth, the rod ends up with negative charge (–), while the cloth is left with an equal amount of positive charge (+).
c Unlike most other materials, metals are good conductors of electricity.

6 a Below, ammeters are being used to measure the current in different parts of a circuit.

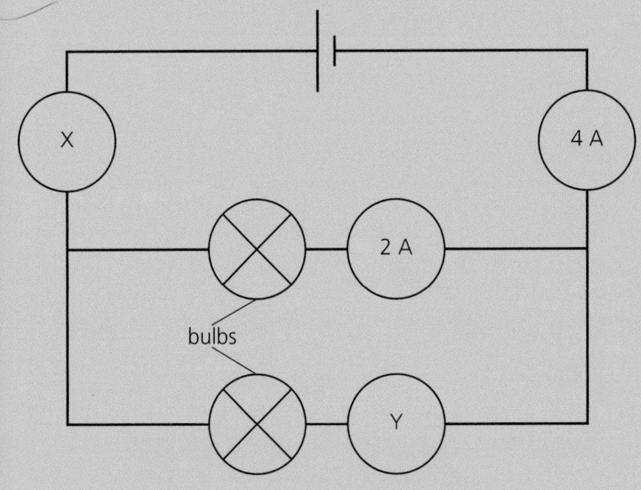

i Have the bulbs been connected to the battery in *series* or in *parallel*?
ii What is the reading on ammeter X? Give a reason for your answer.
iii What is the reading on ammeter Y? Give a reason for your answer.
iv If one of the bulbs is removed, so that there is a gap between its connecting wires, what will be the effect on the other bulb?

b Below, voltmeters are being used to measure the voltage across different parts of a circuit.

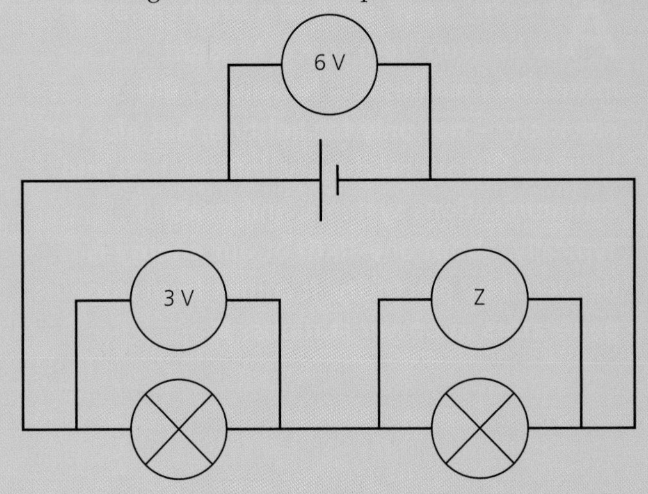

i Have the bulbs been connected to the battery in *series* or in *parallel*?
ii What is the reading on voltmeter Z? Give a reason for your answer.
iii If one of the bulbs is removed, so that there is a gap between its connecting wires, what will be the effect on the other bulb?

7 a What is the principal energy transformation which takes place when a 2 kW, 230 V, two bar electric fire is turned on?
b What is the power rating of the fire? Write a sentence explaining exactly what your answer means.
c To which part of the electric fire is the earth wire always connected? Explain what might happen if the fire became faulty and there was no Earth wire.
d Where should the switch for turning the fire on and off be positioned? Explain your answer.
e From the figures given in **a** calculate the current flowing through the fire.
f What is the most appropriate fuse for this circuit?
g Why would it be dangerous to connect two fires like the one described above to the same socket in a ring main?
h If any electrical appliance is found to be faulty when it is switched on, what is the first thing you must do?

Chapter 6

Magnets and currents

At night, a city like this is bright enough to be seen from space. Modern industrial societies rely heavily on the use of electricity – not only for lighting, but also for running factory machinery, information and communications systems, and heating. Typically, about one-sixth of our energy is delivered by electricity. It comes from huge generators in power stations. ■

6.01 Magnets and fields

Poles of a magnet

If a small bar magnet is dipped into iron filings, the filings cling to its ends, as shown on the right. The magnetic forces seem to come from two points, called the **poles** of the magnet.

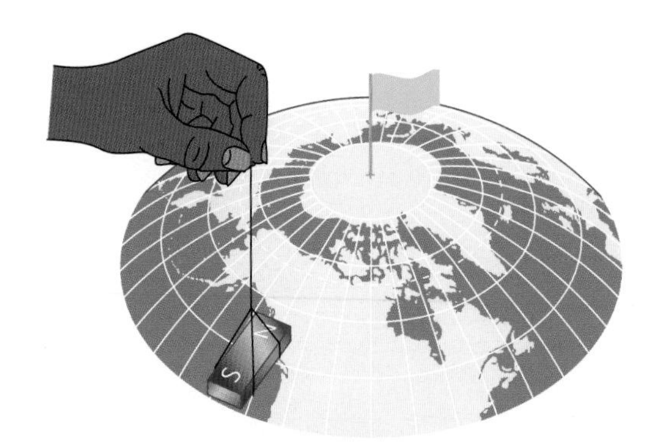

The Earth pulls on the poles of a magnet. If a bar magnet is suspended, it turns until it lies roughly north–south, as shown in the diagram above. This effect is used to give the two poles of a magnet their names:

- The **north-seeking pole** (or **N pole** for short)
- The **south-seeking pole** (or **S pole** for short)

In the diagram below, you can see what happens if the ends of similar magnets are brought together. There are forces between the poles:

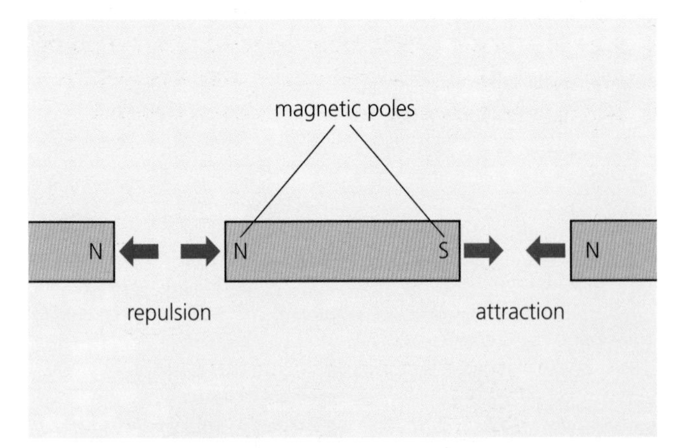

Like poles repel. Unlike poles attract.

The closer the poles are, the greater the force between them.

Permanent and temporary magnets

If pieces of iron and steel are placed near a magnet, they *become* magnets. The magnet **induces** magnetism in them. It attracts them because the poles nearest each other are different.

When the pieces of metal are pulled away, the steel keeps its magnetism, but the iron does not. The steel has become a **permanent magnet**. The iron was only a **temporary magnet**.

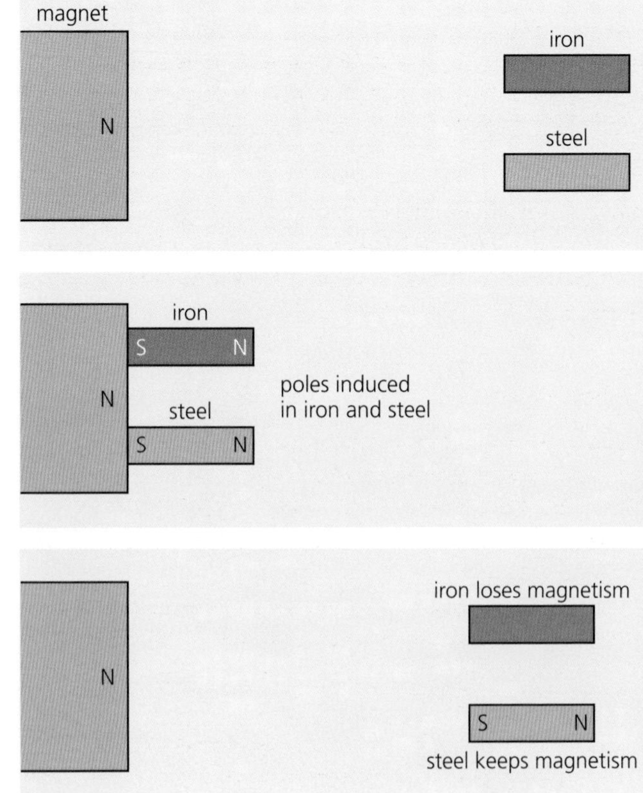

Magnetic materials

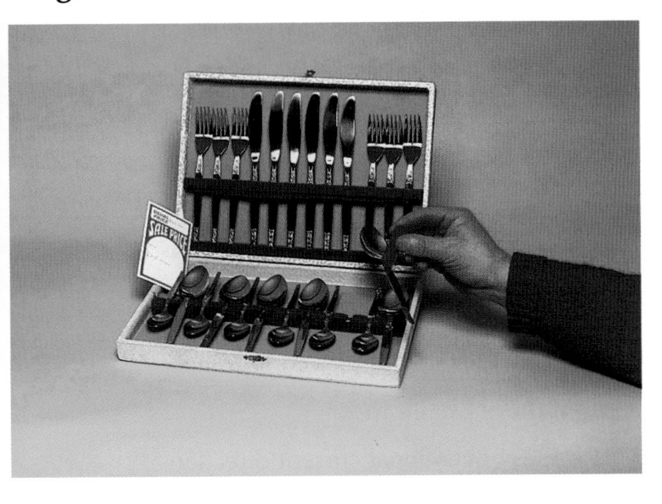

Is this worth buying? Check it with a magnet. Ordinary steel is attracted to a magnet, but the very best quality stainless steel isn't. If the cutlery is expensive, it shouldn't do this.

Materials that can be magnetized and are attracted to magnets are called **magnetic materials**. All strongly magnetic materials contain iron, nickel, or cobalt. For example, steel is mainly iron.

Magnetic materials are described as *soft* or *hard*, depending on how well they keep their magnetism when magnetized:

Soft magnetic materials such as iron and Mumetal are easy to magnetize, but their magnetism is only temporary. They are useful in electromagnets, for example, where the magnetic effect needs to be 'switched' on and off.

Hard magnetic materials such as steel and Alcomax are more difficult to magnetize but do not easily lose their magnetism. They are used for permanent magnets.

Field around a magnet

A magnet has a **magnetic field** around it. This is where there are forces on any magnetic material. You can study the field using a small **compass**, as below. The 'needle' is a tiny magnet which is free to turn on its spindle. The forces from the poles of the magnet make it line up with the field.

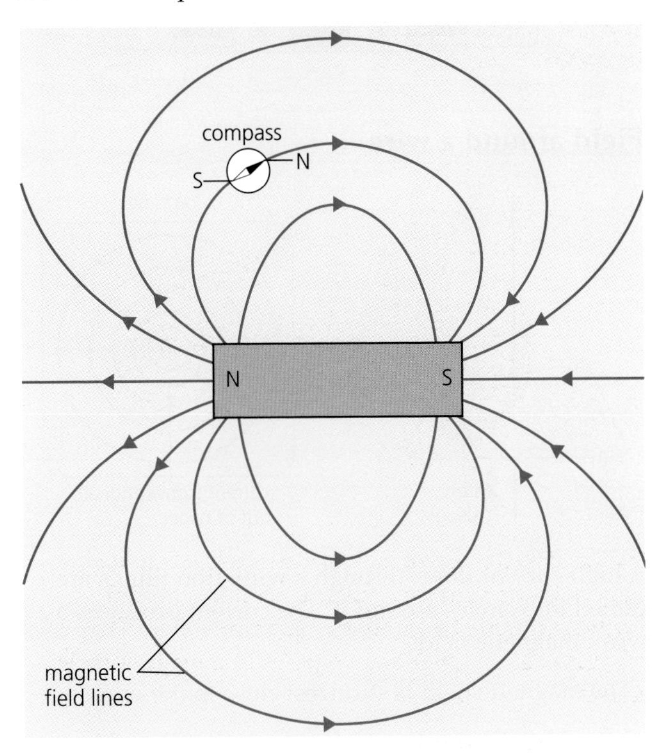

The Earth is a weak magnet. Its field will turn a compass needle – or any suspended magnet – so that it points roughly north – south.

The field above has been shown using magnetic **field lines**. These run from the N pole of the magnet to the S pole. They show the direction in which the N end of a compass needle would point. The magnetic field is strongest where the field lines are closest together.

Questions

1 Why are the poles of a magnet called N and S?

2 What type of magnetic pole:

a attracts an N pole? b repels an S pole?

3 How can you show that there is a field around a magnet?

4 In the diagram on the right, pieces of iron and steel are being attracted to the end of a magnet.

a Copy the diagram. Draw in any magnetic poles on the iron and steel.

b If the lower ends of the iron and steel start to move, which way will they move, and why?

c What happens to each of the metals when it is taken away from the magnet?

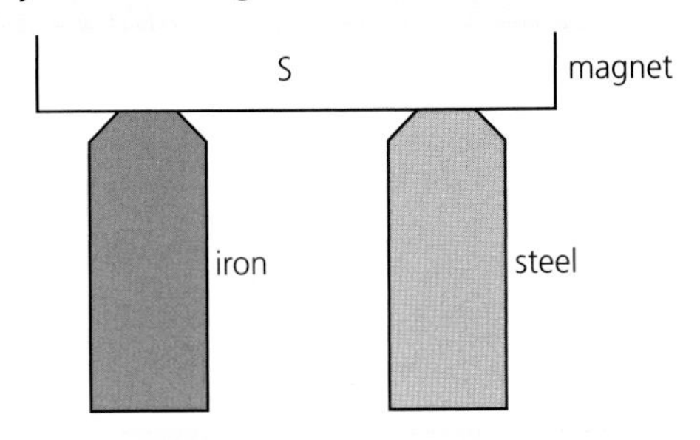

6.02 Magnetism from currents

Make a recording on this tape and 45 minutes of sound becomes over 100 metres of varying magnetism along the tape. But the tape isn't magnetized by a magnet. It is magnetizd by a current passing through a piece of wire.

Field around a wire

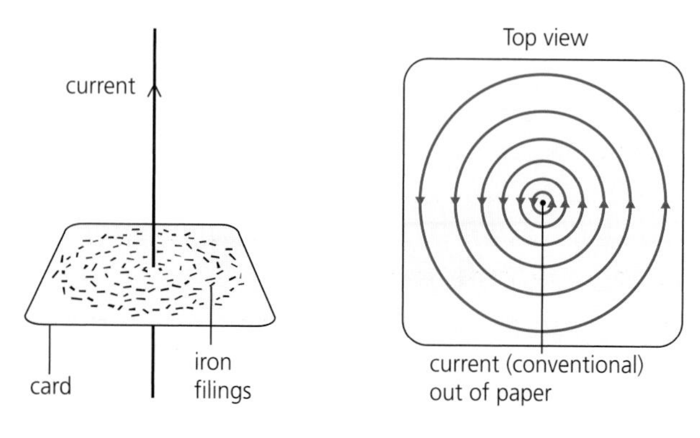

A high current flows through a wire. Iron filings are pulled into circles around it. The current produces a weak magnetic field:

The magnetic field is strongest close to the wire.

Increasing the current makes the magnetic field stronger.

Field around a coil

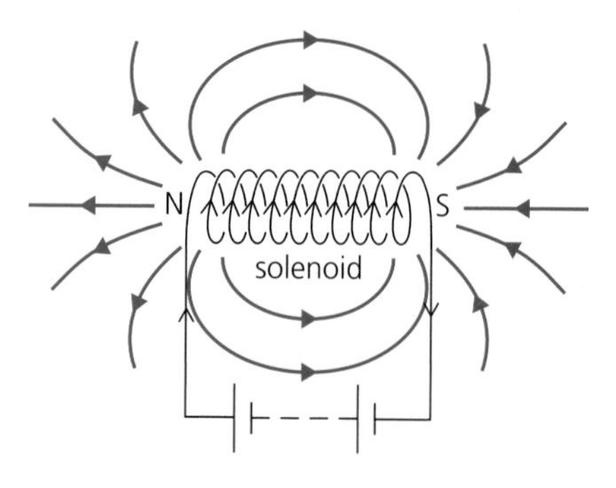

A current flows through a long coil, called a **solenoid**. A magnetic field is produced. The field is like the field around a bar magnet. The solenoid behaves as if it has magnetic poles at its ends.

Increasing the current makes the magnetic field stronger.

Increasing the number of turns on the coil makes the magnetic field stronger.

Magnetic rules

Current flows from + to –.

This is the conventional current direction.

Magnetic field lines run from N to S.

The right-hand grip rule for field direction:

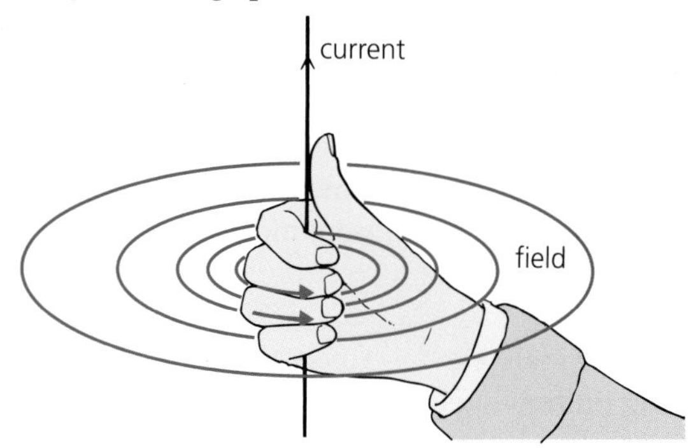

Imagine your right hand gripping the wire so that your thumb points the same way as the current. Your *fingers* curl the same way as the *field* lines.

The right-hand grip rule for poles:

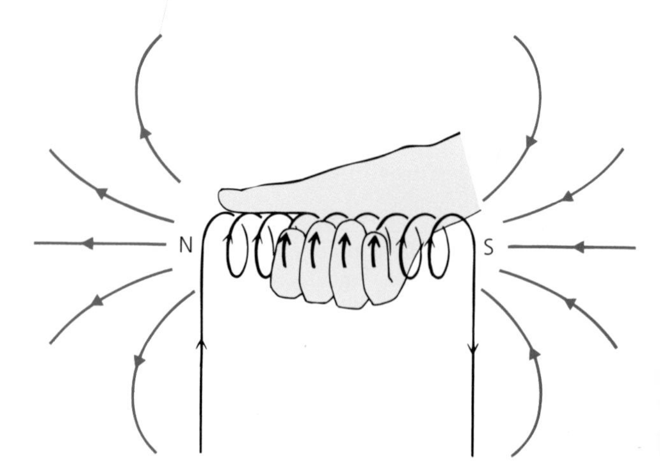

Imagine your right hand gripping the solenoid so that your fingers curl the same way as the current. Your *thumb* will then point to the *north* pole of the solenoid.

Making magnets . . .

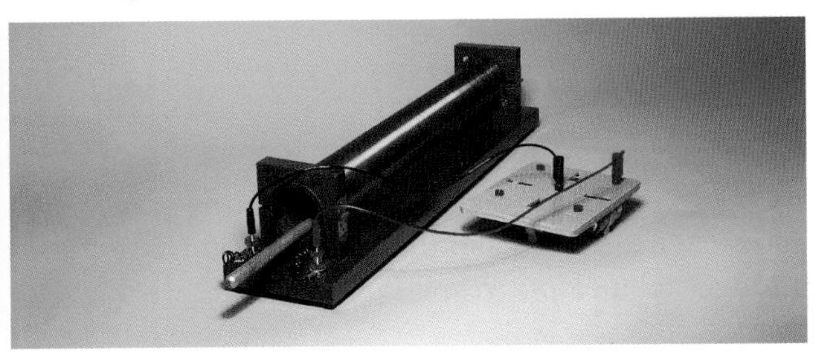

A current flows through a solenoid. In the solenoid is a bar of steel. The steel becomes magnetized and makes the magnetic field much stronger than before.

When the current is switched off, the steel stays magnetized. It has now become a permanent magnet. Nearly all permanent magnets are made in this way.

. . . and demagnetizing them

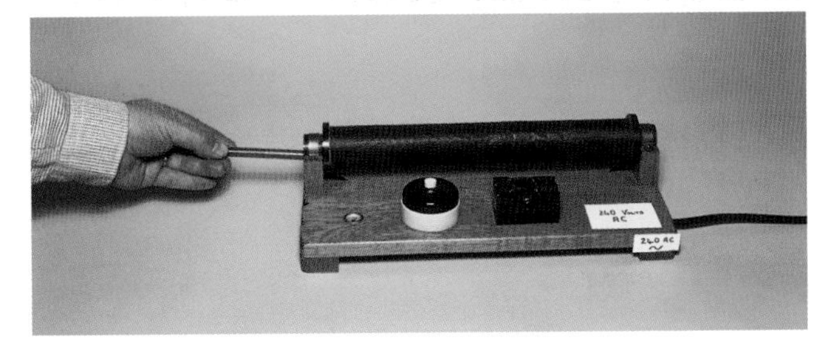

A solenoid can also be used to demagnetize a magnet. The magnet is put in the solenoid. Alternating current (a.c.) is passed through the solenoid. Then the magnet is slowly pulled out.

When a.c. is passing through the solenoid, the magnetic field keeps changing direction very rapidly. This turns the magnetic atoms in the steel out of line.

Making recordings . . .

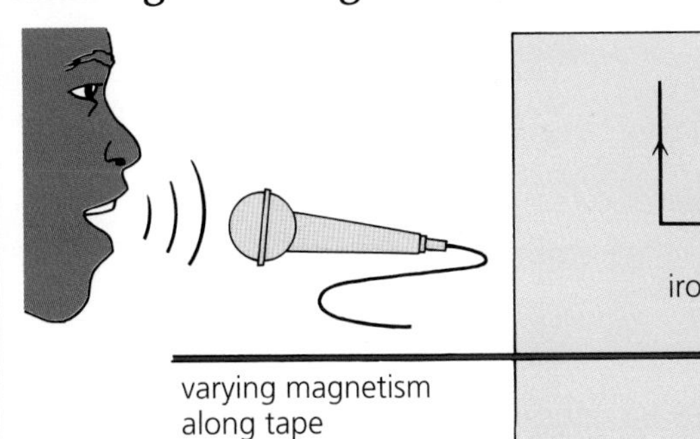

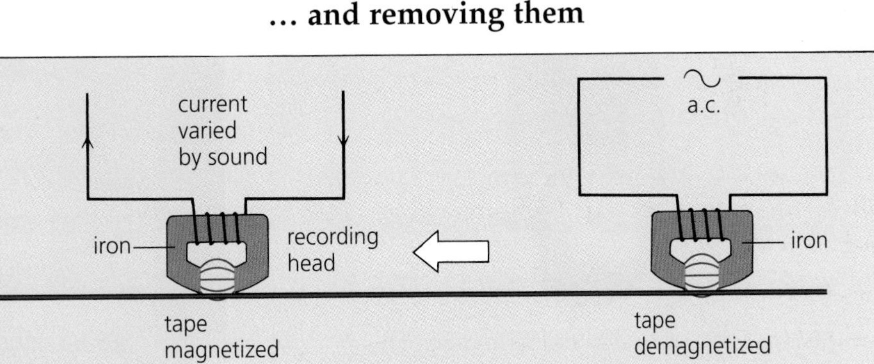

Magnetic tape passes over the recording head in a cassette recorder. The tape is magnetized by the current in the coil. As the sound varies, so does the current – and the strength of magnetism along the tape. Result: a magnetic 'copy' of the original sound waves.

... and removing them

New recordings can't be made until old ones have been removed. This head has a.c. flowing through its coil. It demagnetizes the tape passing over it – ready for the next recording.

Questions

1 This is the end view of a long length of wire. A high current is flowing through the wire. Copy the diagram, and show which way the other compass needles would be pointing.

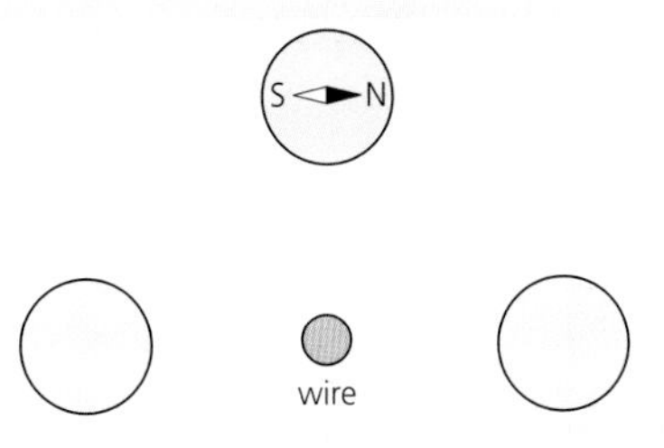

2 All four coils have the same current passing through them. Which one:

a gives the weakest field? Why?

b will still give a magnetic field when the current is switched off? Why?

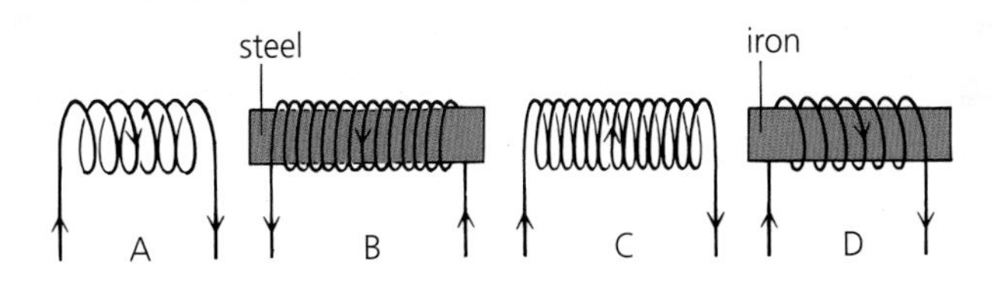

6.03 Electromagnets

Electromagnets can do all the things that ordinary magnets can do. But you can switch them on and off.

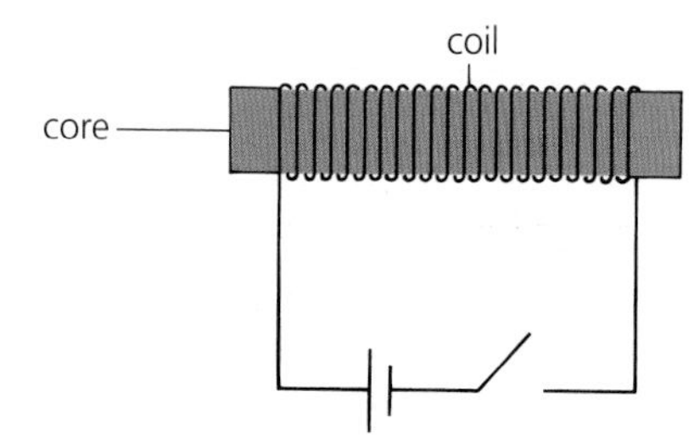

The parts of an electromagnet:

A coil – made from several hundred turns of insulated copper wire. The greater the number of turns, the stronger the field.

A battery – to supply current. The higher the current, the stronger the field.

A core – made from a soft magnetic material like iron. This makes the field much stronger. But its magnetism dies away as soon as the current is switched off.

Using electromagnets

In an electric bell, an electromagnet is switched on and off very rapidly. It keeps pulling the hammer over to the gong, then releasing it.

When sorting scrap metal, electromagnets are used to separate metals like iron and steel from other metals.

There's an electromagnet in a telephone earpiece. As the current through it varies, the pull on a metal plate varies. This makes the plate vibrate and send sound waves into your ear.

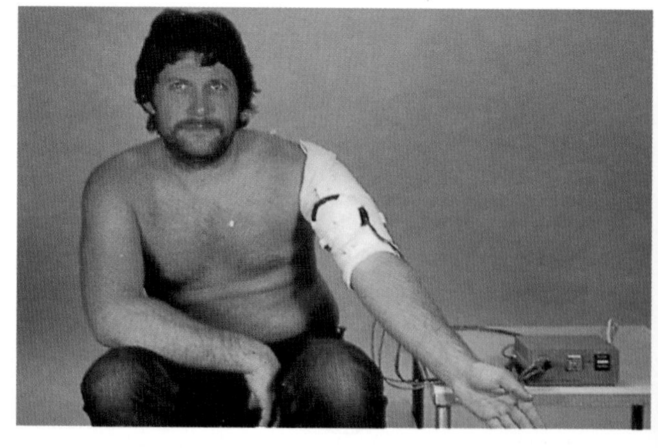

This picture shows a wrap-round electromagnet. Bursts of magnetism actually help broken bones to mend more quickly. No one is quite sure why.

Switches worked by electromagnets

Problem A car starter motor takes a current of over 100 A. It has to be switched on by a lightweight switch, connected to thin cable. This can't handle the high current.

Solution Use an electromagnetic switch or **relay**. With a relay, a large current in one circuit can be switched on by a small current in another circuit.

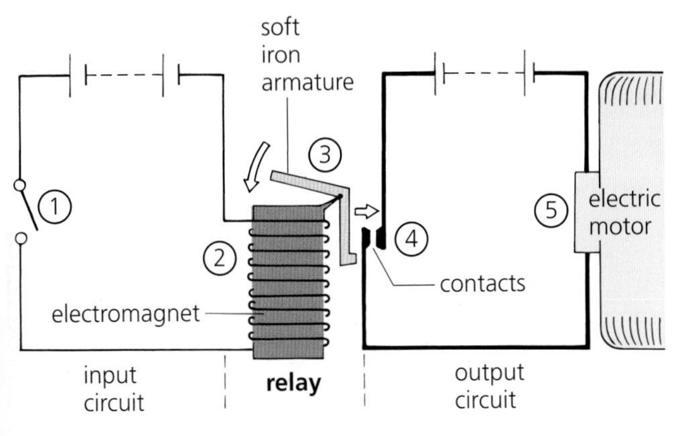

1 When the switch in the input circuit is closed:
2 the electromagnet comes ON,
3 and pulls the iron **armature** towards it.
4 This closes the contacts.
5 So the motor in the output circuit is switched ON.

The **circuit breaker** below is designed to cut off the current in a circuit if it rises above a certain value. The current flows through two contacts and also through an electromagnet. If the current gets too high, the pull of the electromagnet becomes strong enough to release the iron catch, so the contacts open.

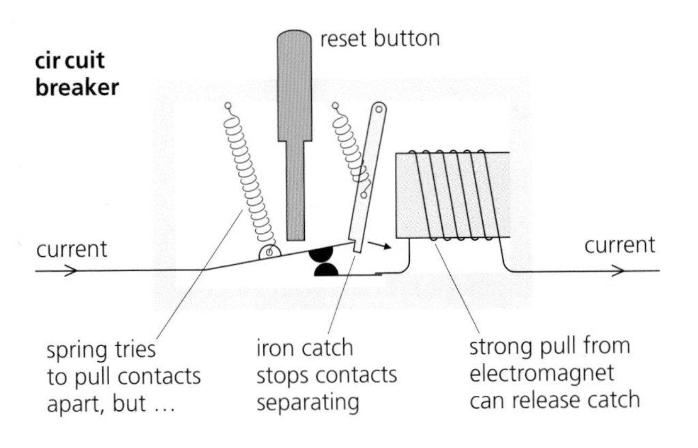

Questions

1 To answer this question, you may need information elsewhere in this book.

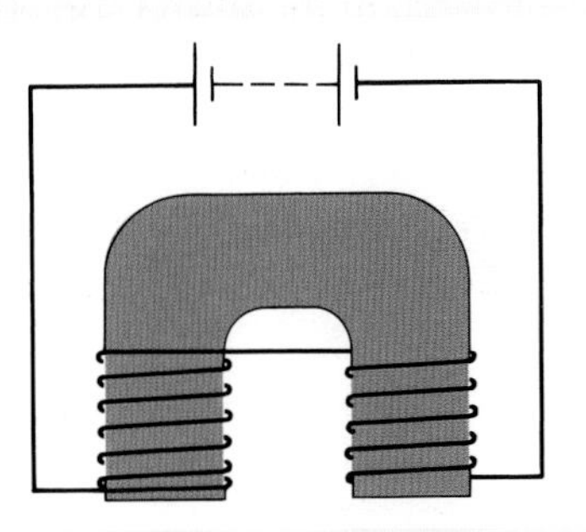

This is a U-shaped electromagnet.

a Name a suitable material for the coil.

b Name a suitable material for the core.

c Explain why steel wouldn't be a suitable material for the core.

d Explain why the wire in the coil needs to be insulated.

e What two changes could you make to give a stronger magnetic field?

f What would be the effect of connecting the battery the other way round?

2 In the diagram on the left, the electric motor is controlled by a relay. Below, the arrangement has been redrawn using circuit symbols.

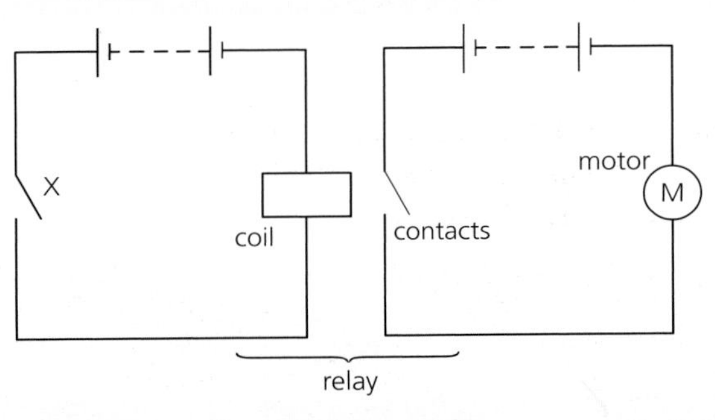

a Explain why the motor is turned on when switch X is closed.

b Phil can't see the point of the relay. It looks very complicated. He wants to know why the motor can't just be turned on and off by a simple switch in the motor circuit. What answer would you give him?

3 The diagram on the left shows a circuit breaker.

a What makes the circuit breaker switch off if the current rises above a certain value?

b What changes would you make to the circuit breaker so that it switches off at a higher current?

6.04 The magnetic force on a current

Put a current into each of these, and something moves:

The loudspeaker cone vibrates.

The pointer moves up the scale.

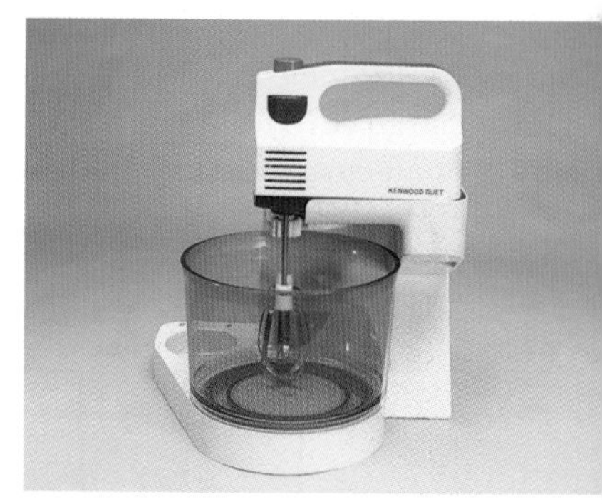

The motor turns.

The movement is caused by a force. A force is produced whenever a current flows with a magnetic field across it.

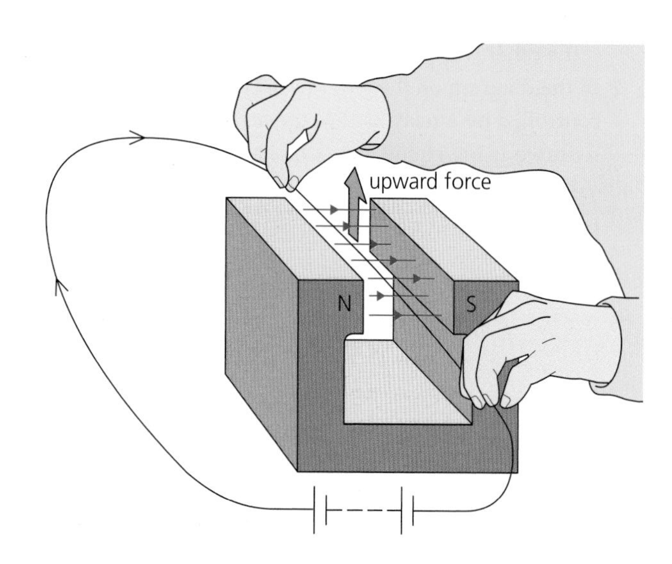

A wire is held between the poles of a magnet. When a current flows through the wire, there is an upward force on it.
The force becomes stronger if:

- the current is increased;
- a stronger magnet is used;
- there is a greater length of wire in the field.

The force isn't always upwards. It depends on the current and field directions. If the wire is in line with the field, there isn't any force at all.

Fleming's left-hand rule

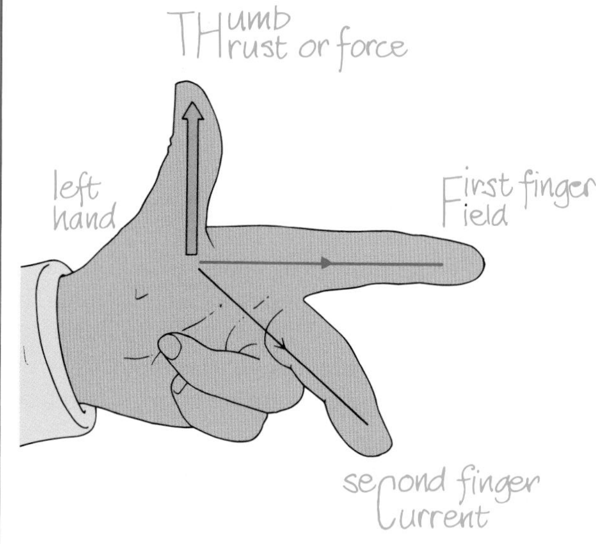

This is a rule for working out the direction of the force when a current is at right angles to a magnetic field.

Hold the thumb and first two fingers of your left hand at right angles. Point your fingers as shown, and your thumb gives the direction of the force.

When you use the rule, remember:

the current direction is from + to –;
the field lines run from N to S.

Turning a coil

A coil lies between the poles of a magnet. A current flows through the coil. The current flows in opposite directions along the two sides of the coil. So one side is pushed *up*, and the other side is pushed *down*. There is a turning effect on the coil.

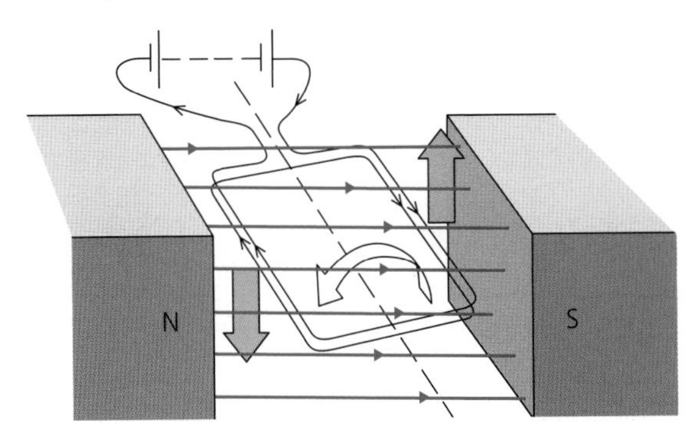

The turning effect is stronger if:

- the current is increased;
- a stronger magnet is used;
- there are more turns on the coil.

Using magnetic forces

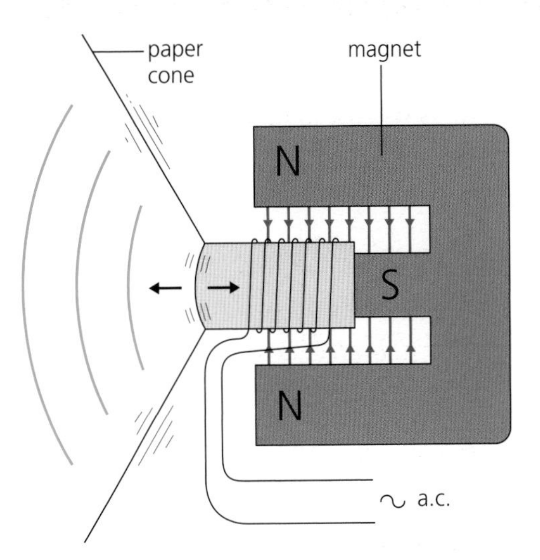

Alternating current passes through the coil of a loudspeaker. The wire in the coil is at right angles to a magnetic field. As the current flows backwards and forwards, the coil is pushed in and out. This makes the cone vibrate and give out sound waves.

Questions

1

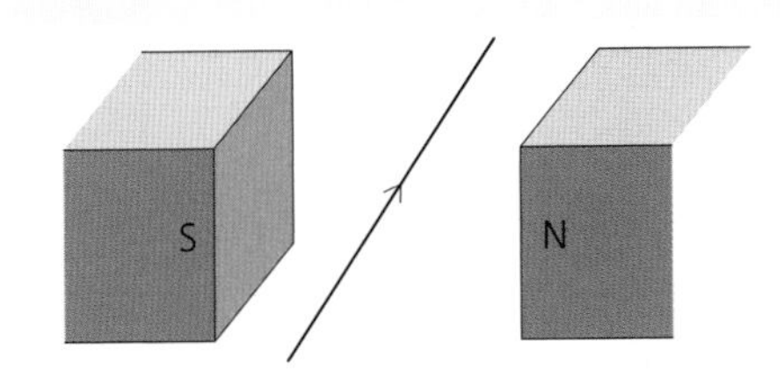

There is a force on the current in the wire above.

a Which of the following statements describes this force correctly?
A The force is towards one of the poles.
B The force is upwards or downwards.

b What would be the effect on the force of using a higher current?

c What would be the effect on the force of reversing the direction of the current?

d Use Fleming's left-hand rule to work out the direction of the force.

2 Some power supplies can deliver alternating current (a.c.). This flows backward, forwards, backwards, forward ... and so on, 50 times per second. What do you think would be the effect of passing a.c. through the wire in question **1**?

3 A student has made the battery tester shown below. It uses a magnet, wire that is flexible and springy, and a pointer. With it, she can check whether a small battery is 'live' or 'dead'.
When she connects a battery to the tester, the pointer moves to the left.

a Why does the pointer move?

b What would happen if the battery she connected delivered less current?

c Can you suggest reasons why she should only connect the battery to the tester briefly and not leave it connected?

d The student wants to make the tester more sensitive – she wants the pointer to move further when a battery is connected. How could she change her design to make this happen?

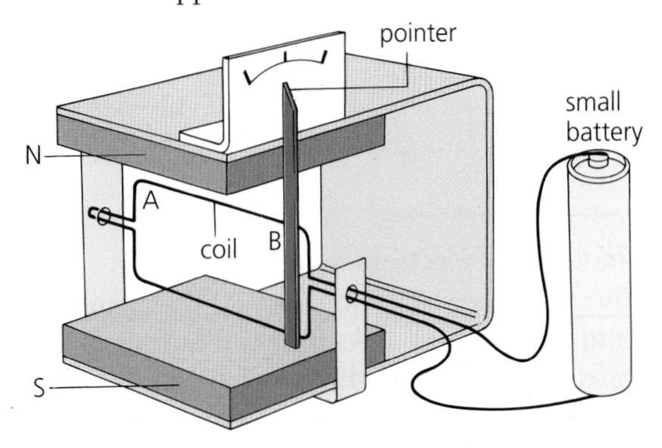

6.05 Electric motors

Electric motors use the magnetic turning effect on a coil. They can power anything from a model car to a submarine.

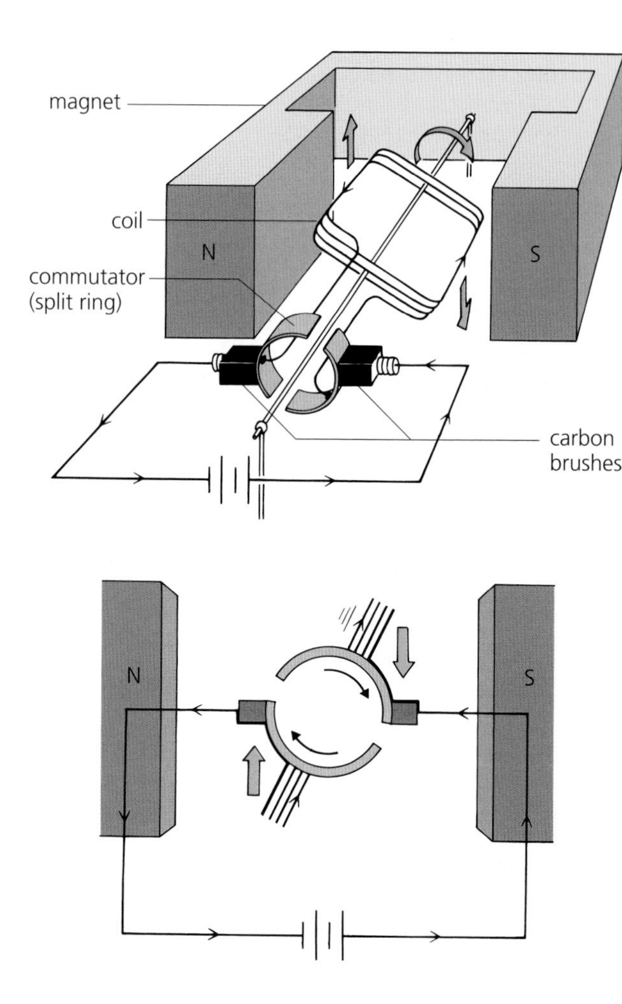

The poles of the **magnet** face one another.

The **coil** is free to rotate between the poles of the magnet.

The **commutator** or split ring is fixed to the coil, and turns round with it.

The **brushes** are two carbon contacts. They connect the coil to the battery.

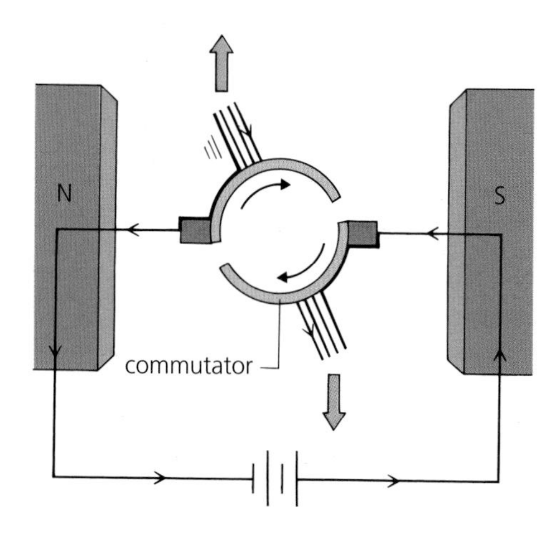

When a current flows through the coil, one side is pushed up, and the other side is pushed down. So the coil turns. However, when the coil is vertical, the forces can't turn it any further because they are pointing the wrong way . . .

. . . As the coil shoots past the vertical, the commutator *changes* the current direction. Now the forces point the other way. So the coil is pushed round another half turn. And so on.

Practical motors usually have several coils set at different angles. This gives smoother running and a greater turning effect.

Some motors use electromagnets rather than permanent magnets. This means that they can run on alternating current (a.c.). As the current flows backwards and forwards through the coil, the magnetic field changes direction to match it. So the turning effect is always the same way.

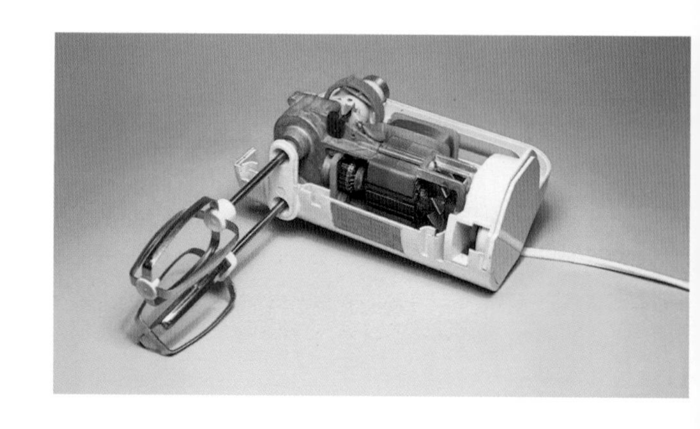

Making a motor

Using a motor kit, you need:
3 metres of plastic-covered copper wire
1 wooden block with metal tube through centre

1 wooden base	1 iron yoke	2 magnets
1 metal spindle	2 split pins	4 studs
2 rubber rings	3 V battery	Sellotape

1 Insulate one end of the tube with Sellotape.

2 Wind coil on wooden block. You need about 10 turns.

3 Strip plastic from ends of wire.
Fix bare ends of wire to tube using rubber rings.

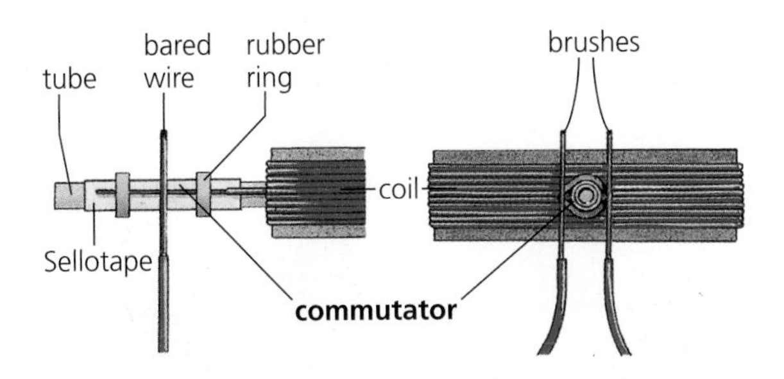

Check the ends are opposite each other and in line with the coil. You have now made the **commutator**.

4 Cut two half-metre lengths of wire.
Bare the ends of the wires.
Fix wires to wooden base using studs. You have now made the **brushes**.

5 Put split pins into base.

6 Push vertical wires (the brushes) towards each other.
Move tube upwards to separate them.

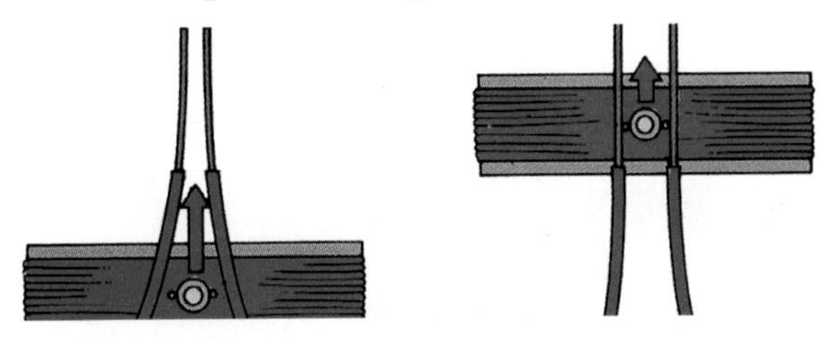

Slide spindle through split pins and tube.
You should now be able to spin the coil.
The brushes should press firmly against the tube and the wire from the coil.

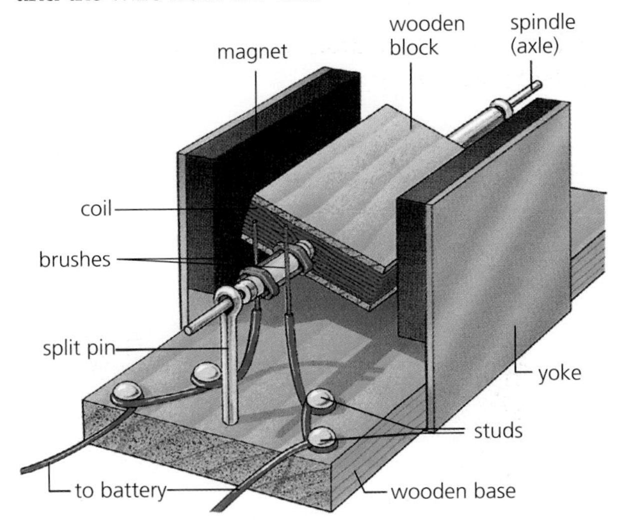

7 Put the two magnets on the yoke to make a single U-shaped magnet. Check that the opposite faces attract each other.

8 Slide yoke into position. Connect wires to battery. Give the coil a flick to start it turning.

Questions

To answer these questions, you will need information from elsewhere in the book.

1 COMMUTATOR BRUSH COIL MAGNET SPINDLE
Which of these:
a is often made from carbon;
b is also known as a split ring;
c turns when current flows through it;
d connects the battery to the split ring and coil;
e changes the current direction every half turn?

2 Someone builds a simple motor following the instructions above. What changes could they make to give the motor a greater turning effect?

3 This is the end view of a simple motor.

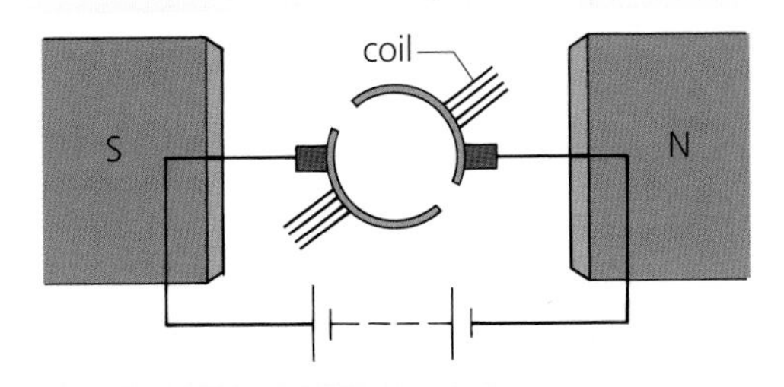

a Why does the coil turn?
b What would be the effect of reversing the magnet?
c What would be the effect of reversing the battery *and* the magnet?
d What is the position of the coil when there is no turning effect on it?

6.06 Power for motion

Engines or motors?

This car is good for special occasions, but not for parking in tight spaces or getting round corners. And it is certainly not good for the environment. The exhaust gases from its huge petrol engine pollute the atmosphere.

The car above is more cramped and not so good for long distances. But it is less polluting. It is powered by an electric motor, so it doesn't have an exhaust pipe. If everyone drove cars like this, conditions in city centres would be much more pleasant.

Storing the energy

These can deliver the same amount of energy:

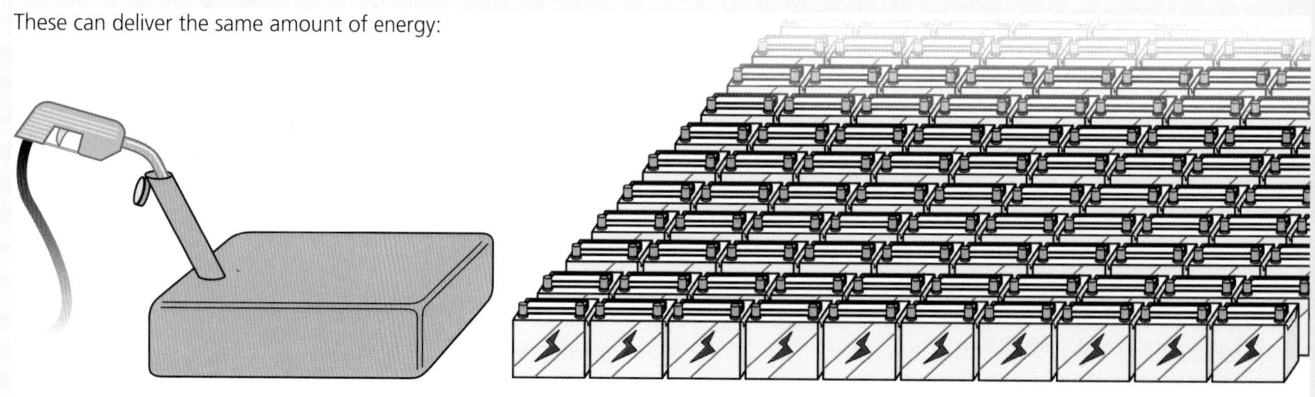

1 full tank of petrol
mass: 50 kg
time to refuel: 3 minutes

150 fully-charged car batteries
mass: 1500 kg (1.5 tonnes)
time to recharge: 3 hours

Electric motors are a clean and efficient way of turning the wheels. But present-day electric cars have one major problem: they need batteries.

Batteries are a relatively poor way of storing energy. Battery-powered cars will never have the performance or range of petrol or diesel models.

Fuel cell future

Fortunately, there is a solution to the battery problem – a source of electricity called a **fuel cell**. When you feed a fuel cell with hydrogen (plus oxygen from the air), chemical reactions deliver a continuous supply of electricity.

The main problem with fuel cells is how to store the hydrogen. It isn't safe or practical to carry large cylinders of this explosive gas. That is why the fuel in the tank is likely to be liquid methanol. A unit called a **reformer** produces hydrogen from the methanol using steam and catalysts.

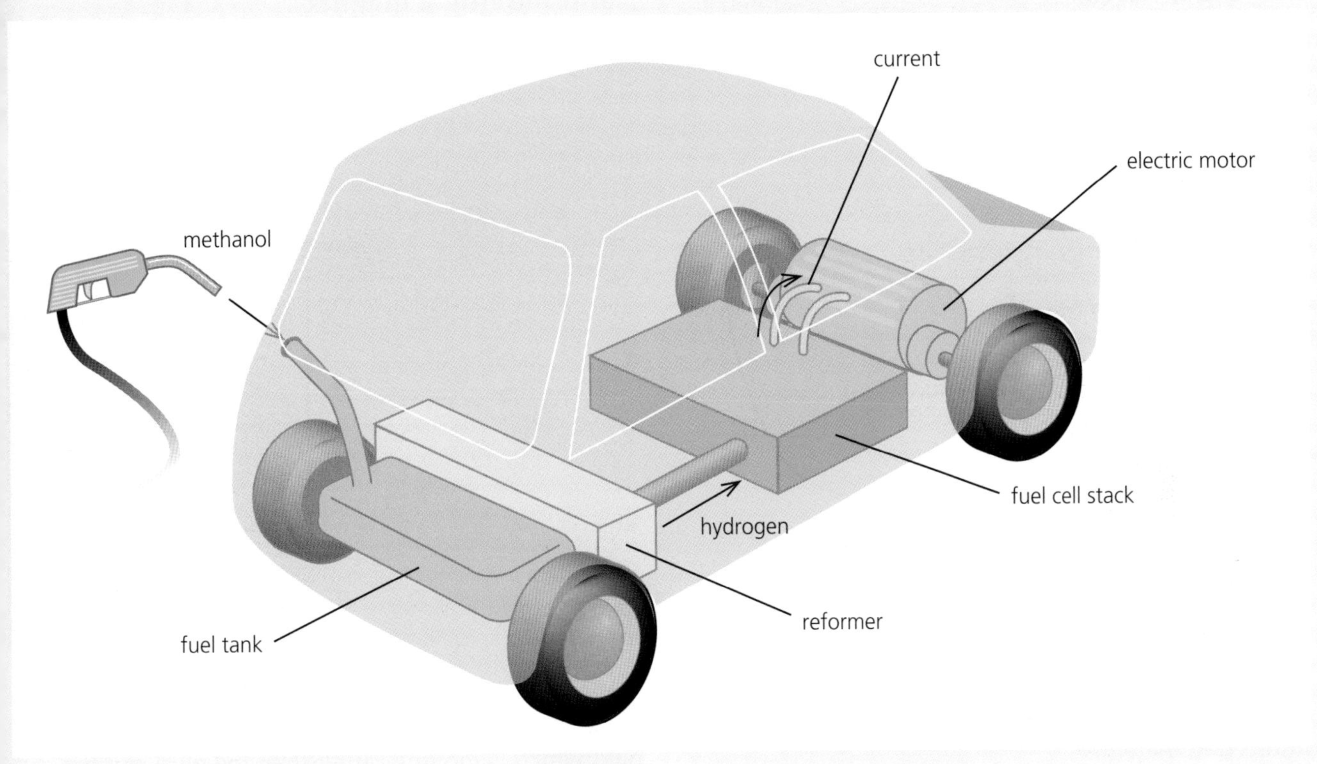

Methanol, or 'wood alcohol', can be made using plant materials grown as a renewable resource. It can also be produced from natural gas. Vehicles with fuel cells will have the range and performance of today's fuel burners, but be more efficient and less polluting.

A fuel cell doesn't need recharging. As long as you feed in the gases, the cell delivers the current. The only waste product is water. Fuel cells have been around for years, but the technology has only recently become cheap enough for cars.

- The batteries in today's electric cars must be recharged by plugging them into a mains-powered charger. Their motors produce no pollution. Can you suggest reasons why, if everyone drove cars like this, the system would still cause atmospheric pollution?
- Can you suggest reasons why cars with fuel cells in are likely to be more successful and popular than battery-powered cars?

Poo-llution problem

Pollution from transport isn't a new problem. In the 1800s, horse-drawn traffic was increasing so much that it was estimated that, by the end of that century, Londoners would be up to their knees in horse manure.

6.07 Electricity from magnetism

You don't need batteries to produce a current. Just a wire or coil, a magnet, and some movement.

Moving a wire...

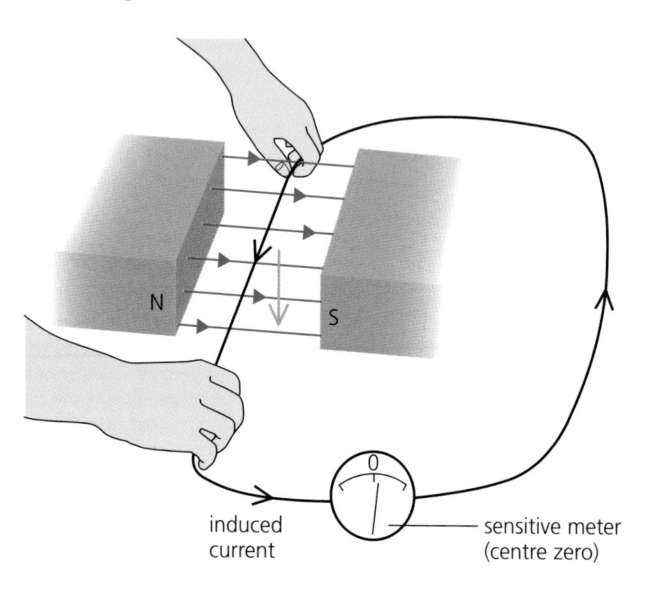

When a wire is moved across a magnetic field, as above, a small voltage is generated in the wire. The effect is called **electromagnetic induction**: a voltage is **induced** in the wire.
As the wire is part of a complete circuit, the voltage makes a current flow. This can be detected using a sensitive meter. The one in the diagram is a centre-zero type. Its pointer moves to the left or right, depending on the current direction.

The induced voltage (and current) can be increased by

- Moving the wire faster.
- Using a stronger magnet.

Doing either of the following will *reverse* the direction of the induced voltage and current:

- Moving the wire in the opposite direction.
- Turning the magnet round so that the field direction is reversed.

If the wire isn't cutting field lines, there is *no* induced voltage or current. This may be because:

- The wire is moving parallel to the field lines.
- The wire isn't moving.

...and moving a magnet

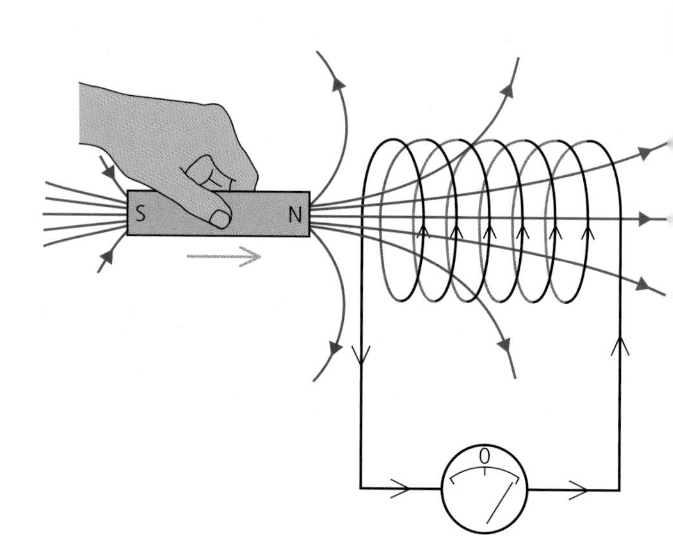

If a bar magnet is pushed into a coil, as above, a voltage is induced in the coil. Here, it is the magnetic field which is moving rather than the wire, but the result is the same: field lines are being cut. As the coil is part of a complete circuit, the induced voltage makes a current flow.

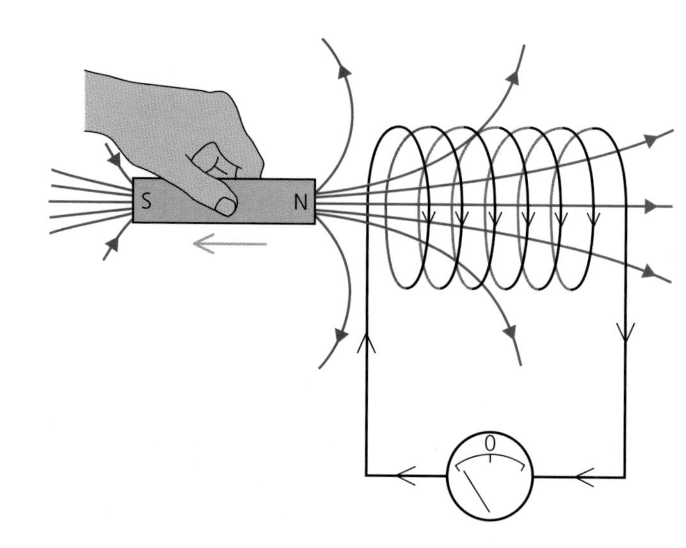

If the magnet is pulled *out of* the coil, the direction of the induced voltage (and current) is reversed.

In the magnet-and-coil experiment on the opposite page, the induced voltage (and current) can be increased by

- Moving the magnet faster.
- Using a stronger magnet.
- Increasing the number of turns on the coil.

Guitar pick-ups are tiny coils with magnets inside them. The magnets magnetize the steel strings. When the strings vibrate, current is induced in the coils, boosted by an amplifier, and used to produce sound.

The playback heads in audio and video cassette recorders contain tiny coils. A tiny, varying voltage is induced in the coil as the magnetized tape passes over it. In this way, the magnetized patterns on the tape are changed into electrical signals which can be used to recreate the original sound or picture.

If the S pole of the magnet, rather than the N pole, is pushed into the coil, this reverses the current direction.

If the magnet is held still, no field lines are cut, so there is no induced voltage or current.

Questions

1

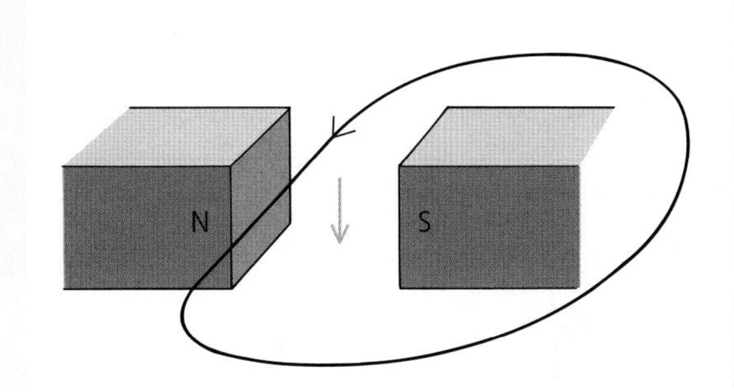

When the wire above is moved downwards, a current is induced in it. What would be the effect of:

a moving the wire upwards through the magnetic field?

b holding the wire still in the magnetic field?

c moving the wire parallel to the magnetic field lines?

2

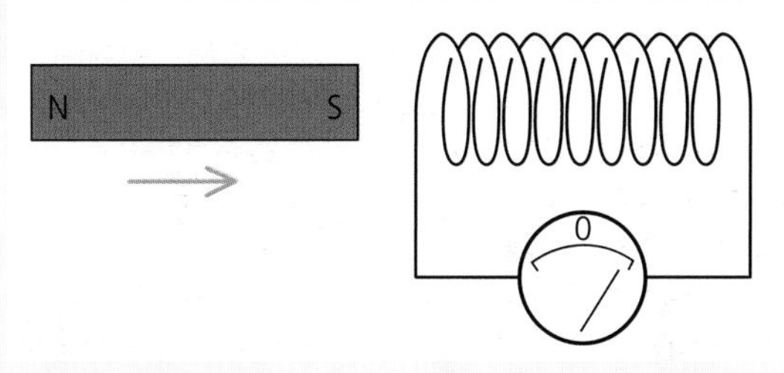

In the experiment above, a current is induced in the coil when the magnet is moved in or out of it.

a What is this effect called?

b Copy and complete the table below to show what happens to the needle of the meter when the magnet is moved in and out of the coil.

Magnet pushed in	Needle moves to right
Magnet in coil, but not moving	
Magnet pulled out	
Magnet pushed in again, but faster	

c What would be the effect of increasing the number of turns on the coil?

6.08 Generators

Turn a **generator** and out comes a current . . .

. . . current for the lights on a bike.

. . . current for the circuits in a car.

. . . current to light up a whole city.

In fact, generators provide over 99% of our electrical energy.

A simple alternator

Most generators give out **alternating current (a.c.)**: the current flows backwards, forwards, backwards, forwards ... and so on. a.c. generators are called **alternators**. The simple one below is supplying the current for a small bulb:

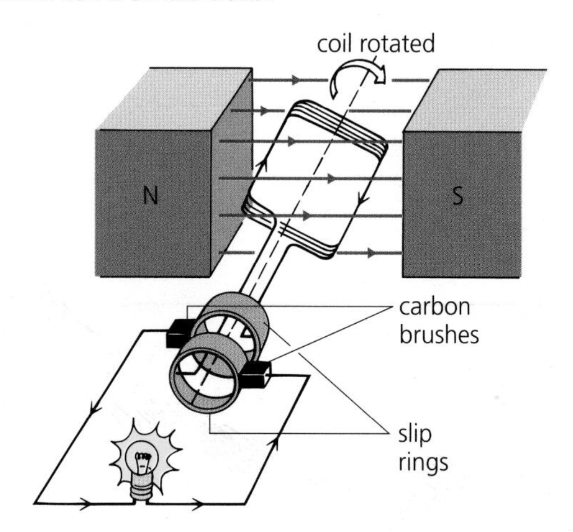

The **coil** is rotated between the poles of a magnet.

The **slip rings** turn with the coil.

The **brushes** are two carbon contacts. They rub against the slip rings, so that the rotating coil is connected to the bulb.

When the coil is rotated, it cuts through magnetic field lines. A voltage is generated. This makes a current flow through the bulb.

As the coil rotates, each side travels upwards through the magnetic field, then downwards. So the induced current flows one way, then the opposite way. The current is alternating.

Turning a motor into a generator

You may have made an electric motor like this.
It can be used to generate a current.
Connect the leads to a milliammeter.
Give the coil a spin. The coil cuts through magnetic field lines, and a current is generated.
The milliammeter reading shows that the current is 'one-way' direct current (d.c.).
However, the flow is very uneven.

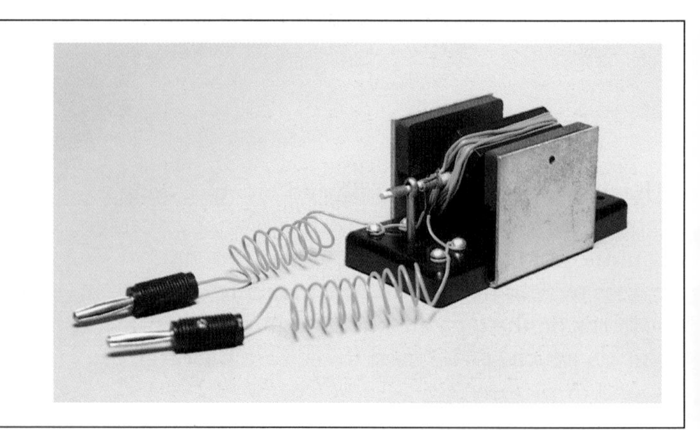

This graph shows how the current from the alternator changes as the coil rotates.
'Forwards' current is plus (+).
'Backwards' current is minus (–).

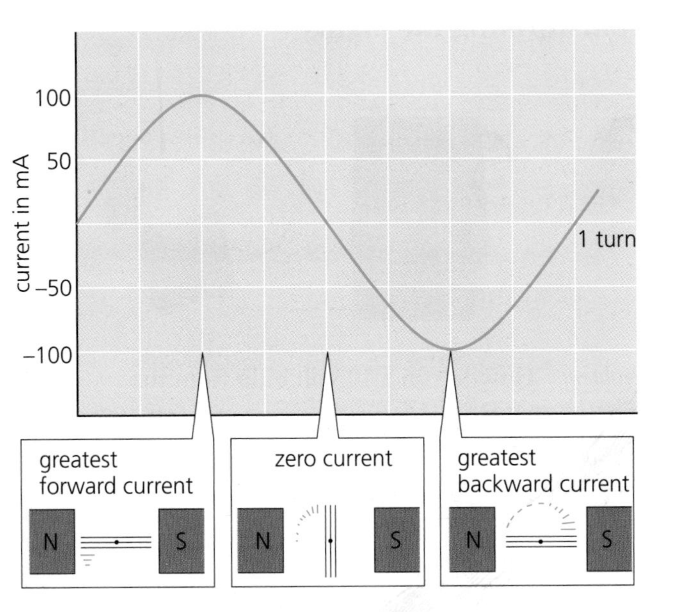

The current is *greatest* when the coil is *horizontal*.
The coil cuts field lines most rapidly in this position.

The current is *zero* when the coil is *vertical*.
The coil doesn't cut field lines in this position.

The alternator would generate a higher current if:

- the coil had more turns;
- a stronger magnet were used;
- the coil were rotated faster.

Alternator facts

- Many alternators use electromagnets instead of permanent magnets. These give a stronger field.
- Alternators in power stations have a rotating electromagnet in the middle, with fixed coils around it. This means that the output current doesn't have to flow through sliding contacts.
- Alternators in power stations have to run at a constant speed. If their speed changed, the mains frequency would change from 50 Hz.
- The alternator in a car is fitted with a device called a rectifier. This changes the alternating current into 'one-way' direct current needed for the car's circuits and charging the battery.

Questions

To answer these questions, you may need information from the previous spread.

1 Copy the boxes. Fill in the first letter of each answer to make a word. This is an essential part of any generator.

[?] It measures small currents.
[?] Type of current from an alternator.
[?] When turned, they produce currents.
[?] Magnetic field lines leave this pole.
[?] Type of energy from a generator.
[?] For more current, a generator coil needs more of these.

2 This is the end view of a simple alternator.

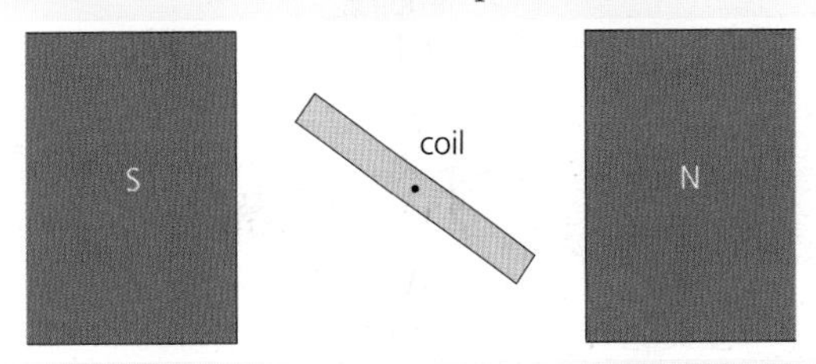

a Redraw the diagram to show the position of the coil when the current is greatest.
b Why is the current greatest in this position?
c Redraw the diagram to show the position of the coil when the current is zero.
d Why is the current zero in this position?

3 This alternator is generating a small current:

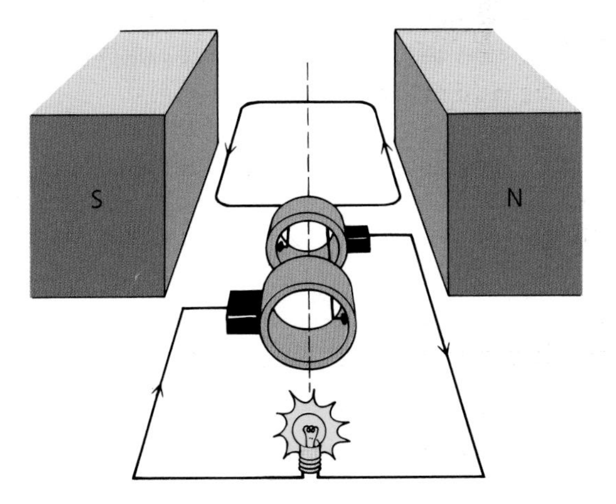

a What would be the effect of using a stronger magnet?
b Describe two ways in which the current would change if the coil were turned faster.
c Explain why the current being generated is a.c. and not d.c.

6.09 Transformers

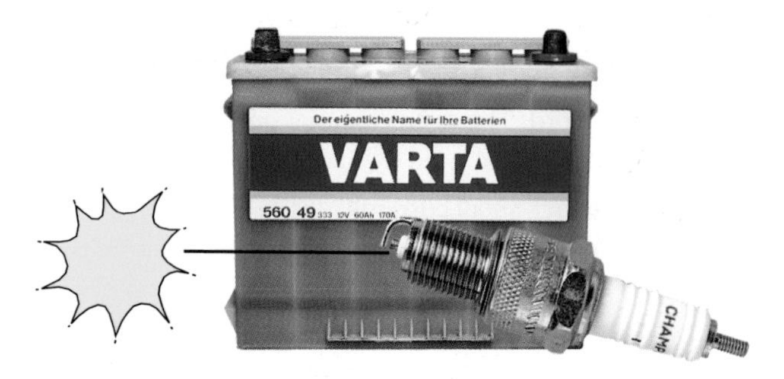

A 12000 volt spark from a 12 volt battery.
This is needed to ignite the petrol in a car engine. The high voltage is generated in a coil; not by pushing a magnet in and out, but by switching an electromagnet on and off.

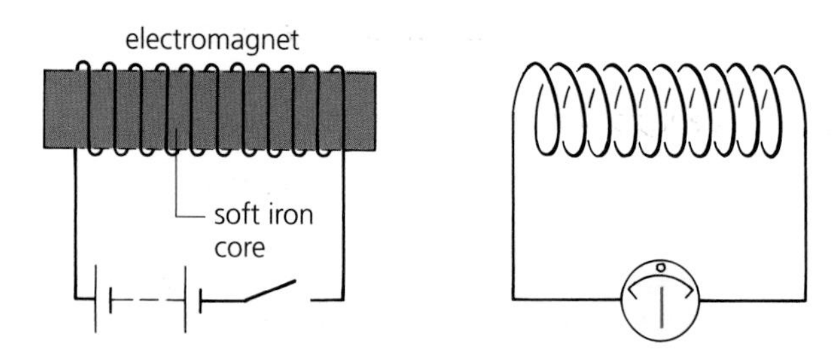

An electromagnet is close to a coil.
Switching on the electromagnet puts a magnetic field around the coil. The effect is the same as pushing a magnet into the coil very fast. A voltage is induced, a current flows, and the meter needle flicks one way. But only for a fraction of a second. When the field is steady, the current stops.

When the electromagnet is switched off, the magnetic field vanishes. The effect is the same as pulling a magnet out of the coil very fast. Just for a moment, the meter needle flicks the other way.

Without the core, the induced voltage would be much less. Can you explain why?

A higher voltage is induced if:

- the core of the electromagnet goes right into the coil;
- the coil has more turns.

The coil in a car engine has many thousands of turns. This gives the thousands of volts needed for the spark plugs. The electromagnet is inside the coil. It runs on only 12 volts. It is switched on and off by a transistor or, in older cars, a set of contacts called 'points'.

Transforming the mains

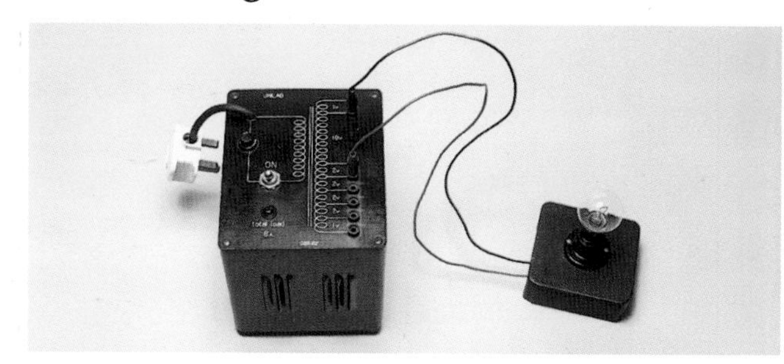

Problem How to run a 10 volt bulb from the 230 volt mains.

Answer Use a **transformer**. Easier still – use a low voltage power supply. It's already got one in it.

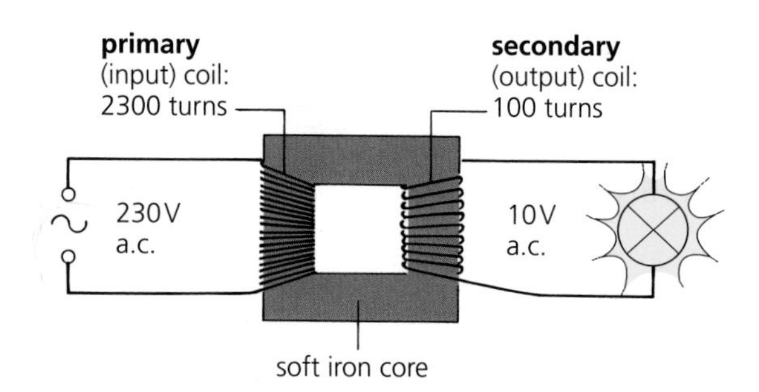

This is one type of transformer.
Alternating current flows through the **primary** or **input coil**. This sets up a changing magnetic field in the **secondary** or **output coil**. The effect is the same as moving a magnet in and out of the coil very fast. An alternating voltage is induced. Alternating current flows. The bulb lights up.

There is a connection between the input and output voltages:

$$\frac{\text{input voltage}}{\text{output voltage}} = \frac{\text{turns on input coil}}{\text{turns on output coil}}$$

In this example,

$$\frac{230}{10} = \frac{2300}{100}$$

The input coil has 23 times the turns of the output coil. The **turns ratio** is 23:1.
The input voltage is 23 times the output voltage.

The transformer wouldn't work on d.c. Direct current would give a steady magnetic field. So no voltage would be induced in the output coil.

Stepping down and up

There are two types of transformer:

Step-down transformer	Step-up transformer
Symbol:	Symbol:
Turns on output coil fewer than turns on input coil	Turns on output coil more than turns on input coil
Output voltage less than input voltage	Output voltage more than input voltage
Used in . . .	Used in . . .
A mains 'power pack' to supply 9V for a radio, keyboard, or computer	A television to supply 25000V for the picture tube

Transformer power

If a transformer doesn't waste any energy, then it must give out as much energy every second as is put in. In other words: its power output (in watts, W) must be the same as its power input. For this to happen, the current must change as well as the voltage.

For example:

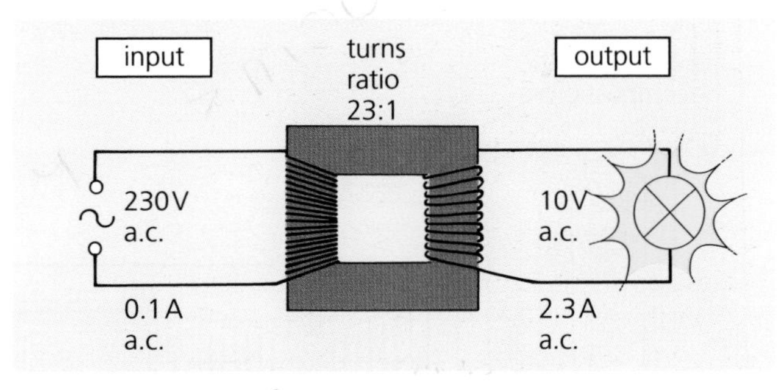

The voltage goes down from:

230V ……………..……to 10V

The current goes up from:

0.1A ……………..……to 2.3A

The power input
= voltage × current

= 230 × 0.1
= 23 W

The power output
= voltage × current

= 10 × 2.3
= 23 W

The voltage has gone *down*. The current has gone *up*. But the power has stayed the *same*.

For any transformer that doesn't waste power:

input voltage × input current = output voltage × output current

Questions

1

Transformer	A	B	C	D
Input voltage in V	240	120	50	100
Input turns	1000	1000	1000	2000
Output turns	500	100	2000	2000

Which transformer:

a is a step-up transformer?
b has the same output voltage as input voltage?
c has a turns ratio of 10:1?
d has an output voltage of 12 V?
e has the highest output voltage?

2 A 23V bulb takes a current of 2A. Its power supply is a transformer connected to the 230V mains.
You have to choose a suitable transformer. You can assume that the transformer wastes no power.
a What turns ratio is needed?
b What power is taken by the bulb?
c What power is taken from the mains?
d What current is taken from the mains?
e Why wouldn't the transformer work on d.c.?

6.10 Power across the country

Mains power comes from huge alternators in power stations.

Transformers step up the voltage before the power is carried across country by overhead cables.

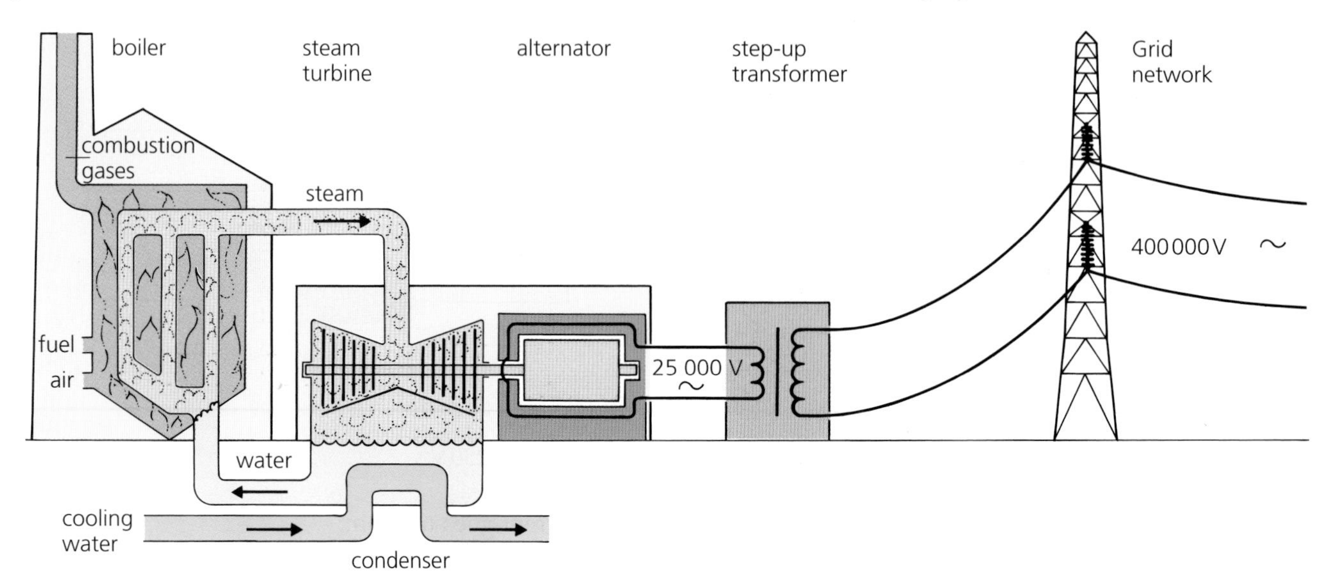

The power station

In the power station, the alternators are driven by huge **turbines**, spun round by the force of high-pressure steam. The steam is made by heating water in a boiler. The heat comes from burning coal, gas, or oil – or from a nuclear reactor.

Huge **cooling condensers** change the steam back into water for the boiler. The condensers need vast amounts of cooling water. So power stations are often built near rivers or the sea.

Why change voltage?

The current from a large alternator can be 20000 A or more. It needs very thick, heavy, and expensive cable to carry it. So a transformer is used to *step up* the voltage and *reduce* the current. Then thinner, lighter, and cheaper cables can be used to carry the power across country.

If a 25000 V alternator produces a current of 20000 A, its power output is 500000000 W.

If the voltage is stepped up to 400000 V, the current drops to 1250 A but the power is still 500000000 W.

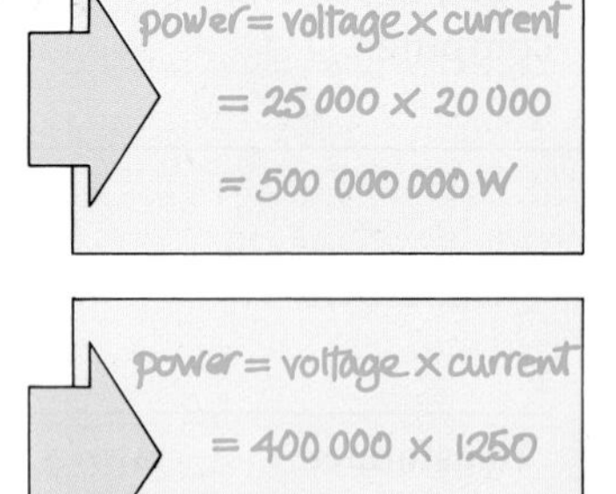

Why a.c.?

If power stations didn't generate alternating current (a.c.), transformers couldn't be used to change the voltage. Direct current (d.c.) voltages can be changed, but this is difficult and expensive. Transformers don't work on direct current.

Then transformers reduce the voltage . . .

. . . before the power is supplied to homes, offices, and factories.

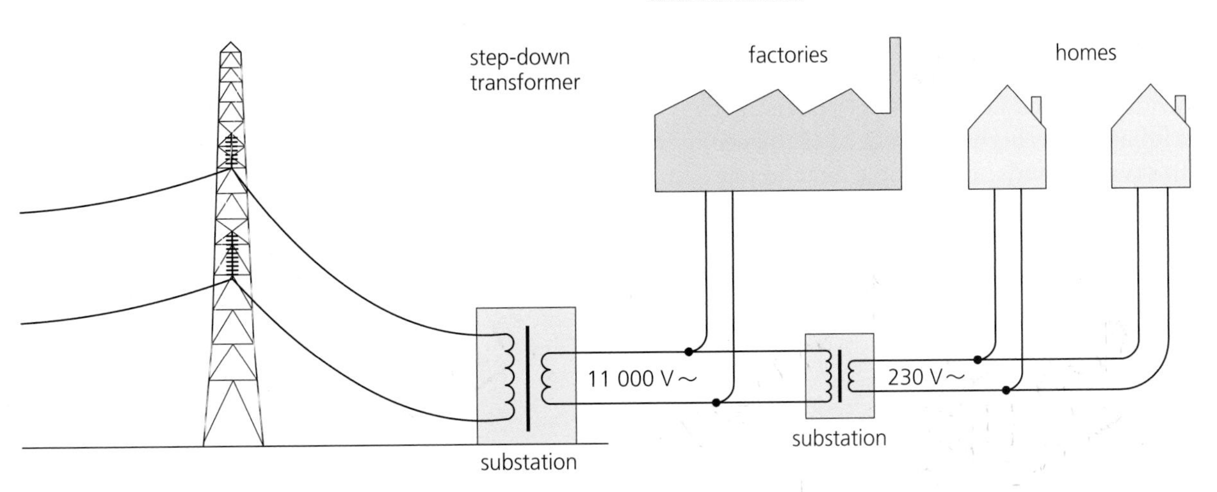

The Grid

Each power station feeds its power to a network of cables and switching stations called the **Grid**. If one area of the country needs more power, it can be supplied by power stations in other areas.

Power from the Grid

Power from the overhead cables is fed to substations. Here, the voltage is stepped down by transformers. Homes take their power at 230 volts. Factories and hospitals take their power at higher voltages.

Questions

To answer these questions, you may need information from the previous spread.
1 MW = 1000 000 W.

1 Explain why:

a Steam is needed in a power station.

b Power stations are often near a river or the sea.

c The voltage is stepped up before power is fed to the overhead cables.

d Power stations generate a.c., and not d.c.

2 The three power stations right were built to supply the towns of Newleigh, Extown, and Oldwich.
Each alternator generates 20 000 V.
Each has a power output of 100 MW.
The stations feed their power to the Grid. The towns take their power from the Grid.

a What is the Grid?

b How many alternators must be working to supply the town of Newleigh?

c Which towns could be supplied by A station alone?

d How much spare power is being supplied to the Grid for use in other areas?

e If B station shuts down, how much power must be supplied to the towns from other parts of the country?

f How much energy (in joules) does each alternator supply in 1 second?

g How much current is being generated by each alternator?

h After the voltage has been stepped up to 400 000 V, how much current does each alternator supply to the Grid?

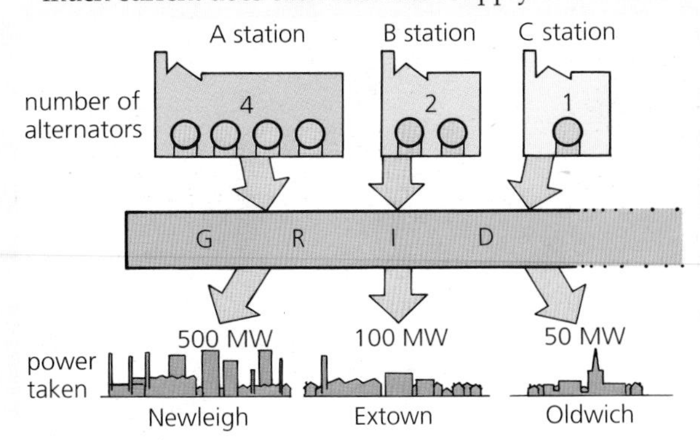

6.11 Power plus

Hidden power

In Snowdonia, the landscape hasn't been spoilt by pylons, because the electricity company has put its power lines underground. But this is an expensive way of sending power. Lower voltages have to be used, and that means higher currents and thicker cables. To save the landscape, people have to pay more for their electricity.

Guaranteed power

Power cuts don't happen very often. But when they do, the results can be serious:

A loss of power here – and 200 cows will need milking by hand.

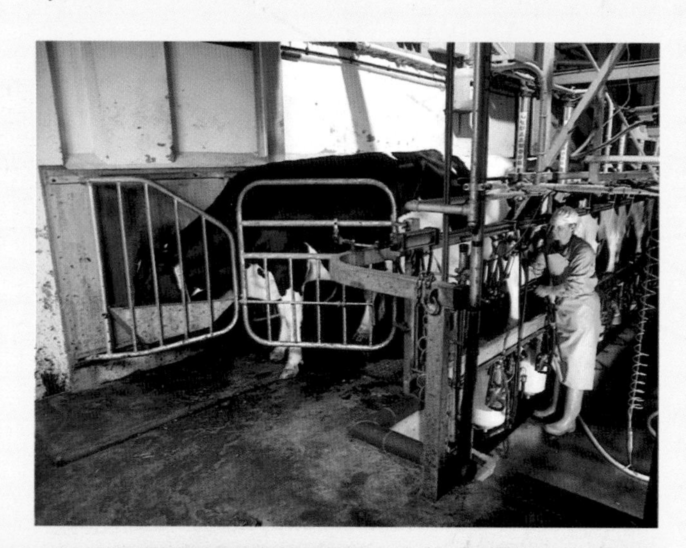

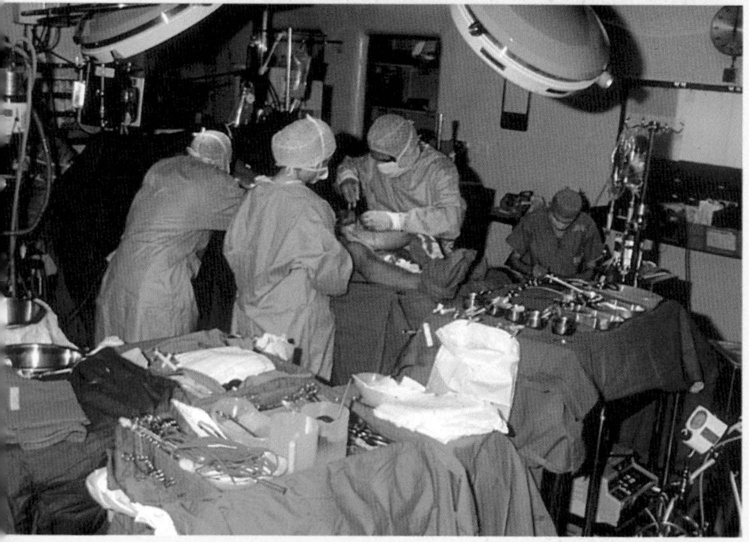

A loss of power here might put someone's life at risk.

For emergencies, most large hospitals and farms have stand-by generators. They are driven by engines which run on petrol, diesel, or bottled gas. They start up automatically if there is a mains failure.

Extra power

Battery hens? In Somerset, hens have solved one farmer's electricity supply problems. He saves their droppings in a tank and collects the gas given off. Then he uses the gas to run the engine which drives his generator.

In Florida, the police have collected so much marijuana in drugs raids that a power station has been specially converted to burn it. One tonne of marijuana gives nearly as much heat as three barrels of oil.

In Edmonton, North London, the council has turned one of its rubbish incinerators into a generating station. Electricity is generated using the heat from burning household rubbish. The council gets rid of its waste. And it keeps its costs down by selling the electricity to the local electricity company.

Acid rain

All over Europe, acid rain is falling. The acid in the rain is only weak. But it is killing fish in the lakes of Norway and Sweden, damaging forests in Germany, and eating into the stonework of old buildings.

In Norway, Sweden, and Germany, they blame the sulphur fumes from Britain's coal-burning power stations. Winds are blowing the fumes across Northern Europe. And the fumes are making the rain acid.

The electricity companies don't agree. They say that there is no firm evidence to link their power stations with acid rain. Sulphur fumes aren't a new problem – factories and road vehicles have been producing them for years.

And as the argument goes on, the acid rain still falls.

Water power

To provide hydroelectric power, a river is dammed to form a lake. Water rushes from the lake to turn generators at the foot of the dam. No pollution. But the landscape is changed, and local animal and plant life is disturbed.

In Sweden, much of their electricity comes from hydroelectric schemes. But plans to build more dams have been dropped. The Swedes don't want to see more countryside destroyed.

In Sri Lanka, they are keen to expand their use of hydroelectricity. Unless they can supply more power from their own resources, they will have to borrow more money to buy oil. And that will keep the country poor.

Make a list of the buildings where you think an emergency generator is essential.

Here are some of the ways in which a town could get its power:

- a hydroelectric power scheme;
- a coal-burning power station;
- a small generator in every building.

How many advantages and disadvantages can you think of for each?

Try to find out:

- where the power stations in your region are sited;
- what fuels they use.

Questions on Chapter 6

1 The diagram below shows a relay switch.

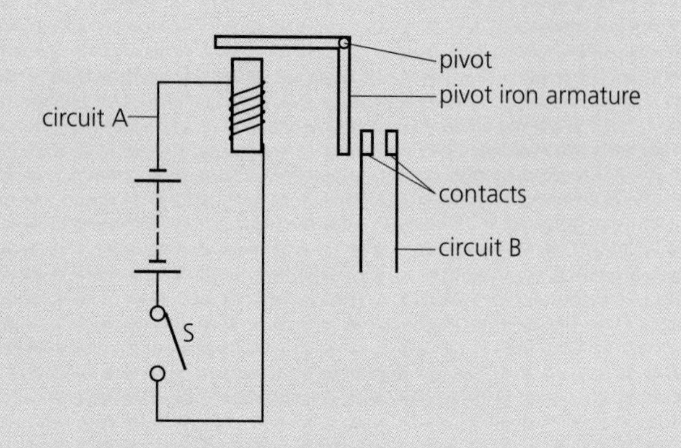

a Explain in detail what happens when the switch S is closed.
b Explain what now happens if switch S is opened.
c What kind of material is the coil wrapped around?
d Suggest one use for a relay switch.

2 The diagram below shows a simple transformer.

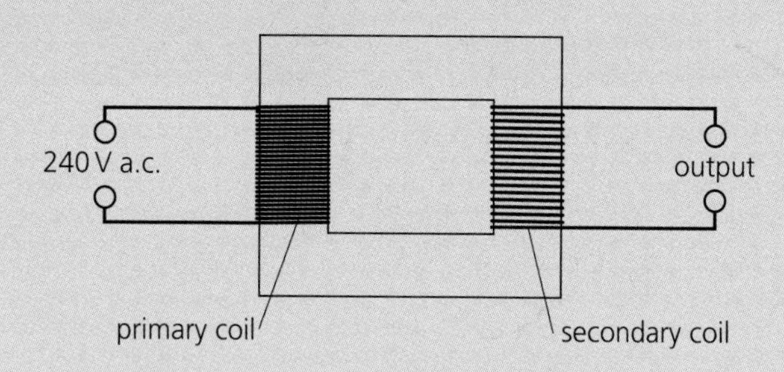

a If there are 1000 turns on the primary coil and 250 turns on the secondary coil calculate the output voltage from the transformer. (Show all your workings.)
b If the current flowing through the primary coil is 0.2 A calculate the current flowing through the secondary coil.
c What assumption have you made in your calculation for both **a** and **b**?
d Explain why a transformer will not work if a direct current supply is connected across the primary coil.
e State one use for:
i a step-up transformer.
ii a step-down transformer.

3 The diagram below shows a moving coil loud speaker.

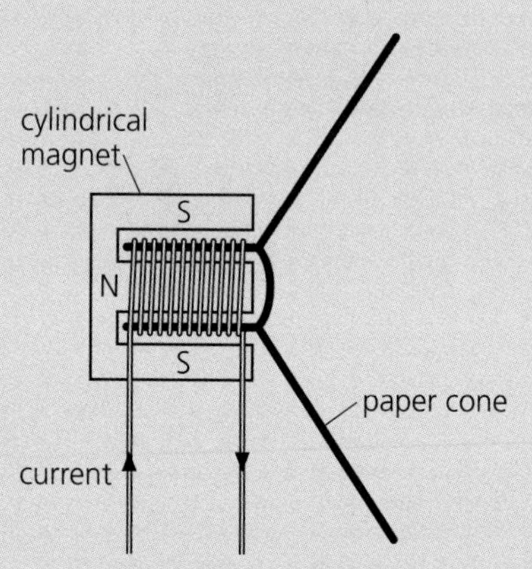

Explain how passing an alternating current through the coil causes the paper cone to produce a sound.

4 Here is an experiment involving two circuits.

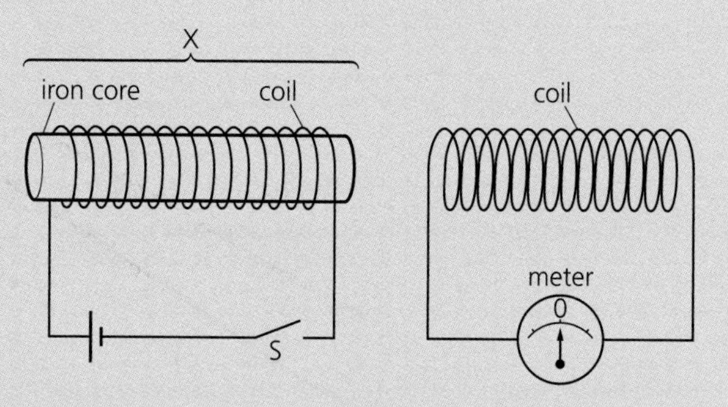

a What name is given to the device marked X?
b Describe what you will observe if you are looking at the meter:
i at the moment switch S is closed;
ii a few seconds later, if switch S is kept closed;
iii at the moment switch S is opened again.
c Name a device which makes use of the principle shown in the experiment above.
d Describe another way in which you could make a current flow in the right-hand circuit without connecting anything else into the circuit.
e With switch S, the magnetic field from the core can be turned on and off. What difference would it make if the core were made of steel rather than iron?

5 The diagram below shows the route followed by domestic electricity in this country.

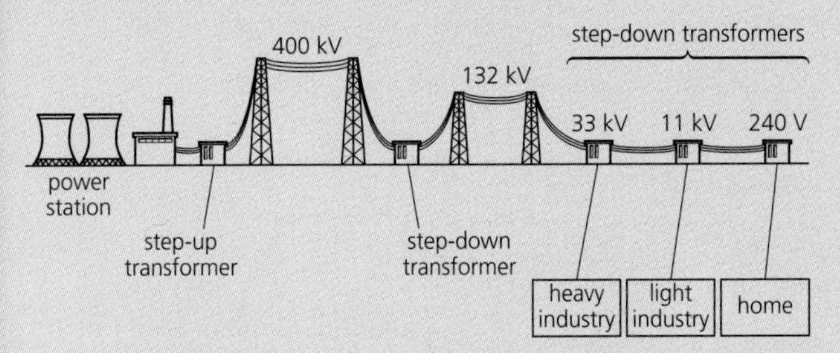

a What device manufactures our electrical energy at a power station? Name three fuels which could be used to power this machine. State the principle energy transformation which takes place.

b Why is the electricity transmitted at high voltage?

c Suggest one reason why the power lines are suspended high above the ground on pylons.

d What happens to the electricity before it enters our homes? In just one sentence explain how this is done.

e Why is alternating current transmitted rather than direct current?

f A transformer has 10 000 turns on its primary coil and 500 turns on its secondary. If a p.d. of 240 V a.c. is applied across the primary coil, calculate the output voltage across the secondary.
Used in this way, this is a __________ transformer.

6 The diagram below shows a simple generator. Rotating the loop of wire causes a current which lights the lamp.

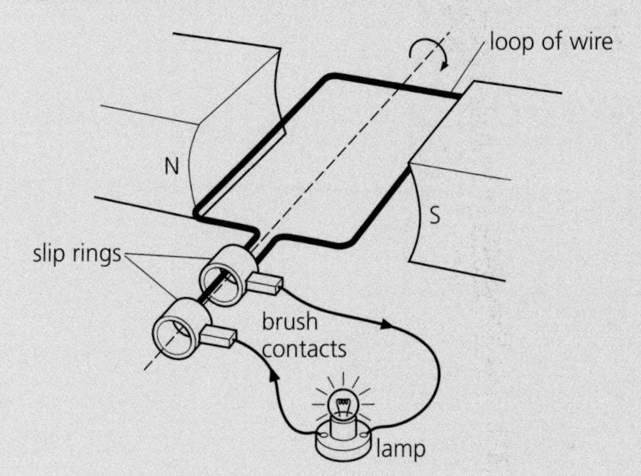

a State **three** ways to increase the current produced by the generator.

b This kind of generator produces 'alternating current'. Explain what is meant by the phrase 'alternating current'.

7 The diagram below shows a simple generator.

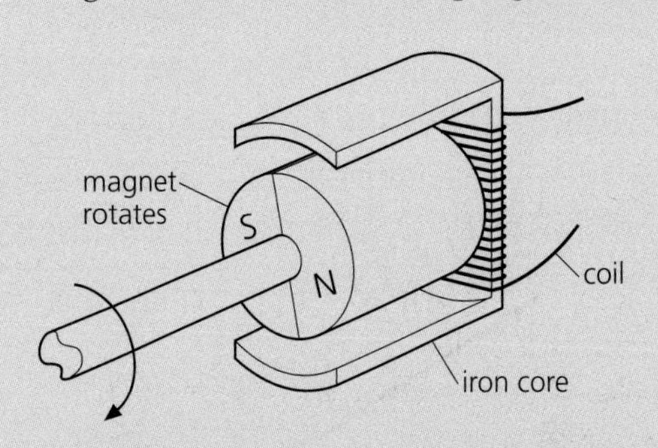

a What happens in the coil of wire when the magnet rotates?

b The ends of the coil are connected to a cathode ray oscilloscope (CRO). The diagram shows the trace on the screen as the magnet rotates.

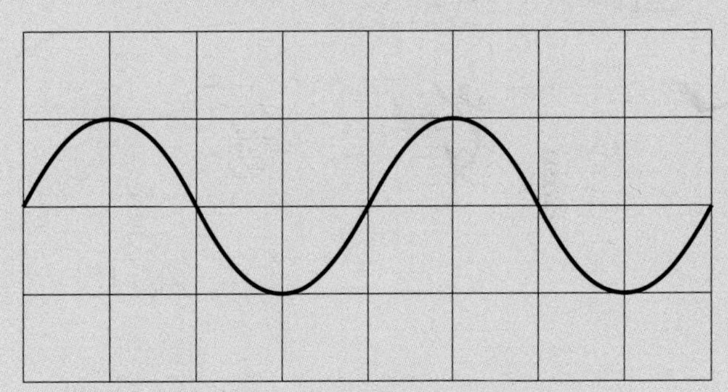

Draw new traces for each of the following changes.

i The magnet rotates at the same speed but in the opposite direction.

ii The magnet rotates at the same speed, in the same direction as the original, but the number of turns on the coil is doubled.

iii The magnet rotates at twice the speed, in the same direction, with the original number of turns on the coil.

Chapter 7
Atoms and nuclei

The aurora borealis, or 'northern lights', seen from a spacecraft above the Earth. The shimmering curtain of light is produced when atomic particles streaming from the Sun strike atoms and molecules high in the Earth's atmosphere. The Earth's magnetic field concentrates the incoming atomic particles above the north and south polar regions, so that is where aurorae are normally seen. ■

7.01 Inside atoms

Atoms are extremely small. There are more than a billion billion of them covering this full stop.

Here is a simple **model** (description) of the atom. There is a tiny **nucleus** made up of **protons** and **neutrons**, with **electrons** in orbit around it:

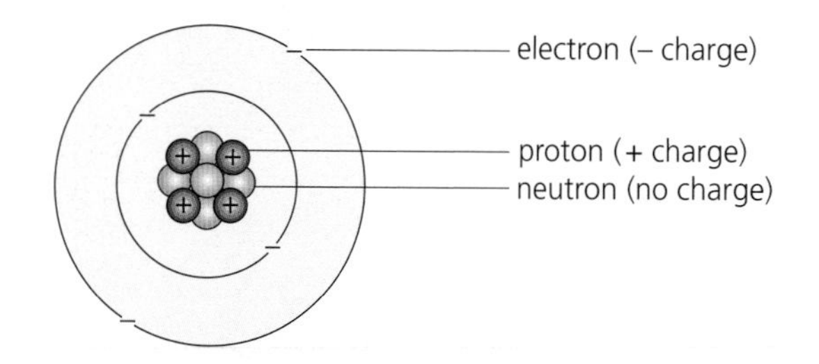

Electrons have almost no mass compared with protons and neutrons. So the mass of an atom is mainly in its nucleus.
Electrons and protons have electric **charge**, but of opposite types. Normally, an atom has the same number of electrons as protons, giving an overall (total) charge of zero.
This chart shows how the masses and charges of the different particles compare, counting the mass of a proton as 1 unit and its charge as +1 unit:

Particle	proton	neutron	electron
Mass	1	1	0
Charge	+1	0	–1

The nucleus is far too small to show in a diagram.
If an atom were the size of this concert hall, its nucleus would be smaller than a pea!

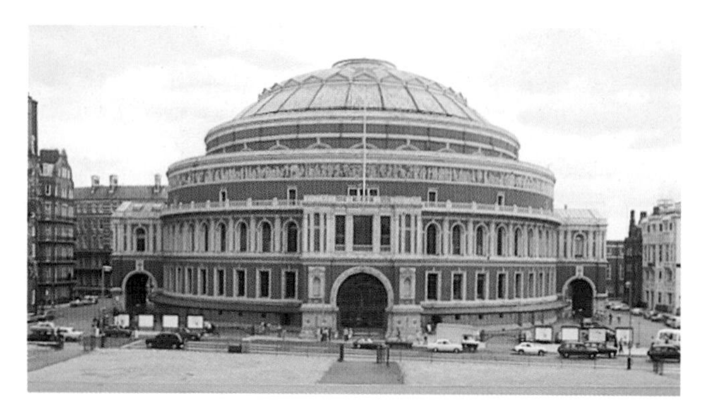

Elements and atomic number
Everything is made up from about 100 simple substances called **elements**. Each element has a different number of protons in its atoms. This is called its **atomic number**. For example:

Element	Chemical symbol	Atomic number (proton number)
hydrogen	H	1
helium	He	2
lithium	Li	3
beryllium	Be	4
boron	B	5
carbon	C	6
nitrogen	N	7
oxygen	O	8
radium	Ra	88
thorium	Th	90
uranium	U	92
plutonium	Pu	94

Isotopes and mass number
The atoms of an element are not all alike. Some have more neutrons than others. These different versions of the element are called **isotopes**. There are some examples on the right.

The total number of protons plus neutrons in the nucleus is called the **mass number** (or **nucleon number**). Isotopes have *different* mass numbers but the *same* atomic number. For example:

Lithium is a mixture of two isotopes with mass numbers 6 and 7. Lithium-7 is the more common. This is the symbol for an atom of lithium-7:

mass number (protons + neutrons) — $^{7}_{3}\mathrm{Li}$ — chemical symbol
atomic number (protons)

The bottom number also tells you the charge on the nucleus relative to a single proton (+1).

Some atoms, elements, and isotopes

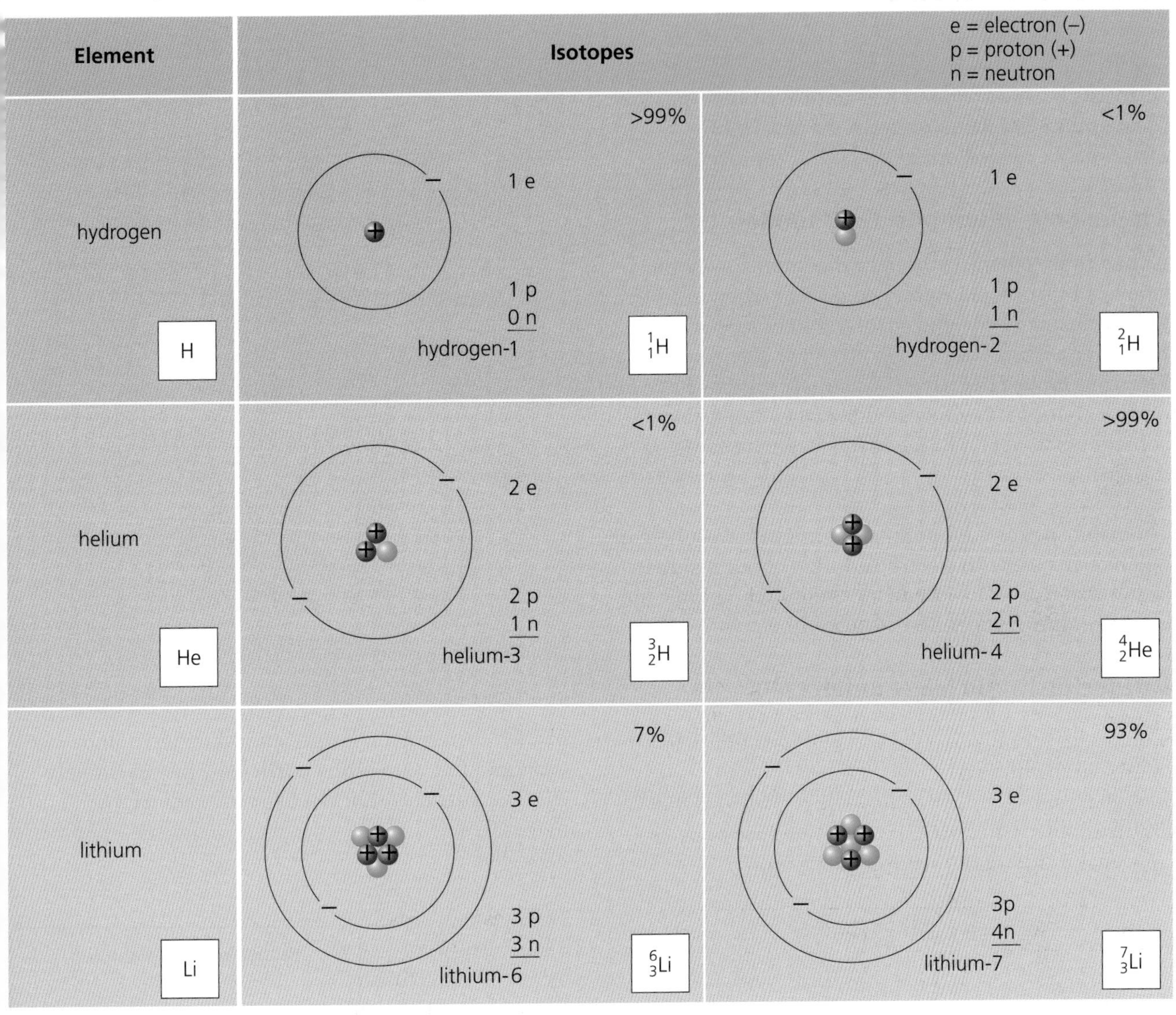

Questions

1

electron proton neutron nucleus

Which of these:

a orbits the nucleus?

b is a particle with a + charge?

c is uncharged?

d is lighter than all the others?

e is made up of protons and neutrons?

f has a – charge?

2 Copy the chart and fill in the blanks:

	Electrons	Protons	Neutrons	Mass number
Sodium-23	11			
Aluminium-27	13			
Strontium-90	38			
Cobalt-60	27			

To answer the following questions, you will need information from the table of elements on the opposite page.

3 Nitrogen-14 can be written $^{14}_{7}$N. How can the following be written?

a Radium-226

b Uranium-235

c Oxygen-16

d Carbon-12

4 Here is some information about four atoms:

Atom A: 3 electrons, mass number 7

Atom B: 142 neutrons, mass number 232

Atom C: 3 neutrons, mass number 6

Atom D: 5 electrons, mass number 11

a Which elements are A, B, C, and D?

b Which pair of atoms are isotopes?

7.02 Models of the atom

Scientists have developed and improved their models (descriptions) of the atom from the results of experiments carried out over the last century.

Thomson's 'plum pudding' model

At one time, scientists thought that atoms were the smallest bits of matter you could have. Then in 1897, J. J. Thomson discovered that atoms could give out tiny, charged particles which he called **electrons**. Electrons have a negative (–) charge; as atoms have no overall charge, this suggested that they must also contain positive (+) charge to balance the charge on the electrons.

Thomson suggested that an atom might be a sphere of positive charge with electrons dotted about inside it rather like raisins in a pudding. People called this the 'plum pudding' model.

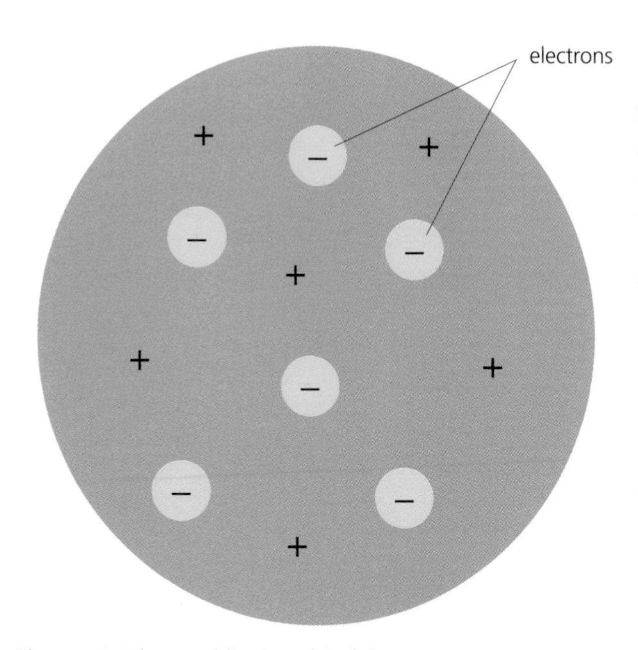

Thomson's 'plum pudding' model of the atom.

Rutherford's nuclear model

In 1911, Ernest Rutherford got two of his assistants, Hans Geiger and Ernest Marsden, to do the experiment below. The results could not be explained by the plum pudding model.

In their experiment, Geiger and Marsden bombarded thin gold foil with **alpha particles** – tiny, positively charged particles shot out by some radioactive materials.

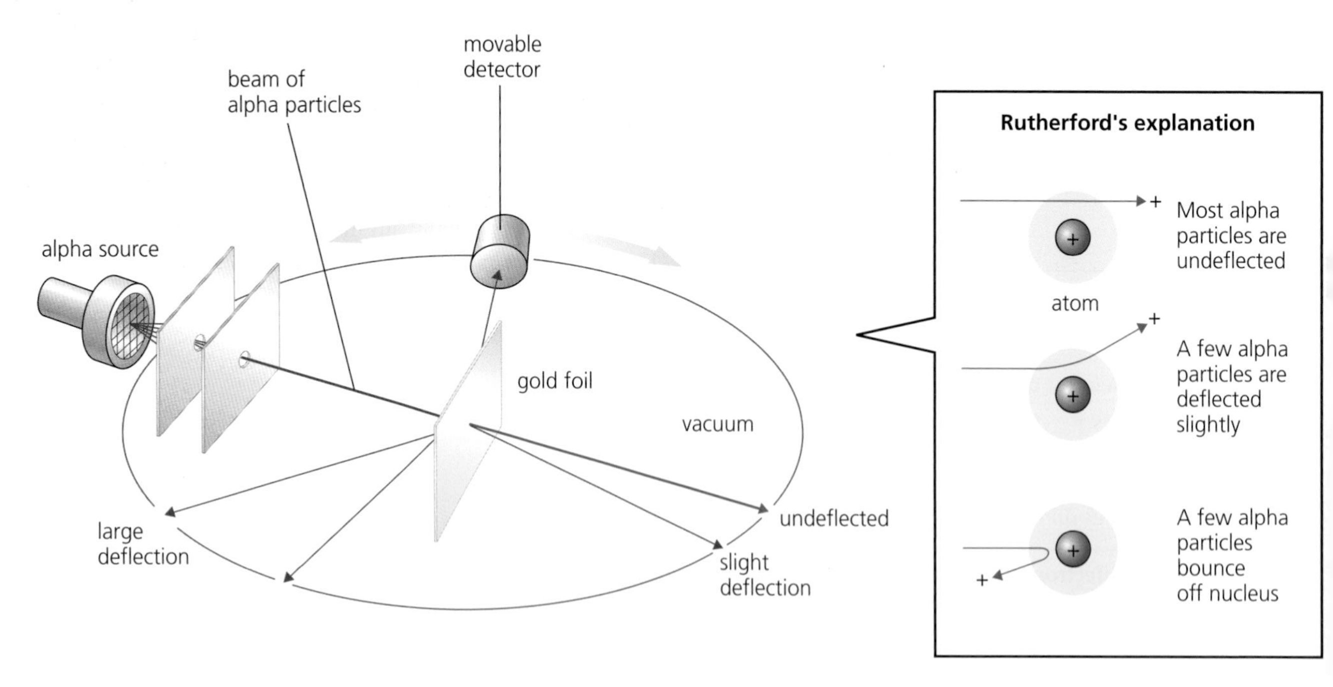

Most of the alpha particles passed straight through the gold atoms, but a few were repelled so strongly that they bounced back or were deflected through large angles. Rutherford concluded that the atom must be largely empty space, with its positive charge and most of its mass concentrated in a tiny **nucleus** at the centre. In his model, the much lighter electrons orbited the nucleus rather like the planets around the Sun. In 1913, Niels Bohr modified Rutherford's model by suggesting that electrons were only allowed to have certain orbits around the nucleus. He did this in order to explain how atoms give out light.

In 1919, Rutherford found that positively charged particles could be knocked out of the nucleus. These were **protons**. In 1932, James Chadwick found that the nucleus also contained uncharged particles, which he called **neutrons**.

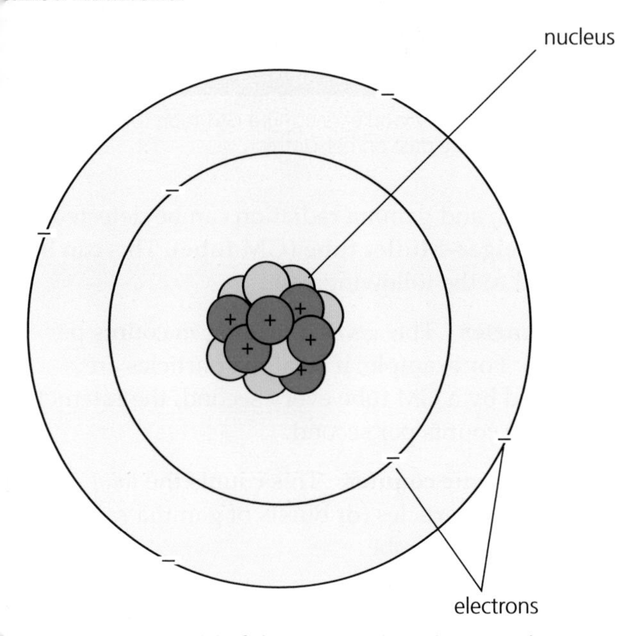

Rutherford–Bohr model of the atom, with nuclear particles included.

Modern models

Since Rutherford's time, scientists have had to develop new models to explain their discoveries. For example, electrons can behave like clouds of charge. They can also behave like waves!

Today scientists use a **wave mechanics** model of the atom. This is a mathematical model, and can't really be shown in a picture.

Drawing a nucleus with electrons around it is still a useful way of representing an atom. However, it's important to remember that the particles don't really have colours. Also, if the nucleus were drawn to the right scale, it would be far too small to see!

Scientists use giant machines like this to smash atomic particles together and find out what they are made of.

Questions

1 What is the difference between Rutherford's nuclear model of the atom and Thomson's 'plum pudding' model?

2 On the right, alpha particles are being fired at a thin piece of gold foil. According to Rutherford's nuclear model of the atom:

a why do most of the alpha particles go straight through the foil?

b why are some alpha particles deflected at large angles?

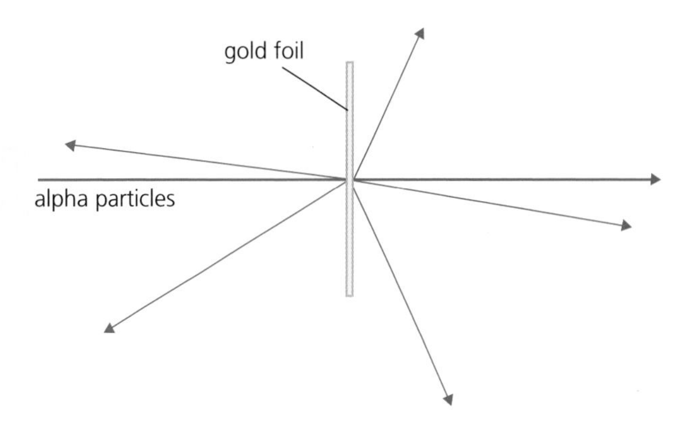

7.03 Nuclear radiation

Some materials contain atoms with unstable nuclei. In time, each nucleus breaks up, or rearranges itself. As it does so, it shoots out a tiny particle, a burst of wave energy, or both. The particles and waves 'radiate' from the nucleus, so they are called **nuclear radiation**. The materials they come from are **radioactive**.

Elements are a mixture of isotopes. In a 'radioactive material', it is particular isotopes that are radioactive. The chart below gives examples.

Isotopes		
Stable nuclei	**Unstable nuclei, radioactive**	**Found in ...**
carbon-12 carbon-13	carbon-14	air, plants, animals
potassium-39 potassium-41	potassium-40	rocks, plants, sea water
	uranium-234 uranium-235 uranium-238	rocks

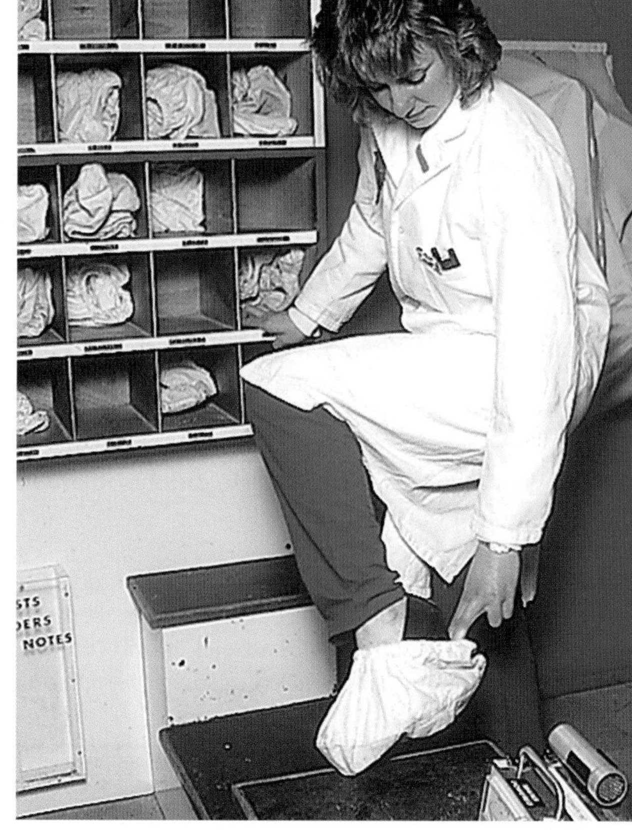

This nuclear laboratory worker is using a GM tube to check for traces of radioactive dust on her clothing.

Alpha, beta, and gamma radiation

There are three main types of nuclear radiation: **alpha particles**, **beta particles**, and **gamma rays**. Gamma rays are the most penetrating:

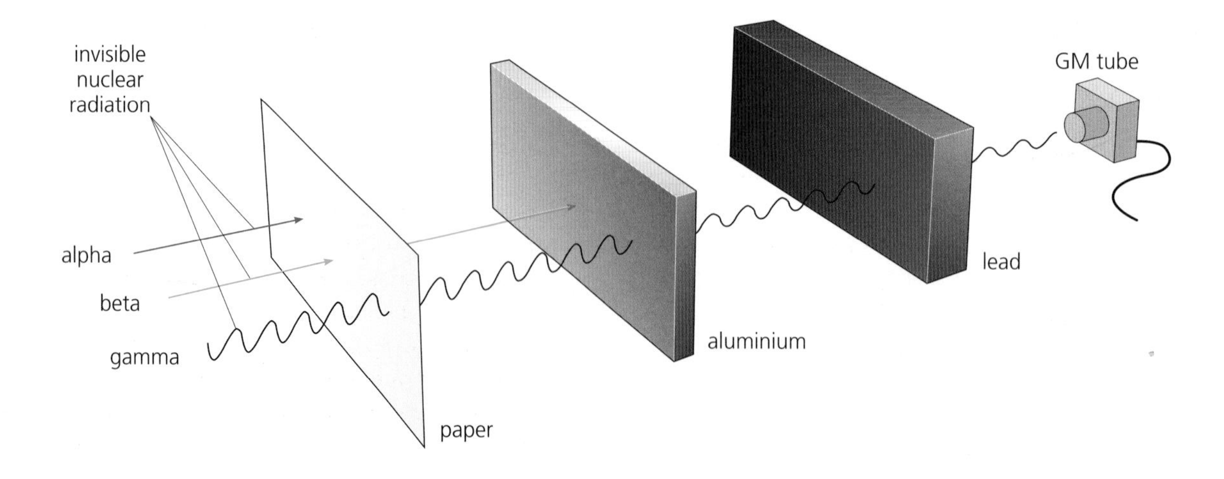

Alpha, beta, and gamma radiation can be detected using a **Geiger–Müller tube** (**GM tube**). This can be connected to the following:

- **A ratemeter** This gives a reading in counts per second. For example, if 50 alpha particles are detected by a GM tube every second, the ratemeter reads 50 counts per second.
- **An electronic counter** This counts the *total* number of particles (or bursts of gamma radiation) detected by the tube.
- **An amplifier and loudspeaker** The loudspeaker makes a 'click' when each particle or burst of gamma radiation is detected.

type of radiation	alpha particles (α)	beta particles (β)	gamma particles (γ)
	each particle is 2 protons + 2 neutrons (it is identical to a nucleus of helium-4)	each particle is an electron (created when the nucleus decays)	electromagnetic waves similar to X-rays
charge compared with +1 for proton	+2	−1	0
mass compared with 1 for proton	4	0	…
speed	up to 0.1 × speed of light	up to 0.9 × speed of light	speed of light
ionizing effect	strong	weak	very weak
penetrating effect	not very penetrating: stopped by a thick sheet of paper, or by skin, or by a few centimetres of air	penetrating, but stopped by a few millimetres of aluminium or other metal	very penetrating: never completely stopped, though lead and thick concrete will reduce intensity

Ionizing radiation

Nuclear radiation can strip electrons from atoms in its path. As a result, the atoms are left electrically charged. Charged atoms (or groups of atoms) are called **ions**, so nuclear radiation causes **ionization**. Ultraviolet and X-rays also cause ionization. Living cells are very sensitive to ionization. It can completely upset their life processes. There is more about this in the next spread.

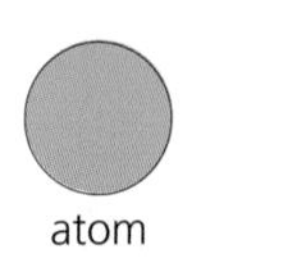

If an atom loses (or gains) an electron, it becomes an ion.

Questions

1 Name one radioisotope which occurs naturally in living things.

2 What is a GM tube used for?

3 Nuclear radiation causes *ionization*. What does this mean?

4 *alpha beta gamma*

Which of these three types of radiation:

a is a form of electromagnetic radiation?

b carries positive charge?

c carries negative charge?

d can penetrate a thick sheet of lead?

e is stopped by skin or thick paper?

f is made up of electrons?

g travels at the speed of light?

h is similar to X-rays?

i is the most ionizing?

j is the least ionizing?

5 What is the difference between the atoms of an isotope that is radioactive and the atoms of an isotope that is not?

7.04 Exposed to radiation

Nuclear power stations produce radioactive waste. The containers that carry the waste must be strong enough to withstand crashes like the one above. If any leaked out, it would be a health hazard.

This monitoring device detects radiation from any radioactive radon gas that may have seeped out of the rocks beneath the building (see right).

Radiation dangers

Because of its ionizing effect, nuclear radiation can damage or destroy living cells. It can stop vital organs in the body working properly, and cause cancer. The stronger the radiation, and the longer the exposure time, the greater the risk.

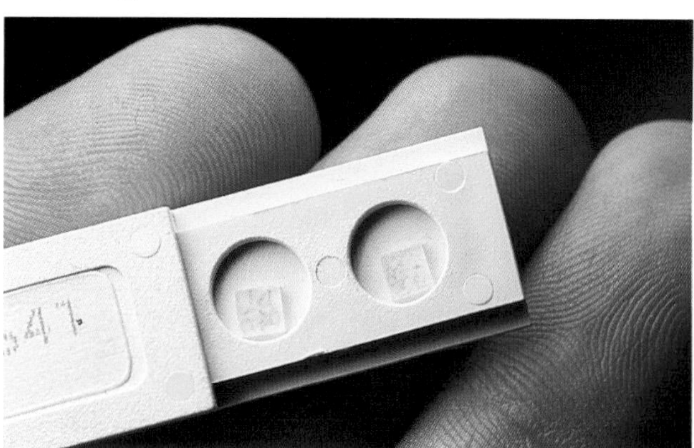

Workers in nuclear power stations have to wear a film badge like the one above. It reacts to nuclear radiation rather like the film in a camera reacts to light. Every month, the film is developed, to check that its wearer hasn't been exposed to too much radiation.

Dangers from inside the body Radioactive gas and dust are especially dangerous because they can be taken into the body with air, food, or drink. Once absorbed, they are difficult to remove, and their radiation can cause damage in cells deep in the body. Alpha radiation is the most harmful because it is the most highly ionizing.

Dangers from outside the body Normally, there is less risk from radioactive sources outside the body. Sources in nuclear power stations and laboratories are well shielded, and their radiation weakens as you move further away. Beta and gamma rays are the most dangerous because they can penetrate to internal organs, while alpha particles are stopped by the skin.

Background radiation

We are exposed to a small amount of radiation all the time because of radioactive materials in our surroundings. This is called **background radiation**. It mainly comes from natural sources such as soil, rocks, air, building materials, food, drink – and even space.

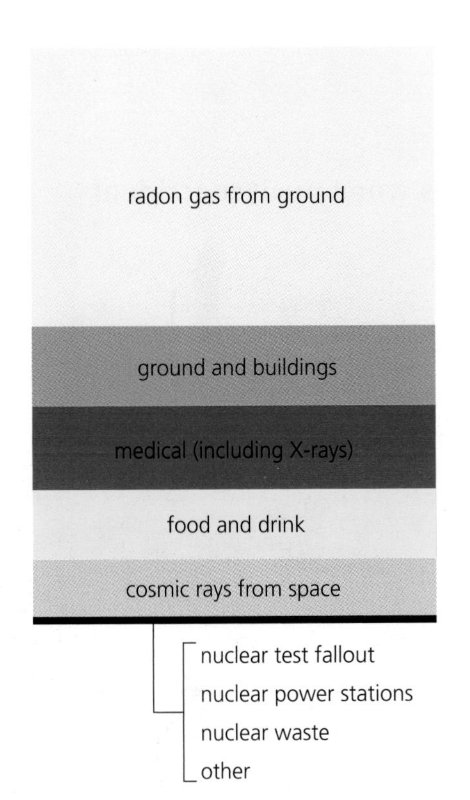

Where background radiation comes from. (These proportions are averages. The actual proportions vary from one area to another.)

In some areas, over a half of the background radiation comes from radioactive radon gas (radon-222) seeping out of rocks – especially some types of granite. In high-risk areas, houses may need extra ventilation to stop the gas collecting. Sometimes, a sealed floor is used to stop the gas entering in the first place.

Questions

1 What is the biggest source of background radiation?
2 Radon gas seeps out of rocks underground. Why is it important to stop radon collecting in houses?
3 a Which is the most dangerous type of radiation from radioactive materials absorbed by the body?
  b Why is this radiation less dangerous outside the body?
4 In the experiment on the right:
  a What is the count rate due to background radiation?
  b What is the count rate due to the source alone?
  c If the source emits one type of radiation only, what type is it? (You may need information from the previous spread to answer this.)

Mutations

Living cells contain a complex chemical called **DNA**. This carries the coded instructions needed to build the body of an animal or plant. The instructions are passed on from generation to generation.

Radiation is one cause of **mutations** (changes) in DNA. Most mutations are harmful, but some are useful. Without mutations, ancient fish with scales would never have evolved into animals with feathers or fur, and we wouldn't be here!

When the radiation from a radioactive source is measured, the reading *includes* any background radiation. To find the reading for the source alone, you must measure the background radiation and take that reading away from the total.

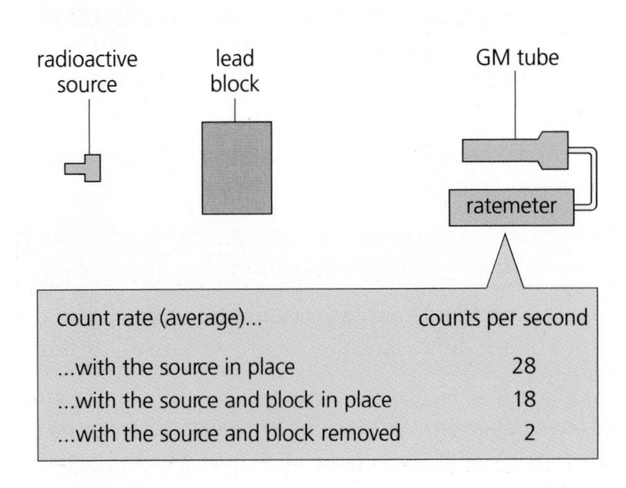

count rate (average)...	counts per second
...with the source in place	28
...with the source and block in place	18
...with the source and block removed	2

7.05 Living with radiation

Nuclear power – how safe?

The disaster at Chernobyl nuclear power station, Ukraine, happened swiftly, without warning. It was in the early hours of April 26 1986 when the cooling system of number four reactor failed. Minutes later, a violent explosion blew the top off the reactor and blasted a huge cloud of radioactive gas high into the atmosphere. Two people were killed outright. Hundreds received massive radiation overdoses. And more than 25 000 had to be evacuated from their homes. Days later, the radioactive cloud had spread as far as Scotland. Its radiation was weak but, all over Europe, radioactive rain was falling. In some areas, people were advised not to eat fresh vegetables, or drink fresh milk, and the sale of meat was banned.

The accident at Chernobyl was the world's worst nuclear accident. In Britain, it convinced many people that all nuclear power stations should be shut down. But the company running the power stations doesn't agree. It claims that:

- A similar disaster can't happen in Britain, because the reactors are of a much safer design.
- Fewer deaths are caused by the use of nuclear fuel than by mining for coal or drilling for oil and gas.
- Nuclear accidents are rare compared with other types of accident – such as air crashes, fires, or dam collapses.
- More nuclear power stations are essential because the world's supplies of oil, coal, and natural gas are running out.

Britain's worst nuclear accident

Windscale (now called Sellafield) in Cumbria. Here, in 1957, a nuclear reactor overheated and caught fire. No one was killed outright, but fourteen workers received radiation overdoses. And small amounts of radioactive gas and dust were released over the local countryside.

An official report said the accident had nearly become a full-scale disaster. The nuclear authorities wanted the report published. But the Prime Minister at the time refused. He thought that it would make people lose confidence in Britain's nuclear industry. Thirty years later, the cabinet records for 1957 were released. Only then did the public discover what had really happened at Windscale.

The search for a nuclear dustbin

To the nuclear authorities, the village of Elstow, near Bedford, seemed like the ideal dumping site for Britain's nuclear waste. Firm rocks underneath meant that the containers wouldn't crack open. And the soft clay soil above would absorb the radiation.

When the dumping plans were announced, the residents of Elstow reacted angrily. There was a storm of protests and the plans were dropped. Now, the authorities are searching for other sites. They've considered drilling storage tunnels under the North Sea. But Norway and Denmark are fiercely opposed to this idea. They're afraid that radioactive materials might leak out and contaminate their coastlines. Meanwhile, the waste from Britain's nuclear power stations is piling up. It's going to be radioactive for hundreds of years. And it's got to be stored somewhere . . .

Gammas keep fruit fresher

These strawberries were picked three weeks before the photograph was taken.

So were these. But these were put straight into a beam of gamma radiation . . .

. . . The radiation stopped the rotting process. So the strawberries look as fresh as the day they were picked. They haven't become radioactive. And their taste has hardly changed at all.

Irradiating food has many advantages. Or so the food producers claim. The radiation stops vegetables sprouting when they are being stored. It kills off the mould which makes food go off. And it destroys bacteria like *Salmonella* which can give you food poisoning. Many supermarkets want to sell fruit treated with radiation. They claim that it will mean better quality for their customers, less waste, and lower prices.

But not everyone likes the idea. The radiation may destroy important vitamins. And it may change some of the chemicals in food – so that they behave like dangerous additives. Irradiated food does last longer. But when you next buy fresh strawberries, how fresh will they really be?

Radioactive precautions

Small radioactive sources are used in many school laboratories. They present almost no risk, as long as the correct safety procedures are followed. The sources need to be stored in lead-lined containers, in locked cupboards, so that exposure times are kept to a minimum. When used in experiments, they must never be held in the hand or placed close to the body.

Most people wouldn't want a nuclear waste dump near their homes, even if they were told that the dump was completely safe. Why not? How many reasons can you think of?

Some supermarkets want to sell fruit and vegetables that have been treated with radiation. Make lists of the points for and against this scheme.

7.06 Radioactive decay

The break-up of unstable nuclei is called **radioactive decay**. It happens at random, and isn't affected by pressure, temperature, or chemical change. You can't tell which nucleus is going to break up next, or when. However, some types of nucleus are more unstable than others and decay at a faster rate.

Activity

The **activity** of a radioactive sample is the average number of nuclei breaking up per second. It is measured in **becquerels (Bq)**. For example: Iodine-128 decays by shooting out beta particles. If, in a sample, 40 nuclei break up every second, then 40 beta particles are shot out every second, and the activity is 40 Bq.

Half-life

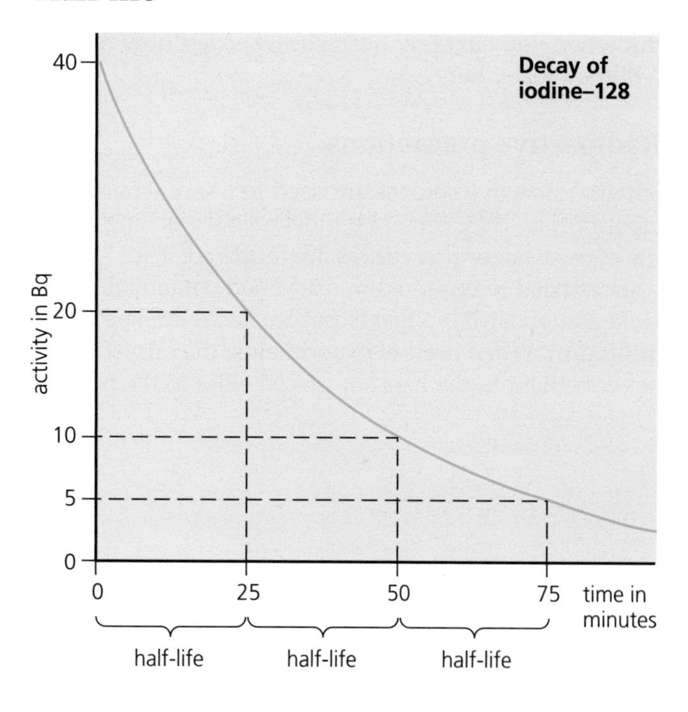

Time in minutes	0	25	50	75
Activity in Bq	40	20	10	5

Above, you can see how a sample of iodine-128 decays. As time goes on, there are fewer and fewer unstable nuclei left to decay, so the activity gets less and less. After 25 minutes, the activity is half its original value. After another 25 minutes, the activity has halved again...and so on. Iodine-128 has a **half-life** of 25 minutes.

Heat from decay

Radioactive decay releases energy. 100 metres underground, the temperature is 50 °C. The heat comes from radioactive materials in the rocks.

The half-life of a radioactive isotope is:

- the time taken for half the nuclei to decay
- the time taken for the activity to halve.

Radioactive isotope	Half-life
radon-222	3.8 days
strontium-90	28 years
radium-226	1602 years
carbon-14	5730 years
plutonium-239	24400 years
uranium-235	710 million years

To get a graph like that on the left, a Geiger–Müller (GM) tube is used to detect the radiation from the sample. Provided you allow for background radiation, the number of counts per second is *proportional* to the activity – but not equal to it, because not all the beta particles go into the detector.

With experimental results, the points on the graph are irregular because decay is a random process. The curve is really a 'line of best fit'.

New atoms from old

When an atom shoots out an alpha or beta particle, the number of protons in its nucleus changes, so it becomes an atom of a different element:

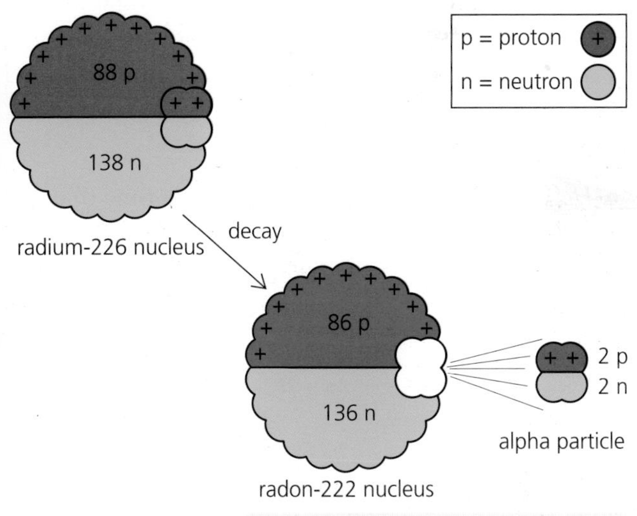

decay products

Alpha decay Above, a radium-226 nucleus decays by shooting out an alpha particle. The nucleus loses 2 protons and 2 neutrons, and becomes a nucleus of radon-222. The decay process can be written as a nuclear equation:

$$^{226}_{88}\text{Ra} \rightarrow {}^{222}_{86}\text{Rn} + {}^{4}_{2}\alpha \quad (\alpha = \text{alpha})$$

The equation uses the same symbol system for nuclei and particles as is used for isotopes.

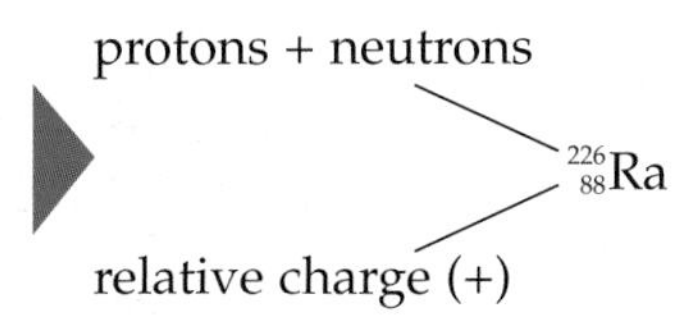

In the equation:

- the top numbers balance (226 = 222 + 4) because the total of protons + neutrons doesn't change.
- the bottom numbers balance (88 = 86 + 2), because the total charge doesn't change.

Beta decay When an iodine-128 nucleus decays, a neutron changes into a proton and an electron. The electron (beta particle) is shot out. The nucleus now has one less neutron than before, but one more proton, making it a nucleus of xenon-129. Again, the nuclear equation balances:

$$^{128}_{53}\text{I} \rightarrow {}^{128}_{54}\text{Xe} + {}^{0}_{-1}\beta \quad (\beta = \text{beta})$$

(A chargeless, almost massless particle called an **antineutrino** is also shot out.)

Gamma decay By itself, this doesn't alter the number of protons or neutrons in the nucleus.

Questions

1 Look at the table of half-lives on the opposite page. If small amounts of strontium-90 and radium-226 both gave the same count rate today, which would give the higher reading in 10 years' time?

2 A GM tube is placed near a weak radioactive material in the lab. There is no shielding round the tube or source to absorb background radiation. This is the graph of count rate against time, using readings taken every half minute:

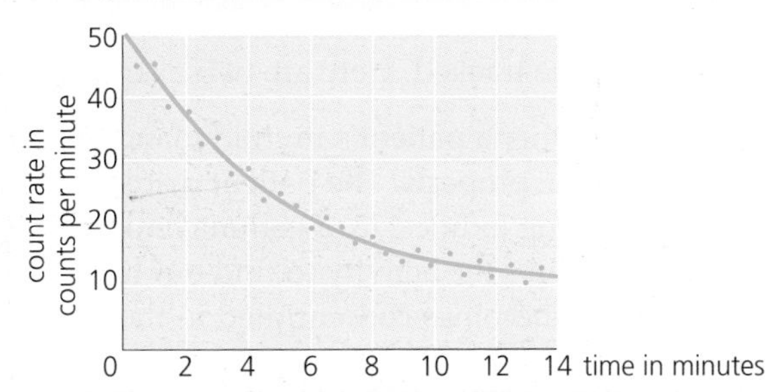

a Why are the points on the graph not on a smooth curve?

b Why does the graph level out above zero?

c What is the half-life of the material? (Give an approximate value, to the nearest minute.)

3 This is how the count rate from a radioactive material changed:

Time in s	0	20	40	60	80	100	120
Count rate in counts/s	57	44	33	25	19	14	11

a Plot a graph of count rate (side axis) against time (bottom axis).

b How long did it take the count rate to fall from 50 to 25 counts/second?

c How long did it take the count rate to fall from 40 to 20 counts/second?

d What is the half-life of the material?

4 The accident at the Chernobyl nuclear reactor released a cloud of radioactive gas and dust into the atmosphere. It contained caesium-137 (half-life 30 years) and iodine-131.

a Here are some measurements of the count rate from a small amount of iodine-131.

Time in days	0	4	8	12
Count rate in counts/s	240	170	120	85

What is the half-life of iodine-131?

b Two months after the accident, scientists were still concerned about the health risks from the caesium, but felt that the iodine was no longer a threat. Can you explain why?

7.07 Using radioactivity

Radioactive isotopes are called **radioisotopes**. Some are produced artificially in a nuclear reactor by bombarding other isotopes with neutrons.
Here are some of the uses of radioisotopes:

Using tracers

Radioisotopes can be detected in small (and safe) quantities, so they can be used as **tracers** – their movements can be tracked. Here are two examples:

- Checking whether a patient's thyroid gland is taking in iodine properly. The patient drinks a liquid containing iodine-123, a gamma emitter. A detector measures the activity to find out how quickly iodine becomes concentrated in the gland.
- Detecting leaks in underground pipes by adding a tracer to the fluid in the pipe.

For leaks like these, artificial radioscopes with short half lives are used so that there is almost no radioactivity left over a few days.

Radiotherapy

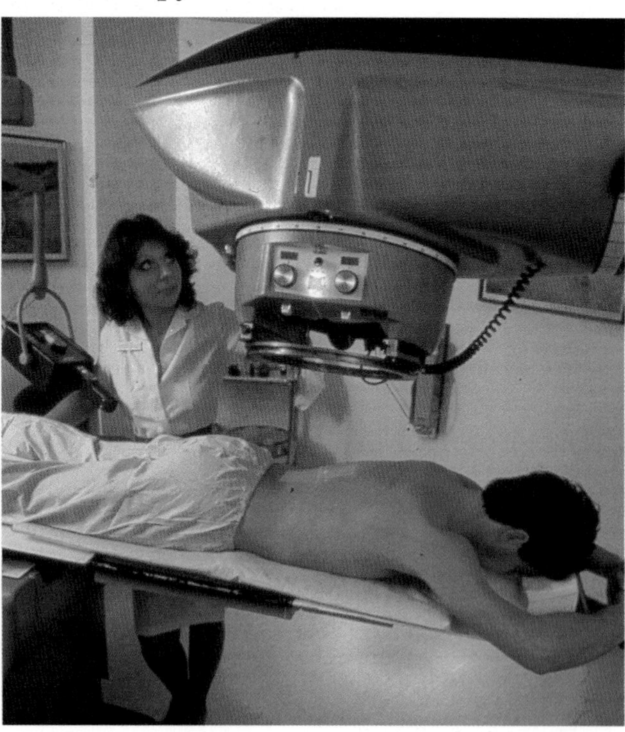

Gamma rays can penetrate deep into the body and kill living cells. So a highly concentrated beam from a cobalt-60 source can be used to kill cancer cells. Treatment like this is called **radiotherapy**.

When choosing a radioisotope for a particular job, here are two factors that must be considered:

- *Penetrating effect* Gamma rays are very penetrating, beta particles less so, and alpha particles least of all.
- *Half-life* A short half-life reduces the time that living things are exposed to harmful radiation.

Sterilization

Gamma radiation from powerful cobalt-60 sources is also used to sterilize medical equipment - in other words, to kill the germs on it. Although gamma radiation is less ionizing than alpha or beta, it is more penetrating, so whole boxes of syringes and other equipment can be placed in the path of the beam.

Thickness monitoring

In some production processes, it is important to keep a steady thickness of material. Here is an example – the production of tyre cord:

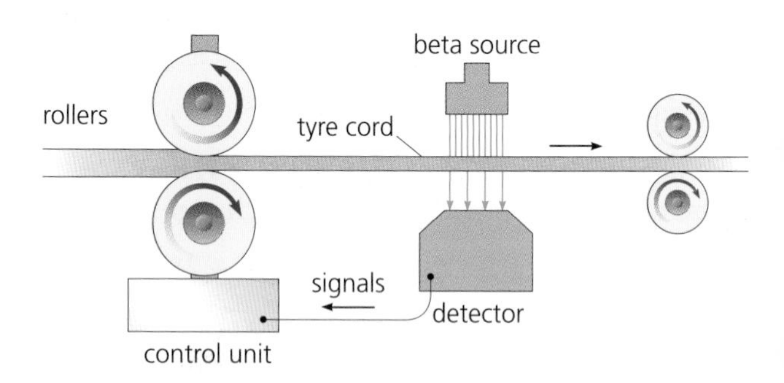

The moving band of tyre cord has a beta source on one side and a detector on the other. If the cord from the rollers becomes too thin, more beta radiation reaches the detector. This sends signals to the control unit, which adjusts the gap between the rollers.

Testing for cracks

Gamma rays are like X-rays, so they can be used to photograph metals to reveal cracks. A cobalt-60 gamma source is compact and does not need an electrical power source, unlike an X-ray tube.

This pipe is being tested for cracks. A gamma source has been put inside the pipe, and an X-ray film wrapped round the outside.

Dating rocks

When rocks are formed, some radioisotopes become trapped in them. But as time goes by, the radioactivity slowly dies away. This idea can be used to estimate their age. For example:

Potassium-40 is trapped when molten material cools to form igneous rock. As the potassium-40 decays, more and more of its stable decay product, argon-40, is created. Provided none of this argon gas has escaped, the age of the rock (which may be hundreds of millions of years) can be estimated from the proportion of potassium-40 to argon-40.

Igneous rock can also be dated from the proportion of uranium to lead isotopes. Lead is the product of a series of decays that start with uranium.

Carbon dating

There is carbon in the atmosphere (in carbon dioxide) and in the bodies of living things. A small amount is radioactive carbon-14, which is continually being formed in the upper atmosphere. While plants and animals are alive, they absorb and give out carbon as they feed and breathe, so the proportion of carbon-14 in their bodies stays the same. But when they die, no more carbon is taken in and the proportion of carbon-14 reduces because of radioactive decay. By measuring the activity of a sample, the age of the remains can be estimated. This is called **carbon dating**. It can be used to find the age of organic materials such as wood and cloth.

The age of remains like this can be found by carbon dating.

Questions

1 a What are *radioisotopes*?
   b Give *two* medical uses of radioisotopes.

2 Give two uses of gamma radiation.

3 In the thickness–monitoring system shown on the opposite page:
   a why is a beta source used, rather than an alpha or gamma source?
   b what is the effect on the detector if the thickness of the tyre cord increases?

4 a What is a radioactive tracer?
   b Describe one use of a radioactive tracer.
   c Why is it important to use radioactive tracers with short half-lives?

5 When molten material cools to form igneous rock, radioactive potassium-40 is trapped in it.
   a As time goes on, what happens to the amount of potassium-40 in the rock?
   b Why does argon-40 build up in the rock?
   c What can scientists learn by measuring the proportions of potassium-40 and argon-40?

7.08 Nuclear energy

The nuclear power station on the right can generate enough power to supply a large city. Like most power stations, it uses heat to make steam to drive the turbines which turn its generators. But the heat doesn't come from burning coal, gas, or oil. It comes from uranium atoms as their nuclei decay (break up) in a **nuclear reactor**.

Radioactive decay is usually a slow process. However, with some nuclei, much faster decay can happen if nuclei are made more unstable by bombarding them with neutrons. That is what happens in a reactor. If a particle penetrates and changes a nucleus, this is called a **nuclear reaction**.

Nuclear fission

Natural uranium is a dense radioactive metal. It is mostly made up of two isotopes: uranium-238 (over 99%) and uranium-235 (less than 1%).
On the right, you can see what happens if a neutron strikes and penetrates a nucleus of uranium-235. The nucleus becomes highly unstable and splits into two lighter nuclei, shooting out two or three neutrons as it does so. The splitting is called **fission**. It releases energy which throws the bits apart.

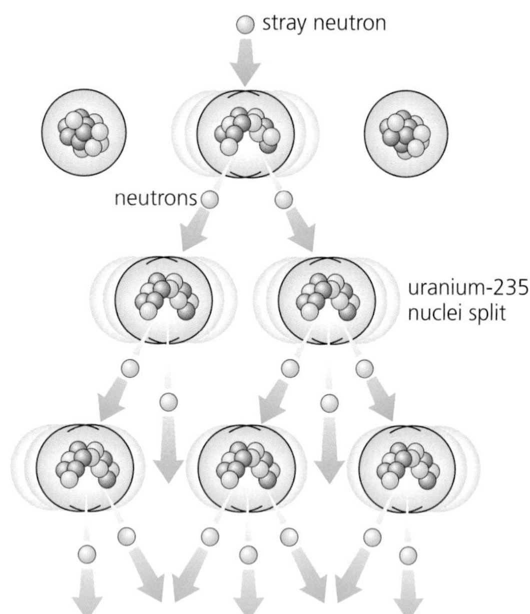

If the neutrons go on to split other nuclei, and so on, the result is a **chain reaction**, as above. This releases energy very rapidly. The new nuclei bump into other atoms and make them move faster. In this way, nuclear energy is changed into heat.

If the chain reaction is *uncontrolled*, the heat builds up so rapidly that the material bursts apart in an explosion. This happens in a nuclear bomb.
If the chain reaction is *controlled*, there is a steady output of heat. This happens in a nuclear reactor.

Energy releases

In a chemical change such as burning, atoms get rearranged. Energy is released as electrons settle into different positions in atoms.

In radioactive decay, nuclear particles get rearranged. The energy released per atom is around a million times greater than that from a chemical change such as burning.

In fission, lots more atoms are involved every second than in natural decay. That is why energy is released much more rapidly.

Fission in a reactor

Most reactors use uranium dioxide as their fuel. The fuel is in sealed cans (or tubes). The natural uranium is enriched with extra uranium-235.

To keep the chain reaction going, the neutrons have to be slowed down, otherwise most get absorbed by the uranium-238. A material called a **moderator** is needed for this. Graphite is used in some reactors, water in others. The rate of the reaction is controlled by raising or lowering **control rods** which absorb neutrons.
A reactor can't blow up like a nuclear bomb. The atoms of uranium-235 are too spread out for an uncontrolled chain reaction to happen.

Nuclear waste

After a fuel can has been in a reactor for three or four years, it must be removed and replaced. The amount of uranium-235 in it has fallen and radioactive products are building up. Some are very dangerous. For example:

- Strontium-90 and iodine-131 are easily absorbed by the body. Strontium becomes concentrated in the bones; iodine in the thyroid gland.
- Plutonium-239 can be used as a nuclear fuel and in nuclear weapons. It is highly toxic. Breathed in as dust, the smallest amount can kill.

Waste from a nuclear reactor is taken to a reprocessing plant. There, unused fuel and plutonium will be removed. The remaining waste will be stored with thick shielding around it. Some of the isotopes have long half-lives, so safe storage will be needed for thousands of years.

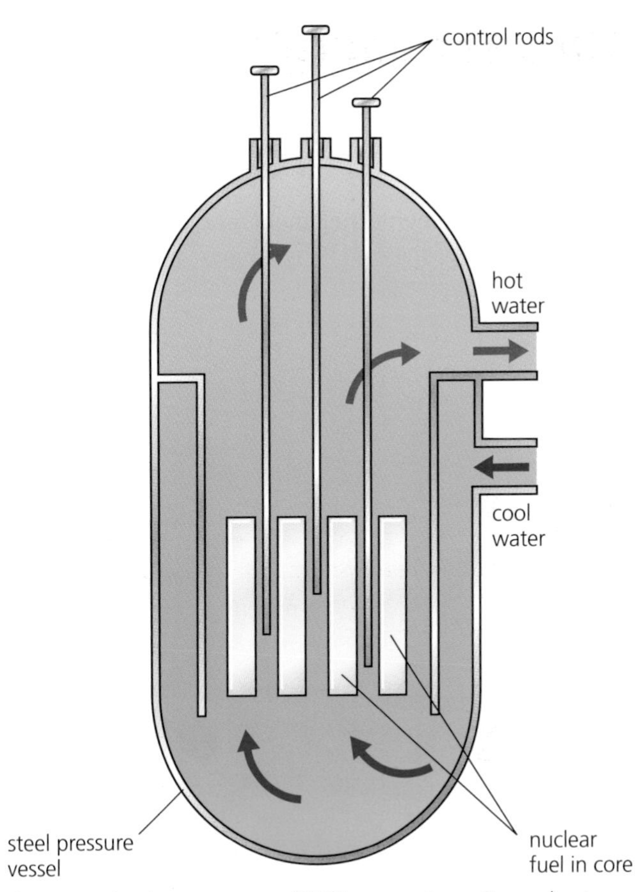

This pressurized-water reactor (PWR) uses water as its moderator. The water also carries the heat away to a boiler to produce the steam for the turbines.

Questions

1 What is meant by:
  a nuclear fission? b a chain reaction?
2 Give an example of:
  a a controlled chain reaction.
  b an uncontrolled chain reaction.
3 Give *two* reasons why the waste from a nuclear reactor is so difficult to deal with.
4 In a typical fission process, uranium-235 absorbs a neutron, creating a nucleus which splits to form barium-141, krypton-92, and some neutrons. Use the data below to find:
  a the number of neutrons in a nucleus of uranium-235.
  b the number of neutrons in the nucleus that splits.
  c the number of neutrons given off by fission.

	atomic number (protons)	mass number (protons + neutrons)
uranium-235	92	235
barium-141	56	141
krypton-92	36	92

7.09 Fusion future

Hydrogen – fuel for the stars

Hydrogen is the lightest element, and the most plentiful. 75% of the Sun is hydrogen. There is also lots of hydrogen on Earth, though most has combined with oxygen to form water (H_2O).

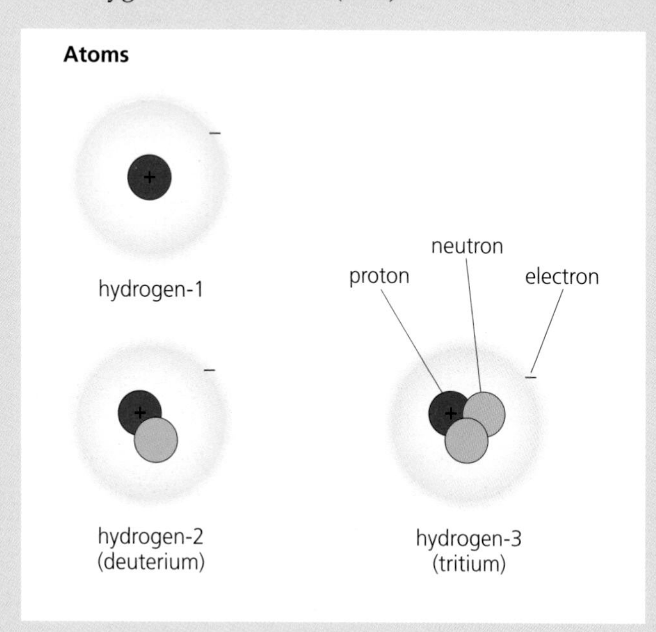

Hydrogen exists in three different versions. By far the most common isotope is hydrogen-1. The others are hydrogen-2 (also called deuterium) and hydrogen-3 (tritium).

The stars are powered by nuclear reactions. Most use hydrogen as their nuclear fuel. One day, it may also be the fuel for reactors on Earth.

Energy from nuclear changes

The protons and neutrons in the nucleus of an atom are held tightly together by a force called, simply, a **strong nuclear force**. However, in some nuclei, they are more tightly held than in others. To get energy out of the nucleus, the trick is to make the protons and neutrons regroup into more tightly held arrangements than before.

Protons and neutrons in 'middleweight' nuclei tend to be the most tightly held, so joining very light nuclei together can release energy, as can splitting up very heavy ones. The two processes, **fusion** and **fission**, are shown on the right.

Fusion

Light nuclei fuse (join) to form heavier ones.

Example

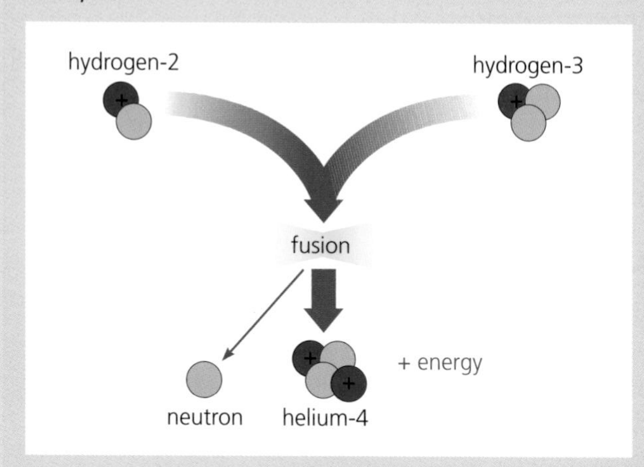

Fusion is difficult to achieve because the nuclei are charged, and repel each other. To beat the repulsion and join up, they must travel very fast. For the above reaction, this means heating the hydrogen to at least 40 million degrees Celsius.

Fission

Very heavy nuclei split to form lighter ones.

Example

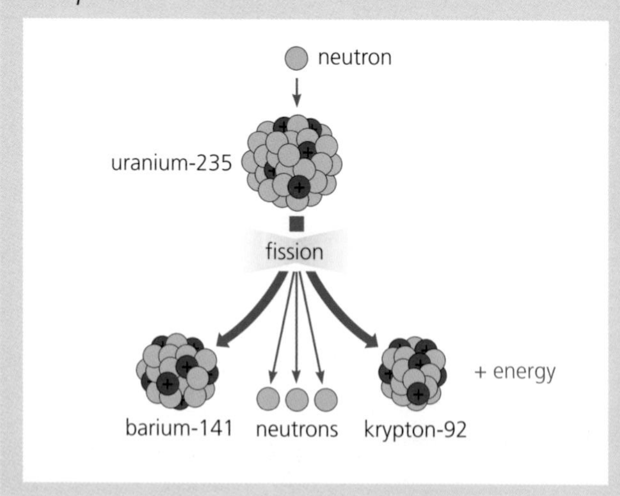

Fission is used in the reactors in nuclear power stations. Technically, it is much easier to achieve than fusion because neutrons are not repelled by nuclei. The core temperature in a nuclear reactor is only a few hundred degrees Celsius.

Building a fusion reactor

Scientists and engineers are trying to design fusion reactors for use as an energy source on Earth. But the problems are immense. Hydrogen must be heated to at least 40 million degrees Celsius and kept hot and compressed, otherwise fusion stops. No ordinary container can hold a superhot gas like this, so scientists are developing reactors that trap the reacting nuclei in a magnetic field.

This magnetic containment vessel, called a **tokamak**, is being used to investigate fusion.

Fusion reactors will have huge advantages over today's fission reactors. They will produce more energy per kilogram of fuel. Their hydrogen fuel can be extracted from sea water. Their main waste product, helium, is not radioactive. And they have built-in safety: if the system fails, fusion stops.

One day, fusion power stations may provide us with safe, 'clean' energy from sea water.

Fusion in the Sun

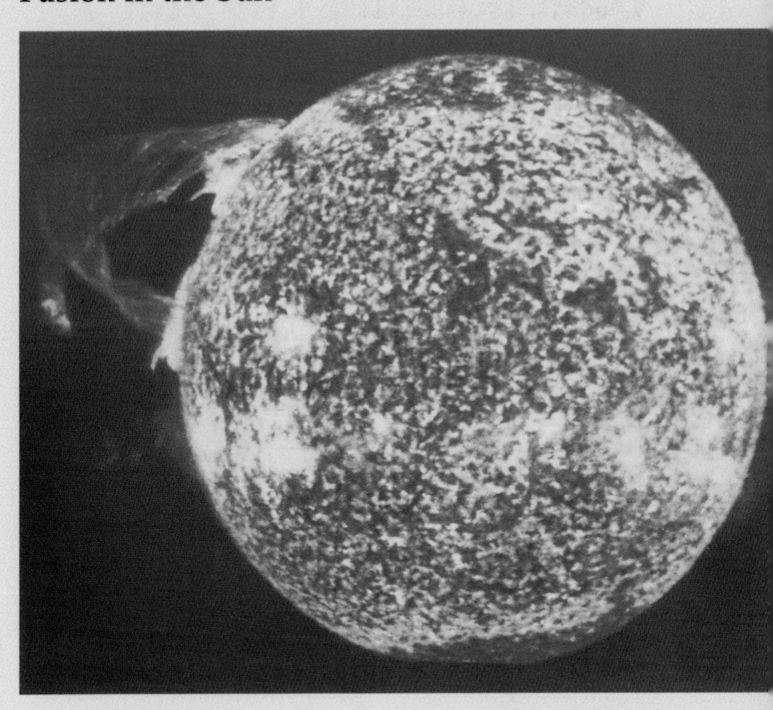

Like most other stars, the Sun gets its energy from the fusion of hydrogen into helium. Deep in its core, the heat output and huge gravitational pull keep the hydrogen hot enough and compressed enough to maintain fusion.

So far, the Sun has used up less than half of its hydrogen. It has enough left to keep it shining for another 6 billion years.

In the Sun, fusion happens at 'only' 15 million degrees Celsius. But the Sun uses different fusion reactions from those being tried on Earth. If the Sun were scaled down to the size of a nuclear reactor, its power output would be too low to be useful.

- What is the difference between nuclear fusion and nuclear fission?
- Can you explain how the Sun gets its energy, and what fuel it uses?
- Can you explain why fusion reactors have been so much more difficult to develop than fission reactors?
- What advantages will power stations with fusion reactors have over today's nuclear power stations?

Questions on Chapter 7

1 Two students are carrying out an experiment to discover how much beta radiation passes through different thicknesses of aluminium.

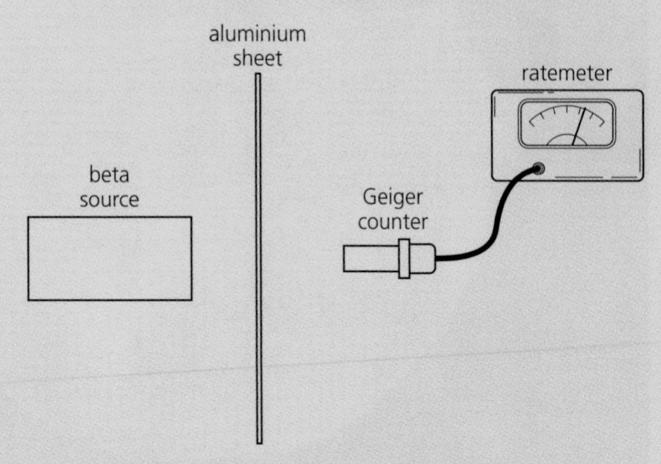

At the beginning of the experiment they measured the background radiation. It was 100 counts per minute.

a Suggest two possible sources of the background radiation.

The students then recorded the count rates for the different thicknesses of aluminium. Their results are shown in the table below.

thickness of aluminium in mm	1.0	2.0	3.0	4.0	5.0	6.0	7.0	8.0	9.0
actual count rate in counts per min	1120	620	300	240	180	150	120	100	100
corrected count rate in counts per min	1020								

b Finish the table by filling in the seven missing corrected count rates.

c Plot a graph of the results (count rate – y axis, thickness of aluminium – x axis).

d Which result does not fit the pattern?

e What is the minimum thickness of aluminium needed to stop beta particles from the source reaching the Geiger counter?

2 Uranium-235 is used as a fuel in nuclear reactors. The following diagram shows how a uranium-235 nucleus absorbs a neutron before breaking in half and releasing these neutrons.

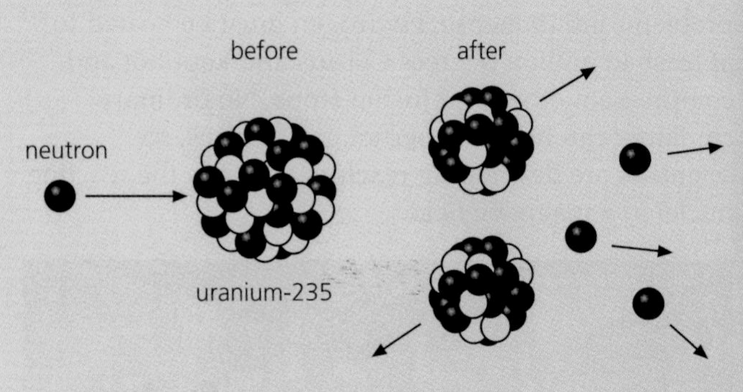

a What is this process called?

b What happens to the three neutrons produced?

c How is the energy released by this reaction used to produce electricity?

d What must happen to the radioactive waste produced by a nuclear power station?

3 The graph below shows how the radiation emitted by a sample of uranium-238 ($^{238}_{92}U$) changes with time.

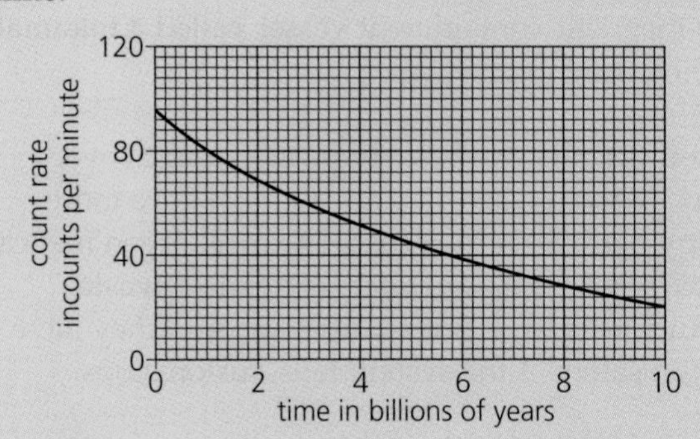

a After how many years has the count rate dropped to 80 counts per minute?

b After how many years has the count rate dropped to 40 counts per minute?

c What is the half-life of uranium-238?

d When an atom of uranium-238 ($^{238}_{92}U$) decays another radioactive nuclide called thorium-234 ($^{234}_{90}Th$) is produced.
What kind of radiation does a uranium-238 atom emit when it decays?

e When thorium-234 decays it emits beta radiation.
What is beta radiation?

f Name one use for beta radiation.

4 In some parts of Britain high levels of background radiation are caused by radon gas. The element radium-224 ($^{224}_{88}Ra$) decays to form radon-220 ($^{220}_{86}Rn$).

a What particle is emitted when radium-224 decays to form radon-220?
b From where within a radium atom is the particle emitted?
c Radium-224 has a 'half life' of 3.6 days. What is meant by the phrase 'half life'?
d If the initial count rate of a sample of radium-224 is 800 counts per second what is the count rate of this sample after **i** 3.6 days **ii** 10.8 days?

5 In a papermaking plant, a radioactive source and detector can be used for testing the thickness of the paper as it is rolled out.

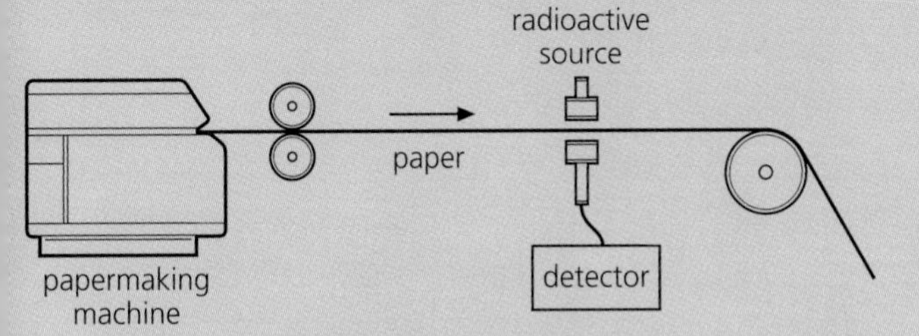

The radioactive source in the diagram above gives out beta particles.
a What are beta particles?
b What device could be used as a detector?
c If the paper is thicker than normal, what effect will this have on the reading on the detector?
d Why should the radioactive source be a beta source, rather than one that gives out alpha particles or gamma rays?
e Some people could be worried that the radiation might 'make the paper radioactive'. What answer would you give them?

6 a The diagram below represents an atom of nitrogen-14 ($^{14}_{7}N$).

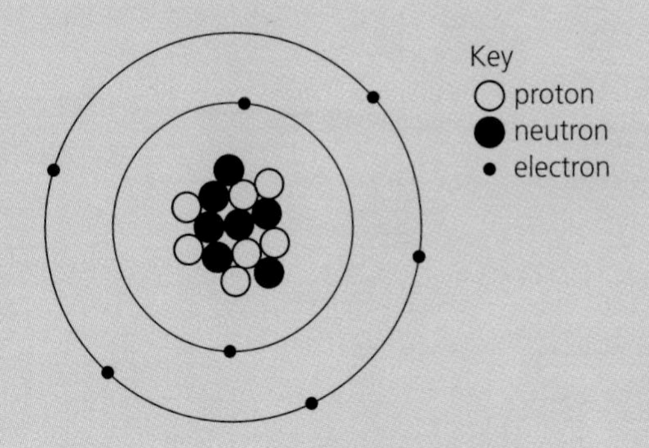

Complete this table of data for nitrogen-14.

Particle	Number in atom	Charge
proton		
neutron		
electron		

b The element chlorine has two 'isotopes'. What are isotopes?
c Draw diagrams of the two isotopes chlorine-35 ($^{35}_{17}Cl$) and chlorine-37 ($^{37}_{17}Cl$).

7 A radioactive source is emitting all three types of radiation α, β and γ.
a What is an α particle?
b What is a β particle?
c What is a γ ray?
d From where are these radioactive particles and rays being emitted?
e Name one piece of apparatus that could be used to detect radiation.
f Name one material through which β particles and γ rays can pass but not α particles.
g Name one material through which only very energetic γ rays can pass.

8 The diagram below shows someone trying to detect a leak in an oil pipe below the ground. A radioactive isotope has been added to the oil in the pipe.

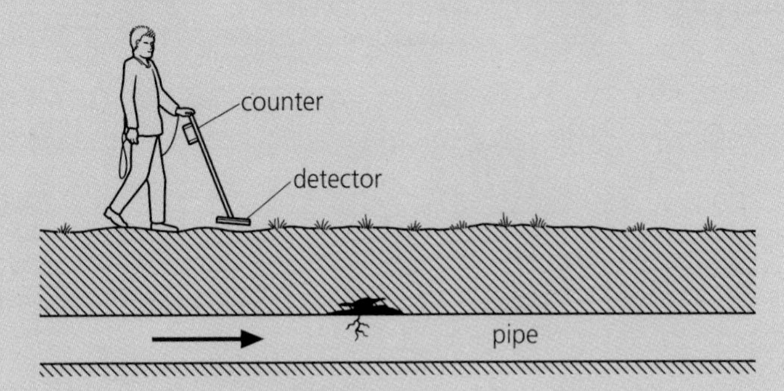

a Describe what happens when the detector passes over the leak. Explain your answer.
b What kind of radiation should the radioactive isotope be emitting? Explain your answer.

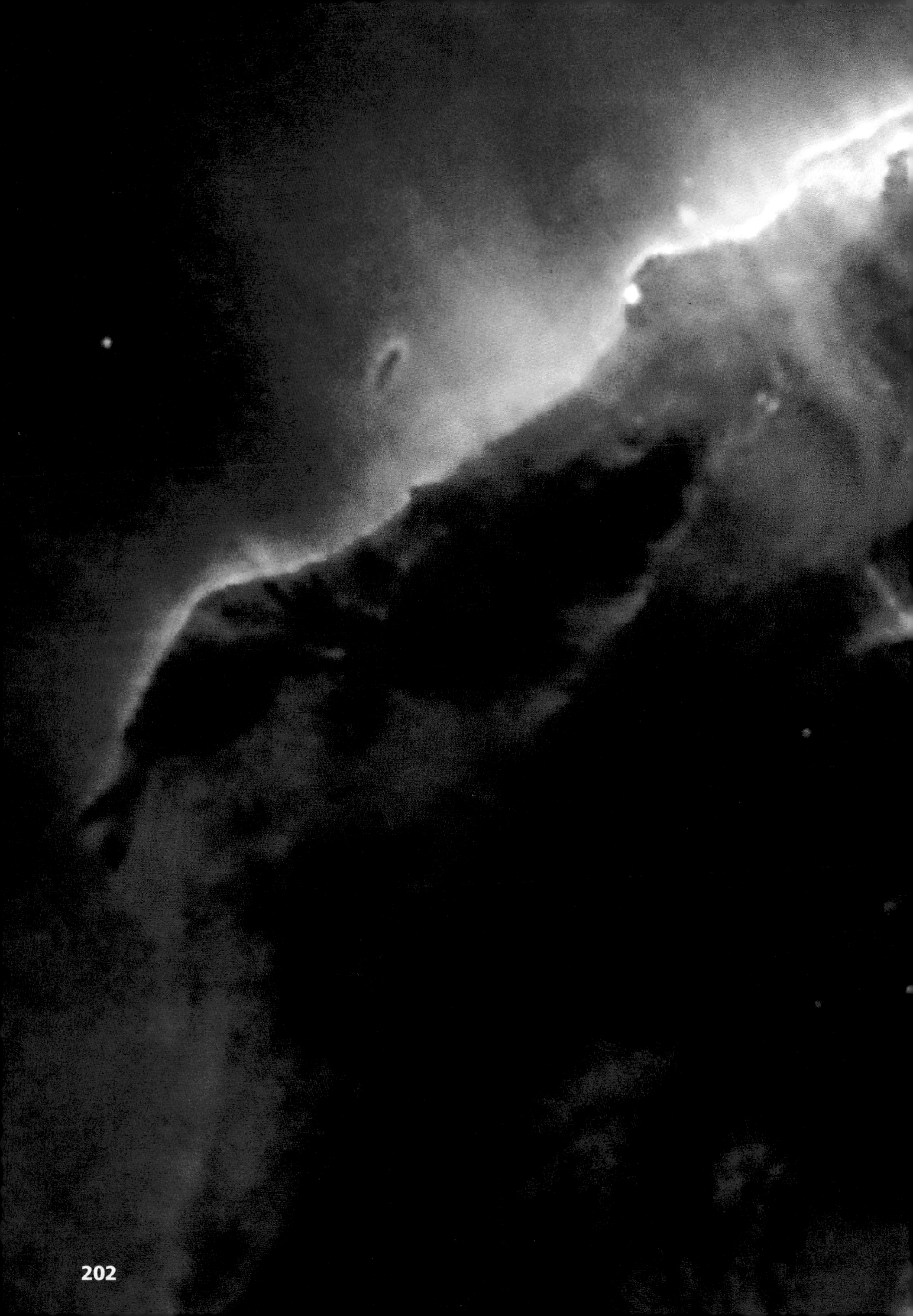

Chapter 8

The Earth in space

Part of the Eagle nebula, as seen by the *Hubble Space Telescope* from its orbit around the Earth. This vast pillar of gas and dust is billions of kilometres across. Within it, new stars are forming as matter is clumped together by the pull of gravity. The picture is also a view back in time. The nebula is so far away that its light takes 7000 years to reach the Earth. ■

8.01 Sun, Earth, Moon, and sky

The Sun is a huge, hot, glowing ball of gas called a **star**. The Earth is a much smaller, cooler ball called a **planet**. The Sun is 150 million km away from us. Other stars only look like points of light because they are much further away.

Earth, orbiting and turning

The Earth moves round the Sun in a path called an **orbit**. One orbit takes just over 365 days, which is the length of our year.

As the Earth moves through space, it slowly turns about a line called its **axis**. This runs from the North Pole to the South Pole. It takes **one day** (24 hours) for the Earth to turn once. As it does so, places move from the sunlit half into the shadow half – in other words, from daytime into night. That is why the Sun appears to rise, move across the sky, and then set.

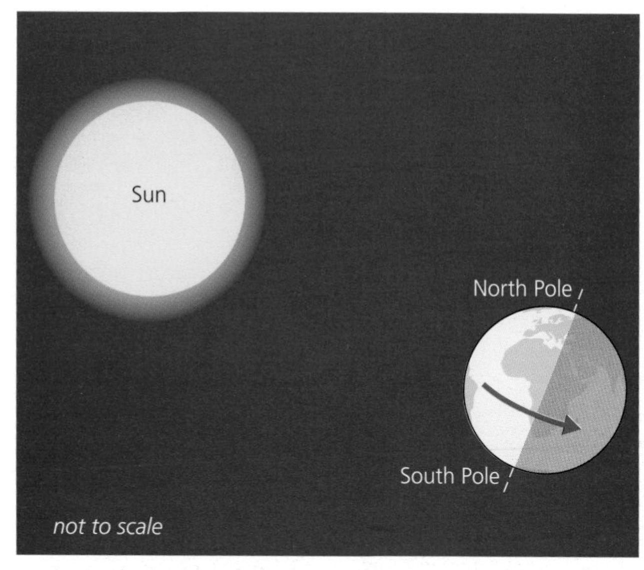

As the Earth slowly turns on its axis, one half is in sunlight while the other half is in shadow.

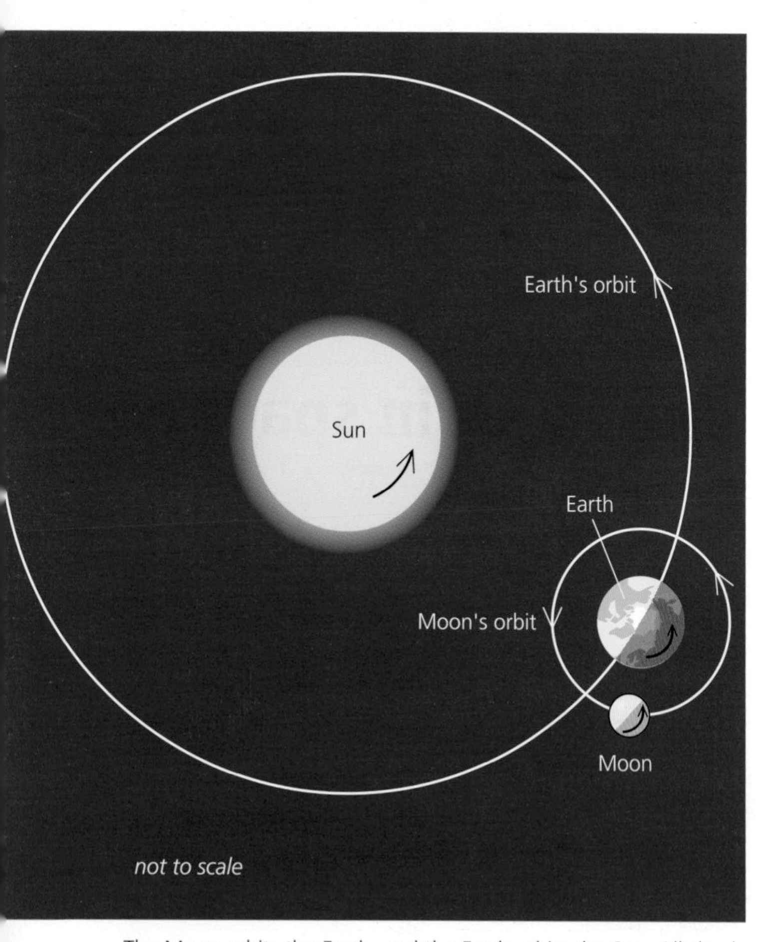

The Moon orbits the Earth, and the Earth orbits the Sun. All slowly turn on their axes the same way.

The Moon

The Moon is in orbit around the Earth. It takes about 28 days for each orbit. It also takes the same time to turn once on its axis, so it always keeps the same face toward us.

The Moon is smaller than the Earth (about a quarter of the diameter) and 380000 km away. It has a rocky surface with lots of craters.

The Moon does not glow like the Sun. You can only see it because its surface reflects sunlight. And you don't see the part that is in shadow. That is why it sometimes looks like a crescent.

Moving across the sky

On a clear night, the sky is full of tiny points of light. Most of these are stars. Like the Sun, they appear to move across the sky as the Earth rotates. However, relative to each other, their positions hardly change by any amount that you could notice.

A few of the dots in the night sky *do* appear to change position. These are other planets in orbit around the Sun. (The word 'planet' comes from an old Greek word meaning 'wanderer'.)

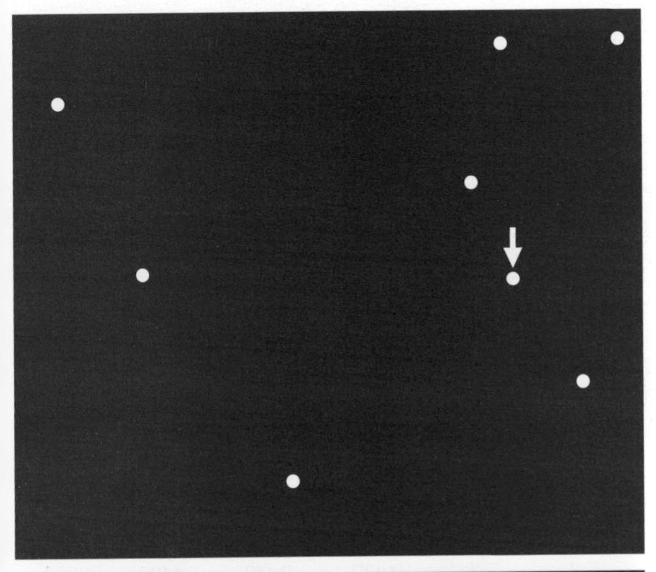

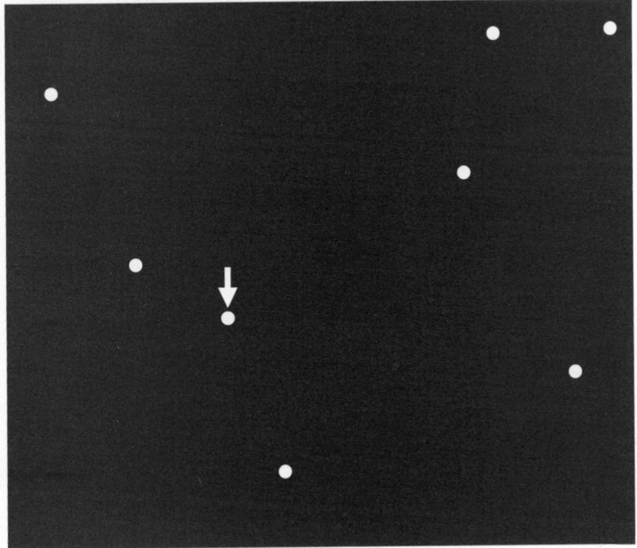

The diagrams above show how the apparent position of a planet (Mars) can change relative to the stars in the background. The apparent position depends on where the planet is in its orbit, and where the Earth is. During the daytime, you can't normally see stars or planets because their light is completed swamped by sunlight.

In the northern hemisphere, the stars appear to move in circles about the Pole Star. Above, you can see the tracks of a few of them over a 12 hour period. In reality, it is the Earth that is rotating.

Questions

1 Give the time taken (to the nearest day) for each of the following:

a One rotation of the Earth on its axis.
b One rotation of the Moon on its axis.
c One orbit of the Earth about the Sun.
d One orbit of the Moon about the Earth.

2

Copy the diagram above. Shade in the part of the Earth that is in shadow. Then write down whether it is daytime or night at each of the following places:

a Britain **b** The North Pole
c The South Pole

3 As the Moon is not hot and glowing like the Sun, why are we able to see it?

4 If you watched it every night for several months, how could you tell whether a point of light in the night sky was a star or a planet?

8.02 The Solar System I

The Earth is one of many planets in orbit around the Sun. Some of these planets have smaller moons in orbit around them. Together, the Sun, planets, and other objects in orbit are known as the **Solar System**.

The Solar System is far too big for the sizes of the planets and their distances from the Sun to be shown on the same scale diagram. That is why two diagrams have been used here, below and on the next page.

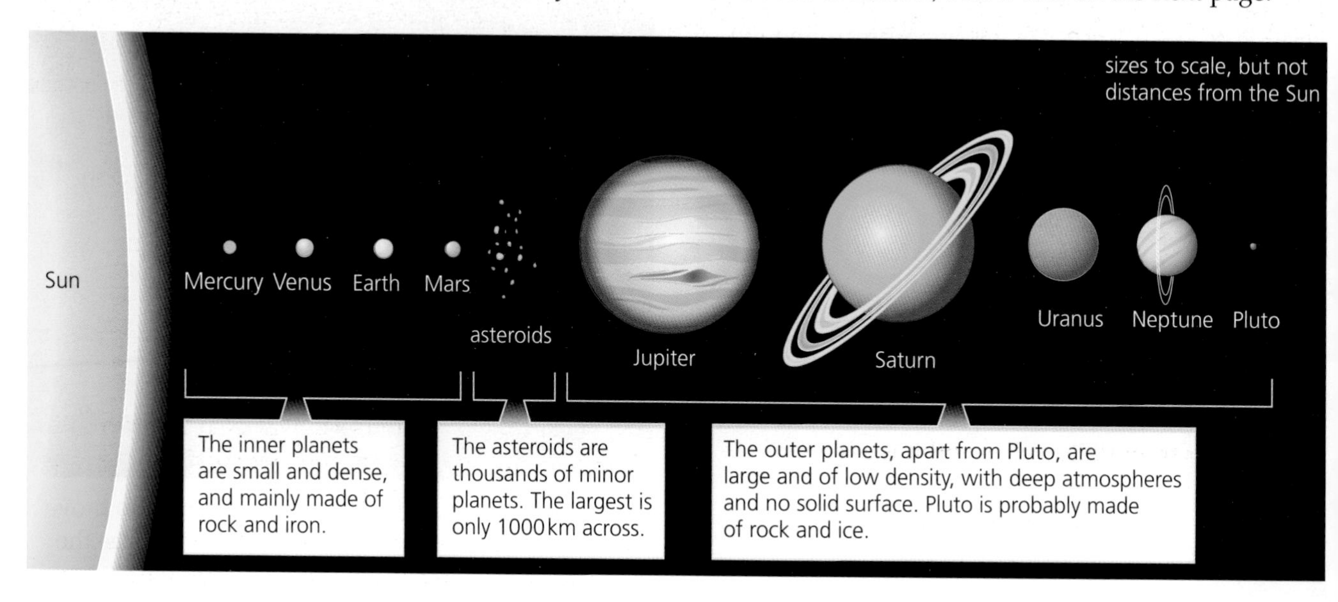

	Mercury	Venus	Earth	Mars	Jupiter	Saturn	Uranus	Neptune	Pluto
Average distance from Sun in million km	58	108	150	228	778	1427	2870	4490	5900
Time for one orbit in years	0.24	0.62	1	1.88	11.86	29.46	84.01	164.08	247
Diameter in km	4900	12100	12800	6800	143000	120000	51000	49000	2300
Mass compared with Earth (Earth = 1)	0.06	0.82	1.00	0.11	318	95.2	14.5	17.2	0.002
Average surface temperature	350 °C	480 °C	22 °C	−23 °C	−150 °C	−180 °C	−210 °C	−220 °C	−230 °C
Number of moons	0	0	1	2	39	30	21	8	1

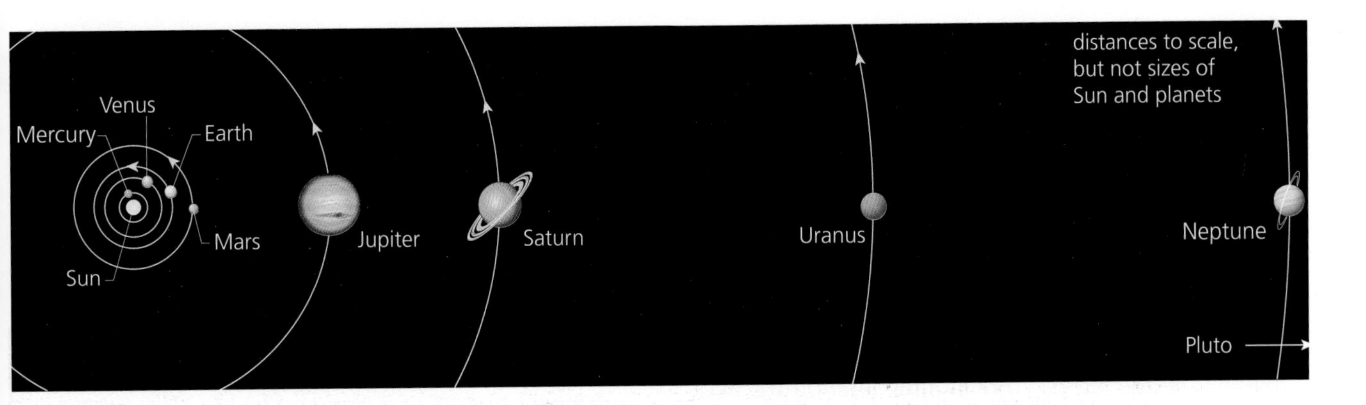

Orbits of the planets

Most of the inner and outer planets have near-circular orbits about the Sun. However, for Mercury, Mars, and Pluto, the orbit is more of an **ellipse** (a stretched-out circle).

The planets all travel round the Sun in the same direction. They also travel in approximately the same plane, apart from Pluto, whose orbit is slightly tilted.

The further a planet is from the Sun, the slower it travels, and the more time its orbit takes.

Gravity in action

Gravity pulls us to the Earth. But scientists have found that there is a gravitational pull between *all* masses:

- Small masses have a weaker pull than large masses.
- Distant masses have a much weaker pull than close masses.

The pull between everyday things is far too weak to detect. It only becomes strong if one of the things has a huge mass, like a planet.

The gravitational force between a planet and the Sun holds the planet in orbit around the Sun. Without it, the planet would drift off through space.

The gravitational force between a moon and its planet holds the moon in orbit around the planet.

Questions

1 From Earth, Venus looks like a bright dot. Why is it bright if it is not hot like a star?

2 Which planets are smaller than the Earth?

3 Which planets have less mass than the Earth?

4 Which planet travels round the Sun at the highest speed?

5 **a** Which planets are colder than the Earth?
b Why do you think that they are colder?

6 One planet has an atmosphere mainly composed of carbon dioxide which causes severe global warming. Which planet do you think it is? What clue is there in the table on the opposite page?

7 A tiny object called Ceres takes 4.6 years to orbit the Sun. Between the orbits of which other planets does Ceres lie? Explain your answer.

8 The diagram below shows the Sun and two planets.
a What is the name of the force that holds the planets in their orbits?
b Which of the two planets has the stronger force on it (if both have about the same mass)?
c Which of the two planets takes the longer time to go round the Sun?

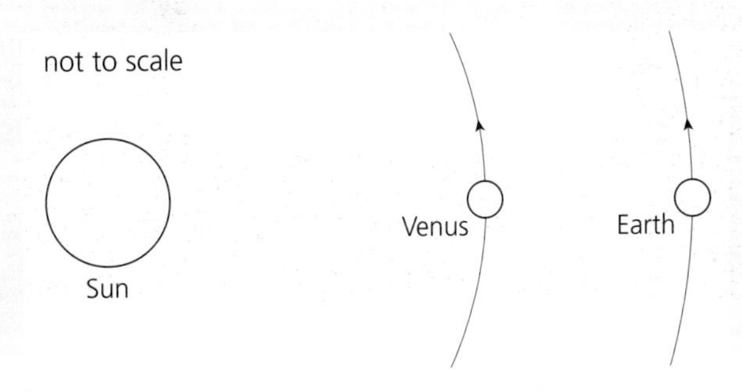

8.03 The Solar System II

More about the planets

Mercury is the planet nearest the Sun. It has a cratered surface and no atmosphere.

Venus is the brightest object in the night sky (apart from the Moon). Its atmosphere is mainly carbon dioxide. It is covered by thick clouds of sulphuric acid.

Earth is the only planet in the Solar System known to support life.

Mars is sometimes called 'the red planet' because of its surface colour. It has a thin atmosphere, a dusty surface, and polar caps. Although it seems to be a dead, dry planet now, water may once have flowed on its surface.

The asteroids have diameters from a few kilometres up to 1000 km. Some have highly elliptical orbits which cross the paths of other planets.

Jupiter is more massive than all the other planets put together. It is mainly gas (hydrogen) and has no solid surface.

Saturn too is mainly gas. It is surrounded by a series of 'rings'.

Uranus is mainly gas and ice.

Neptune is similar to Uranus, but with a more violent atmosphere.

Pluto is small and icy. Its orbit is elliptical, and takes nearly 250 years to complete. Although called the 'outermost planet', it is actually inside Neptune's orbit at present.

To astronomers, 'ice' does not necessarily mean frozen water. It can also mean frozen carbon dioxide, methane, or ammonia.

This asteroid, photographed by the *Galileo* spacecraft, is over 50 km long.

Saturn's rings are millions of pieces of ice and rock, each in its own orbit about the planet.

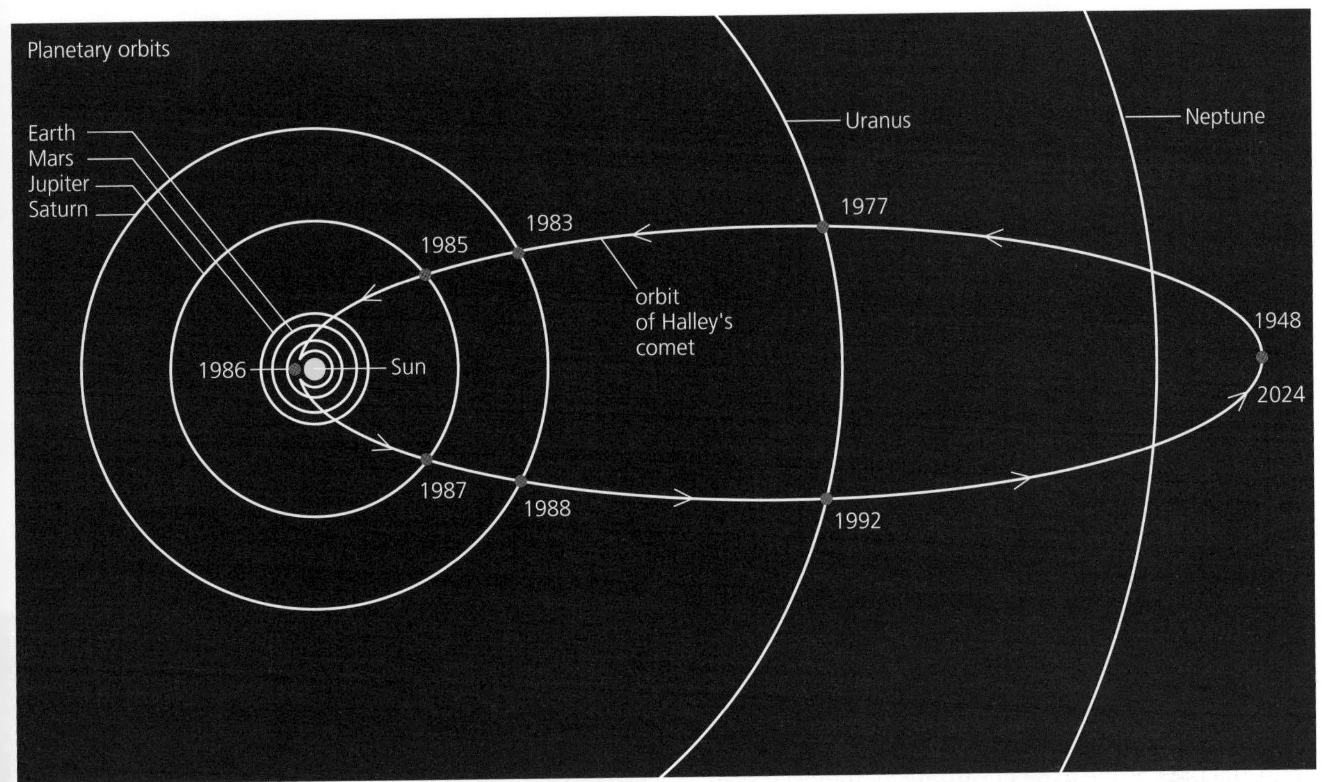

The orbit of Halley's comet. The red dots show where the comet was – and will be – between 1948 and 2024.

Comets, meteors, and meteorites

Other objects orbiting the Sun include **comets** and millions of small bits of rock and ice.

Comets have highly elliptical orbits. A comet has least speed when furthest from the Sun. This is also when the Sun's gravitational pull on it is weakest. As it moves closer to the Sun, it speeds up.

In the 'head' of a comet, there is an icy lump, perhaps several kilometres across. Heated by the Sun, dust and gas stream off it into space, forming a huge 'tail' millions of kilometres long. This is visible because it reflects the sunlight.

As the Earth moves through space, it runs into tiny grains of material which hit the atmosphere so fast that they burn up. Each one causes a streak of light called a **meteor**. Rarely, a larger chunk of material reaches the ground without completely burning up. The chunk is called a **meteorite**.

Questions

1 Which planet is most easily visible from Earth?

2 What are Saturn's rings?

3 If Pluto is now closer to the Sun than Neptune is, why is Pluto called the 'outermost planet'?

4 Why would it be difficult for astronauts to land on Jupiter?

5 What is the difference between a meteor and a meteorite?

6 The diagram below shows the orbit of a comet.

- **a** At which point (X, Y, or Z) is the Sun's gravitational pull on the comet strongest?
- **b** At which point does the comet have most speed?
- **c** At which point does the comet have least speed?
- **d** How is the tail of the comet formed?
- **e** Why is the tail of the comet visible?

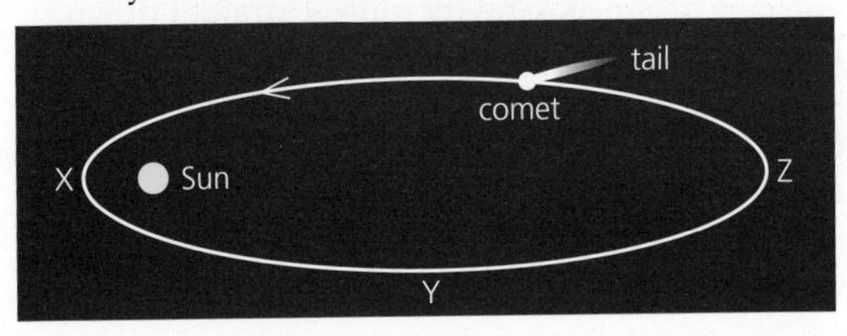

8.04 Satellites in orbit

The Moon is a natural satellite of the Earth. However, most of the Earth's satellites are artificial. They have been built, and put into orbit by rockets.

To keep moving without power, a satellite must be above the Earth's atmosphere, where there is no air resistance to slow it. A high orbit needs less speed than a low one. However, the launch rocket must leave the Earth faster in order to 'coast' further into space when its engines have burned all their fuel and shut down.

The time taken for one orbit is called the **period**. The higher the orbit of a satellite, the longer the period.

Here are two commonly used orbits:

Polar orbit Survey satellites are often put into a low polar orbit – one that passes over the North and South Poles. As the Earth turns beneath them, they can scan the whole of its surface.

Geostationary orbit The satellite orbits at the same rate as the Earth turns, so appears to stay in the same position in the sky. Communications satellites are normally in this type of orbit. On the ground, the dish aerials sending and receiving the signals can point in a fixed direction.

All geostationary satellites orbit at the same height above the equator. There is a limit (about 400) to the number of satellites that can be put in this orbit without their signals interfering.

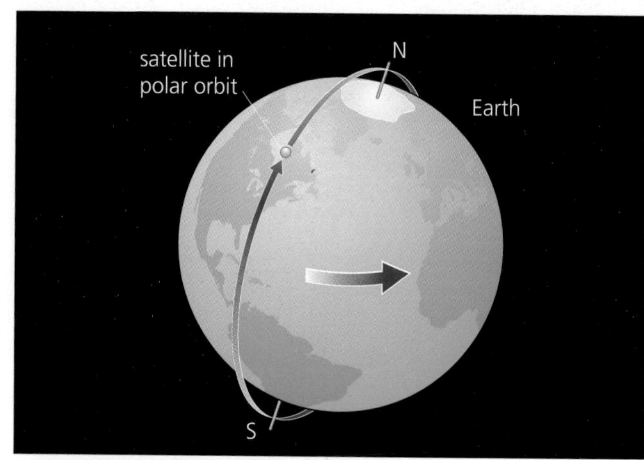

For a low polar orbit, a speed of 29 100 km/hour (18 100 m.p.h.) is required.

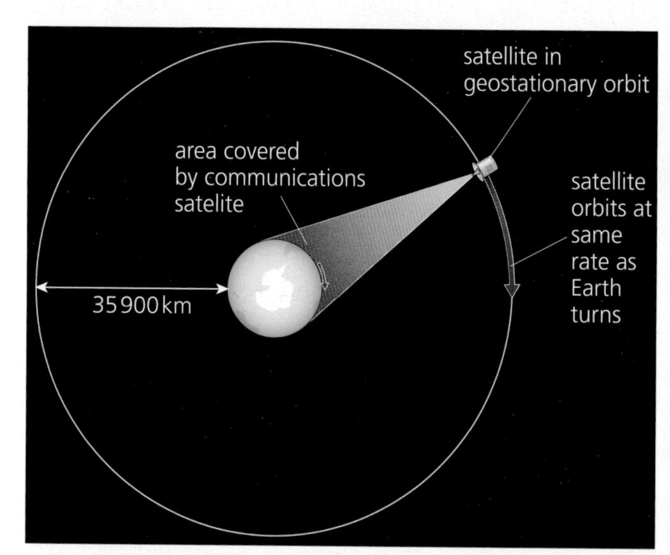

For a geostationary orbit, a satellite must be 35 900 km above the equator, with a speed of 11 100 km/hour.

Why a satellite stays up

In the 'thought experiment' on the right, an astronaut is on a tall tower above the atmosphere. She is so strong that she can throw a ball at the speed of a rocket!

Ball A is dropped. Gravity pulls it straight down.

Ball B is thrown horizontally. Gravity pulls it down, but it also moves sideways at a steady speed.

Ball C is also thrown horizontally, but so fast that the curve of its fall matches the curve of the Earth. The ball is in orbit. With no air resistance to slow it, it will keep its speed and stay in orbit.

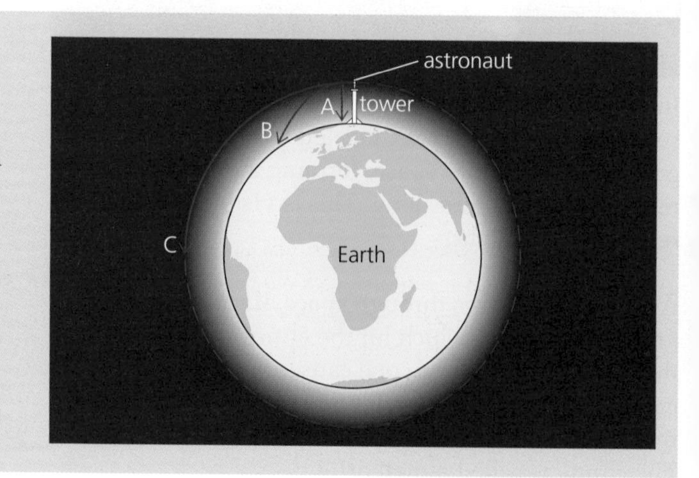

Communications satellites pass on telephone and TV signals from one place to another.

Some TVs get their pictures from a satellite like this.

Monitoring satellites study the weather and other conditions down on the Earth.

This picture was taken from a weather satellite over Europe.

Research satellites Some of these carry telescopes for looking at stars and planets. Above the atmosphere, they get a much clearer view.

This is the *Hubble Space Telescope*. It uses radio signals to send its pictures back to Earth.

Navigation satellites send out radio signals which ships, aircraft, or people on the ground can use to find their position.

This **GPS (global positioning system)** receiver uses time signals from satellites to calculate its position.

Questions

1 A survey satellite is in a low polar orbit.
- **a** What is the advantage of this type of orbit?
- **b** Why must the satellite be above the atmosphere?
- **c** Give *three* other uses of satellites.

2 A satellite is launched from a rocket when the rocket is travelling horizontally. What will happen to the satellite if the rocket is:
a too fast? **b** too slow?

3 TV satellites are in orbit and moving. Yet, down on the ground, the dish aerials that receive the signals point in a fixed direction. How is this possible?

4 Satellite A is put into one orbit around the Earth. Satellite B is put into a higher orbit.
- **a** Which satellite has the greater speed?
- **b** Which satellite takes the longer time to orbit the Earth?

8.05 Sun, stars, and galaxies

The Sun is one star of billions. There are bigger and brighter stars, but they all look like tiny dots because they are much further away from us.

Constellations

The brightest stars seem to form patterns in the sky. The groups are called **constellations**. They have names like Orion, the Great Bear, and Pisces. But the stars in a constellation aren't really grouped together. For example, one star may be much further away than another, but look just as bright because it is bigger or hotter.

For practical reasons, astronomers still divide up the sky into constellations. It helps them find where different stars are.

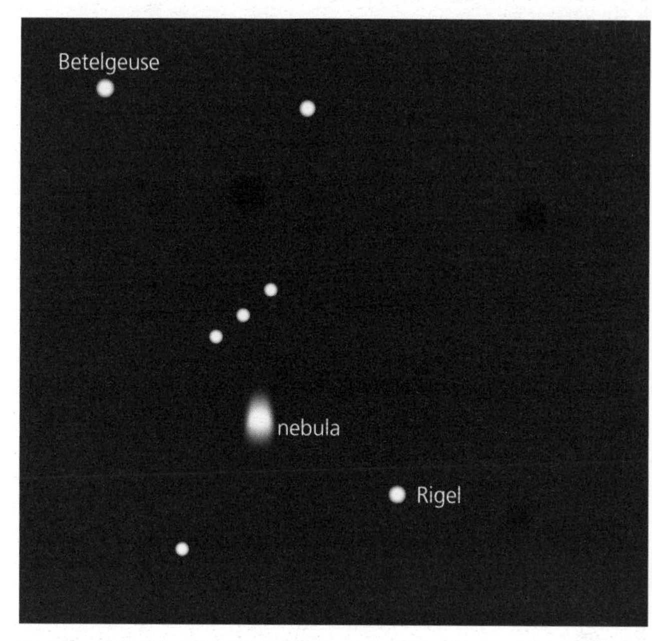

The constellation of Orion. Its stars aren't really in a group. Rigel is nearly twice as far away as Betelgeuse.

Energy from a star

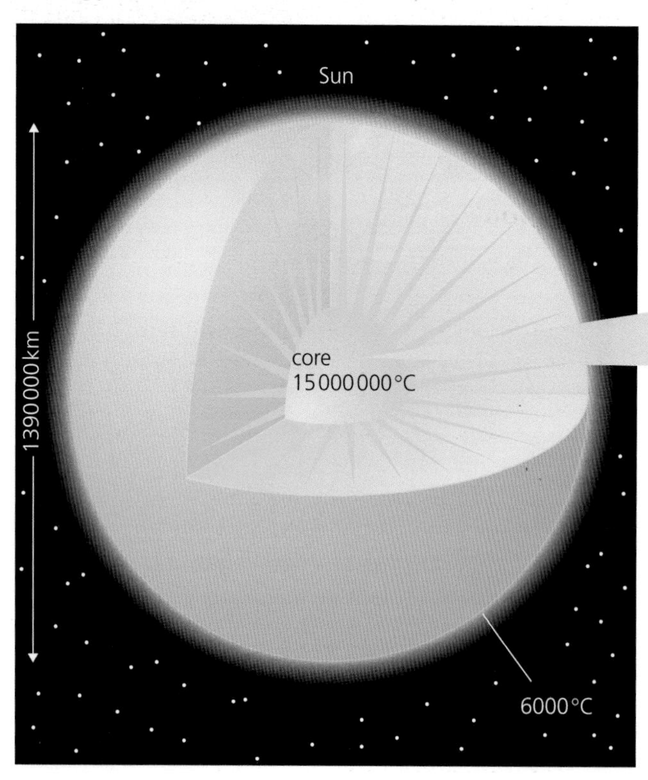

Nuclear fusion happens in the Sun's core, where the temperature and pressure are high enough to keep the reactions going:

Nuclei of hydrogen atoms fuse (join) together to make nuclei of helium. The changes release huge amounts of energy.

Fusion can also make heavier elements. All the heavier elements have come from fusion in stars.

The Sun is 75% hydrogen gas. It gets its energy from a process called **nuclear fusion**, in which the hydrogen (the lightest element) is slowly converted into helium (the next lightest).

The Sun has enough hydrogen left to keep it shining for another 6000 million years.

Light years

Light is the fastest thing there is. But it can still take many years for it to travel the vast distances between stars.

Astronomers have special units for measuring distances in space. For example: one **light year** is the distance travelled by light in one year. It is about 9 million million kilometres.
The nearest star to us (other than the Sun) is Proxima Centauri. It is 4 light years away.

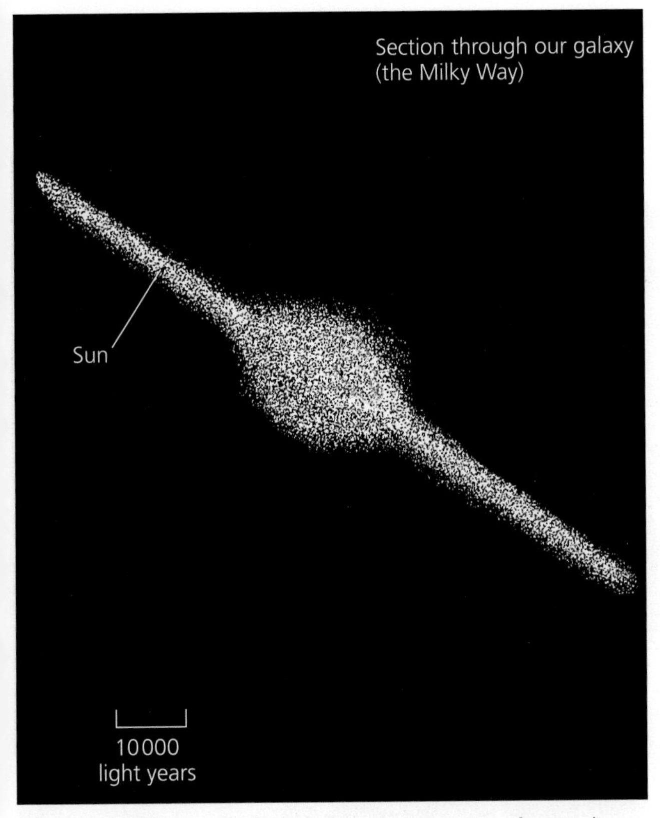

Our own Sun is about halfway out from the centre of our galaxy.

The Andromeda Galaxy is 2 million light years away. Its light has taken 2 million years to reach us.

Galaxies

The Sun is a member of a huge star system called a **galaxy**. This contains over 100 billion stars, and is nearly 100000 light years across. The galaxy is slowly rotating, and is held together by gravitational attraction.

Our galaxy is called the **Milky Way**. You can see the edge of its disc as a bright band of stars across the night sky. It is just one of many billions of galaxies in the known **Universe**.

Light travels through space at 300000km per second. At this speed, light takes ...	
8 minutes...	to reach us from the Sun
6 hours...	to reach us from the furthest planet (Pluto)
4 years...	to reach us from the nearest star (other than the Sun)

Questions

1 What element is the Sun mostly made of?

2 The Sun is a giant nuclear reactor.
  - a What element does the Sun use as its fuel?
  - b What is the name of the process by which the Sun gets its energy?
  - c What is the main element formed in the Sun by this process?

3 Explain what is meant by these terms:
  - a galaxy
  - b Milky Way
  - c constellation
  - d light year

4 Stars in the same constellation appear to form a group. Are they really in a group? If not, explain why not.

5 Give an *approximate* value for each of these:
  - a The temperature in the Sun's core.
  - b The number of stars in our galaxy.
  - c The diameter of our galaxy, in light years.
  - d The time taken for light to travel from the Sun to the Earth.
  - e The distance from Earth to the nearest star (other than the Sun) in light years.
  - f The distance from Earth to the nearest star (other than the Sun) in kilometres.

8.06 The birth and death of stars

Birth of a star

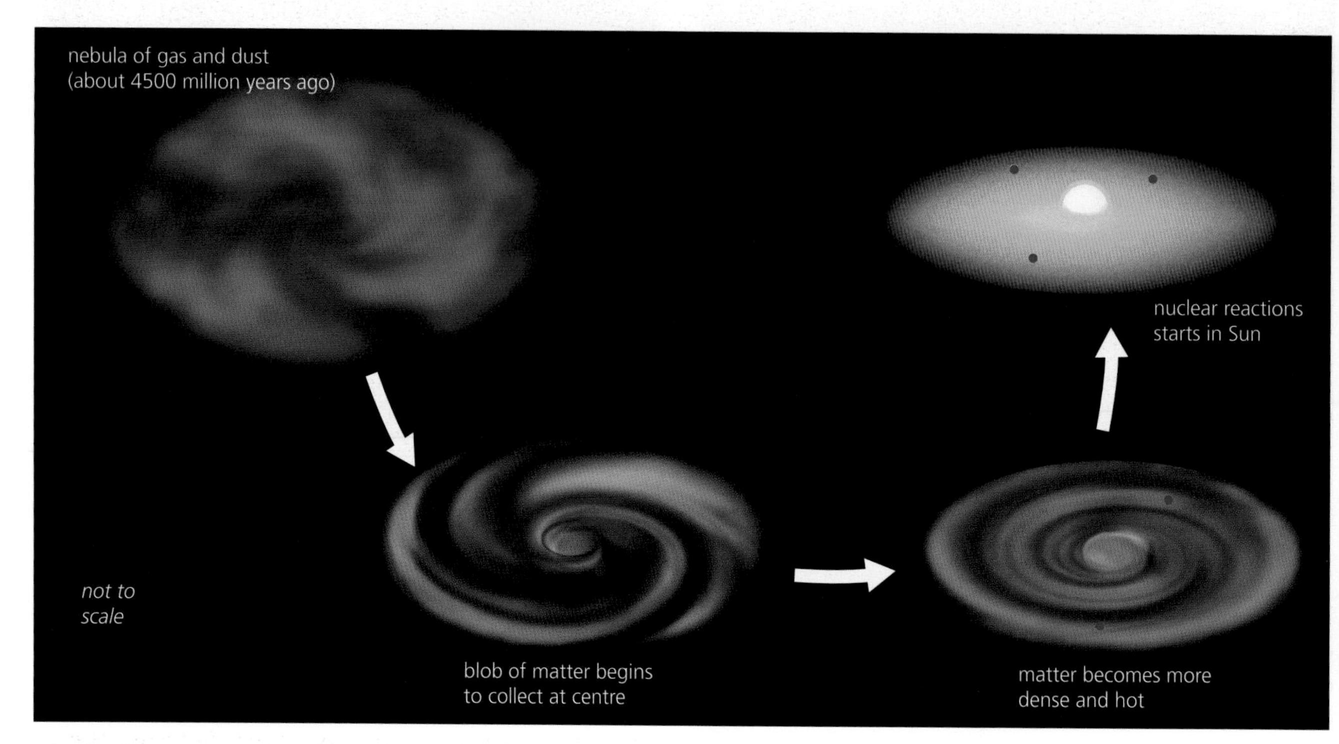

The Sun is a rather average, middle-aged star. Scientists think that it and the rest of the Solar System formed about 4500 million years ago in a huge cloud of gas and dust called a **nebula**. There, gravity slowly pulled the gas and dust into blobs.

In the centre of the nebula one blob grew bigger than all the rest. It would become the Sun. Around it, smaller blobs formed. These would be planets and moons.

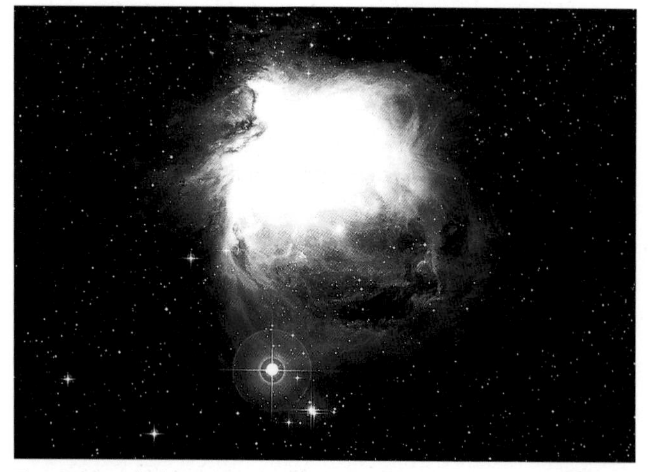

The Great Nebula in the constellation of Orion. Stars are born in clouds of gas and dust such as this.

As more and more material was pulled in, gravitational potential energy was changed into thermal energy, so the central blob became hotter and hotter. Eventually, its core became so hot and compressed that fusion started, and it 'lit up' to become a star. Other stars formed – and are being formed – in the same way.

Death of a star

In the Sun's core, the heating effect is so intense that it stops gravity pulling the material further inwards. However, in about 6000 million years' time, the core will have used up its hydrogen fuel, and will collapse. At the same time, the Sun's outer layer will expand and cool to a red glow. The Sun will have become a star called a **red giant**.

Eventually, the Sun's outer layer will drift into space, leaving a hot, dense core called a **white dwarf**. This tiny star will use helium as its fuel. When this runs out, the star will fade for ever.

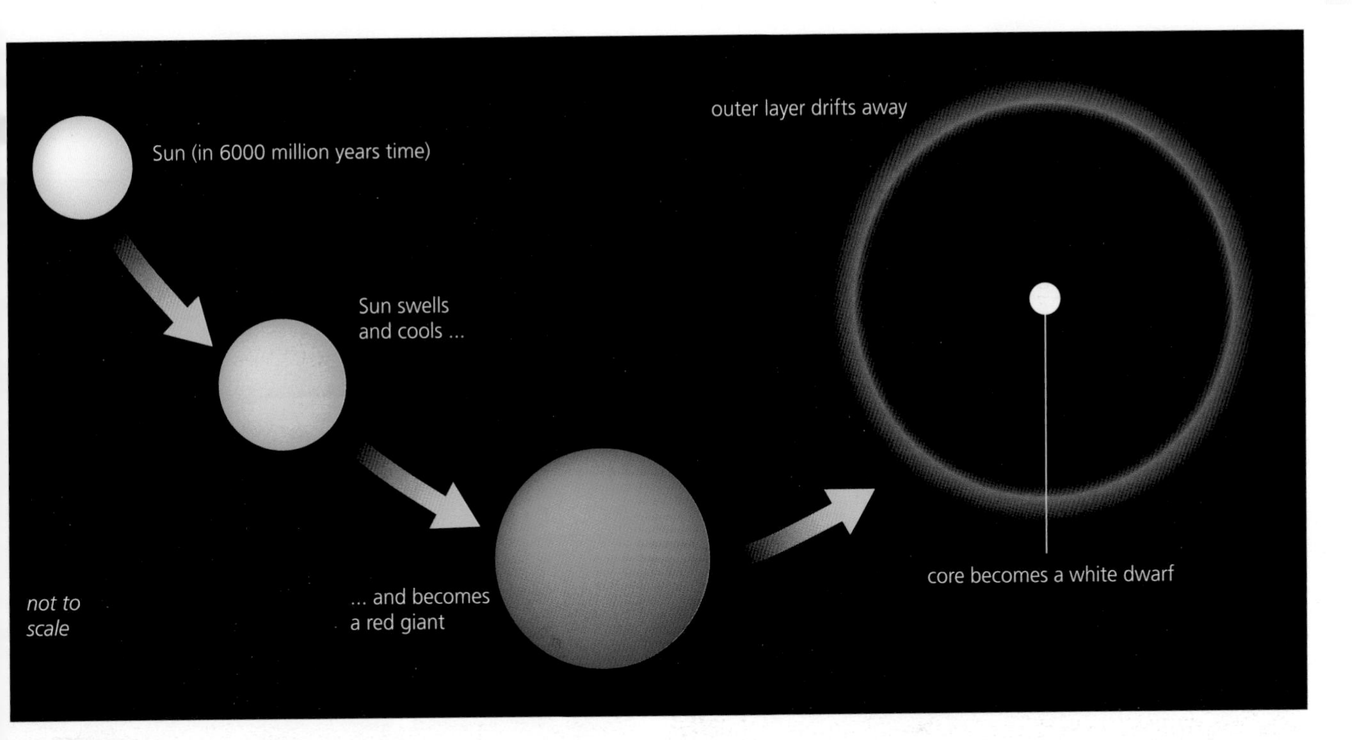

Supernovae and black holes

If a star is much more massive than the Sun, it dies a different death. It blows up in a gigantic nuclear explosion called a **supernova**, leaving a very dense core called a **neutron star**.

When the most massive stars of all explode, the core cannot resist the pull of gravity and goes on collapsing. The result is a **black hole**.

Nothing can escape from a black hole, not even light. So a black hole can't be seen. However, if gases from a nearby star are pulled into it, they give off X-rays, and these can be detected.

The Crab Nebula: the remains of a supernova.

Made from stardust

In stars, fusion reactions change lighter elements into heavier ones. However, to make very heavy elements (gold and uranium for example), the extreme conditions within a supernova are needed. The Sun and inner planets contain very heavy elements. This suggests that the nebula in which they formed contained 'stardust' from an earlier supernova.

Questions

1 Like other stars, the Sun formed in a *nebula*.
  a What is a nebula?
  b What force made matter in the nebula collect together in blobs?
  c About how long ago was the Sun formed?
  d What else formed in the nebula at the same time as the Sun?

2 One day, the Sun will become a *red giant*.
  a What is a red giant?
  b When will the Sun become a red giant?
  c What will eventually happen to the Sun, after it has been a red giant?

3 **a** What is a *supernova*?
  b After a supernova has occurred, what is left at its centre?

4 If a black hole cannot be seen, how can its presence be detected?

5 Scientists think that the nebula in which the Sun formed contained material from an earlier supernova. What reason do they have for suggesting this idea?

8.07 The expanding Universe

There are billions of galaxies in the Universe. The most distant are so far away that their light has taken more than 10 billion years to reach us. The light started its journey almost right back at the beginning of time itself.

The expanding Universe

When objects move away from Earth at high speed, the light waves from them become 'stretched out' so that the wavelengths are shifted towards – or beyond – the red end (the longer-wavelength end) of the visible spectrum. This is called **red shift**.

In the 1920s, Edwin Hubble observed that light from distant galaxies is red shifted, and that, in general, the red shift increases with the distance of the galaxy. This suggests that the galaxies are receding (moving away) from us at high speed. We seem to be living in an expanding Universe.

Stars are made from matter from the big bang. And we are made from matter that came from stars.

With radio telescopes like these, scientists have detected radio waves from the most distant parts of the Universe – including microwaves which may be red-shifted 'leftovers' from the big bang.

The big-bang theory

According to this theory, the Universe began more than 10 billion years ago when a single, incredibly dense, hot 'superatom' expanded in a burst of energy called the **big bang**. Everything in the Universe came from it. Here are two pieces of evidence to support the theory:

- As the galaxies appear to be rushing apart, they may once have once have been together in the same space.
- Radio telescopes have picked up faint background radiation from every direction in space. This may be the red-shifted 'leftovers' of radiation from the big bang, and is commonly called the 'microwave background'.

The big bang was not an explosion into existing space. Space itself started to expand. To think about this, it helps to use a simple model of an expanding Universe like the one on the next page. There, space is represented by a two-dimensional surface: the elastic surface of an inflating balloon. Really, space is three-dimensional because you can move through it upwards, forwards, or sideways.

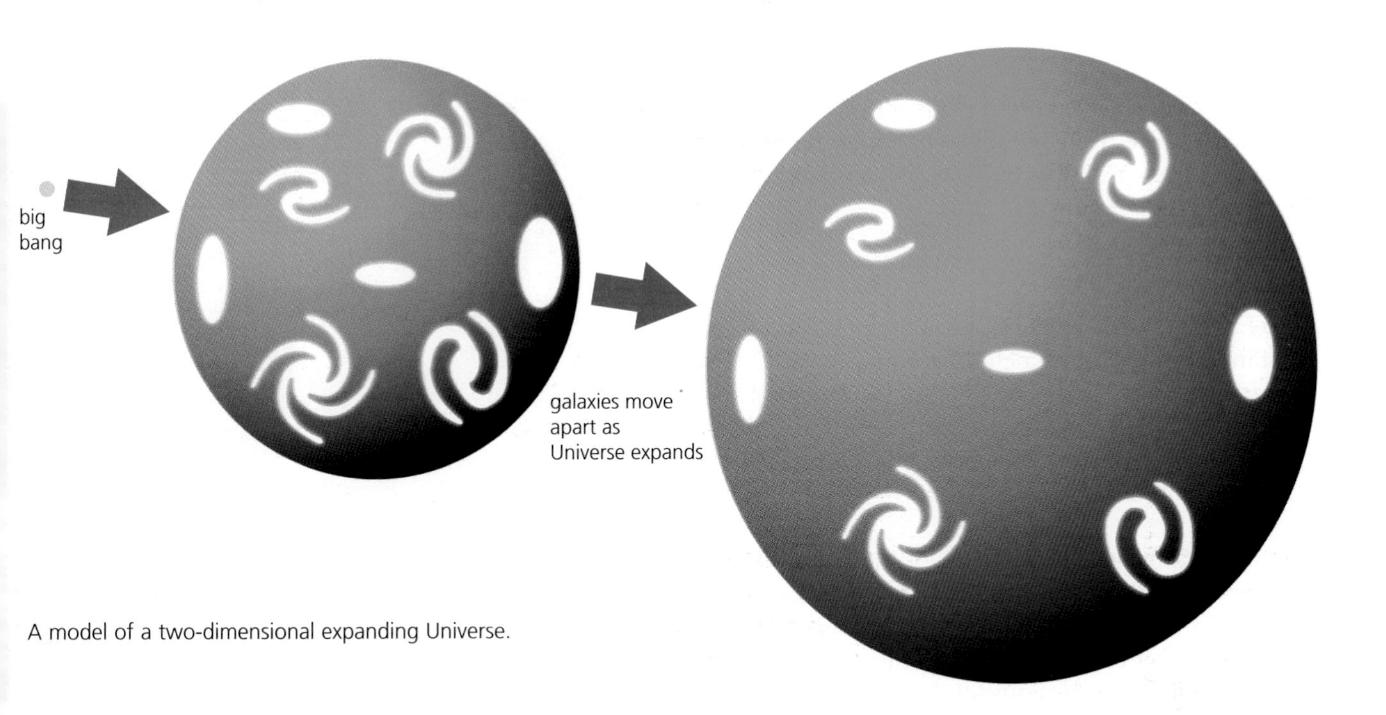

A model of a two-dimensional expanding Universe.

Imagine that you are on one of the galaxies above as the balloon inflates. It doesn't matter which galaxy you are on. All the other galaxies appear to be moving away from you.

The fate of the Universe

Until recently, scientists thought that gravitational attraction must be slowing the expansion. If so, the fate of the Universe depends on its total mass – which isn't accurately known. If the mass is *less* than a certain critical value the Universe will keep expanding for ever. If it is *more* than the critical value, the expansion will eventually stop and be followed by a contraction ... and a big crunch!

Recently, scientists have been getting some very puzzling results. These suggest that the expansion may be speeding up! But no one knows why.

Estimating the age of the Universe

Scientists have estimated the rate at which the galaxies appear to be moving apart. The value has not been agreed, but is thought to be about $\frac{1}{15000}$ km per year per million km of separation. This is called the **Hubble constant**. From it, it is possible to work out that the galaxies must have started to separate about 15 000 million years ago. If so, that is when the big bang occurred.

Questions

1 To answer this question, you may need to look back at other spreads to find the information you need.

5   5 million   5 billion   15 billion

Which of the above numbers could be a possible value for each of the following?

a The separation between two neighbouring galaxies, in light years.

b The separation between two neighbouring stars, in light years.

c The distance from Earth to the most distant galaxies observed, in light years.

d The age of the Universe, in years.

2 Light from distant galaxies shows red shift.

a What is meant by *red shift*?

b What is thought to be the cause of the red shift?

3 What evidence is there that the Universe may have started with a big bang?

4 If the expansion of the Universe is slowing down, what force is causing this to happen?

5 The value of the Hubble constant is uncertain. If its value is $\frac{1}{10000}$ km per year per million km separation, how old is the Universe?

8.08 Looking for life

Does life only exist on Earth?

Scientists would love to find evidence of intelligent life out in space. They would be happy to find *any* form of life, even simple bacteria. But so far, their search is proving difficult.

A home for life

The Earth is a special place. It has the rare conditions that make life possible, including liquid water, and a distance from the Sun which makes the temperature just right. It even has a big bodyguard, Jupiter, whose gravitational pull stops many comets and asteroids smashing into it.

But is Earth the *only* home for life? Within the Solar System, two other candidates are Mars and Europa – a moon of Jupiter. Mars seems to be a dead planet now, but water once flowed there. Europa has a warm interior and may have liquid water beneath its icy surface.

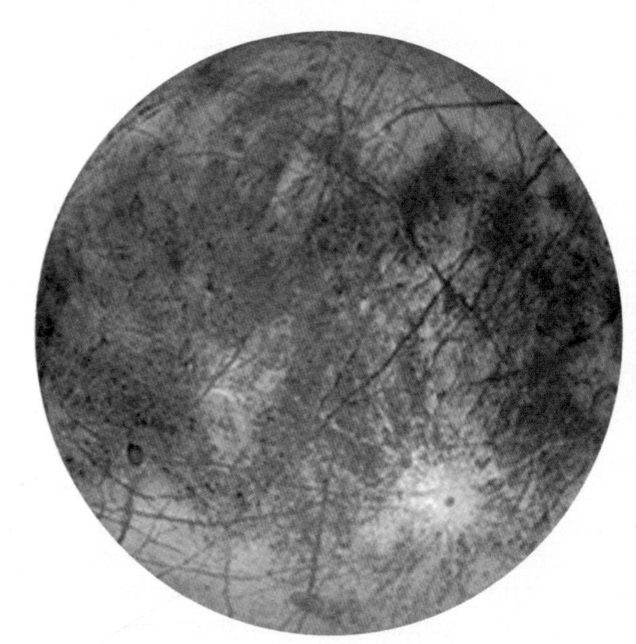
Could life exist beneath the icy surface of Europa?

Living things change the land, sea, and air. For example, if life had not evolved on Earth, there would be much less oxygen in our atmosphere and no fossils in the rocks. So conditions on Mars and Europa may give clues about the existence of life there now or in the past.

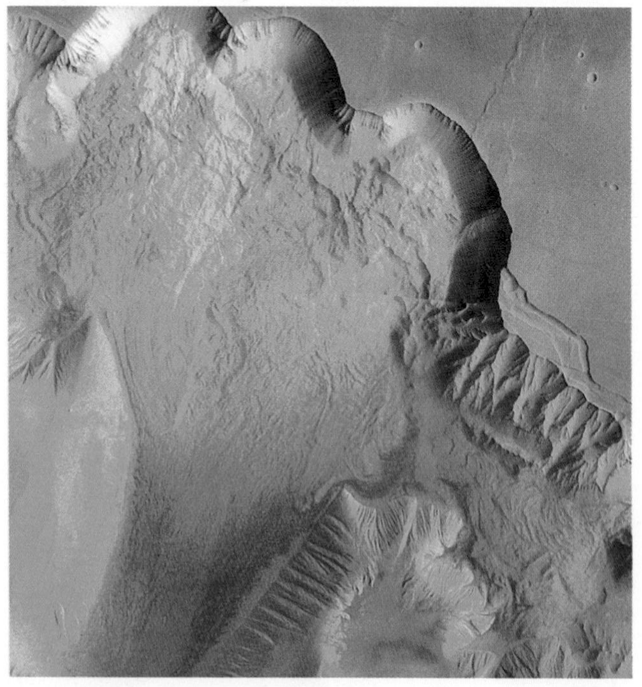
Has simple life ever existed on Mars? These valleys suggest that water once flowed there ...

... but this wheeled robot found no evidence of life when it landed on Mars.

Beyond the Solar System, there are over 100 billion 'suns' (stars) in our galaxy, and more than 100 billion galaxies. It seems unlikely that there are no other Earth-like planets out there somewhere. But we just don't have any evidence, or much chance of finding any.

SETI

Spacecraft can be sent to places in our Solar System, but a visit to even the nearest star would take thousands of years. If we want to detect life far out in space, we have to hope that the life is intelligent and sending out signals. The search for these signals is called the **SETI** project (the Search for Extra-Terrestrial Intelligence). It has been going on for over 40 years.

Stars naturally give off radio waves which can be picked up by radio telescopes like the one above. Scientists analyse them for signals that might have been made by intelligent life.

If signals are ever found, communicating with their senders will be almost impossible. Radio waves take about 4 years to reach us from the nearest star, and 2 million years from our neighbouring galaxy, Andromeda. If we send signals now, it will be 2 million years before any Andromedans receive them. As for visits from Andromedans ... nothing can travel faster than radio signals, so visits are likely to be completely out of the question.

Little green men

In the late 1960s, physicist Jocelyn Bell was analysing data from a radio telescope, when she noticed strange signals coming from a distant star. They were pulses so regular and rapid that, for while, no one thought that they could be natural. Maybe the signals had been sent by distant aliens, or 'little green men' as they became known.

The **LGM** (**little green men**) theory was soon abandoned. What Jocelyn Bell had discovered was a new type of star called a **pulsar** – a small, rapidly spinning neutron star. It sends out radio beams whose pulses are rather like the flashes seen when a lighthouse beam sweeps round and round.
Maybe the *next* time strange pulses are found, they really will be coming from little green men.

- Why are scientists likely to concentrate on Mars and Europa when searching for evidence of simple life elsewhere in the Solar System?
- If an alien probe analysed samples from the Earth's surface and atmosphere, what clues might it find that there could be life here?
- What is the SETI project?
- Why, in the immediate future, are astronauts unlikely to visit planets around other stars?
- Why, if we ever pick up radio signals from distant aliens, will it be extremely difficult to exchange messages with them?

Questions on Chapter 8

1 The diagram shows the path of a satellite placed in a low polar orbit round the Earth.

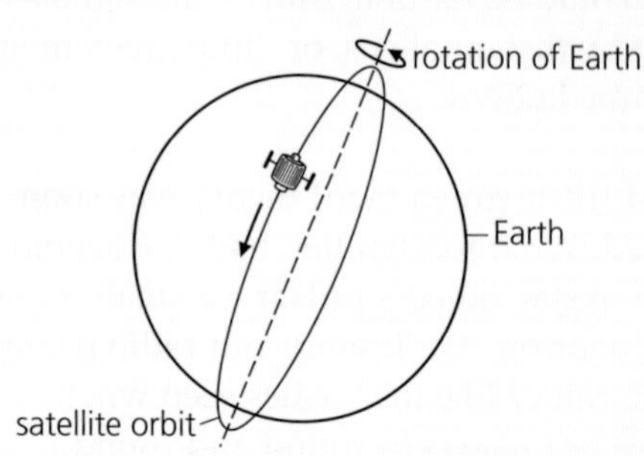

It takes the above satellite 2 hours to orbit the Earth.

a How many orbits will the satellite complete in one full day?

b Explain why a low polar orbit is useful for weather satellites.

c Describe one other use for a satellite in this kind of orbit.

d Why would this kind of orbit be no use for a communications satellite?

e What is a geostationary orbit?

2 Here is some data about the planets:

Planet	Diameter of planet in km	Average distance from Sun in million km	Time for one orbit in years	Average surface temperature in °C
Mercury	4900	58	0.2	350
Venus	12 000	108	0.6	480
Earth	12 800	150	1.0	22
Mars	6800	228	1.9	–23
Jupiter	143 000	778	11.9	–150
Saturn	120 000	1427	29.5	–180
Uranus	52 000	2870	84.0	–210
Neptune	49 000	4497	164.8	–220
Pluto	3000	5900	247.8	–230

Use the above table to answer the following questions.

a Which is the largest planet?

b Which is the smallest planet?

c Which planet is closest to the Sun?

d Which planet takes almost twelve Earth years to orbit the Sun?

e How long is a year on the planet Mercury? Explain your answer.

f How would you expect a planet's surface temperature to depend on its distance from the Sun? Do the data in the above table support this? Explain your answer.

3 **meteorite** **galaxy** **supernova**
big bang **constellation** **black hole**
moon **comet** **Solar System**

Which of the above is the best match for each of the following descriptions?

a A rocky object orbiting a planet.

b The Sun, its planets, and other objects in orbit.

c A small rocky object which collides with a planet, and may be a fragment from an asteroid.

d A clump of ice, gas, and dust, usually in a highly elliptical orbit around the Sun.

e A huge group of many millions of stars.

f A gigantic explosion that occurs when a very massive star has used up its nuclear fuel.

4 The Sun is a star. It formed in a nebula about 4500 million years ago. The diagram below shows what is likely to happen to the Sun in about 6000 million years' time.

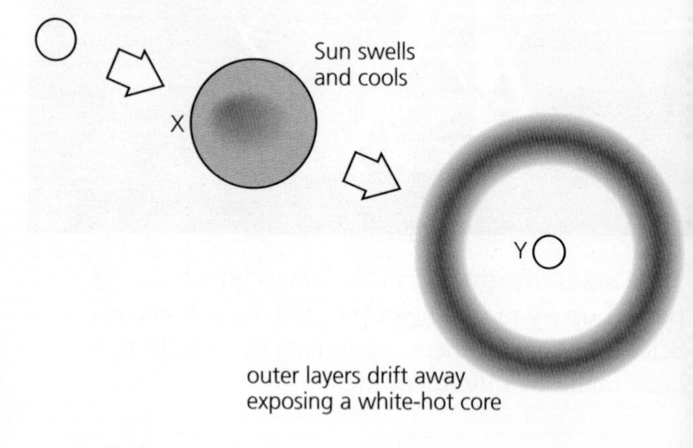

a What is a nebula?

b What makes matter in a nebula collect together to form a star?

c The Sun gets its energy from nuclear reactions that change hydrogen into helium. What is this process called?

d What type of star has the Sun become at X in the diagram above?

e What type of star is left when the core, Y, is exposed?

5 **a** Explain carefully how stars form.
b Why do stars heat up as they form?
c Explain how planets are formed around a young star.
d The light from distant stars and galaxies show a 'red shift' in their spectra.
i Explain what is meant by the phrase 'red shift'.
ii What does this 'red shift' tell us about these stars and galaxies?
iii Using this information scientists have devised a theory to explain how the Universe may have begun. What is this theory called?

6 **a** Name one luminous object in the night sky.
b Name one non-luminous object in the night sky.
c The diagrams show the constellation Taurus on two nights a month apart.

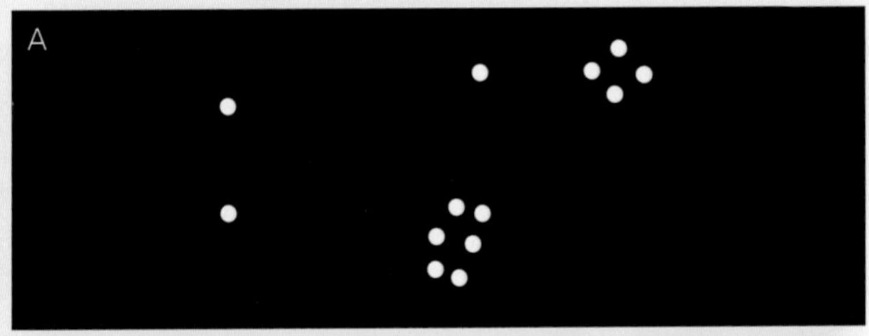

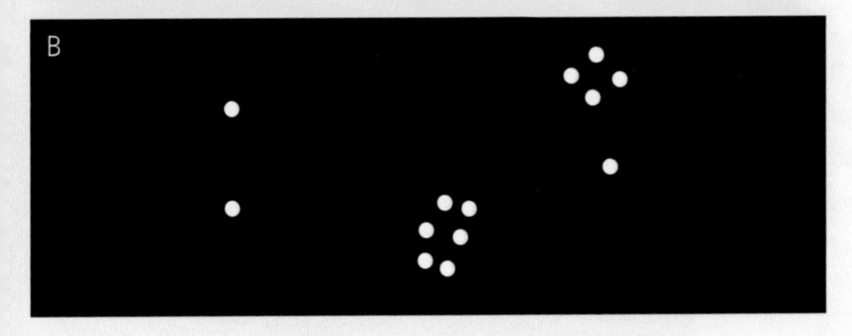

i What evidence is there that one of the objects is a planet? Make a sketch to show which object it is.
ii Why will the planet not always appear to be among the stars of Taurus?
d **i** What is a satellite?
ii Name one artificial satellite.
iii Name one natural satellite.

7 The diagram shows the orbit of a comet.

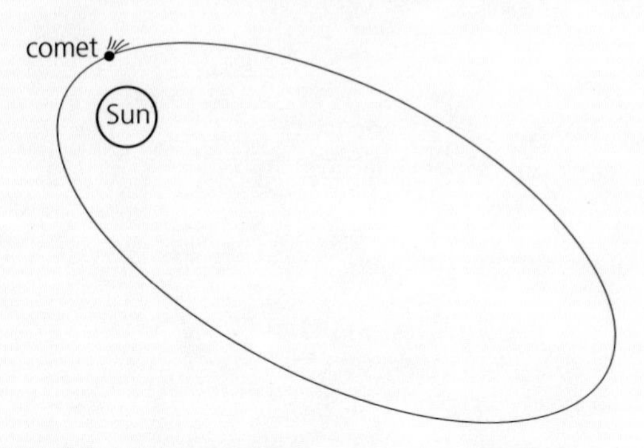

a What is a comet?
b What is the shape of a comet's orbit?
c Where in a comet's orbit is it moving the slowest? Explain your answer.

8 The diagram below shows two identical satellites, A and B, in orbit around the Earth.

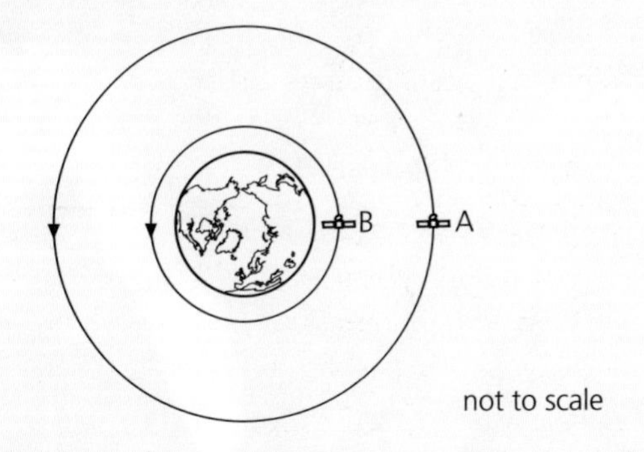

a Which satellite is pulled most strongly by the Earth's gravitational field?
b Which satellite has the highest speed?
c Which satellite will take longest to complete one orbit of the Earth?
d Satellite A is in a geostationary orbit. What does this mean?
e Why are communications satellites normally put into geostationary orbits?

Further topics

To do this, you need courage, a good sense of balance, a strong cable, and a long pole. The pole helps to lower the tightrope walker's centre of gravity, which makes him more stable. It also reduces the speed at which he rotates if he starts to tip to one side, so that he has got time to take correcting action. The walker's weight makes the cable stretch slightly, but not enough for there to be any risk of it snapping.

FT1 Turning effects

What's needed to turn these?

Something which increases the turning effect of your hand.

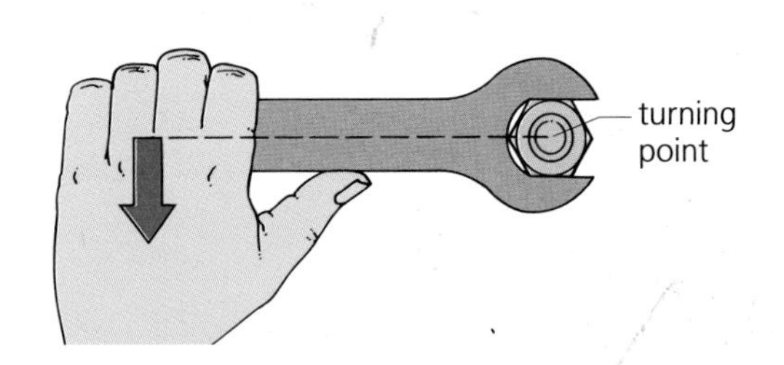

The nut is easy to turn with a spanner.

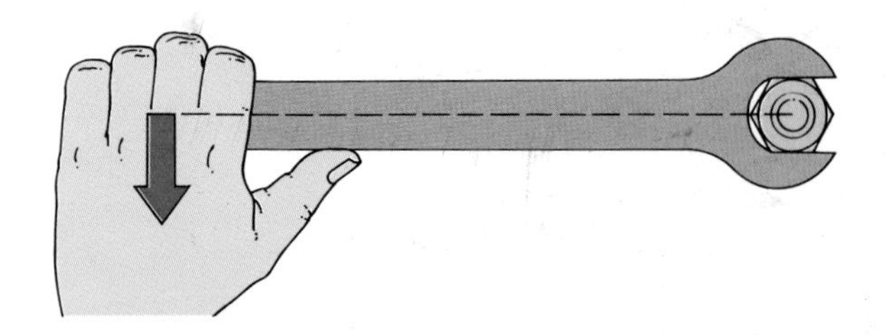

It is easier still if the spanner has a long handle. You can increase the turning effect in two ways:

1 Increase the force.

2 Move the force further away from the turning point of the nut.

Moments

The turning effect of a force is called a **moment**. It can be calculated as follows:

Moment = force × distance from turning point

Moments are **clockwise** or **anticlockwise** depending on which way they turn. For example:

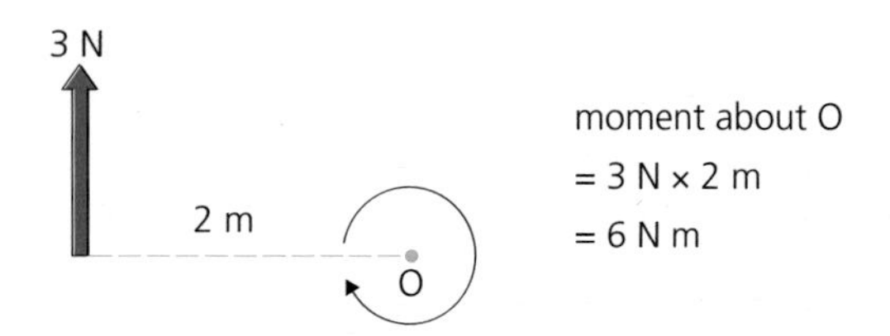

This force has a clockwise moment of 6 N m about point O.

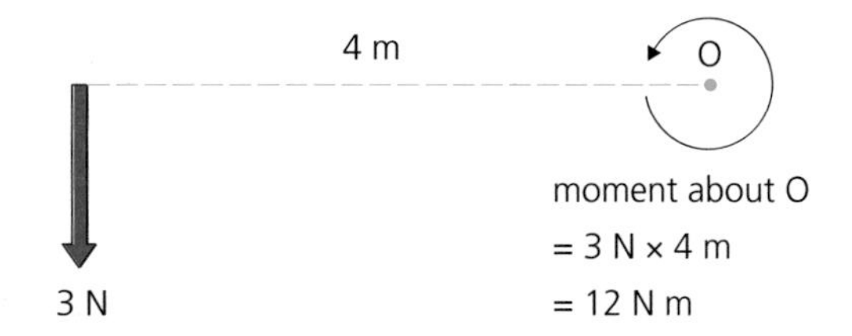

This force has an anticlockwise moment of 12 N m about point O. It has twice the turning effect, but in the opposite direction.

Torque

In engines and motors, several forces act together to produce a turning effect. The turning effect is called a **couple** or **torque**. Typical torque values are:

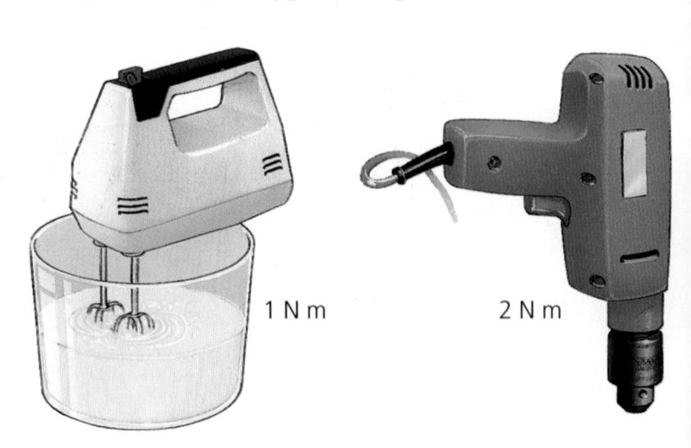

Moments in balance

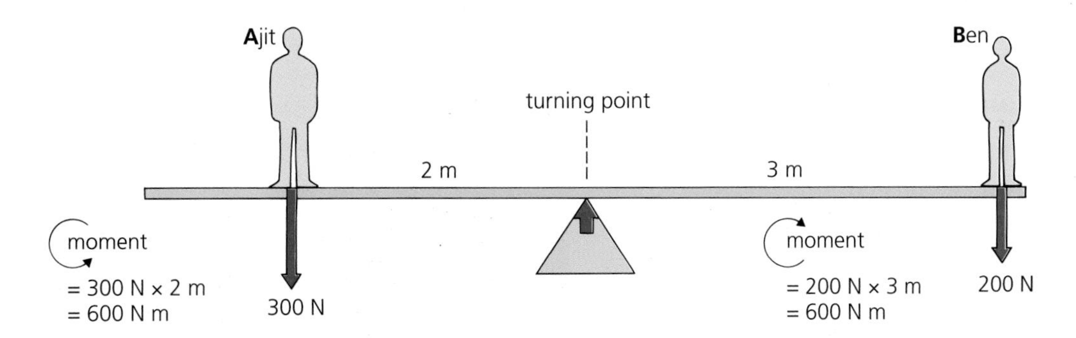

There are two turning effects at work on the see-saw: Ajit has an **anticlockwise** turning effect; Ben has a **clockwise** turning effect. The two moments are equal. So their turning effects cancel and the see-saw balances. This is an example of the **principle of moments**:

> If something is in balance, about the turning point the total clockwise moment is equal to the total anticlockwise moment.

The principle works in more complicated cases as well. In the diagram below, there is one anticlockwise moment about the turning point, but two clockwise moments. Add up the two clockwise moments.

The total is the same as the anticlockwise moment. So the see-saw balances.

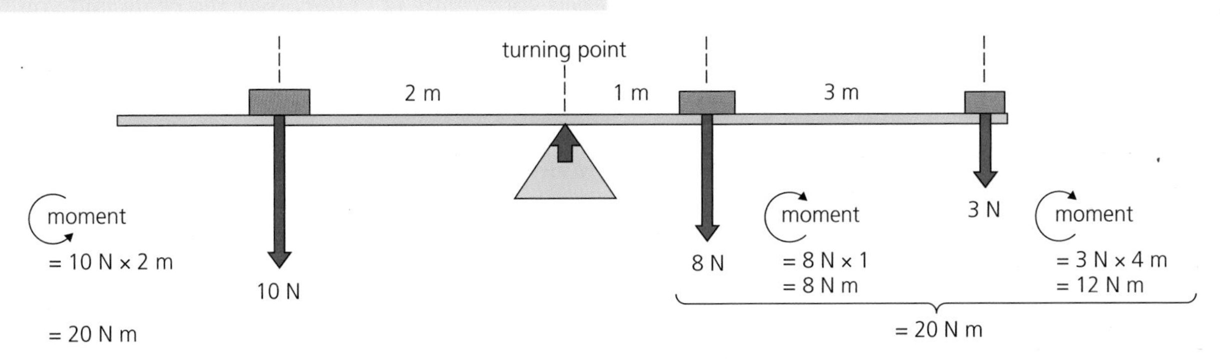

Questions

1

O, 2 m, 3 N (A)

O, 1 m, 5 N (B)

O, 3 m, 3 N (C)

O, 0.5 m, 12 N (D)

a Which force has the greatest moment about O?
b Which forces have the same moment about O?
c Which force has the least moment about O?

2

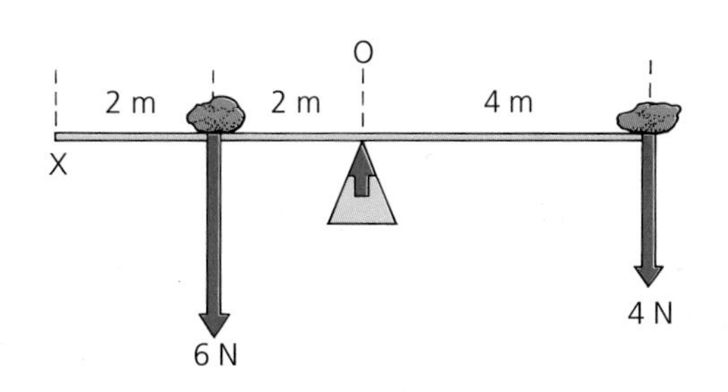

Someone is trying to balance a plank with stones.
a Calculate the moment of the 4N force about O.
b Calculate the moment of the 6N force about O.
c Will the plank balance? If not, which way will it tip?
d What extra force would be needed at X to balance the plank?

FT2 Centre of gravity

Balancing for Gold

Most people would find it impossible to walk along such a narrow beam, let alone perform handstands and somersaults on it.

The secret lies in how you position your weight. Every particle in your body has a small gravitational force acting on it. Together, these forces act like a single force pulling at just one point.

This single force is your **weight**.

The point is called your **centre of gravity** or **centre of mass**.

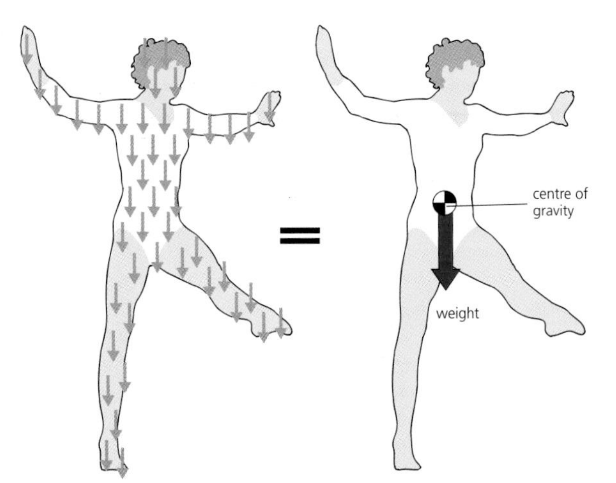

Keep your centre of gravity over the beam and you stay on. Allow it to move to one side, and your weight produces a turning effect which tips you off.

Simple shapes, like a metre rule, often have a centre of gravity exactly in the middle. Vehicles usually have a low centre of gravity because most of their heavy mechanical parts are low down.

Finding the centre of gravity of a flat piece of card

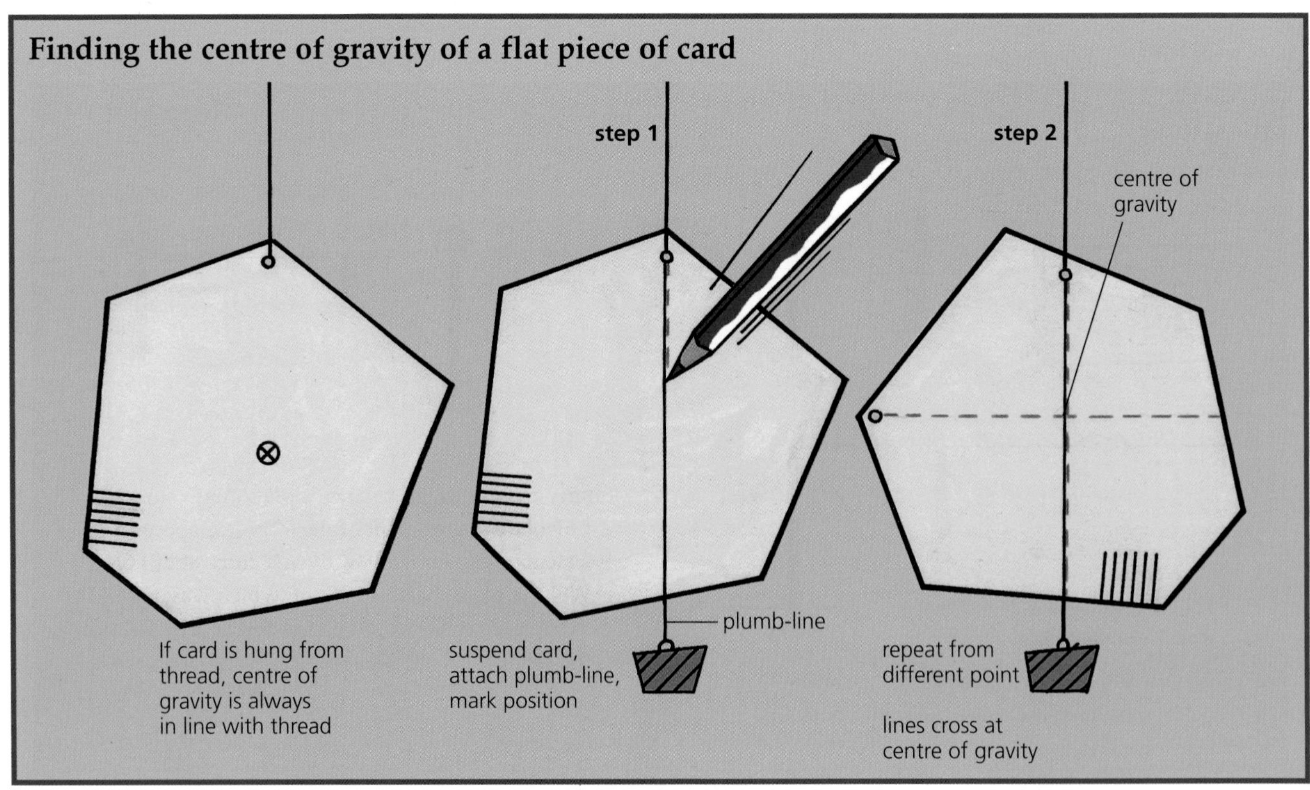

How stable?

base

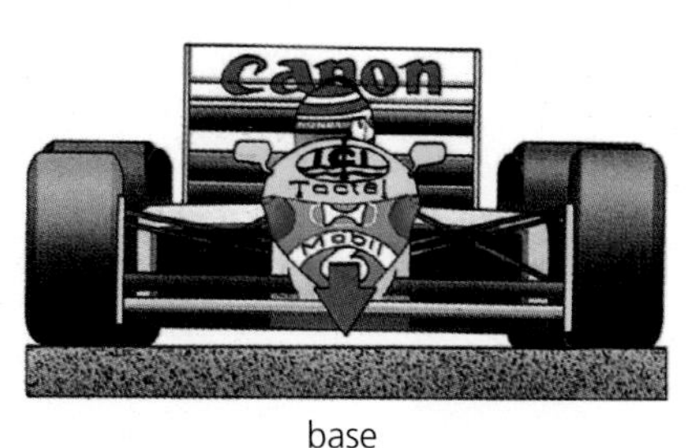

base

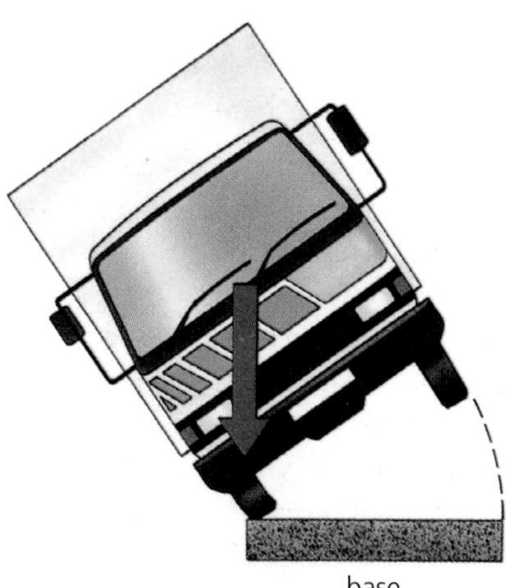

base

If something won't topple over, its position is stable:

This truck is in a stable position. If it starts to tip, its weight will pull it back again. As long as its centre of gravity stays above its base, it won't topple over.

This racing car is even more stable than the truck. It has a lower centre of gravity and a wider base. It could be tipped much further before it started to topple.

Clever stunt driving – but it has put the truck in an unstable position. If the truck tips any further, its centre of gravity will pass over the edge of its base. Then its weight will pull it right over.

Supporting the weight

On the right, someone weighing 500 N is standing on a beam which rests on two trestles. These exert upward forces X and Y to support the weight. Assuming for simplicity that the beam is of negligible weight, then, wherever the person stands, $X + Y$ must always equal 500 N. However, if the person is nearer X than Y, as shown, then X will be larger than Y.

You could find the value of X by taking moments about B. The clockwise moment of X about B must equal the anticlockwise moment of the 500 N force about B. From this, you can work out X. And, knowing X, you can then find Y.

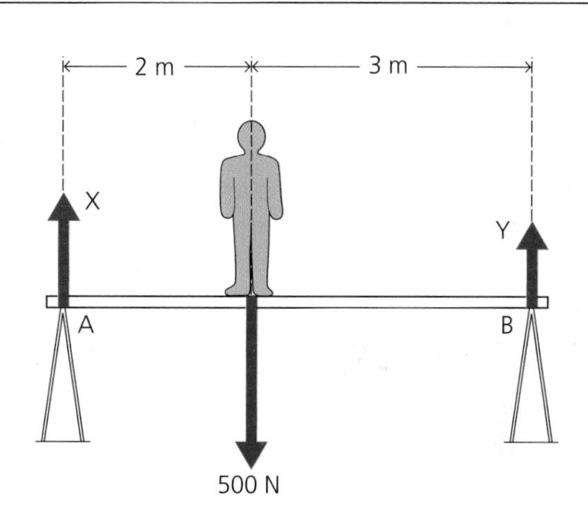

Questions

1 In the diagram, the kitchen stool is about to topple over. Copy the diagram and mark on the position of the centre of gravity.
Would the stool be MORE stable, or LESS stable, if it had:

a a higher centre of gravity?

b a wider base?

Explain why three-legged stools aren't as stable as stools with four legs.

2 a Redraw the diagram below, showing the weight of the plank as a force arrow.

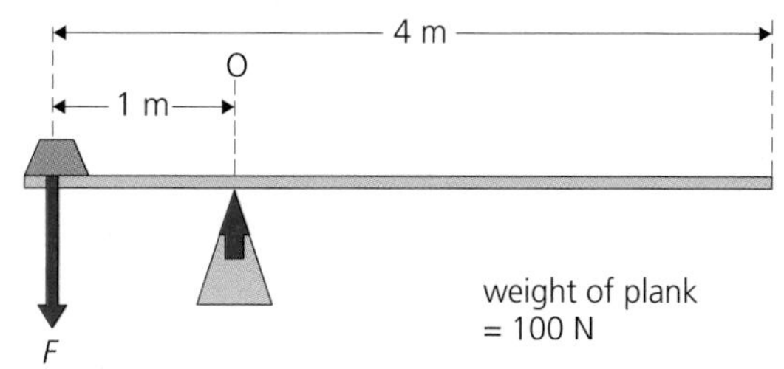

b How far is this force from the point O?

c What is the moment of this force about O?

d If the plank balances, what must be the moment of the force F about O?

e What is the value of F?

FT3 **Stretching and compressing**

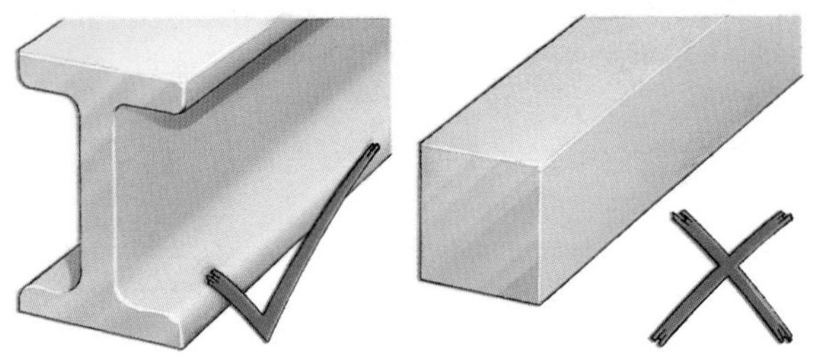

An I-section beam has a much greater resistance to bending than a solid square-section beam made from the same amount of metal.

At 555 metres, the CN tower in Toronto is one of the tallest buildings in the world. However, its steel and concrete structure isn't quite as rigid as it looks. In high winds, the top can sway up to half a metre. And the tower is actually shortened by several centimetres because the structure is compressed by its own weight.

Whenever several forces act on something, its shape changes – though sometimes only by a small amount. Some things are designed to bend and twist; some springs for example. However, the steel frames used in most modern buildings are designed to change shape as little as possible. The frames are made using I-section beams. In every case, the more cross-sectional ('end-on') area the bar has, the more it resists being put out of shape.

Elastic and plastic

To engineers, these don't have quite the same meaning as in everyday language.

Bend a ruler a little. Then release it. It goes back to its original shape.

Materials which behave in this way are **elastic**.

Press a piece of Plasticine, then release it. It doesn't return to its original shape. Materials which behave in this way are **plastic**.

A bumper on a car is elastic – provided it isn't bent too far. Given too much force, it passes its **elastic limit** and stays out of shape.

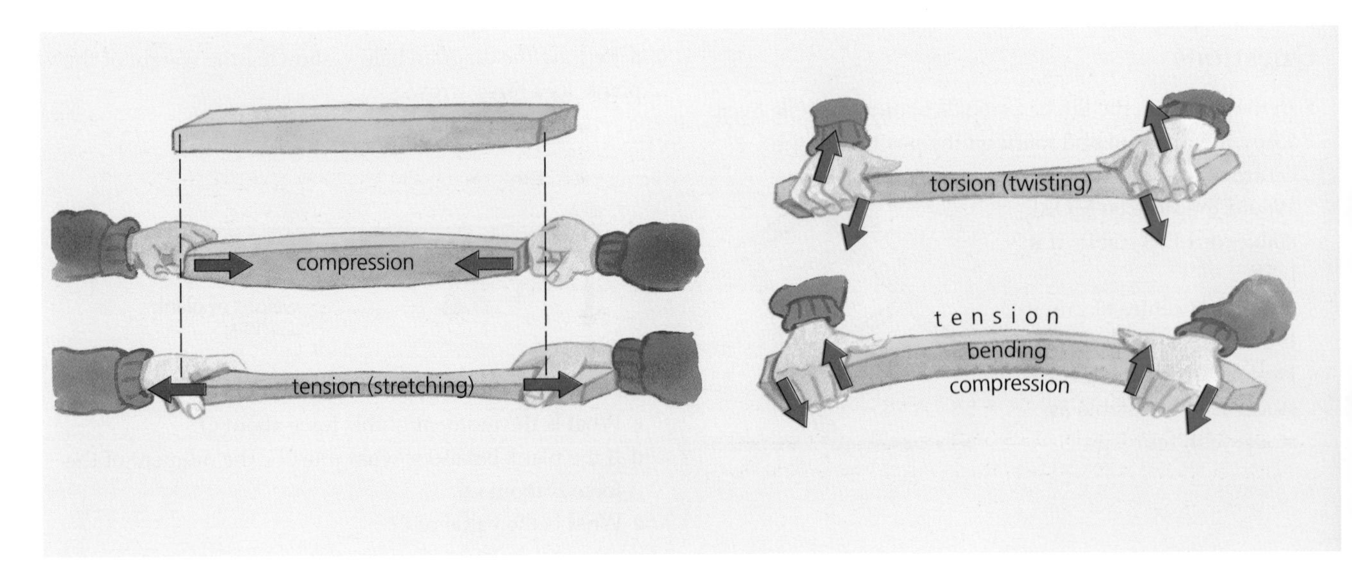

Hooke's law

Many materials obey a simple law when compressed or stretched. Take the case of a spring:

The spring is stretched in stages by hanging masses from one end. The stretching force is called the **load**. As $g = 10\,N/kg$, there is a 1 N load for every 100 g hung from the spring.
Each time the load is changed, the **extension** of the spring is measured. The extension is the difference between the stretched length of the spring and its original unstretched length.
Typical readings are shown in the chart.

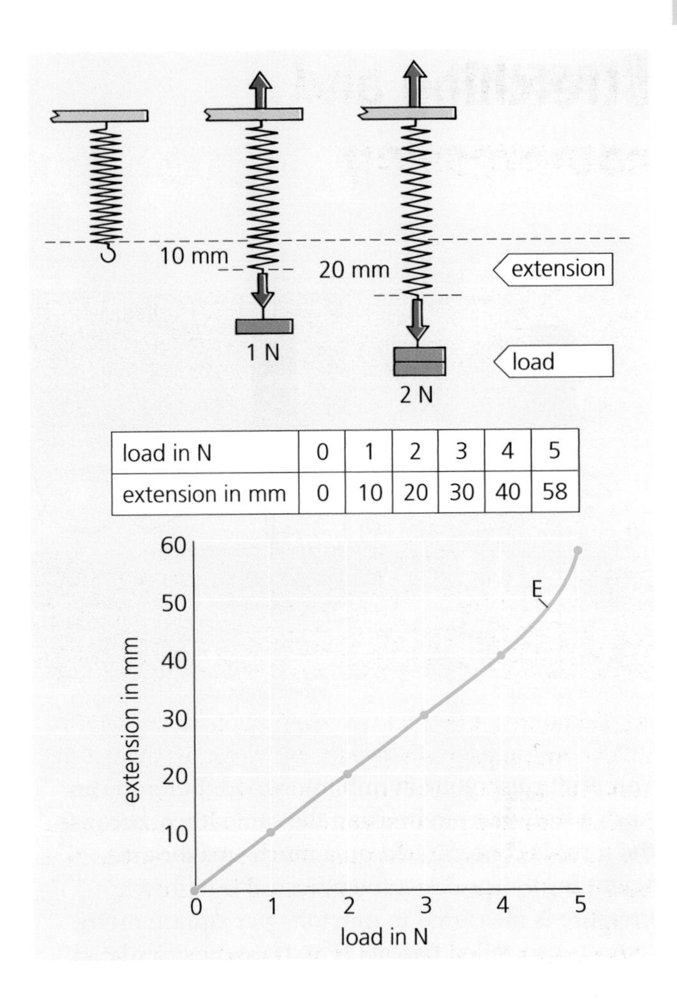

load in N	0	1	2	3	4	5
extension in mm	0	10	20	30	40	58

The readings can be used to plot a graph of extension against load.
Up to the point X:

1 The graph is a straight line through the origin.
2 Every extra 1 N of load produces the same extra extension (10 mm in this case).
3 If the load is doubled, the extension is doubled, and so on.

Mathematically, these all mean that the extension is directly proportional to the load. This is sometimes called **Hooke's law**.

Steel bars don't stretch as much as springs. But they obey the same law. So do glass, wood, and many other materials. However, rubber does not. When a rubber band is stretched, the graph line is curved, not straight.

E is the **elastic limit**. If this point is passed, the spring doesn't go back to its original length when the load is removed. It ends up longer than before.

Questions

1 a Write down the parts of the ridge tent which are under tension; in compression; bending.

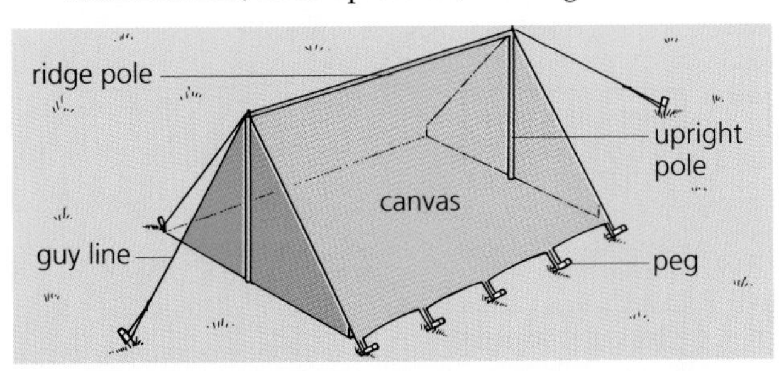

b What would happen to the ridge pole if its elastic limit were exceeded?

c The force on the guy line is increased. The guy line doesn't break. What does happen to it? How would the result be different if a thicker guy line, made from the same material, were used?

2 The table shows the readings taken in a spring-stretching experiment:

Load in N	0	1	2	3	4	5	6
Length in mm	40	49	58	67	76	88	110
Extension in mm							

a Copy and complete the table.
b What is the unstretched length of the spring?
c Plot a graph of extension against load.
d Mark the elastic limit on your graph. What happens to the spring beyond this point?
e What load is needed to produce an extension of 35 mm?
f What load is needed to make the spring stretch to 65 mm long?

Pressure

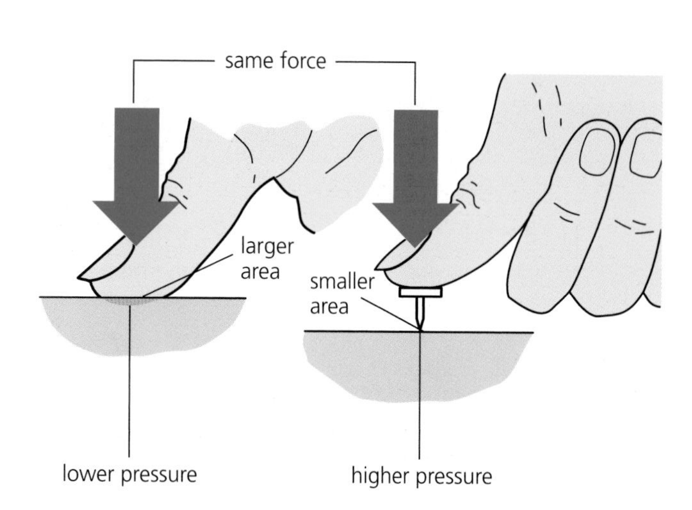

You can't push your thumb into wood. But you can push a drawing pin in using the same force, because the force is concentrated on a much smaller area. Scientifically speaking, the **pressure** is higher. Pressure is measured in **newtons per square metre** (**N/m²**), also called **pascals** (**Pa**). It can be calculated with this equation:

$$\text{pressure} = \frac{\text{force}}{\text{area}}$$

where force is measured in newtons (N), and area in square metres (m^2).

For example:

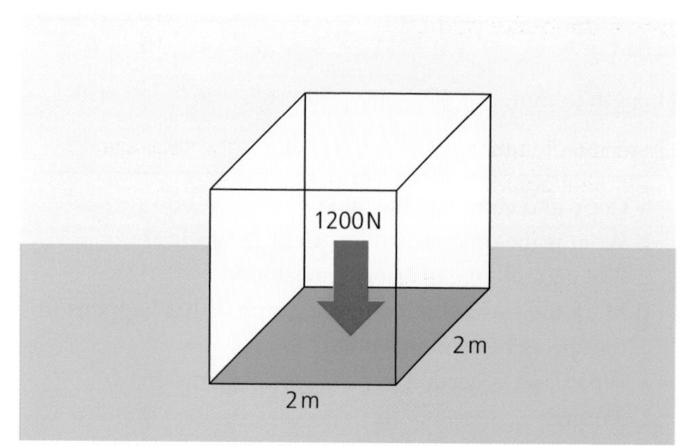

Above, a force of 1200N pushes (at right angles) on an area measuring 2 m × 2 m. So the area is 4 m^2. Therefore:

$$\text{pressure} = \frac{\text{force}}{\text{area}} = \frac{1200}{4} = 300\,\text{Pa}$$

Skis reduce the pressure on the snow by increasing the area over which your weight is spread.

Liquid pressure

The deeper you go into a liquid, the greater the pressure becomes. This pressure pushes in all directions:

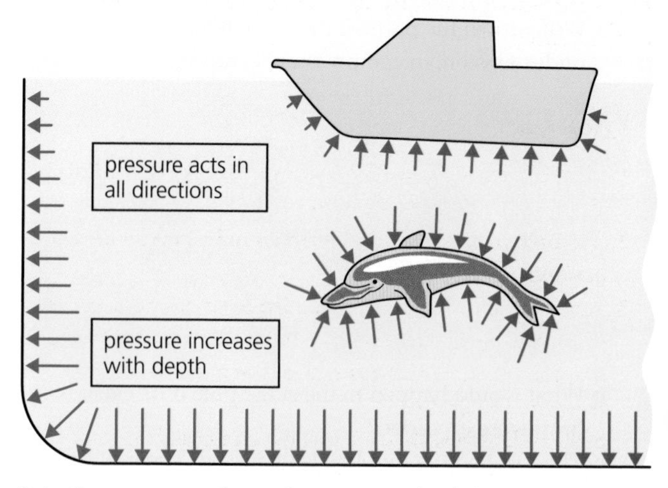

It is the pressure from the water which keeps a boat afloat. Water pressing on the hull produces an upward push called an **upthrust** which is strong enough to support the weight of the boat.

Hydraulic machines

These are machines in which liquids are used to transmit forces. Machines like this rely on two features of liquids:

- Liquids cannot be squashed. They are virtually incompressible.
- If a trapped liquid is put under pressure, the pressure is transmitted throughout the liquid.

The diagram below shows a simple hydraulic jack. When you press on the narrow piston, the pressure is transmitted by the oil to the wide piston. It produces an output force which is larger than the input force. In other words, it is a **force magnifier**.

The shovel on this digger is moved hydraulically.

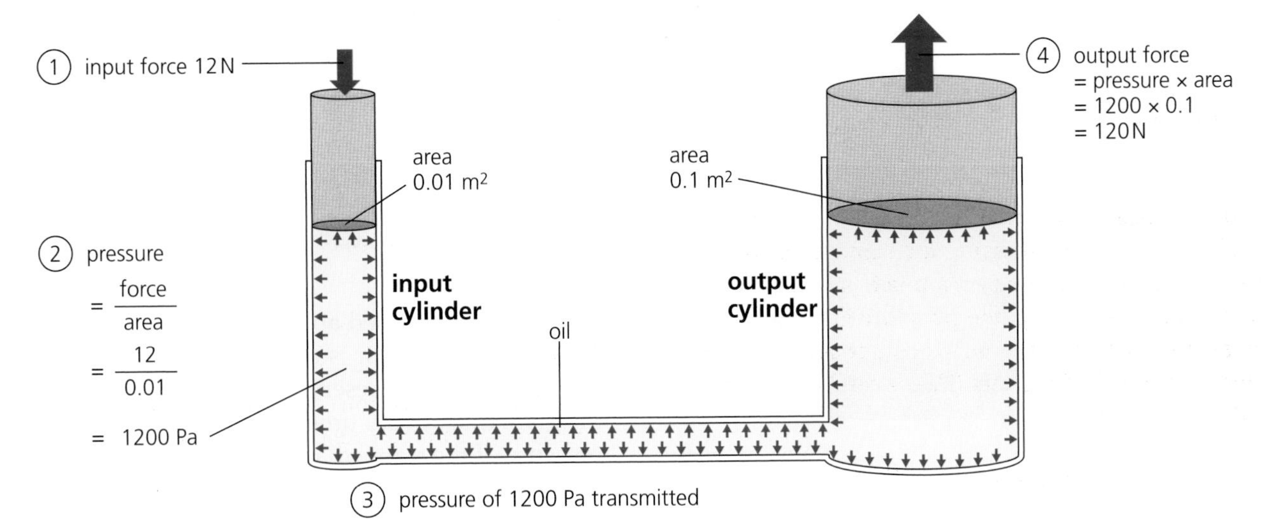

Follow the sequence of circled numbers 1–4 on the diagram above. They show you how to use the link between pressure, force, and area to calculate the pressure transmitted by the liquid, and then the output force.

Car brakes work hydraulically. When the brake pedal is pressed, a piston puts pressure on trapped brake fluid. The pressure is transmitted, by pipes, to the wheels. There, the pressure pushes on pistons which move the brake pads.

Questions

1 Why is it easier to walk on soft sand if you have flat shoes rather than shoes with small heels?

2 If a force of 12 N presses (at right angles) on an area of $4 m^2$, what is the pressure?

3 A rectangular block measures 4 m × 3 m × 2 m. It weighs 600 N and rests with one face on level ground. Draw a diagram to show the position of the block when the pressure under it is:

a as high as possible. **b** as low as possible.

Calculate the pressure in each case.

(Area of a rectangle = length × width)

4 In the simple hydraulic system on the right:

a what is the pressure of the oil?

b what is the output force?

c if the diameter of the output cylinder were greater, how would this affect the output force?

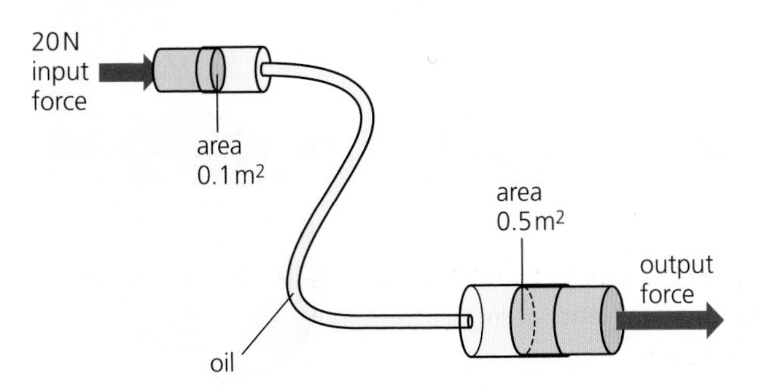

FT5 Squashed gases

Pressure problems

This diver is hunting for pearl oysters. At 30 metres, she is ten times deeper than the bottom of a swimming pool. She has been underwater for over two minutes. And she isn't using any breathing apparatus. The pressure on the diver is around four times that of atmospheric pressure. To survive, she has to expand her lungs to the limit before diving. Even so, on reaching the seabed, her lungs are so squashed that the air in them takes up only a quarter of its normal volume.

More squashed air

Pump air into a motor cycle tyre and it is squashed into about one-third of its normal space. Then, the tyre is full of air at roughly three times the outside pressure. Like all gases, air has a greater pressure when its volume is reduced.

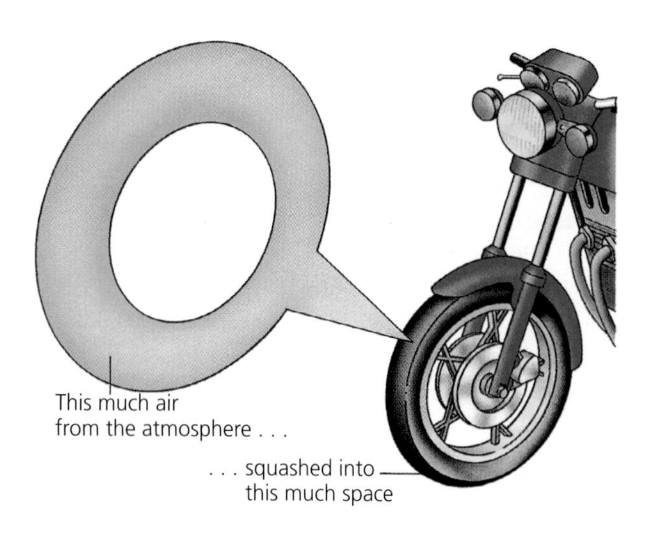

How pressure and volume are linked

This is the equipment you might use to find the connection between the pressure of a gas and its volume:

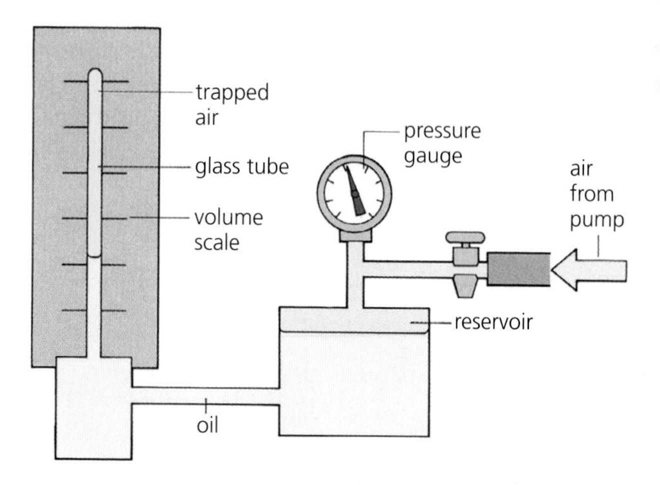

The gas is air, trapped above the oil in the glass tube. The volume of the air is reduced in stages by pumping outside air into the reservoir. This forces more oil up the glass tube. Every time the volume is reduced, the pressure of the trapped air is measured on the gauge. Squashing the air warms it slightly, so you have to wait a few moments after each reading for the air to settle to its original temperature.

Here are some typical readings:

volume in cm^3	50	40	25	20	10
pressure in mm of mercury	800	1000	1600	2000	4000

There are two connections between the readings:

1 If the *volume* is *halved* then the *pressure* is doubled, and so on.

2 Multiplying the *pressure* by the *volume* gives the same value every time – in this case, 40000.

The air obeys **Boyle's law**:

If a fixed mass of gas is kept at a steady temperature, pressure × volume stays the same.

Most other gases obey this law too.

Using Boyle's law

This is the type of problem you could solve using Boyle's law:

Problem A diver working on the seabed is breathing out air bubbles. The air in each bubble has a volume of $2 cm^3$, and a pressure of 3 atmospheres. Up on the surface, the pressure is 1 atmosphere. *What is the volume of a bubble when it reaches the surface?*

If the temperature doesn't change, pressure × volume stays the same. So,

pressure on seabed × volume on seabed = pressure at surface × volume at surface

Filling in the figures,

$3 atm \times 2 cm^3 = 1 atm \times$ volume at surface

Rearrange this, and the volume of the bubble at the surface works out to be $6 cm^3$.

Concentrating the molecules

The diagrams show why the pressure rises when a gas is squashed:

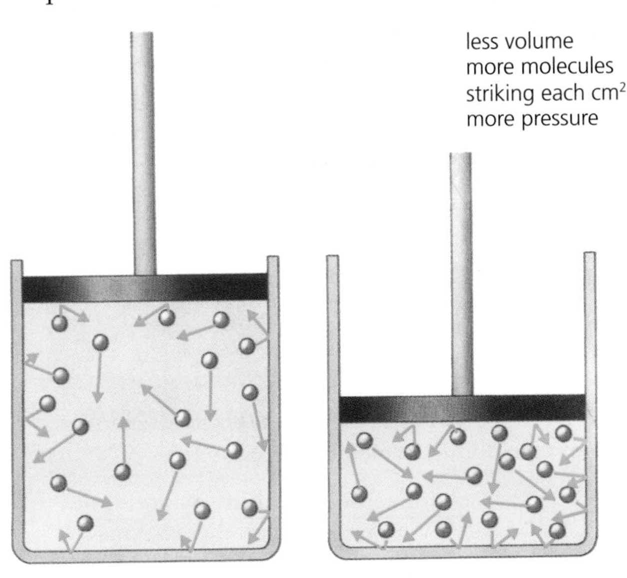

The pressure is caused by fast-moving gas molecules colliding with the sides of the container. If the gas is compressed into a smaller space, the molecules become more concentrated. Each square centimetre of the container sides has more molecules striking it. So the pressure is greater.

Pressure units

Here are some of the units of pressure you may come across:

pascal (Pa) This is the SI unit of pressure. It is a pressure of 1 newton per square metre (N/m^2).

kilopascal (kPa) This is 1000 Pa.

atmosphere (atm) This is 101 325 Pa. It is standard atmospheric pressure: the pressure of the atmosphere at the Earth's surface.

mm of mercury (mmHg) Atmospheric pressure is measured using a barometer. At standard atmospheric pressure, the height of the column in a mercury barometer is 760 mm. So 1 atm = 760 mmHg.

millibar (mb) Meteorologists use this unit. 1 mb = 100 Pa. So standard atmospheric pressure is about 1000 millibars.

Questions

1 According to Boyle's law, if a gas is squashed into a quarter of its original volume, and the temperature does not change, what happens to the pressure?

2 This question is about the experiment and the table of readings on the opposite page.

a If the *volume* of the gas were only $5 cm^3$, what would the *pressure* be?

b Plot a graph of *pressure* (side axis) against *volume* (bottom axis).

c From your graph, read off the *pressure* of the gas when the *volume* is **i** $30 cm^3$ **ii** $15 cm^3$.

d Plot a graph of *pressure* against 1/*volume*. (First, use a calculator to work out values of 1/*volume*.) What shape is your graph?

3 The balloon right contains $6 m^3$ of helium at a pressure of 100 kPa. As the balloon rises through the atmosphere, the pressure falls and the balloon expands. Assuming that the temperature does not change, what is the volume of the balloon when the pressure has fallen to:

a 50 kPa?

b 40 kPa?

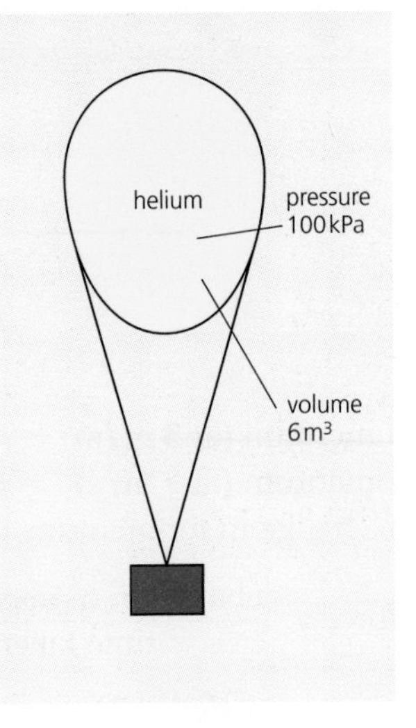

FT6 Momentum

On the right, you can see a massive truck travelling very fast. People sometimes say that a truck like this has lots of **momentum**. However, to scientists, momentum is something that can be calculated. They use this equation:

momentum = mass × velocity

For example, if a model car of mass 2kg has a velocity of 3m/s:

momentum = 2 × 3 = 6kgm/s

Like velocity, momentum is a vector, so a + or – is often used to show its direction. For example:

if car moves to right: momentum = +6kgm/s
if car moves to left: momentum = –6kgm/s

Force and momentum

There is a link between force and momentum:

$$\text{force} = \frac{\text{change in momentum}}{\text{time taken}}$$

You could use this equation to calculate the force in newtons (N) needed to make a 2kg model car accelerate from 3m/s to 9m/s in 4 seconds:

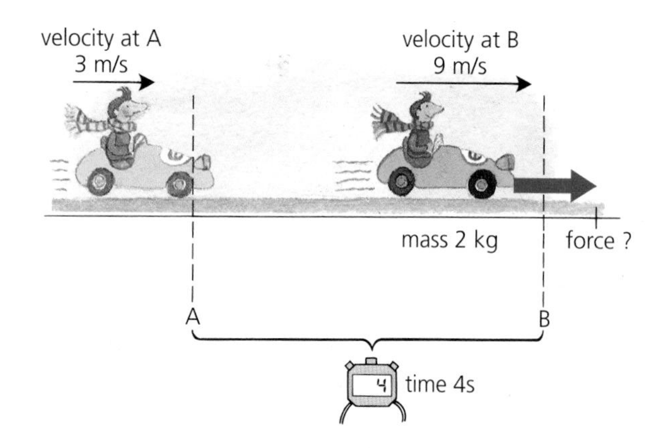

momentum (at 3 m/s) = 2 × 3 = 6kgm/s
momentum (at 9 m/s) = 2 × 9 = 18kgm/s
So, change in momentum = 18 – 6 = 12kgm/s

$$\text{S force} = \frac{\text{change in momentum}}{\text{time taken}} = \frac{12}{4} = 3$$

So, force needed = 3N

Equation links

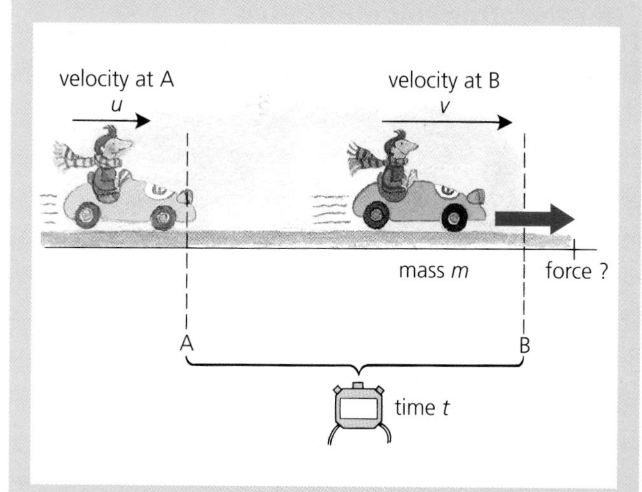

Above, a force makes a car of mass m accelerate from velocity u to velocity v in time t.

$$\text{force} = \frac{\text{change in momentum}}{\text{time taken}} = \frac{mv - mu}{t} \quad (1)$$

$$= m\left(\frac{v-u}{t}\right)$$

But $\left(\frac{v-u}{t}\right)$ is the car's acceleration.

So, force = mass × acceleration (2)

This shows that (1) and (2) are really different versions of the same equation. This equation is sometimes called **Newton's second law of motion**.

Conserving momentum

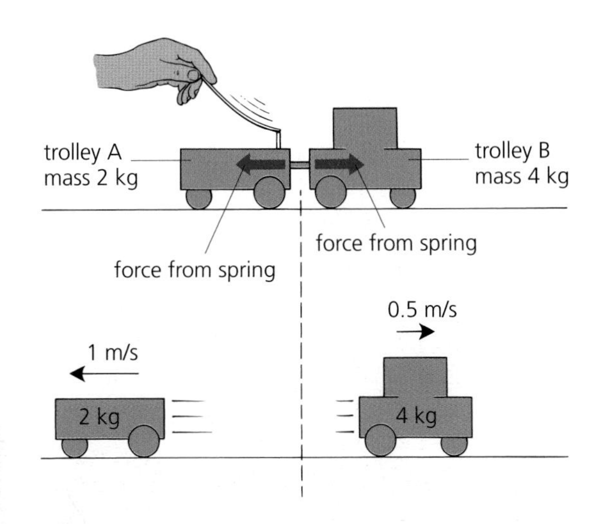

At first, the trolleys A and B above are at rest. Then a spring is released between them so that they shoot off in opposite directions. The trolley with the lower mass gains the higher velocity.

The diagram shows some typical mass and velocity values. Using these, you can work out the momentum changes taking place (note: a + or – is used to show motion to the right or left):

Before spring is released:
total momentum of trolleys = 0

After spring is released:
momentum of B = 4 × (+0.5) = +2 kg m/s
momentum of A = 2 × (–1) = –2 kg m/s

So, total momentum of trolleys = 2 + (–2) = 0

Note that the total momentum *after* the spring is released is exactly the same as it was *before*. This is an example of the **law of conservation of momentum**:

> Things may push or pull on each other but, if there is no force on them from outside, their total momentum stays the same.

You may be able to see why this law applies to the trolleys. The forces on A and B are equal but opposite. They act for the same time. So they produce equal but opposite changes in momentum. The change to the left cancels the change to the right, so the total momentum is unchanged.

Rocket thrust

Engineers can use the equation linking force and momentum to calculate the **thrust** (force) from a rocket or jet engine. For example:

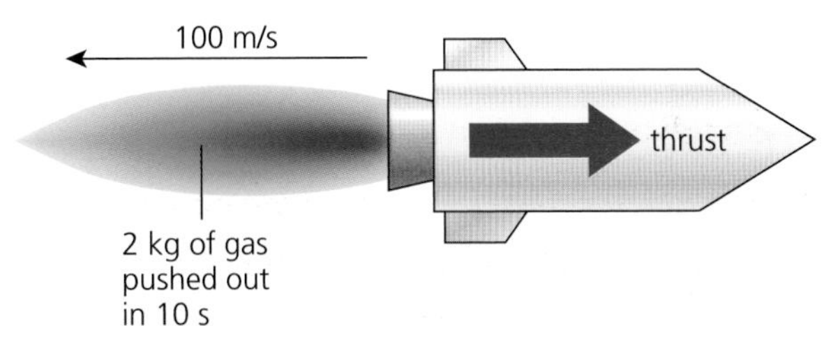

In 10 seconds, a model rocket pushes out 2 kg of exhaust gas at a velocity of 100 m/s.

change of momentum of exhaust gas
= 2 × 100 = 200 kg m/s

$$\text{force} = \frac{\text{change in momentum}}{\text{time}} = \frac{200}{10} = 20\,\text{N}$$

This force pushed the exhaust gas backwards.
By Newton's third law, an equal but opposite force must be pushing the rocket forward. So:

thrust from rocket engine = 20 N

Questions

	mass in kg	velocity in m/s
car	1000	5
motor cycle	200	30

1 In the table:
  a What is the momentum of the car?
  b Which has more momentum, the car or the motor cycle?
  c Which would have more momentum if they were both travelling at the same velocity?

2 What force is needed to make a 10 kg mass accelerate from 2 m/s to 4 m/s in 5 seconds?

3 What is the force from a rocket engine which, in 2 seconds, pushes out 4 kg of exhaust gas at a velocity of 200 m/s?

4 An astronaut floating in space kicks against a rock also floating in space. If the astronaut has a mass of 100 kg, the rock has a mass of 200 kg, and the rock gains a velocity of 2 m/s to the right, what velocity does the astronaut gain to the left?

FT7 Curves and circles

Downwards, sideways . . .

Below, you can see what happens if one ball is dropped and another is thrown sideways at the same time. (Here, the balls are heavy and the effects of air resistance are too small to notice.)

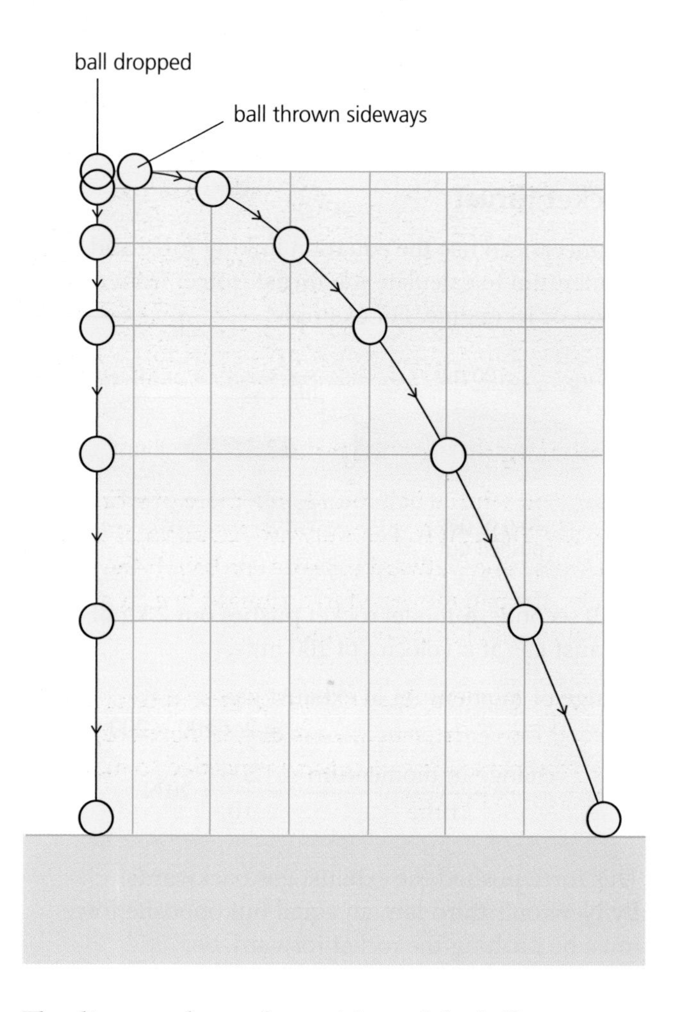

The diagram shows the positions of the balls at regular time intervals (every 1/10 second). If you study the diagram, you will notice two things:

- Both balls hit the ground at the same time. They have exactly the same downward acceleration (g, $10 m/s^2$).
- As it falls, the second ball moves sideways over the ground at a steady speed. In other words, its horizontal velocity is constant.

Results like this show that, if something is falling freely, its vertical and horizontal movements are quite independent of each other.

. . . and into orbit

The diagram below shows a 'thought experiment'. An astronaut is standing on a tall tower, high above the atmosphere, where there is no air resistance. She is so strong that she can throw a ball at the speed of a rocket!

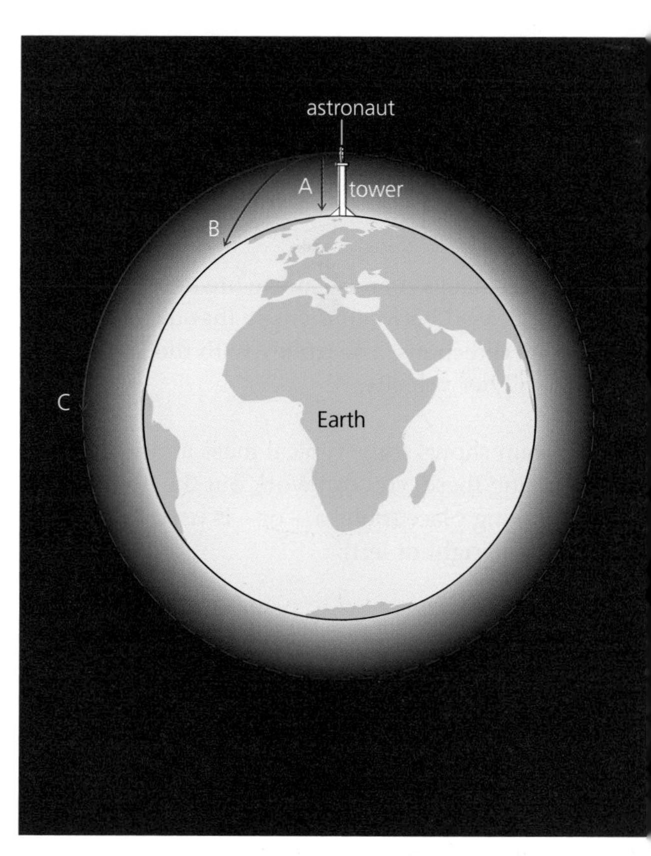

Ball A is dropped. It accelerates downwards, straight to the ground.

Ball B is thrown horizontally. It too accelerates downwards. But it also moves sideways at a steady speed.

Ball C is thrown horizontally, but much faster. Once again, the ball is falling. But this time, its sideways speed is so fast that the curve of the fall matches the curve of the Earth. The ball is accelerating downwards, but getting no closer to the ground! It is in **orbit** around the Earth.

Satellites are put in orbit by fast, powerful rockets. For a near-Earth orbit, the speed required is about 8 km/s (18 000 m.p.h.). In orbit, a satellite is in free fall, just like a ball.

Moving in circles

Many orbits are circular. Below, you can see another example of circular motion: a ball being whirled round on the end of a piece of string. The person in the middle keeps the ball moving at a steady speed.

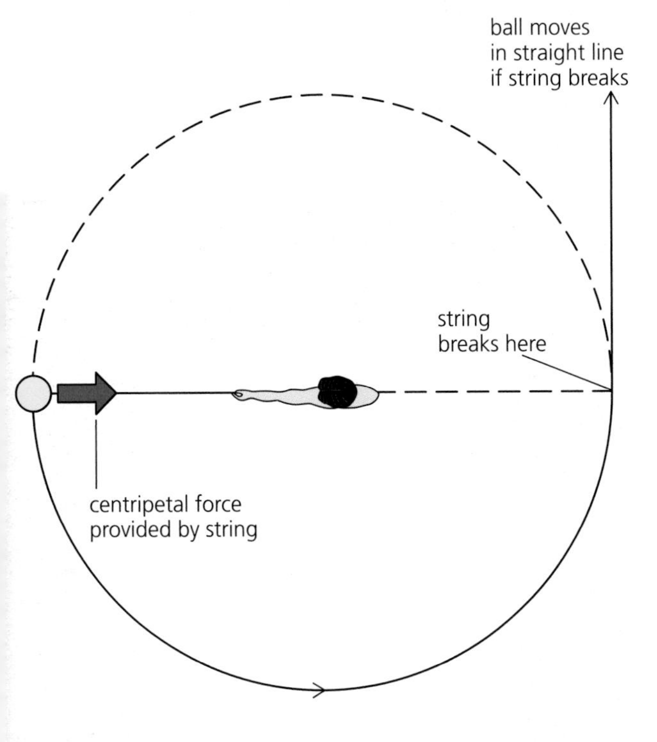

An inward force is needed to make the ball move in a circle. This is called the **centripetal force**. Without it, the ball would move in a straight line, as predicted by Newton's first law of motion.

With the ball above, the string provides the centripetal force. *More* force is needed:

- if the mass of the ball is *greater*;
- if the speed of the ball is *greater*;
- if the radius of the circle is *less*.

For a satellite orbiting the Earth, gravity provides the centripetal force needed to make it move in a circle.

For a car cornering at high speed, sideways friction from the tyres provides the centripetal force needed to make it turn the corner.

Centrifugal or centripetal?

When you whirl a ball round on a piece of string, you may say that you feel an outward 'centrifugal force'. But there is no outward force on the ball. If the string breaks, the ball moves off in a straight line, at a tangent. It isn't flung outwards.

Moving a ball in a circle doesn't *produce* a centripetal force. If the centripetal force is, say, 20 newtons, this tells you that a 20 newton force is needed to make the ball move in the circle.

Questions

1 Below, one bullet is shot from a gun at 50 m/s while another is dropped. The dropped bullet takes 2 seconds to reach the sea. There is no air resistance.

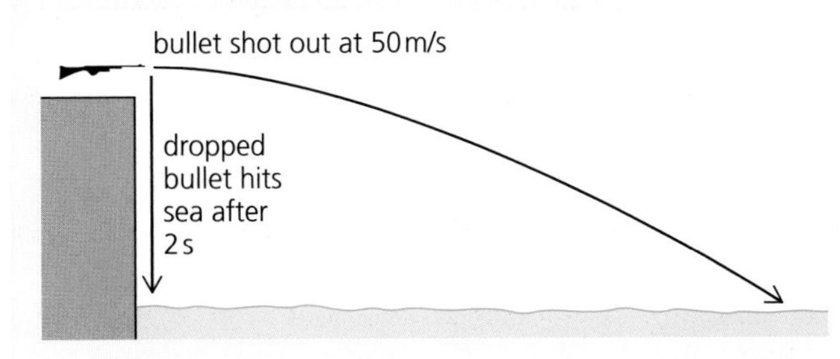

a How long does the bullet from the gun take to reach the sea?

b What is the horizontal velocity of this bullet when it reaches the sea?

c How far is it from the cliff when it reaches the sea?

2 A car goes round a corner:

a What provides the centripetal force?

b Is *more* force or *less* force needed if the car is **i** heavier? **ii** faster? **iii** going round a tighter curve?

c What would happen to the car if there were no centripetal force?

Further exam-style questions

1 A car driver drives from his home at a slow, steady speed. On reaching the motorway he accelerates rapidly and then travels at a high constant speed. Leaving the motorway he decelerates and comes to a halt at a junction.

a Sketch a speed–time graph for the driver's journey.

b Sketch a distance–time graph for the driver's journey.

c Calculate the driver's average speed in km/h if he travels 40 km in 30 minutes.

2 The diagram below shows a velocity–time graph for a free-fall parachutist.

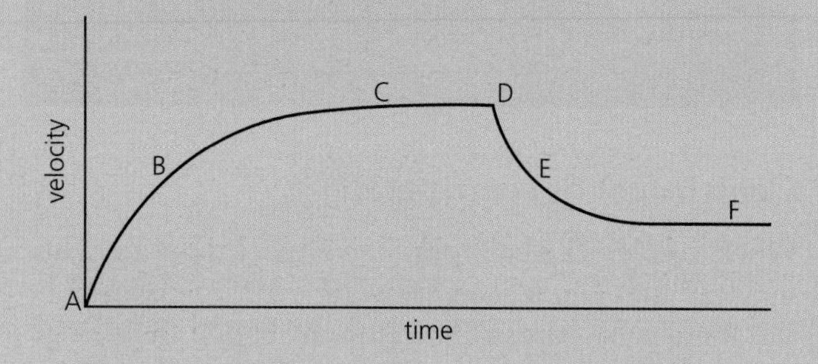

Assuming the acceleration due to gravity is 10 m/s^2:

a What is the acceleration of the parachutist at point A on the graph?

b Why is the acceleration of the parachutist decreasing in part B of the graph?

c Explain why the parachutist is travelling at his terminal velocity in part C of the graph.

d What has happened at point D on the graph?

e What is happening to the parachutist in part E of the graph?

f What is happening to the parachutist in part F of the graph?

3 An electric motor is a device for changing electrical energy into kinetic energy. Suggest a device which will carry out the following energy changes:

a Electrical energy to heat and light energy.

b Chemical energy to electrical energy.

c Light energy to electrical energy.

d Sound energy to electrical energy.

e Electrical energy to sound.

f Chemical energy to heat and light.

4 a Explain the following sentences.
Coal is a non-renewable source of energy.
Wind is a renewable source of energy.

b Name one other non-renewable source of energy.

c Name one other renewable source of energy.

d Give one advantage and one disadvantage of using the source of energy you have given as an answer for **c**.

5 The diagram below shows a simple series circuit containing a cell, a switch, and a bulb. When the switch is closed, a current of 0.2 A flows through the bulb.

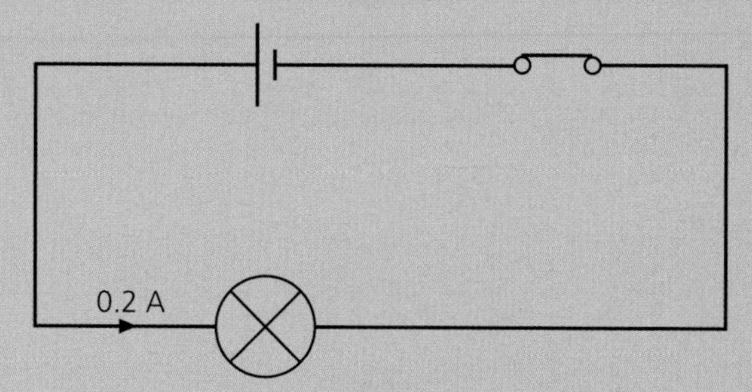

a What current will flow if a second, identical bulb is connected in series with the first?

b What current will flow from the cell if the second bulb is now connected in parallel with the first bulb?

6 The diagram below shows a battery, ammeter, and bulb connected in series. A voltmeter is connected in parallel with the bulb.

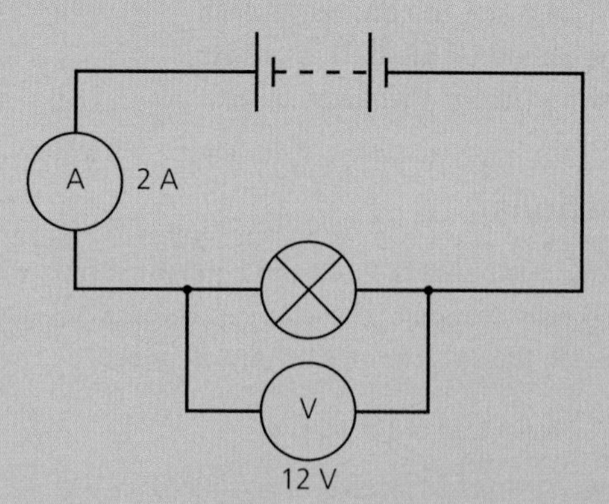

a Calculate the power of the bulb.

b How much energy is converted by the bulb in 10 seconds?

c What energy change takes place inside the bulb?

7 a There are three commonly available fuses that can be used in a three-pin mains plug. These are rated at 3 A, 5 A, and 13 A. Electricity from the mains is supplied at 240 V.
Which of these three fuses would be suitable for use with each of the following appliances?
i A bulb rated at 60 W.
ii A TV set rated at 600 W.
iii A hair drier rated at 1.1 kW.
iv A kettle rated at 2 kW.
b Explain what happens to a fuse if too much current passes through the circuit.

8 The diagram below shows the inside of a three-pin plug.

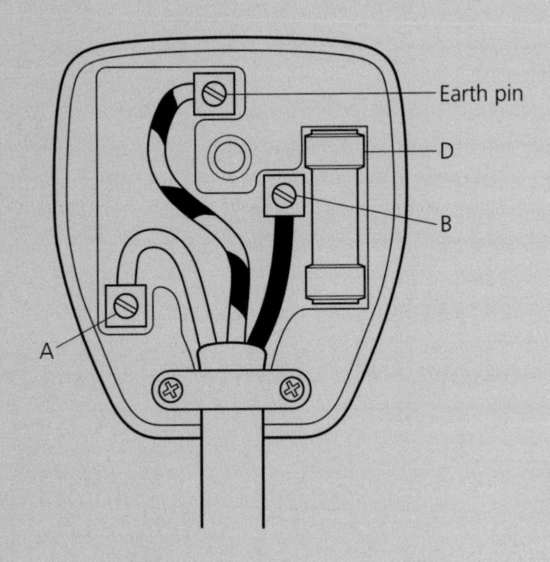

a What is the name of pin A?
b What is the name of pin B?
c What is the colour of the wire connected to the Earth pin?
d Explain why there is an Earth pin.
e What is D?

9 a If electrical energy costs 7p per kW h, calculate the cost of running the following:
i A 3 kW fire for 6 hours.
ii A 1.2 kW hair drier for 30 minutes.
iii A 100 W bulb for 10 hours.
b What is the National Grid?

10 The diagram below shows two resistors connected in parallel.

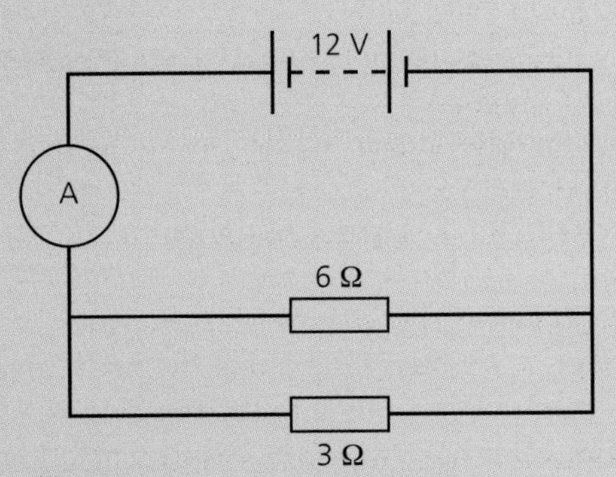

a What is the component A?
b Calculate the current flowing through the 6 Ω resistor.
c Calculate the current flowing through the 3 Ω resistor.
d What current flows through A?

11 A student using the circuit shown below investigates the relationship between the current flowing through a resistor and the p.d. (voltage) across it.

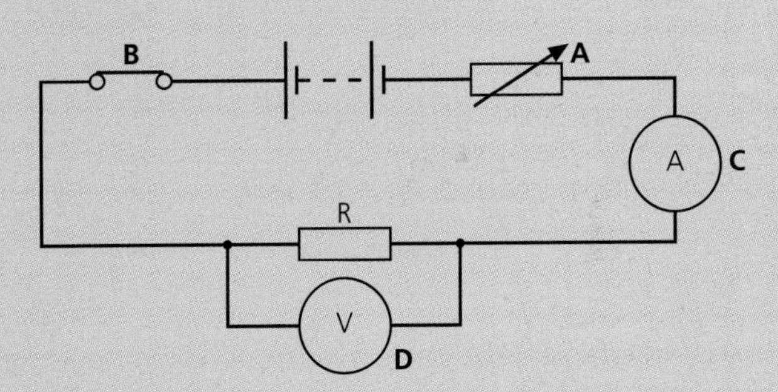

a What is **A**?
b What is **B**?
c What is **C**?
d What is **D**?

The student's results are shown in the table below.

p.d. (V)	0	2	4	6	8	10	12
current (A)	0	0.25	0.50	0.80	1.00	1.25	1.50

e Plot a graph of p.d. against current.
f Which result appears to have been measured incorrectly?
g Does the resistor obey Ohm's law? Explain your answer.
h What is the resistance of the resistor R?

12 A car headlamp is rated at 12 V 36 W.

a What energy change takes place inside the bulb?

b At what rate does this energy change take place, in J/s?

c Calculate the current which flows through the bulb.

d Calculate the resistance of the bulb.

13 The graph below shows part of the journey of a bus driver. After travelling along the main road for several minutes he pulls into the bus station. Sometime later he drives out of the bus station and continues his journey.

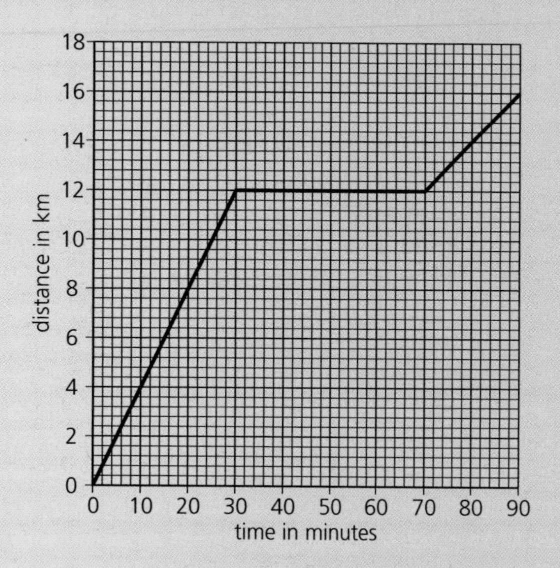

a How far did the bus driver travel before pulling into the bus station?

b How long did the bus driver stop in the bus station?

c What was the average speed of the bus before pulling into the bus station?

d Was the journey after the stop at a faster or slower speed? Explain your answer.

14 The diagram below shows waves being produced in a ripple tank by a wave machine.

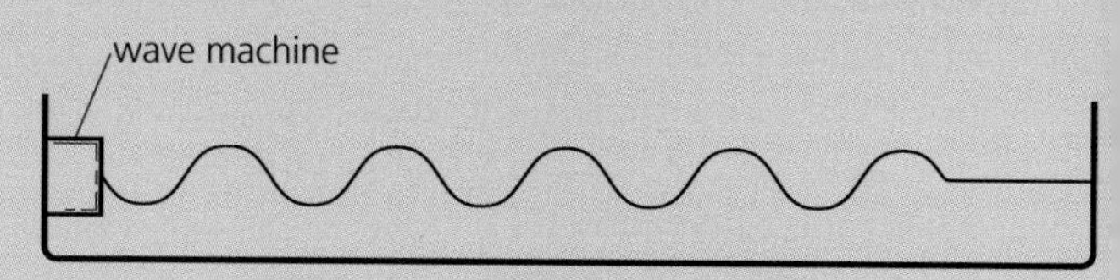

a How many water waves are shown in the diagram?

b If the above waves were produced in 2.5 seconds, what is their frequency?

c If the wavelength of the water waves is 5 cm, calculate their speed.

15 A crane lifts a load of 500 N through a height of 30 m in 20 s.

a What kind of energy has the load gained after the lift has been completed?

b Calculate the work done by the crane.

c Suggest one reason why the crane will have done more work than the value you calculated in **b**.

d Calculate the power of the crane.

16 The diagram below shows a bar magnet, and a coil of wire connected to a sensitive ammeter.

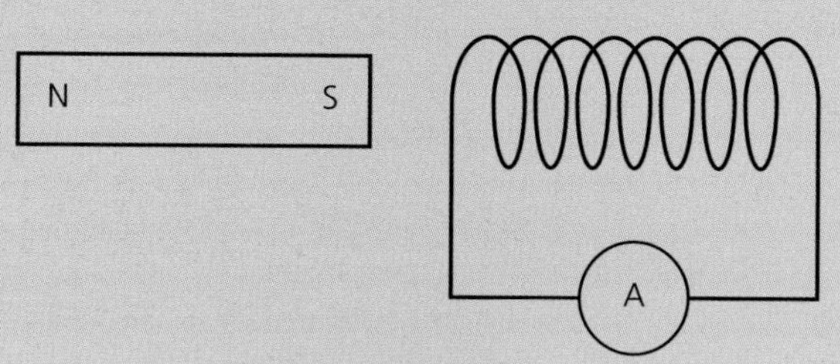

a As the magnet was pushed slowly into the coil, the ammeter pointer moved 10 divisions to the right.
What would you expect to happen if:

i the magnet is pulled slowly out of the coil?

ii the magnet is held stationary inside the coil?

iii the magnet is turned around so that its north pole is nearer the coil, and then pushed quickly into the coil?

b Explain in your own words why the ammeter deflects.

17 The diagram below shows the flow of heat from the inside of a house to the outside through a cavity wall.

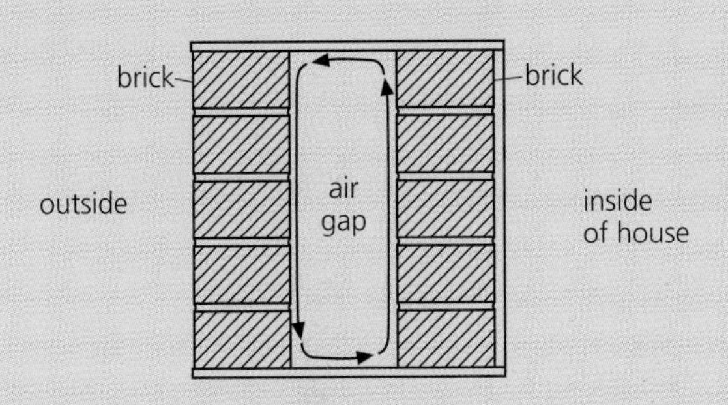

- **a** Why will heat flow from the inside of a house to the outside?
- **b** By what method is heat transferred through the bricks?
- **c** By what method is heat transferred across the air gap?
- **d** Suggest what could be done to reduce the rate at which heat flows across the air gap.

18 The diagram below shows the flow of energy through a coal-burning power station.

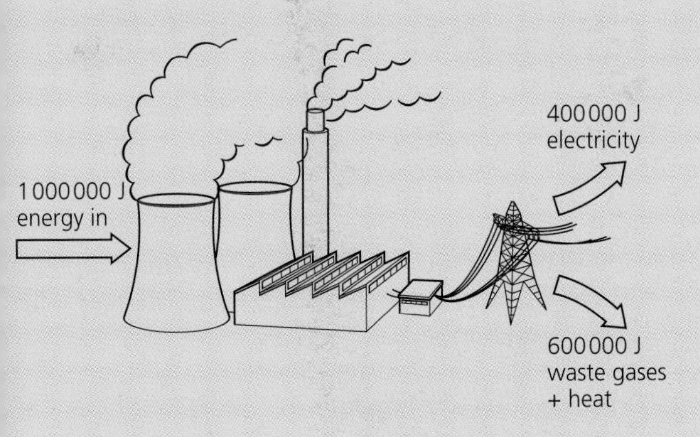

$$\text{efficiency} = \frac{\text{useful energy output}}{\text{total energy input}} \times 100\%$$

- **a** Calculate the efficiency of the above power station.
- **b** Explain how the energy released when the coal is burned is used to produce electricity.
- **c** How is this electrical energy then sent to towns and cities many miles from the power station?

19 The diagram below shows how light travels along an optical fibre.

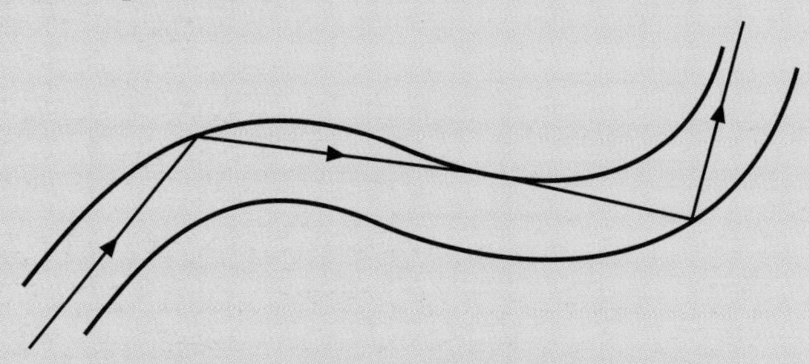

- **a** Explain why the ray of light does not emerge from the sides of the optical fibre.
- **b** Describe one use of an optical fibre.

20
- **a** Name the two types of seismic wave which are emitted when an earthquake occurs.
- **b** What is a longitudinal wave?
- **c** What is a transverse wave?
- **d** Which seismic wave is transverse?
- **e** Which seismic wave cannot travel through a liquid?

21 The diagram below shows the northern part of the Earth.

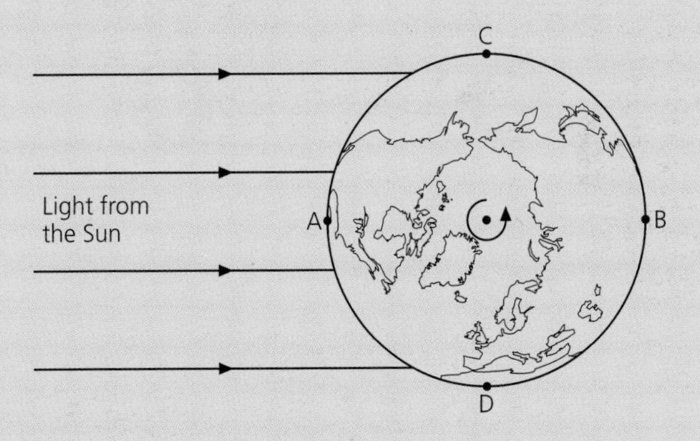

- **a** Approximately what time of day is it on the Earth's surface at:
  - **i** point A on the Earth's surface?
  - **ii** point B on the Earth's surface?
  - **iii** point C on the Earth's surface?
  - **iv** point D on the Earth's surface?
- **b** How long does it take the Earth to make one complete rotation around its axis?

22 The diagram below shows what happens to the radiation from three different radioactive substances when different materials are put in front of them.

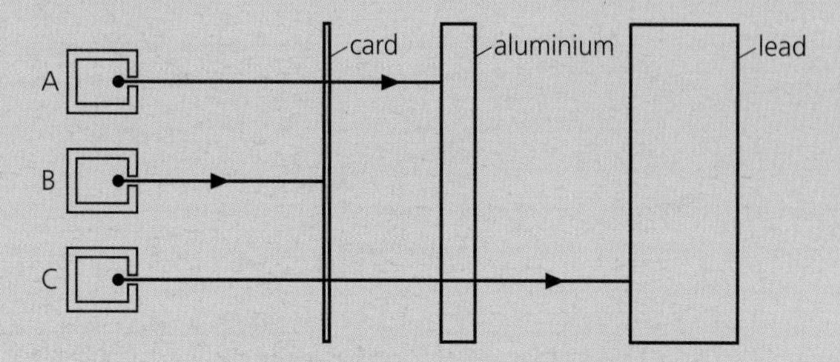

a Which type of radiation is being emitted by each of the three sources?

b Which of these three types of radiation are charged?

c Which of these three types of radiation is the strongest ionizer?

d Name one way in which all three types of radiation could be detected.

23 The diagram below shows a toy car.

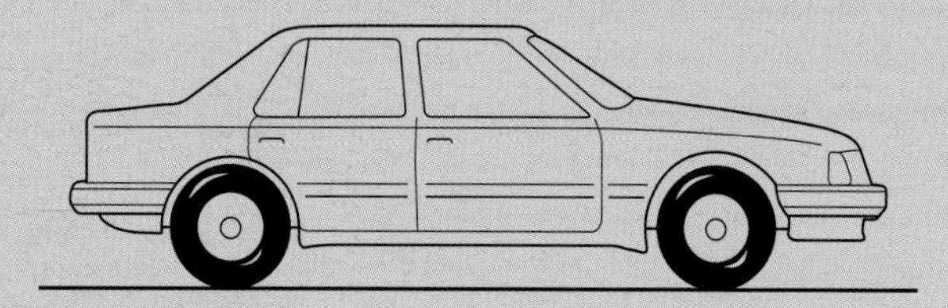

a Name three energy sources which could be placed in the car to make it move.

b What kind of energy does the car have when it is moving?

c Explain as fully as you can the phrase 'renewable source of energy'.

24 The diagram below shows a tumble dryer.

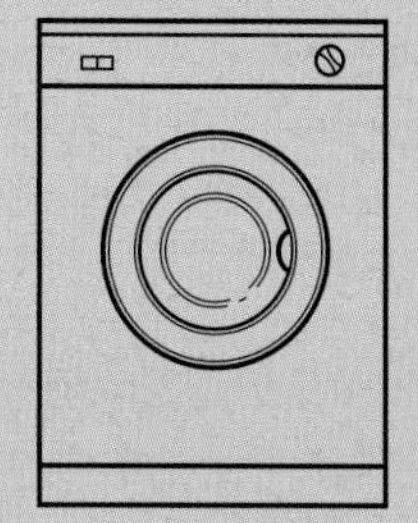

a Copy out the sentence below and fill in the missing words.

The tumble dryer converts __________ energy into __________ energy and __________ energy.

b The power of the dryer is 1.5 kW. Calculate the number of Units of electricity it uses if it is turned on for 40 minutes.

c Calculate the cost of using the dryer for this time if the cost of 1 Unit of electricity is 9p.

25 This question is about the electromagnetic spectrum.

a Which statement about electromagnetic waves is correct?

A They all have the same wavelength.

B They all have the same frequency.

C They all travel at the same speed in air.

b Name TWO types of electromagnetic wave which could be used to cook food.

c Name ONE type of electromagnetic wave used for communicating over large distances.

26 The diagram below shows a sledge sliding across some ice.

a As sledges slide across the ice, they slow down and eventually stop. Explain why this happens.

b Write down **two** effects the sliding sledges will have on the ice.

27 Prisms can be used to alter the direction of a ray of light.

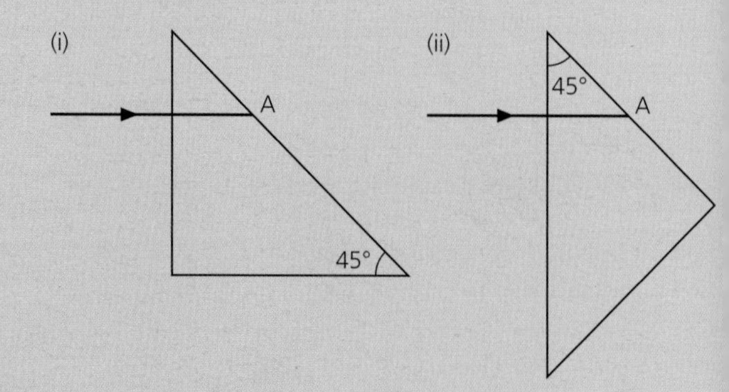

a Copy the diagrams above into your book and complete them showing accurately the paths the rays will take.

b What happens to each of the rays at point A inside the prisms?

c By how many degrees does each prism alter the directions of the rays of light?

d Name one use of a reflecting prism.

28

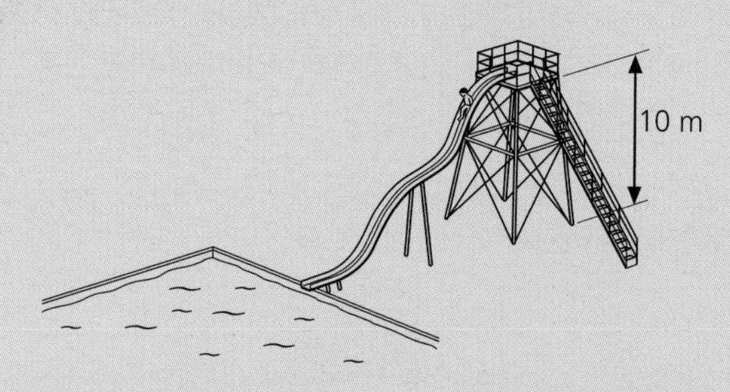

The diagram above shows a water slide. It is 10 m high.

A boy weighing 600 N climbs to the top of the slide.

a Calculate the work done by the boy in climbing to the top of the slide.

b What kind of energy has the boy gained when he is at the top of the slide?

c If it takes the boy 10 seconds to climb to the top of the slide, calculate his power during this time.

d What kind of energy does the boy have just before hitting the water at the bottom of the slide?

e What happens to this energy after the boy has come to a stop in the water?

29 a What are P waves?

b How are P waves different from S waves?

c The graph below shows how the speed of P waves change as they travel through the Earth.

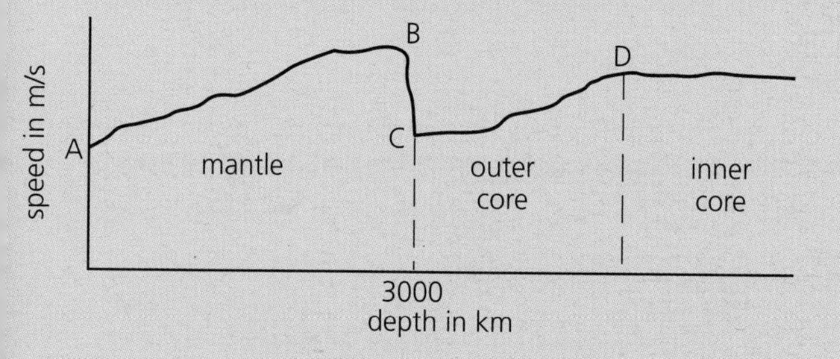

i What is happening to the speed of the P waves between A and B? Explain your answer.

ii What happens to the speed of the P waves at a depth of 3000 km? Explain your answer.

30 Most of the energy requirements for industrialized countries come from burning fossil fuels.

a Name three fossil fuels.

b Why are these fuels called fossil fuels?

c Why are they described as non-renewable sources of energy?

d Explain how burning fossil fuels may contribute to:

i global warming;

ii acid rain.

e Name three alternative sources of energy. Give one advantage and one disadvantage of using each of the alternative sources you have named.

31

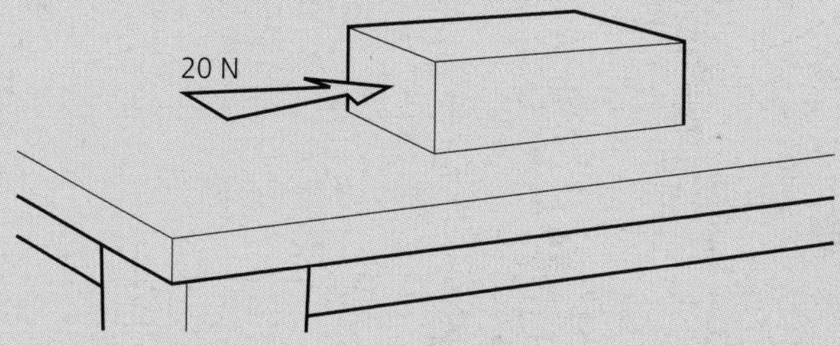

The diagram above shows a box weighing 10 N on a table. A horizontal force of 20 N is applied to the box but it does NOT move!

a Copy the diagram of the box into your book and add other arrows showing the forces acting on the box. Where possible show the sizes of the forces.

b In which direction are frictional forces acting?

c How could these frictional forces be reduced?

d If the applied force is increased to 50 N and the box moves 50 cm calculate the work done on the box.

32 The diagram below shows a graph for a short car journey.

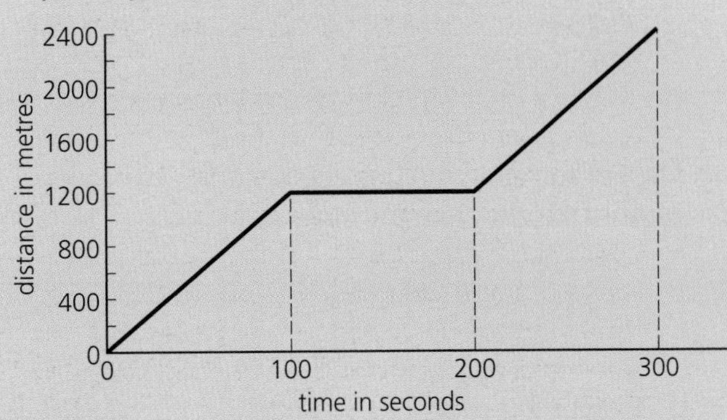

a Describe how the car is moving during the first 100 seconds.

b Describe the motion of the car between 100 seconds and 200 seconds.

c Calculate the speed of the car during the first 100 seconds.

d Calculate the average speed of the car for the whole journey.

33 The diagram below represents an atom of beryllium. It has a mass number of 9.

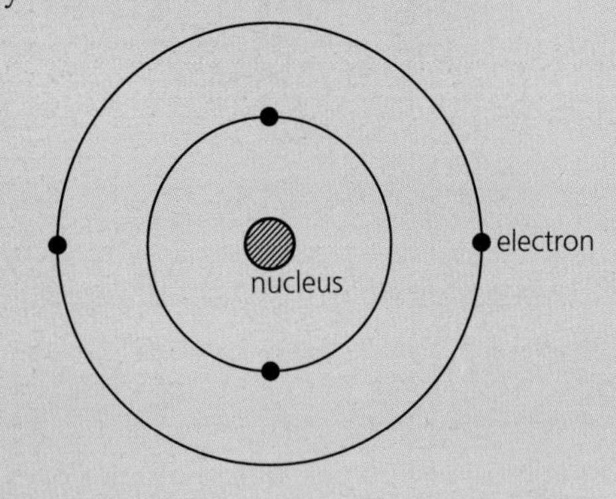

a What is the proton number for beryllium?

b How many charged particles are there in the atom?

c How many uncharged particles are there in the nucleus?

d What are the positively charged particles in the nucleus called?

e Explain how the electrons are held in orbit around the nucleus.

f What is:

i a positive ion?

ii a negative ion?

34 Satellites are often placed in polar orbits or geostationary orbits around the Earth.

a Sketch a diagram of the Earth. Add a typical polar orbit and geostationary orbit to your diagram.

b Give one use for a satellite in each of these orbits.

c What forces keep satellites in orbit around the Earth?

d Describe in detail how the Solar System was formed. Draw diagrams to illustrate your explanation.

35 The diagram below shows the wiring of a 13 A three-pin plug.

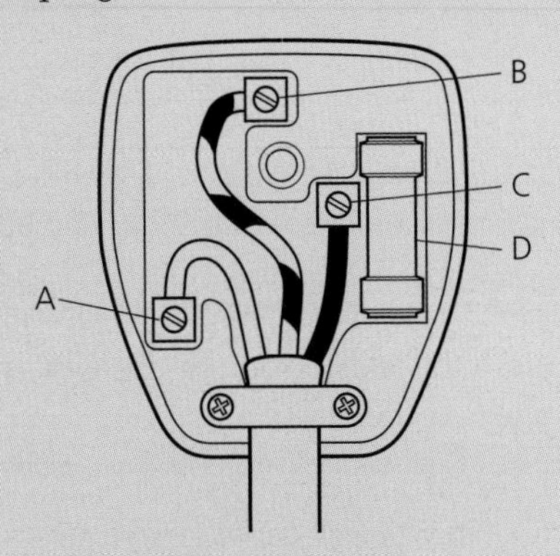

a Copy the table below into your books. Fill in the empty spaces.

Wire	Name	Colour
A		
B		green and yellow
C		

b What is D and what does it do?

c Many domestic appliances are 'double insulated'. What does this phrase mean?

d A 500 W drill is connected to the 230 V mains supply. What size fuse should the drill's plug contain: 1 A, 3 A, or 13 A?

36 a Different parts of the electromagnetic spectrum are used for different jobs.
Choose words from this list to complete the table below.

X-rays **light** **microwaves**
radio waves **ultraviolet rays**

Type of radiation	What the radiation is used for
	to send along optical fibres
	to give skin a tan (but can cause cancer in cells)
	to 'see' inside the body
	to send information to and from satellites

b The diagram shows the electromagnetic spectrum.

shortest wavelength → longest wavelength

gamma rays	X rays	ultra-violet rays	light	A	micro-waves	B

i What are A?
ii What are B?

c Where does gamma radiation come from?

37 Ultrasonic waves are used to examine a developing baby inside its mother's womb.
a What are ultrasonic waves?
b Why are ultrasonic waves rather than X-rays used to examine the developing baby?
c Calculate the wavelength of an ultrasonic wave of frequency 30 kHz.
(The speed of sound in air is 340 m/s.)

38 A steam engine is powered by coal. The coal is burned to heat water and change it into steam. The steam is used to move parts of the engine.
a What kind of energy is stored in the coal?
b Steam engines are typically 20–25% efficient in converting the energy stored in the coal into kinetic energy. Suggest four ways in which the stored energy of the coal is lost in non-useful ways.
c Coal is a non-renewable source of energy. Name one renewable fuel.

39 a A radioactive material is thought to be emitting beta radiation. Describe with the help of a diagram how you would confirm that this was true.
b Explain what is meant by the half-life of a radioactive substance.
c The background count in a laboratory is 100 counts per minute. When a radioactive substance was taken out of its lead lined container, the count rate rose to 1000 counts per minute but after 10 minutes had fallen to 325 counts per minute. Calculate the half-life of the substance.
d What would be the *measured* count rate of the substance be after a further 5 minutes?

40 a State the two conditions necessary for total internal reflection to take place.
b Draw diagrams to show how using total internal reflection a prism can turn a ray through **i** 90° or **ii** 180°.
c Explain with diagrams how light travelling down an optic fibre is unable to escape through the walls of the fibre.
d Describe in detail one use of optic fibres.

41 The diagram below shows a room being heated by a radiator.

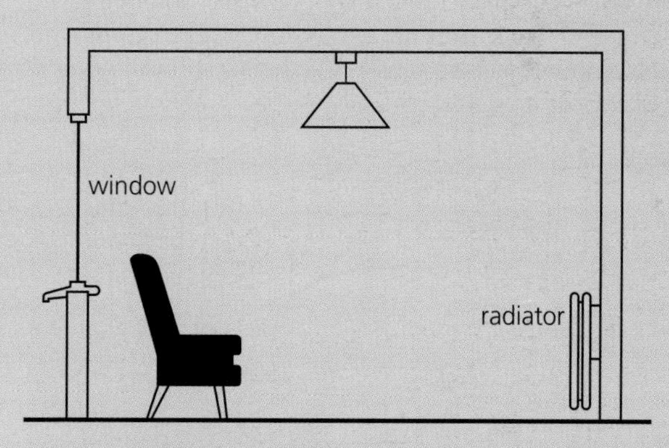

a Describe in detail how the whole room is heated by the radiator. You may draw a diagram if you wish.
b Explain why when the sun shines the black chair becomes very warm.
c If the chair were white, would it still become very warm in the sun? Explain your answer.
d What could be done to the window to reduce any heat escaping through it?

Revision and exam guidance

How to revise

There is no one method of revising which works for everyone. It is therefore important to discover the approach that suits you best. The following rules may serve as general guidelines.

Give yourself plenty of time

Leaving your revision until the last minute reduces your chances of success. There are very few people who can revise everything 'the night before' and still do well in an examination the next day. You need to plan your revision timetable for some weeks before the examinations start.

Plan your revision timetable

Plan your revision timetable well before the examinations start. Once you have done this, follow it – don't be sidetracked. Stick your timetable somewhere prominent where you will keep seeing it – or better still put several around your home!!!!

Relax

You will be working very hard revising. It is as important to give yourself some free time to relax as it is to work. So, build some leisure time into your revision timetable.

Ask others

Friends, relatives, teachers will be happy to help if you ask them. Go and talk to them if you are having any difficulties – don't just give up on something that is causing you a problem. And don't forget your parents too!

Find a quiet corner

Find the conditions in which you can revise most efficiently. Many people think they can revise in a noisy, busy atmosphere – most cannot! And don't try and revise in front of the television – it doesn't generally work. Revision in a distracting environment is very inefficient.

Use routemaps/checklists/pathways...to help you

Use routemaps, checklists or other listing device to help you work your way logically through the material. When you have completed a topic, mark it off. You can also mark off topics you already feel confident about. That way you won't waste time revising unnecessarily.

Make short notes, use colours

As you read through your work or your textbooks make brief notes of the key ideas and facts as you go along. But be sure to concentrate on understanding the ideas rather than just memorizing the facts. Use colours and highlighters to help you.

Practice answering questions

As you finish revising each topic try answering some questions. At first you may need to refer to your notes or textbooks. As you gain confidence you will be able to attempt questions unaided, just as you will in the exam.

Give yourself a break

When you are working, work for perhaps an hour then reward yourself with a short break of 15 to 20 minutes while you have a coffee or cola (then go back for another period of revision.

Success in examinations

If the thought of an examination fills you with dread, then you are probably not fully prepared. Of course everybody will be a bit nervous about an important examination, but there is no reason why you should fall apart and fail to do yourself justice if you know what to expect before you go in.

If you have worked hard for two years and put in a lot of effort, there are some steps you can take to ensure that your examination results reflect this.

Be prepared

Make sure you have everything you need ready the night before, including pens, pencils, ruler, and calculator. Your teacher can tell you what mathematical skills you are expected to have, or they are listed in your syllabus. Make sure you are familiar with these well in advance.

Read carefully

Before you start, read the paper all the way through and make sure you know exactly what you have to do. Turn over all the pages. Then, when you are ready to start, read each question more than once to make sure it really does say what you think it says. Follow the instructions to the letter, as marks can only be awarded for precise answers to the question asked, not for any other information about the subject.

Plan your time

Work out how much time you should spend on each question, based on how many marks it has. Don't spend ages racking your brains to think of the answer to the last part of a question – go on and start the next question instead. You will probably get more marks for answering the beginning of all the questions than for finishing one or two questions completely, but not attempting later questions. If you have time left at the end, you can go back and think about the more difficult parts when you will be feeling more relaxed.

Present your work clearly

Remember that the examiner will have a large pile of papers to mark in a short space of time. Struggling to read your writing or to follow an illogical argument will not help, so write as clearly as you possibly can in the time available and think through what you are going to write before you start. The examiner is trying to award you marks – make it easy to find them.

If you are drawing diagrams, draw them clearly and simply, using single lines where appropriate. Label the diagrams and make sure the label lines point exactly to the relevant structures.

Stay calm

If you find a question you have no idea about, do not panic! Breathe slowly and deeply and have another look. It's likely that if you stay calm and think clearly, it will start to make more sense, or at least you may be able to answer part of it. If not, then don't agonise about it but concentrate first on the questions you *can* answer.

Chapter summaries/checklists

Photocopy the lists of topics below and put a cross against those that are *not* included in your examination specification. (Your teacher should be able to tell you which they are.) Tick off the other items on the lists as you revise. The spread numbers in brackets tell you where to find more information.

1 Units and measurement

❑ Units for measuring length, mass, and time. (1.01)
❑ The use of milli and kilo. (1.01)
❑ Units for measuring volume. (1.01)
❑ Symbols (abbreviations) for units. (1.02)
❑ The meaning of density. (1.02)

2 Forces and motion

❑ Calculating speed. (2.01)
❑ The difference between speed and velocity. (2.01)
❑ Calculating acceleration. (2.01)
❑ The meaning of retardation. (2.01)
❑ Representing motion using distance-time and speed-time graphs. (2.02)
❑ The shape of a distance-time graph
- if something is moving at a steady speed
- if something is moving at a higher steady speed
- if something is accelerating
- if something is stopped. (2.02)

❑ Calculating speed from a distance-time graph. (2.02)
❑ The shape of a speed-time graph
- if something is moving at a steady speed
- if something is accelerating. (2.02)

❑ What the gradient of distance-time graph tells you. (2.03)
❑ What the gradient of speed-time graph tells you. (2.03)
❑ What the area under a speed-time graph tells you. (2.03)
❑ Velocity-time and displacement-time graphs. (2.03)
❑ Recording the motion of a trolley using ticker-tape, and interpreting the data collected. (2.04)
❑ The motion of object in free fall. (2.05)
❑ The acceleration of free fall, g. (2.05)
❑ Measuring g. (2.05)
❑ The unit of force: the newton. (2.07)
❑ Measuring force. (2.07)
❑ The resultant of two forces acting in the same direction, or in opposite directions. (2.07)
❑ The link between force, mass, and acceleration: Newton's second law of motion. (2.08)
❑ The difference between weight and mass. (2.10)
❑ Defining gravitational field strength. (2.10)
❑ Why the weight of an object can vary from one place to another. (2.10)
❑ wo meanings of g. (2.10)
❑ How an object moves if the forces on it are balanced: Newton's first law of motion. (2.11)
❑ The effects of friction. (2.11)
❑ erminal speed. (2.11)
❑ The meanings of reaction time, thinking distance, braking distance, and stopping distance. (2.12)
❑ The factors affecting a vehicle's stopping distance. (2.12)
❑ How a vehicle's kinetic energy increases with speed. (2.12)
❑ How all forces exist in pairs: Newton's third law of motion. (2.13)

3 Energy

- ❑ Calculating work done. (3.01)
- ❑ The meaning of energy. (3.01)
- ❑ The unit of work and energy: the joule. (3.01)
- ❑ The different forms of energy. (3.01)
- ❑ Energy transformations (changes). (3.02)
- ❑ The law of conservation of energy. (3.02)
- ❑ The link between work done and energy transformed (changed). (3.02)
- ❑ Calculating gravitational potential energy. (3.03)
- ❑ Calculating kinetic energy. (3.03)
- ❑ Adding energy values. (3.03)
- ❑ The meaning of efficiency. (3.04)
- ❑ The meaning of power. (3.04)
- ❑ The unit of power: the watt. (3.04)
- ❑ How to measure your useful power output. (3.04)
- ❑ What happens to the wasted energy if the efficiency of an engine or motor is less than 100%. (3.05)
- ❑ How thermal power stations (nuclear power stations and fuel-burning power stations) work. (3.06)
- ❑ The limited efficiency of thermal power stations. (3.06)
- ❑ The pollution problems caused by thermal power stations. (3.07)
- ❑ Why fuel-burning power stations may be contributing to global warming. (3.07)
- ❑ The alternatives to thermal power stations, including hydroelectric and tidal power stations and wind farms. (3.07)
- ❑ How electricity supply companies cope with varying demand. (3.08)
- ❑ Which types of power station can be brought 'on line' quickly. (3.08)
- ❑ How a pumped storage scheme works. (3.08)
- ❑ The difference between renewable and non-renewable energy resources. (3.09)
- ❑ Different energy resources, and the advantages and disadvantages of each type. (3.09)
- ❑ Examples of good and poor thermal conductors. (3.11)
- ❑ Uses of thermal insulators in the house. (3.11)
- ❑ Why metals are the best thermal conductors. (3.11)
- ❑ Why wool, feathers, and plastic foam are good thermal insulators. (3.11)
- ❑ Convection currents and why they occur. (3.12)
- ❑ Examples and uses of convection in liquids and gases. (3.12)
- ❑ The nature of thermal radiation. (3.13)
- ❑ How different surfaces compare as emitters, reflectors, and absorbers of thermal radiation. (3.13)

4 Rays and waves

❑ The characteristics (features) of light. (4.01)
❑ The speed of light. (4.01)
❑ The laws of reflection. (4.02)
❑ How and where an image is formed in a flat mirror. (4.02)
❑ The refraction of light. (4.03)
❑ Why water (or a glass block) looks less deep than it really is. (4.03)
❑ How a prism forms a spectrum. (4.03)
❑ Total internal reflection. (4.04)
❑ The meaning of critical angle. (4.04)
❑ Uses of reflecting prisms. (4.04)
❑ Optical fibres and their uses. (4.04)
❑ The difference between transverse and longitudinal waves. (4.05)
❑ The meanings of wavelength, amplitude, frequency, and period. (4.05)
❑ The unit of frequency: the hertz. (4.05)
❑ The link between speed, frequency, and wavelength. (4.05 and 4.12)
❑ Demonstrating reflection, refraction, and diffraction in a ripple tank. (4.06)
❑ How diffraction depends on the size of the gap through which the waves are passing. (4.06)
❑ Electromagnetic waves. (4.07)
❑ Radio waves, microwaves, and their uses. (4.07 and 4.08)
❑ Infrared rays, ultraviolet rays, and their uses. (4.07)
❑ X-rays, gamma rays, and their uses. (4.07)
❑ The difference between analogue and digital signals. (4.08)
❑ The advantages of digital transmission. (4.08)
❑ How radio waves are diffracted. (4.08)
❑ How radio waves travel long distances. (4.08)
❑ How sound waves are produced. (4.09)
❑ Why sound cannot travel through a vacuum. (4.09)
❑ Displaying waveforms on an oscilloscope screen. (4.09 and 4.12)
❑ The speed of sound. (4.10)
❑ The reflection of sound: echoes. (4.10)
❑ The link between frequency and pitch. (4.12)
❑ The link between amplitude and loudness. (4.12)
❑ What ultrasound is. (4.14)
❑ How ultrasound can be used for cleaning and breaking, echo-sounding, metal testing, scanning the womb, and quality control. (4.14)
❑ Detecting seismic waves. (4.15)
❑ The difference between P-waves and S-waves. (4.15)
❑ What seismic waves reveal about the Earth's inner structure. (4.15)
❑ What tectonic plates are. (4.16)
❑ The evidence for plate movements. (4.16)
❑ The different types of movement at plate boundaries. (4.17)
❑ How plate movements contribute to the recycling of rocks. (4.17)

5 Electricity

- ❑ Electrical conductors and insulators. (5.01)
- ❑ Why metals are good electrical conductors. (5.01)
- ❑ Basic principles of a simple circuit. (5.02)
- ❑ Measuring current. (5.02)
- ❑ The unit of current: the ampere. (5.02)
- ❑ The unit of charge: the coulomb. (5.02)
- ❑ The link between charge, current, and time. (5.02)
- ❑ The conventional current direction. (5.02)
- ❑ Measuring voltage (PD). (5.03)
- ❑ The unit of voltage: the volt. (5.03)
- ❑ Cells in series. (5.03)
- ❑ The link between energy, voltage, and charge. (5.03)
- ❑ The link between resistance, voltage, and current. (5.04)
- ❑ The unit of resistance: the ohm. (5.04)
- ❑ Heating elements and resistors. (5.04)
- ❑ Using a variable resistor. (5.05)
- ❑ The properties of LDRs, thernistors, and diodes. (5.05)
- ❑ Interpreting current-voltage graphs. (5.05)
- ❑ The properties of series and parallel circuits. (5.06)
- ❑ How to solve circuit problems. (5.07)
- ❑ Using the equation linking V, I, and R. (5.07)
- ❑ Rules for currents and voltages in series and parallel circuits. (5.07)
- ❑ The features of a mains circuit. (5.08)
- ❑ The function of the fuse and earth wire in a mains circuit. (5.08)
- ❑ Why some appliances have double insulation. (5.08)
- ❑ How to wire a mains plug safely. (5.08)
- ❑ Choosing the correct fuse value. (5.08)
- ❑ The hazards of mains electricity. (5.09 and 5.12)
- ❑ The difference between AC and DC. (5.09)
- ❑ The meaning of power. (5.10)
- ❑ The unit of power: the watt. (5.10)
- ❑ The link between power, voltage, and current. (5.10)
- ❑ Calculating electrical energy in joules and in kilowatt hours. (5.11)
- ❑ Calculating the cost of electricity. (5.11)
- ❑ The two types of electric charge. (5.13)
- ❑ The forces between charges. (5.13)
- ❑ How charges come from the atom. (5.13)
- ❑ Why charged objects attract uncharged ones. (5.13)
- ❑ The dangers of static electricity. (5.14)
- ❑ Using static electricity in inkjet printers and photocopiers, and for ash removal. (5.14)
- ❑ What ions are. (5.15)
- ❑ How ionized gases and liquids conduct. (5.15)
- ❑ The chemical effect of an electric current: electrolysis. (5.15)

6 Magnets and currents

❑ The two types of magnetic pole. (6.01)
❑ The forces between magnetic poles. (6.01)
❑ Permanent and temporary magnets. (6.01)
❑ Magnetic and non-magnetic materials. (6.01)
❑ The magnetic field around a magnet. (6.01)
❑ The magnetic field around a current-carrying wire. (6.02)
❑ The magnetic field around a current-carrying coil. (6.02)
❑ Factors affecting the magnetic field from a coil. (6.02)
❑ The electromagnet. (6.03)
❑ Factors affecting an electromagnet's field strength. (6.03)
❑ How a magnetic relay works. (6.03)
❑ How a circuit breaker works. (6.03)
❑ The force on a current in a magnetic field, and the factors affecting it. (6.04)
❑ How a moving-coil loudspeaker works. (6.04)
❑ The turning effect on a current-carrying coil in a magnetic field. (6.04)
❑ How a simple DC motor works. (6.05)
❑ Electromagnetic induction and the factors affecting it. (6.07 and 6.09)
❑ Demonstrating an induced voltage in a coil. (6.07 and 6.09)
❑ How a simple alternator (AC generator) works. (6.08)
❑ The AC output from an alternator. (6.09)
❑ The action of a transformer. (6.09)
❑ The equation linking a transformer's input and output voltages. (6.09)
❑ The difference between a step-up and step-down transformer. (6.09)
❑ The equation linking a transformer's input and output powers. (6.09)
❑ The transmission and distribution of mains power across country. (6.10)
❑ Why AC is used for power transmission. (6.10)
❑ Why power is transmitted at high voltage. (6.10)

7 Atoms and nuclei

- ❑ The particles in an atom and the charges they carry. (7.01)
- ❑ The meaning of atomic number. (7.01)
- ❑ The meaning of mass number. (7.01)
- ❑ What isotopes are. (7.01)
- ❑ The symbols used to represent isotopes. (7.01)
- ❑ The 'plum pudding' model of the atom. (7.02)
- ❑ Evidence for an atom having a nucleus. (7.02)
- ❑ Radioactive materials and the radiation they produce. (7.03)
- ❑ How nuclear radiation can be detected. (7.03)
- ❑ Alpha particles and their properties. (7.03)
- ❑ Beta particles and their properties. (7.03)
- ❑ Gamma rays and their properties. (7.03)
- ❑ Ionizing radiation. (7.03)
- ❑ The dangers of nuclear radiation. (7.04)
- ❑ Which form of radiation is most dangerous
  - when the source is inside the body
  - when the source is outside the body. (7.04)
- ❑ The main sources of background radiation. (7.04)
- ❑ Allowing for background radiation in experiments. (7.04)
- ❑ Radiation as a cause of mutations. (7.04)
- ❑ What happens during radioactive decay. (7.06)
- ❑ Measuring the activity of a radioactive sample. (7.06)
- ❑ The unit of activity: the becquerel. (7.06)
- ❑ How the rate of radioactive decay changes with time. (7.06)
- ❑ The meaning of half-life. (7.06)
- ❑ Working out half-life from a decay graph. (7.06)
- ❑ The changes in the nucleus that occur during alpha decay. (7.06)
- ❑ The changes in the nucleus that occur during beta decay. (7.06)
- ❑ Writing nuclear equations. (7.06)
- ❑ What radioisotopes are. (7.07)
- ❑ Using radioisotopes
  - as tracers
  - in radiotherapy
  - to find cracks in metals
  - for thickness monitoring
  - for dating old materials. (7.07)
- ❑ What happens during nuclear fission. (7.08)
- ❑ What a chain reaction is. (7.08)
- ❑ The controlled chain reaction in a nuclear reactor. (7.08)
- ❑ The problems of nuclear waste. (7.08)

8 The Earth in space

- ❑ The Sun is a star. (8.01 and 8.05)
- ❑ How the Earth's rotation causes day and night. (8.01)
- ❑ The Earth's orbit around the Sun. (8.01)
- ❑ The Moon's orbit around the Earth. (8.01)
- ❑ Why we always see the same face of the Moon. (8.01)
- ❑ The apparent motion of planets and stars. (8.01)
- ❑ What the Solar System is. (8.02)
- ❑ The relative sizes and distances apart of the Sun and planets. (8.02)
- ❑ The orbits of the planets around the Sun. (8.02)
- ❑ How planets give off light. (8.02)
- ❑ The link between a planet's distance from the Sun and the time for an orbit. (8.02)
- ❑ The inner planets. (8.02 and 8.03)
- ❑ The outer planets. (8.02 and 8.03)
- ❑ The asteroids (minor planets). (8.02 and 8.03)
- ❑ How orbits depend on gravity. (8.02)
- ❑ Comets and their orbits. (8.03)
- ❑ Meteors and meteorites. (8.03)
- ❑ Satellites and their uses. (8.04)
- ❑ What a geostationary orbit is. (8.04)
- ❑ What constellations are. (8.05)
- ❑ How stars get their energy. (8.05)
- ❑ The light year as a unit of distance. (8.05)
- ❑ The distance to the nearest star. (8.05)
- ❑ The Milky Way. (8.05)
- ❑ Galaxies. (8.05)
- ❑ The Universe. (8.05 and 8.07)
- ❑ Nebulae. (8.06)
- ❑ The formation of the Sun: the birth of the Solar System. (8.06)
- ❑ The death of a star. (8.06)
- ❑ Red giants and white dwarfs. (8.06)
- ❑ Supernovae and the formation of new elements. (8.06)
- ❑ Neutron stars and black holes. (8.06)
- ❑ The expanding Universe. (8.07)
- ❑ The big-bang theory and the evidence for it. (8.07)
- ❑ The age of the Universe. (8.07)
- ❑ The Hubble constant. (8.07)
- ❑ The fate of the Universe. (8.07)
- ❑ The search for extra-terrestrial life. (8.08)

Further topics

- ❑ Calculating the moment of a force. (9.01)
- ❑ The factors affecting the moment of a force. (9.01)
- ❑ The principle of moments. (9.01)
- ❑ The meaning of centre of gravity (centre of mass). (9.02)
- ❑ Finding the centre of gravity of an object by experiment. (9.02)
- ❑ Stable and unstable positions. (9.02)
- ❑ The different types of equilibrium. (9.02)
- ❑ The difference between elastic and plastic behaviour. (9.03)
- ❑ The meaning of elastic limit. (9.03)
- ❑ How the extension changes with load when a spring is stretched. (9.03)
- ❑ Hooke's law, and how it applies to metal springs and wires. (9.03)
- ❑ The meaning of pressure. (9.04)
- ❑ The unit of pressure: the pascal. (9.04)
- ❑ The link between pressure, force, and area. (9.04)
- ❑ The pressure in a liquid. (9.04)
- ❑ How hydraulic machines work. (9.04)
- ❑ The link between the pressure of a gas and its volume: Boyle's law. (9.05)
- ❑ A molecular explanation for Boyle's law. (9.05)
- ❑ Defining momentum. (9.06)
- ❑ The link between force and momentum. (9.06)
- ❑ The law of conservation of momentum. (9.06)
- ❑ The meaning of centripetal force. (9.07)
- ❑ The path of an object that is thrown sideways. (9.07)
- ❑ How an object can stay in orbit around the Earth. (9.07)
- ❑ The factors on which centripetal force depends. (9.07)

Glossary

The spread numbers in brackets tell you where to find more information.

acceleration If the velocity of something increases by 10 m/s every second, then its acceleration is 10 m/s^2. (2.01)

acceleration of free fall, *g* Near the Earth's surface, this is 10 m/s^2. (2.05, 2.10)

activity The average number of unstable nuclei decaying (breaking up) per second in a radioactive material. If 100 nuclei are decaying per second, the activity is 100 becquerels (Bq). (7.06)

alpha particles Positively (+) charged particles given off by some radioactive materials. Each alpha particle is made up of two protons and two neutrons. (7.03)

alternating current (AC) Current which flows backwards and forwards, backwards and forwards... and so on. Mains current is like this. (5.08–5.09)

alternator An AC (alternating current) generator. (6.08)

ammeter An instrument that measures current, in amperes (A). (5.02)

ampere (A) Unit of electric current. (5.02)

amplitude For a wave displayed on the screen of an oscilloscope, this is the height of a 'peak' above the centre line. (4.05, 4.12)

analogue signals Signals which vary continuously in the same way as the source. (4.08)

asteroids Sometimes called minor planets, these lumps of rock mostly have orbits between those of Mars and Jupiter. (8.02–8.03)

atomic number The number of protons in an atom. Sometimes called the protons number. (7.01)

background radiation The low level of radiation that is always present, mainly because of radioactive materials in the ground and air. (7.04)

battery A collection of electric cells – although the word is commonly used for a single cell as well. (5.01, 5.03)

beta particles Negatively (+) charged particles given off by some radioactive materials. Each beta particle is an electron. (7.03)

big-bang theory The theory that the Universe was created when a single, incredibly dense, hot 'superatom' expanded, more than 10 billion years ago. (8.07)

black hole What is left when a very massive star collapses at the end of its life. A black hole's gravity is so strong that nothing can escape, not even light. (8.06)

cell A device that pushes current round a circuit when chemicals inside it react. (5.01, 5.03)

charge This is carried by some of the particles in atoms. There are two types: positive (+) and negative (–). Amounts of charge are measured in coulombs (C). (5.01–5.02, 5.13–5.15, 7.01)

circuit breaker An electromagnetic switch that turns of the current in a circuit if this gets too high. It does the same job as a fuse but, unlike a fuse, can be reset. (6.03)

comet An icy lump of material that moves around the Sun in a highly elliptical orbit. Its 'tail' is a thin stream of gas and dust that reflects sunlight. (8.03)

conductor (electrical) A material that lets an electric current flow through it. Metals are the best conductors. (5.01)

conductor (thermal) A material that lets heat (thermal energy) flow through it. Metals are the best conductors. (3.11)

constellation Stars that appear to form a group or pattern when viewed from Earth. Usually, the stars are at different distances and not related at all. (8.05)

convection Process in which heat (thermal energy) is carried by a circulating flow of liquid or gas (air, for exzample). (3.12)

core The Earth's central zone. It is mostly molten (melted) iron, although the inner core is solid. (4.15)

coulomb (C) Unit of electric charge. (5.02)

critical angle If a ray strikes an internal face of a transparent block or liquid at an angle greater than this, all the light is reflected and none is refracted. (4.04)

crust The Earth's outer, rocky layer. (4.15)

current A flow of charge. It is measured in amperes (A). (5.02)

density If a material with a mass of 1000 kg has a volume of 1 cubic metre, then its density is 1000 kg/m^3. (1.02)

diffraction The spreading or bending that occurs when waves travel through gaps or past obstacles. (4.06, 4.08)

digital signals Signals made up of a series of pulses, representing 0s and 1s. The 0s and 1s must be decoded to recreate the information being sent. (4.08)

diode A component that allows current to flow through it in one direction but not the other. (5.05)

direct current (DC) Current which always flows in the same direction. The current from a battery is like this. (5.09)

echo A reflected sound, heard a short time after the original sound was sent out. (4.10)

efficiency If an engine or motor has an efficiency of 0.25 (25%), only a quarter of the energy supplied to it is delivered as work (useful energy output). The rest is wasted. (3.04)

electrolysis Process in which chemical changes occur when a current flows through a liquid. (5.15)

electromagnet A coil wound round a core of iron or mumetal. It becomes magnetized when a current is passed through the coil, but loses its magnetism when the current is switched off. (6.03)

electromagnetic induction Process in which a voltage is generated in a wire or coil because the magnetic field around it is moving or changing. (6.07–6.09)

electromagnetic waves A family of waves whose members are radio waves (including microwaves), infrared, light, ultraviolet, X-rays, and gamma rays. (4.07)

electron Negatively (–) charged particle that moves around the nucleus of an atom. In a circuit, the 'electricity' in the wires is a flow of electrons.(5.01, 7.01)

energy Things have energy, if they can be used to do work – in other words, to make forces move. Energy is measured in joules (J). (3.01–3.02)

fission The splitting of nuclei of 'heavy' atoms, such as those of uranium, to form lighter nuclei. It is the process used in today's nuclear reactors to release energy as heat. (7.08)

force A push or pull. It is measured in newtons (N). (2.07)

frequency The number of oscillations (vibrations) per second, or the number of waves per second. It is measured in hertz (Hz). If 100 waves are sent out per second, the frequency is 100 Hz. (4.05, 4.12)

friction The force that opposes the motion of one material over (or through) another. (2.11–2.12)

fuse A small piece of wire than overheats, melts, and breaks a circuit if the current gets too high. (5.08)

galaxy A huge system of billions of stars. (8.05, 8.07)

gamma rays Electromagnetic waves given off by some radioactive materials. They are similar to X-rays. (7.03)

Geiger–Müller tube (GM tube) Device used for detecting radiation from radioactive materials. (7.03)

generator A machine that produces a voltage when its shaft is turned. (3.06, 6.08)

geostationary orbit An orbit specially chosen so that a satellite appears stationary in the sky. This is because it orbits at the same rate as the Earth turns. (8.04)

gravitational field strength (of Earth), g Near the Earth's surface, this is 10 N/kg. In other words, there is a gravitational pull of 10 N on each kg of mass. (2.10)

half-life The time taken for the activity of a radioactive sample to halve. Also the time taken for half the unstable nuclei present to decay (break up). (7.06)

hertz (Hz) Unit of frequency. If there are 100 vibrations per second, or 100 waves being sent out per second, the frequency is 100 Hz. (4.05, 4.12)

insulator (electrical) A material that does not let an electric current flow through it. (5.01)

insulator (thermal) A material that is a very poor conductor of heat (thermal energy). (3.11)

ion Electrically charged atom (or group of atoms). (5.15, 7.03)

isotopes Different versions of an element. Isotopes have the same number of protons (and electrons) in their atoms, but a different number of neutrons. (7.01)

joule (J) Unit of energy and work. 1000 joules equals 1 kilojoule (kJ). (3.01)

kilogram (kg) Unit of mass. (1.01)

kilowatt-hour (kWh) Unit of energy used by electricity supply companies. It is the energy taken in 1 hour by an appliance with a power of 1 kW. (5.11)

kinetic energy The energy something has because of its motion. (3.01, 3.03)

light year The distance travelled by light in one year. It is nearly 10 000 000 000 000 kilometres. (8.05)

light-dependent resistor (LDR) A component whose resistance varies as it gets lighter or darker. (5.05)

longitudinal waves Waves in which the oscillations (vibrations) are backwards and forwards. (4.05)

magma Hot, molten (melted) rock. (4.16–4.17)

magnetic field The region around around a magnet where forces act on any magnetic materials that are there. (6.01)

magnetic material A material that is attracted to a magnet, and can be magnetized. All magnetic materials contain oron, nickel, or cobalt. (6.01)

magnetic poles Points on a magnet where the magnetic forces appear to come from. Each magnet has an N-pole and an S-pole. (6.01)

mantle The deep zone of rock that lies between the Earth's crust and core. It is mostly solid, but flexible. (4.15)

mass The amount of matter in something. It is measured in kilograms (kg). (1.01)

mass number The total number of protons and neutrons in an atom. Sometimes called the nucleon number. (7.01)

meteorite A lump of rock from space that strikes the Earth (or other planet or moon). (8.03)

metre (m) Unit of length. 1000 metres equals 1 kilometre (km). (1.01)

moment The turning effect of the force. It is equal to the force × perpendicular distance to pivot (turning point). (9.01)

moon large, rocky object that orbits a planet. (8.01–8.02)

nebula A huge cloud of gas and dust in space. In it, new stars are formed. (8.06)

neutron Uncharged particle in the nucleus of an atom. (7.01)

neutron star The very dense core of a supernova. (8.06)

newton (N) Unit of force. A force of 1 N will make a mass of 1 kg accelerate at 1 m/s^2. (2.08)

nuclear reactor A large chamber in which nuclear reactions take place. In the reactors in nuclear power stations, the reactions release energy as heat. (7.08)

nucleus The centre of an atom, made up (in most cases) of protons and neutrons. (7.01)

ohm (Ω) Unit of electrical resistance. (5.04)

optical fibre This glass or plastic fibre, used in communications for carrying signals in the form of pulses of light or infrared. (4.04, 4.08)

orbit Circular or elliptical path followed by an object as it moves around a planet, moon, or Sun. (8.01–8.04)

period The time between one wavefront (or wave 'peak') passing and the next. (4.05)

pitch How high a note sounds to the ear. The higher the frequency of the sound waves, the higher the pitch. (4.12).

planet large object (such as the Earth) that orbits a star (such as the Sun). (8.01–8.02)

potential energy The energy something has because of a change in position or shape. (3.01, 3.03)

power The rate at which work is done or energy is transformed (changed into another form). It is measured in watts (W). 1 watt is equal to 1 joule per second. (3.04, 5.10)

proton Positively (+) charged particle in the nucleus of an atom. (7.01)

radiation Any form of particle or wave energy that radiates (spreads out) from its source. Light, sound, alpha, beta, and gamma rays are all forms of radiation. (3.13, 4.01, 4.07, 4.09, 7.03)

radiation (nuclear) Particles or waves shot out from the unstable nuclei of atoms in radioactive materials. The main types are alpha particles, beta particles, and gamma rays. (7.03)

radiation (thermal) Rays, such as those from the Sun, that have a heating effect when something absorbs them. The rays are mostly infrared. (3.12)

radioactive decay The break up of unstable nuclei in the atoms of a radiuoactive material. (7.06)

radioactive material A material that gives off nuclear radiation – usually alpha, beta, or gamma rays. (7.03)

radioisotope An isotope that is radioactive. (7.07)

red giant A star near the end of its life, which has expanded and is glowing red. (8.06)

refraction The bending that occurs when waves (such as light or sound waves) pass at an angle from one material into another. (4.03, 4.06)

relay An electromagnetic switch in which a small current in one circuit can be used to switch on or off a much larger current in another. (6.03)

resistance This is measured in ohms (Ω). The higher the resistance of a conductor, the less current flows through it for each volt across it. (5.04)

retardation (deceleration) If the velocity of something decreases by 10 m/s every second, then the retardation is 10 m/s^2. (2.01)

satellite Any object that orbits the Earth (or other planet). Most satellites are put into orbit by rockets. However, the Moon is a natural satellite of the Earth. (8.04)

second (s) Unit of time. (1.01)

seismic waves Vibrations that travel through the Earth and are caused by earthquakes. They include P waves and S waves. (4.15)

solenoid A long coil through which a current can flow. (6.02)

speed If something travels a distance of 10 m in 1 second, its average speed is 10 m/s. (2.01)

star A huge, hot, glowing ball of gas, such as the Sun. It is powered by nuclear reactions. (8.01, 8.05–8.06)

Sun This is a star. (8.01, 8.05–8.06)

supernova A gigantic explosion that occurs when a massive star is at the end of its life. (8.06)

tectonic plates Huge sections of the Earth's crust (and upper mantle) that slowly move on the material beneath them. (4.16–4.17)

thermistor A component that has a large change in resistance when its temperature changes. (5.05)

total internal reflection If light strikes an internal face of a transparent block or liquid at a large enough angle, all the light is reflected and none is refracted. This is called total internal reflection. (4.04)

transformer A device used to increase or decrease the voltage of an AC supply. (6.09–6.10)

transverse waves Waves in which the oscillations (vibrations) are from side to side (or up and down). (4.05)

turbine A wheel with blades which are pushed round by steam, gas, or water. In power stations, the generators are turned by turbines. (3.06)

ultrasound Sound waves with frequencies that are too high for the human ear to hear. (4.14)

Universe All the galaxies: everything that exists. (8.05, 8.07)

velocity Speed in a particular direction. It is measured in m/s. An arrow, or a + or −, can be used to show its direction. (2.01)

virtual image The type of image seen in a flat mirror. Unlike the image formed by a cinema projector, the rays don't actually pass through it. (4.02)

volt (V) Unit of voltage. (5.03)

voltage The higher a battery's voltage, the more energy is given to each electron pushed out into the circuit. The higher the voltage across a bulb (or other component), the more energy is spent by each electron as it passes through. (5.03).

voltmeter An instrument that measures voltage, in volts (V). (5.03)

volume The amount of space something takes up. It is measured in cubic metres (m^3). A smaller unit of volume is the cubic centimetre (cm^3), or millilitre (ml). 1 cm^3 = 1 ml = 1/1 000 000 m^3. (1.02)

watt (W) Unit of power. It is equal to 1 joule per second. (3.04, 5.10)

wavelength The distance between wavefronts: in other words, the distance between one wave 'peak' and the next. (4.05)

weight The strength of the Earth's gravitational pull on an object. Being a force, it is measured in newtons (N). (2.10)

white dwarf The hot, dense core left when a red giant star has lost its outer layer. (8.06)

work Work is done whenever a force makes something move. 1 joule (J) of work is done when a force of 1 newton moves something a distance of 1 metre (in the direction of the force). (3.01)

Appendix 1: Equations

$$\text{speed (m/s)} = \frac{\text{distance moved (m)}}{\text{time taken (s)}}$$

velocity (m/s) is speed in a particular direction

$$\text{acceleration (m/s}^2\text{)} = \frac{\text{change in velocity (m/s)}}{\text{time taken (s)}}$$

weight (N) = mass (kg) × gravitational field strength

(gravitational field strength = g = 10 N/m^2 near Earth's surface)

force (N) = mass (kg) × acceleration (m/s^2)

work done (J) = force × distance moved (m) in direction of force

work done (J) = energy transformed (J)

(energy transformed can also be called energy transferred)

gain in gravitational potential energy (J)
= weight (N) × gain in height (m)
= mass (kg) × g × gain in height (m)

$$\underset{\text{(J)}}{\text{kinetic energy}} = \frac{1}{2} \times \underset{\text{(kg)}}{\text{mass}} \times \underset{\text{(m/s)}}{\text{speed}^2}$$

$$\text{power (W)} = \frac{\text{energy transformed (J)}}{\text{time taken (s)}} = \frac{\text{work done (J)}}{\text{time taken (s)}}$$

$$\text{efficiency} = \frac{\text{useful energy output (J)}}{\text{energy input (J)}} = \frac{\text{useful work done (J)}}{\text{energy input (J)}} = \frac{\text{useful power output (W)}}{\text{power input (W)}}$$

$$\underset{\text{(J)}}{\text{energy transformed}} = \underset{\text{(W)}}{\text{power}} \times \underset{\text{(s)}}{\text{time}}$$

$$\underset{\text{(kW h)}}{\text{energy transformed}} = \underset{\text{(kW)}}{\text{power}} \times \underset{\text{(hours)}}{\text{time}}$$

For waves:
speed (m/s) = frequency (Hz) × wavelength (m)

$$\text{resistance (}\Omega\text{)} = \frac{\text{voltage (V)}}{\text{current (A)}}$$

power (W) = voltage (V) × current (A)

energy transformed (J) = voltage (V) × charge (C)

charge (C) = current (A) × time (s)

For a transformer:

$$\frac{\text{input voltage (V)}}{\text{output voltage (V)}} = \frac{\text{turns on input coil}}{\text{turns on output coil}}$$

$$\text{density (kg/m}^3\text{)} = \frac{\text{mass (kg)}}{\text{volume (m}^3\text{)}}$$

$$\text{pressure (Pa)} = \frac{\text{force (N)}}{\text{area (m}^2\text{)}}$$

moment of a force (N m) =
force (N) × perpendicular distance from pivot (m)

Appendix 2: Units and symbols

Units and symbols

Quantity	*Unit*	*Symbol*
mass	kilogram	kg
length	metre	m
time	second	s
force	newton	N
weight	newton	N
pressure	pascal	Pa
energy	joule	J
work	joule	J
power	watt	W
voltage	volt	V
current	ampere	A
resistance	ohm	Ω
charge	coulomb	C
temperature	kelvin	K
temperature	degree Celsius	°C

Bigger and smaller

To make units bigger or smaller, prefixes are put in front of them:

micro (μ)	= 1 millionth	= 0.000001	$= 10^{-6}$
milli (m)	= 1 thousandth	= 0.001	$= 10^{-3}$
kilo (k)	= 1 thousand	= 1000	$= 10^{3}$
mega (M)	= 1 million	= 1000000	$= 10^{6}$

For example

1 micrometre	= 1 μm	= 0.000 001 m
1 millisecond	= 1 ms	= 0.001 s
1 kilometre	= 1 km	= 1000 m
1 megatonne	= 1 Mt	= 1000000 t

Electrical symbols

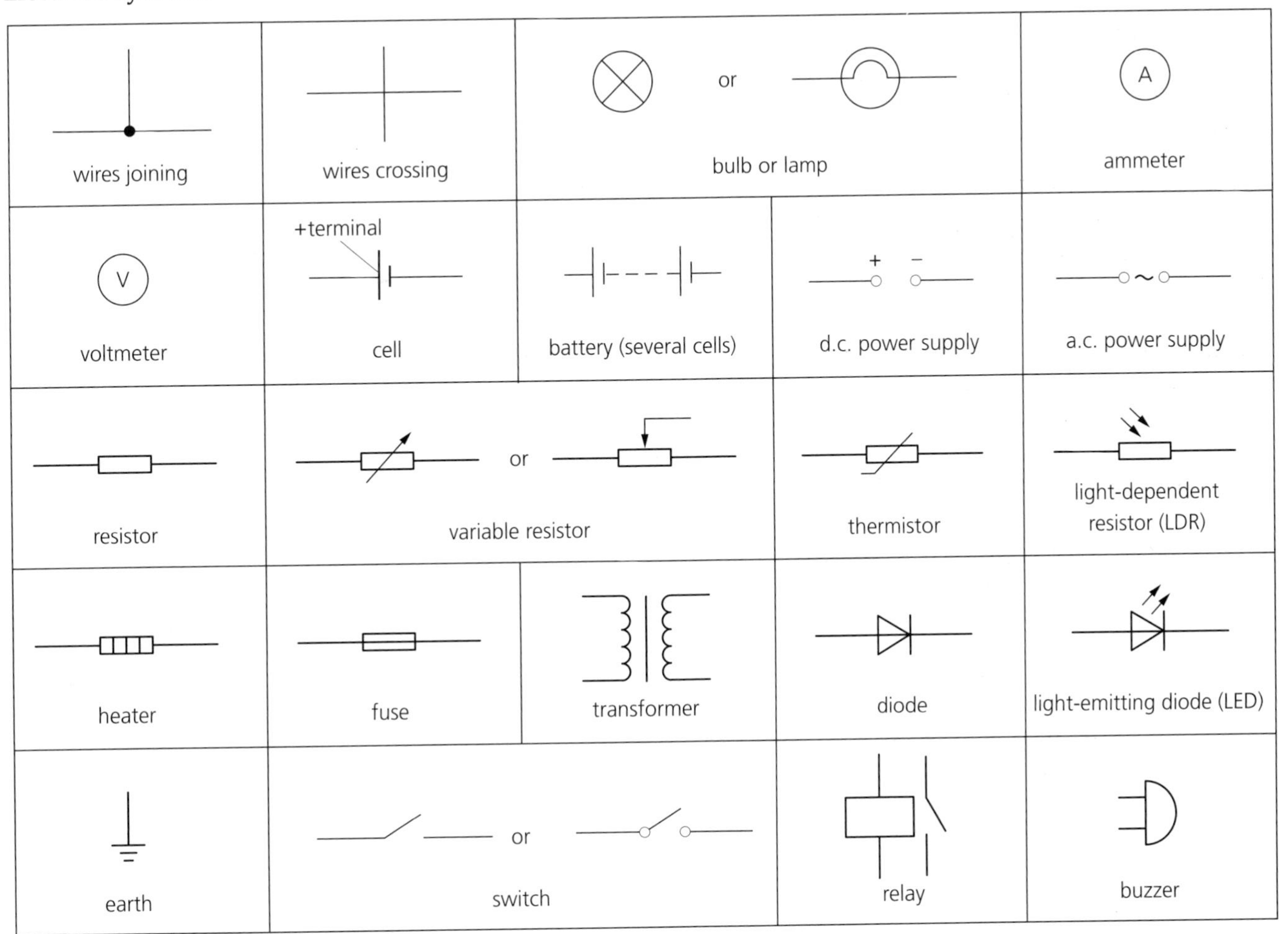

Answers

Note: the answers are in three sections:
- end-of-spread questions
- end-of-chapter questions
- further exam-style questions

Answers to end-of-spread questions

■ **1.01** (page 11)
1 metre; mass, kg; second, s **2** millimetre, tonne, milligram, millisecond, litre, centimetre **3 a** 1600 g **b** 1450 mm **4 a** 1000 **b** 10 **c** 100 000 **d** 100 **e** 1 000 000 **5 a** 1000 mm **b** 1500 mm **c** 1534 mm **d** 1.652 m **6 a** 2750 mm 1600 m **c** 6500 mg **d** 1.5 m **e** 1.750 kg **7** kg, 1000 cm **8** 750 cm^3, 0.75 l **9** 24 cm^3, 192 cm^3

■ **1.02** (page 13)
1 volt (after Volta), watt, joule; abbreviation starts with a capital **2 a** 2700 kg **b** 27 000 kg **3 a** 1 m^3 of water **b** 1 kg of petrol **4 a** X **b** Y **c** X **5** X – steel, Y – aluminium

■ **2.01** (page 21)
1 a 25 m/s **b** doesn't keep steady speed **2 a** 10 m **b** 50 m **c** 100 m **d** 9 s **3** 1st row 7 s; 2nd row 12 m/s, 20 m/s; 3rd row 4 m/s^2 **4** acceleration, second, speed, 3 m/s **5 a** 30 m/s **b** 50 m/s **6** 2.5 m/s^2 **7** 4 m/s^2

■ **2.02** (page 23)
1 b up to 2 s; from 2 s to 5 s; 5 s to 7 s; 7 s to 9 s **c** 56 m; 8 m/s **d** 3 s; 36 m; 12 m/s **2 a** 40 m/s **b** 20 s **c** 50 s **d** 40 m/s; 2 m/s **e** 4 m/s^2

■ **2.03** (page 25)
1 a speed **b** acceleration **c** distance travelled **2 a** 3 m/s^2 **b** 6 m/s^2 **c** 150 m **d** 525 m **e** 25 s **f** 21 m/s

■ **2.04** (page 27)
1 a D **b** C **c** A **3 a** 0.1 s **b** 5 **c** 0.1 s **d** 20 mm **e** 200 mm/s **f** 100 mm; 1000 mm/s **g** 800 mm/s **h** 800 mm/s^2

■ **2.05** (page 29)
1 a false **b** true **c** true **2** 1st row 4 s, 5 s; 2nd row 20 m/s; 3rd row 10 m/s; 4th row 10 m/s^2 **3 a** 10 m/s^2, **b** 50 m/s, **c** 25 m/s, **d** 125 m **4** yes

■ **2.07** (page 33)
1 a newton (N) **b** 200 kN **2** A 10 N to right; B 2 N to left; C zero **3** tow rope, parachute (air resistance), weight (gravity)

■ **2.08** (page 35)
1 a 4 N **b** 1 N **c** 8 N **2** force 5 N, acceleration 10 m/s^2 **3 a** A, D **b** B **c** C **4 a** winner Honda, loser Boeing **5 a** 9 m/s^2 **b** 6 m/s^2 **c** zero

■ **2.10** (page 39)
1 a weight, force **b** newtons **c** pull, stronger **2** 20 N, 40 N, 5 N **3** should be mass of 1 kg **4** A if dropped will accelerate at 10 m/s^2 B weighs 10 N **5 a** B **b** A and D **c** C **d** C **6 a** 1.6 m/s^2 **b** 1.6 N/kg **c** 100 N

■ **2.11** (page 41)
1 a stay still **b** keep moving at steady speed in straight line **2 a** useful **b** nuisance **c** nuisance **d** useful **e** useful **f** useful **g** useful **h** nuisance; **c, f** **3 b** terminal speed **c** 600 N **d** 60 kg **e** more air resistance, so greater force opposing motion

■ **2.12** (page 43)
1 a how far car travels before brakes applied while driver reacts **b** how far car travels after brakes are applied **2** driver tired, affected by alcohol **3** airbags, seat belts, crumple zone **4** B, C, D **5 a** 15 m **b** 18 m **6 a** 50 m **b** about 100 m

■ **2.13** (page 45)
2 a Rocket **b** Equal **c** Action **d** Compressor **e** Third **f** Isaac **g** Opposite **h** Newton **3** no air to take in; would have to carry huge amounts of oxygen **4** rock would gain more speed than astronaut **5** Sue; forces are not an action–reaction pair

■ **3.01** (page 53)
1 a 18 J **b** 6 J **c** 0.1 J **2 a** petrol, chocolate, sugar, chips, batteries **b** hot tea **c** car **3 a** burning **b** eating

■ **3.02** (page 55)
1 a D **b** A **c** F **d** E **e** B **2** 3500 J

■ **3.03** (page 57)
1 a A 32 J; B 1 J **b** A 5 J; B 10 J **c** A 37 J; B 11 J **2 a** 100 000 kg **b** 8000 m/s **c** 100 000 m **d** 100 000 MJ **e** 3 200 000 MJ **f** 3 300 000 MJ **g** changed into heat

■ **3.04** (page 59)
1 a 1000 J **b** 10 s **c** 100 J **d** changed into heat **2 a** 500 N **b** 10 000 J **c** 250 W **d** because of friction, resistance from snow

■ **3.05** (page 61)
1 a 75 J **b** changed into heat **2** engines can't use all input energy to produce motion **3 a** less energy wasted as heat **b** very low power input, so power wasted is very low **4** filament bulb less efficient, so more energy wasted **5 a** 6000 J **b** 300 W **c** 0.6 (60%)

■ **3.06** (page 63)
1 coal, oil, natural gas, nuclear fuel **2 a** turning turbines **b** condense steam **3 a** in turbines **b** heat **c** X 2000 MW, Y 1500 MW **d** X 0.36 (36%); Y 0.27 (27%)

■ **3.07** (page 65)
1 water from behind dam **2 a** useful energy output is 25% of energy input **b** B; build cost per MW output is low, quick start-up **c** E **d** A **e** A; fitting FGD units **f** no fuel burned

■ **3.08** (page 67)
1 to meet rapid increase in demand **2 a** B **b** C **3** wind farm, tidal power scheme **4 a** to store energy **b** when demand for electricity is low **c** turns generators **d** uses spare capacity when demand is low, helps supply when demand is high

■ **3.09** (page 69)
1 renewable can be replaced **2** biomass, winds, tides are renewable **3** Sun → plants → oil → petrol **4** hydroelectric, tidal, wave

■ **3.11** (page 73)
1 a traps air **b** aluminium conducts heat away more quickly **2** insulation in attic, walls; air in double glazing **3** contain free electrons **4 a** more; U-value for window more than for wall it replaces **b** yes

■ **3.12** (page 75)
1 a cold air sinks because of convection **b** no convection because air can't circulate **c** because of convection **d** floats upwards in denser, cooler water **2** because of convection **3 b** 12 °C **c** 7 min

■ **3.13** (page 77)
1 a and **b** dull black **c** white **2 a** B **b** C **3 a** and **b** white reflects Sun's radiation **c** black absorbs Sun's radiation

■ **4.01** (page 85)
1 B and C **2** CDs, telephone systems, surgery **3** solar cells produce electricity **4** 300 000 km/s

■ **4.02** (page 87)
2 a no **b** yes **3 a** 20 m **b** 7.5 m

■ **4.03** (page 89)
2 20p coin isn't in same position as its image **3 a** diamond **b** glass **c** ray bent less in left drawing, no change in right drawing **4 a** violet **b** red

■ **4.04** (page 91)
1 for internal reflection above this angle, there is no refracted ray **2 b** no; critical angle for water more than 45° **3 a** carrying telephone signals, endoscope **b** rear reflector

■ **4.05** (page 93)
1 a transverse **b** 20 mm; 6 mm; 15 mm **2** wave 1: 32 m/s; wave 2: 32 m/s, 2 m; wave 3: 32 m/s, 32 Hz **3 a** B **b** A **c** C **d** B

■ **4.06** (page 95)
1 a reduces; change direction **c** reflected **2 b** diffraction **c** less diffraction

■ **4.07** (page 97)
1 a infrared **b** ultraviolet **2** same speed, travel through empty space **3 a** ultraviolet **b** infrared **c** microwaves **d** gamma rays **e** infrared **f** light **g** gamma rays **4** 3 m

■ **4.08** (page 99)
1 analogue varies continuously, digital pulses represent numbers **2** make signals larger **3 a** pulses of light or infrared **b** better quality, can carry more sets of information **c** carry more signals, less power loss **4** long waves diffract more than VHF **5** reflected by ionosphere **6** 0.33 m

■ **4.09** (page 101)
1 a 10 mm **b** yes **2 a** vibrations **b** vacuum **c** longitudinal waves **d** pressure

■ **4.10** (page 103)
1 aircraft, meteoroid 2 a 330 m b 660 m c 3300 m d 33 m 3 yes, less echo in bedroom 4 a 0.1 s b 140 m

■ **4.12** (page 107)
1 a B lower pitch than A b B 2 a Z b Z c Y d Y 3 a 0.5 m b 165 Hz

■ **4.14** (page 111)
1 sound with higher frequency than human ear can hear 2 a measuring depth of water b measures time for reflection of ultrasound pulses 3 a safer for baby and mother b breaking up kidney stones 4 cleaning, testing for flaws in metals 5 a middle pulse further to left b middle and right pulse further to left 6 a lower volume b reduce gap between rollers c ultrasound volume will rise, so gap will be increased by signals

■ **4.15** (page 113)
1 a P waves; received first b S waves
2 refraction because of speed change as rock density changes 3 a B; only P waves travel through core b 3000 km c S waves can't pass through it

■ **4.16** (page 115)
1 jigsaw fit of continents 2 rock and fossil patterns, sea-floor spreading 3 huge pieces of crust (and upper mantle) 4 a near plate boundaries, where crust moves relative to other crust b crust weak and cracked at plate boundaries 5 convection currents in mantle

■ **4.17** (page 117)
1 molten rock 2 a and b towards each other c past each other 3 heating effect of friction 4 rocks heated 5 crystal size

■ **5.01** (page 123)
1 current 2 a copper b PVC 3 a cell b generator 4 a any two mains appliances b electric drill, food mixer c iron, toaster 5 contain free electrons 6 a 3 hours b £1 (100p)

■ **5.02** (page 125)
1 X 1.8 A, Y 0.76 A 2 a conventional current direction b right terminal is +; electron flow is opposite to conventional direction 3 a 3 A b 3 A c 3 A 4 a 40 C b 40 s c 5 A

■ **5.03** (page 127)
1 a C b A; spent in bulb 2 4 V, 6 V 3 a 6 V b 9 J c 3 J 4 a B b A c 1000 C d 12 000 J

■ **5.04** (page 129)
1 23 Ω 2 1st row 4 Ω; 2nd row 1 A, 4 Ω; 3rd row 0.5 A, 4 Ω 3 a 4.4 A b 1.2 Ω c 1.9 Ω d 2.4 Ω; at 5 A

■ **5.05** (page 131)
1 bulb brighter; less resistance in circuit 2 a LDR b diode c thermistor 3 B 4 a 2 Ω b 4 Ω 5 reverse; voltage/current has higher value

■ **5.06** (page 133)
1 full voltage across each, independently switched 2 B in series, others go OFF; C in parallel, other stays ON 3 a X b Z 4 a A OFF, B ON b A OFF, B OFF c 8 V d 8 V

■ **5.07** (page 135)
1 a 1 Ω b 15 V c 3 A d 0.5 A e 2 V 2 a 3 A b 6 A c 9 A d 1.3 Ω 3 a 2 A b 6 A

■ **5.08** (page 137)
1 a live b earth c live d neutral e earth f neutral 2 from top: (3), 13, 3, 3, 13, 3
3 wire to bulb live even when switch is off; stops casing ever becoming live

■ **5.09** (page 139)
1 full voltage across each, independently switched 2 fuses (or circuit breakers)
3 a breaks circuit if current is too high b can be reset 5 a.c. goes backwards and forwards, d.c. goes one way 6 current goes backwards and fowards 50 times a second
7 switch off at socket, pull out plug 8 a Y b Z

■ **5.10** (page 141)
1 a 1150 W b 11 2 A 460 W (drill), B 690 W (toaster), C 92 W (stereo player) 3 a A 0.46 kW, B 0.92 kW, C 1.15 kW, D 0.023 kW, E 0.046 kW b A 2 A, B 4 A, C 5 A, D 0.1 A, E 0.2 A c A, D, E need 3 A; B, C need 13 A 4 a 2 A b 12 W c 4 A d 48 W

■ **5.11** (page 143)
1 J, kJ, kW h 2 a 1000 W, 3600 s, 1 kW h, 3 600 000 J b 3 600 000 J 3 A 0.5 kW h, B 1.5 kW h, C 3 kW h, D 24 kW h 4 Donna's father 5 a £1 (100p) b 10p c 2p 6 £84 (840p) 7 720 J

■ **5.13** (page 147)
1 a attract b repel c attract 2 a takes electrons from sleeve b attracting charges closer than repelling charges

■ **5.14** (page 149)
1 a sparks when aircraft refuelled b earthing 2 a pushed down b inkjet printer c pulled up

■ **5.15** (page 151)
1 charged atoms (or groups of atoms)
2 a rises b air becomes ionized
3 electroplating

■ **6.01** (page 157)
1 north-seeking, south-seeking 2 a and b S pole 3 using compass (or iron filings)
4 a N poles at top, S poles at bottom b apart, S poles repel c steel stays magnetized, iron doesn't

■ **6.02** (page 159)
2 a A; fewest turns with no core b B; steel stays permanently magnetized (hard magnetic material)

■ **6.03** (page 161)
1 a copper b iron c would stay magnetized d so that current flows through coil and not magnet e more turns, more current f reverse magnetic field 2 a coil closes contacts, completes motor circuit b switch would have to handle much higher current 3 a magnetic field pulling on catch b fewer turns on coil

■ **6.04** (page 163)
1 a B b stronger force c force reversed d upward 2 wire will vibrate 3 a turning effect on coil b move less c to avoid overheating wire, discharging battery d more turns on coil

■ **6.05** (page 165)
1 a brush b commutator c coil d brush e commutator 2 stronger magnet, more turns on coil 3 a upward force on one side, downward force on other (current directions opposite) b coil turns opposite way c turn direction unchanged d vertical

■ **6.07** (page 169)
1 a current reversed b and c no current
2 a electromagnetic induction b from top: needle...doesn't move, moves to left, moves further to right c higher meter readings

■ **6.08** (page 171)
1 Milliammeter, Alternating, Generators, N, Electrical, Turns 2 a coil horizontal b cutting field lines fastest c coil vertical d not cutting field lines 3 a higher current b higher current, higher frequency c as coil turns, each side moves up and down through field

■ **6.09** (page 173)
1 a C b D c B d B e A 2 a 10:1 b 46 W c 46 W d 0.2 A e magnetic field doesn't change

■ **6.10** (page 175)
1 a to turn turbines b for cooling water c reduces current in cables d transformers only work with a.c. 2 a supply network b 5 c Extown, Oldwich d 50 MW e 150 MW f 100 000 000 J g 5000 A h 250 A

■ **7.01** (page 183)
1 a electron b proton c neutron d electron e nucleus f electron 2 1st row 11, 12, 23; 2nd row 13, 14, 27; 3rd row 38, 52, 90; 4th row 27, 33, 60 3 a $^{226}_{88}$Ra b $^{235}_{92}$U c $^{16}_{8}$O d $^{12}_{6}$C
4 a A lithium; B thorium; C lithium; D boron; b A and C

■ **7.02** (page 185)
1 Rutherford's model has nucleus 2 a atoms are mostly empty space b some alpha particles bounce off nucleus

■ **7.03** (page 187)
1 carbon-14 2 detecting alpha, beta, gamma radiation 3 creates ions (makes atoms gain or lose electrons) 4 a gamma b alpha c beta d gamma e alpha f beta g gamma h gamma i alpha j gamma 5 radioactive: atoms have unstable nuclei

■ **7.04** (page 189)
1 radon gas from ground 2 radon is radioactive 3 a alpha b can't penetrate skin 4 a 2 counts per second b 26 counts per second c gamma

■ **7.06** (page 193)
1 radium-226 **2 a** decay happens at random **b** because of background radiation **c** 3 minutes **3 b** 50 s **c** 50 s **d** 50 s
4 a 8 days **b** iodine has shorter half-life, so activity drops more quickly

■ **7.07** (page 195)
1 a radioactive isotopes **b** tracers, radiotherapy **2** radiotherapy, testing metals for cracks **3 a** alpha completely stopped, gamma not stopped at all **b** less beta detected **4 a** small amount of radioactive material that can be tracked **b** checking thyroid function **c** almost no radiation left after a few days **5 a** there is less **b** decay product of potassium-40 **c** age of rock

■ **7.08** (page 197)
1 a nuclei splitting **b** fission sequence which keeps itself going **2 a** heat released in nuclear reactor **b** nuclear bomb explosion
3 highly radioactive, some long half-lives
4 a 143 **b** 144 **c** 3

■ **8.01** (page 205)
1 a 1 day **b** 28 days **c** 1 year **d** 28 days
2 a and **b** night **c** daytime **3** reflects sunlight **4** planet appears to move relative to stars

■ **8.02** (page 207)
1 reflects sunlight **2** Mercury, Venus, Mars, Pluto **3** same as for **2** **4** Mercury **5 a** Mars, Jupiter, Saturn, Uranus, Neptune, Pluto **b** further from Sun **6 a** Venus; hotter than Mercury, but further from Sun **7** Mars and Jupiter; orbit time is between these two
8 a gravity **b** Venus **c** Earth

■ **8.03** (page 209)
1 Venus **2** pieces of rock and ice **3** elliptical orbit takes it further out **4** no solid surface **5** meteor is flash of light, meteorite reaches ground **6 a** X **b** X **c** Z **d** dust and gas stream off **e** reflects sunlight

■ **8.04** (page 211)
1 a travels over whole of Earth's surface **b** to keep speed **c** communications, navigation, research **2 a** go out into space **b** fall back to Earth **3** geostationary orbit, so satellite orbits at same rate as Earth turns
4 a A **b** B

■ **8.05** (page 213)
1 hydrogen **2 a** hydrogen **b** nuclear fusion **c** helium **3 a** star system **b** our galaxy **c** a pattern of stars in the sky **d** distance travelled by light in 1 year **4** no; at different distances from Earth **5 a** 15 000 000 °C **b** 100 billion **c** 100 000 light-years **d** 8 minutes **e** 4 light-years **f** 9 million million km

■ **8.06** (page 215)
1 a huge cloud of gas and dust **b** gravity **c** 4500 million years **d** planets and moons **2 a** huge red star **b** 6000 million years from now **c** core will become white dwarf **3 a** gigantic explosion of massive star **b** neutron star **4** X-rays from gases pulled in **5** presence of very heavy elements in our Solar System

■ **8.07** (page 217)
1 a 5 million **b** 5 **c** 15 billion **d** 15 billion
2 a lengthened wavelengths of light **b** galaxies rushing away from us **3** galaxies rushing apart, background radiation from all directions **4** gravity **5** 10 000 million years

■ **FT1** (page 225)
1 a C **b** A and D **c** B **2 a** 16 N m **b** 12 N m **c** no; clockwise **d** 1 N

■ **FT2** (page 227)
1 a less **b** more; smaller base **2 b** 1 m **c** 100 N m **d** 100 N m **e** 100 N

■ **FT3** (page 229)
1 a tension – guy lines, canvas; compression – ridge pole, upright poles; bending – pegs, ridge pole **b** bend permanently **c** stretches; stretches less **2 b** 40 mm **d** at 48 mm extension; permanently stretched **e** 3.9 N **f** 2.8 N

■ **FT4** (page 231)
1 larger area, so less pressure **2** 3 Pa
3 a 100 Pa **b** 50 Pa **4 a** 200 Pa **b** 100 N **c** greater

■ **FT5** (page 233)
1 four times original pressure
2 a 8000 mmHg **c i** 1330 mmHg **ii** 2660 mmHg **d** straight line **3 a** 12 m^3 **b** 15 m^3

■ **FT6** (page 235)
1 a 5000 kg m/s **b** motor cycle **c** car **2** 4 N **3** 400 N **4** 4 m/s

■ **FT7** (page 237)
1 a 2 s **b** 50 m/s **c** 100 m **2 a** friction from the tyres **b i**, **ii**, and **iii** more **c** go straight on

Answers to end-of-chapter questions

Chapter 1 (page 16)
1 metre, m; kilogram, kg; time second; current, A; degree Celsius, °C, or kelvin, K; m^2; volume; force, N
2 **a** 1000 **b** 1000 **c** 1 000 000 **d** 4 000 000 **e** 500 000
3 **a** 3 m **b** 0.5 kg **c** 1.5 km **d** 0.25 s **e** 500 ms **f** 750 m **g** 2500 g **h** 800 mm
4 24 cm^3, 4 cm, 10 cm, 5 cm
5 **a** t, g, kg **b** m, km **c** cm^3, ml **d** s **e** kg/m^3
6 **a** X: 0.1 m^3, Y: 0.05 m^3 **b** 800 kg **c** Y **d** X: petrol, Y: water

Chapter 2 (pages 48–49)
1 gravity, accelerates, air resistance, falls at a steady speed
2 **a** 5 m/s^2 **b** 3000 N **c** to overcome frictional forces
3 **a i** between feet and ice **ii** between ice and bobsleigh **b** streamline themselves **c** stopping
4 **a** reaction time, weather
5 **a** decelerates **b** accelerates **c** constant speed **d** streamlining and lubricating
6 **a** 10 **c** 3s **d i** gravity **ii** air resistance **iii** downward **iv** equal **e** lower terminal velocity
7 **a** 2 m/s^2 **b** 1.5 m/s^2, –1.5 m/s^2 **c** 10 m/s^2
8 **a** 0.2 m/s^2 **b** 0.2 kg **c** 200 000 N
9 **a** Jane **b** Emma **c** 5 s **d** 7 m/s **e** increases by 2 m/s every second **f** 1.5 m/s^2 **g** 12 m
10 **a** high **b** high **c** high **d** low **e** high **f** low
11 **a** acceleration, constant speed, deceleration, stopped, acceleration, constant speed

Chapter 3 (pages 80–81)
1 **a** double-glazing, roof insulation, cavity wall insulation, carpets and underlay, draught excluders **b** to permit air changes for ventilation
2 **a** 24 000 J **b** 2000 J **c** 150 J, gravitational potential energy
3 **a** 20 J **b** 2 500 000 J **c** 1250 J; heat
4 **a** kinetic **b i** friction **ii** heat
5 **a** 500 N **b** 10 000 J **c** electrical to gravitational potential **d** 1000 W or 1 kW **e** 20000 J **f** friction, weight of bucket **g** lighter bucket, lubrication
6 **a** 40 000 kg **b i** 1 MJ **ii** 2 MJ all potential energy is converted to kinetic energy **c** 1.2 MJ **d** less demand
7 **a** good absorber **b** prevent heat loss **c** convection current **d** more sunlight **e** 2 kW **f** 5 m^2 **g i** non-polluting **ii** intermittent
8 **a** 'water jacket'; fibreglass/foam **b** heats whole tank because hot water rises by convection **c i** 1000 **ii** 3000 J **iii** 1 260 000 J
9 **a** non-polluting **b** intermittent energy **c** noise, unsightly

Chapter 4 (pages 118–119)
1 **b** 325 m/s **c** 3 m/s
2 total internal reflection
3 **a** B louder **b** C higher pitch **c** B **d** C **e** 1.5 m **f** 440 Hz
4 **a i** 20 kHz **ii** Y **b i** scanning unborn babies **ii** less dangerous **iii** cleaning
5 **a** wavelength **b** frequency **d i** radio, microwaves **ii** ultraviolet, gamma rays **iii** infrared, microwaves
6 **a** longitudinal waves (e.g. sound) have backwards–forwards oscillations, transverse waves (e.g. light) have side-to-side oscillations **b** speed changes because of density changes **c** S waves cannot travel through liquid core **d** from travel times, distances from common origin can be worked out, so origin computed
7 **b** changes direction
8 **b i** higher pitch **ii** louder sound **iii** different tone

Chapter 5 (pages 152–153)
1 **a** ammeter **b** variable resistor **c** voltmeter **e** 0.79 A **f** 8 Ω **g** increases
2 **a** ordinary: 0.1 kW, low-energy: 0.02 kW **b** 20 kW h **c** 100 kW h **d** £8 **e** heat

3 a 2 A b 12 W c 6 J d 2 C
4 a i S_1 ii S_1 and S_2 b 8.5 A c 13 A d Y e safety f blue g brown h i fuse rating too high – fault may not blow fuse ii double insulation
5 a electrons (–) repelled by negative terminal b rod takes electrons (–) from cloth, which is left with more + charges than – c contain free electrons
6 a i parallel ii 4 A iii 2 A iv no effect b i series ii 3 V iii goes out
7 a electrical energy to heat and light energy b 2 kW c casing d live wire e 8.3 A f 13 A g too large a current h turn it off

Chapter 6 (pages 178–179)
1 c soft magnetic material such as iron
2 a 60 V b 0.8 A c 100% efficient d stationary magnetic field e i increasing voltage for overhead cables ii decreasing voltage for overhead cables
3 as current changes direction repeatedly, magnetic force on coil changes direction repeatedly, causing core to vibrate and produce sound waves
4 a electromagnet b i needle moves ii needle stationary iii needle moves in opposite direction c transformer d insert magnet e core would be permanently magnetized
5 a generators; coal, oil, gas; chemical energy to electrical energy b less energy loss c safety d voltage decreases, step-down transformer e change voltage using transformers f 12 V; step-down
6 a stronger magnet, more loops of wire, faster rotation b current direction alternates between forwards and backwards

Chapter 7 (pages 200–201)
1 a rocks, e.g. granite, nuclear power stations b 520, 200, 140, 80, 50, 20, 0, 0 d 3rd e 8.0 mm
2 a fission b begin more reactions c energy released heats water to make steam to drive turbines and generators d buried deep underground
3 a 1 billion b 5.6 billion c 4.6 billion years d alpha particle e fast-moving electrons f quality control for paper
4 a alpha particle b nucleus c time for half the sample to decay d i 400 counts per second ii 100 counts per second
5 a electrons b Geiger–Müller tube c smaller d alpha unable to pass through paper, gamma count unaffected by paper thickness
6 a 7 positive, 7 neutral, 7 negative b same element but different numbers of electrons
7 a 2 protons joined with 2 neutrons b electron c electromagnetic wave d nucleus e Geiger–Müller tube f card g lead
8 a increase count rate; high concentration of radioactive material b gamma; high penetration power needed

Chapter 8 (pages 220–221)
1 a 12 b can cover whole of surface c surveying d dish aerials on Earth would have to change direction constantly/lose contact e matches Earth's rate of turning, so satellite appears at fixed position in sky
2 a Jupiter b Pluto c Mercury d Jupiter e 0.2 Earth years f hotter closer to Sun
3 a moon b Solar System c meteorite d comet e galaxy f supernova
4 a cloud of dust and gas b gravity c fusion d red giant e white dwarf
5 a and c see p. 214 b release of gravitational potential energy d i increase in wavelength ii moving away at high speed iii big-bang theory
6 a star b moon/planet c ii moving across stars d i object orbiting a planet ii weather satellite iii Moon
7 a lump of ice and dust with gas b elliptical c far away from Sun
8 a B b B c A d above same place on Earth e constant contact

Answers to further exam-style questions (pages 238–245)

1 c 80 km/h
2 a 10 m/s^2 b air resistance c balanced forces d opens parachute e deceleration f lower terminal velocity
3 a bulb b battery d solar cell d microphone e loudspeaker f burning gas
4 a can't be replaced, can be replaced b oil, gas c tidal d non-polluting, high initial costs
5 a 0.1 A b 0.4 A
6 a 24 W b 240 J c electrical to heat and light
7 a i 3 A ii 3 A iii 5 A iv 13 A b melts
8 a neutral b live c yellow/green d safety e fuse
9 a i £1.26 ii 4.2p iii 7p b a network of pylons and cables carrying electrical energy from power stations to homes
10 a ammeter b 2 A c 4 A d 6 A
11 a variable resistor b switch c ammeter d voltmeter f 4th g yes h 8 Ω
12 a electrical energy to heat and light energy b 36 J/s c 3 A d 4 Ω
13 a 12 km b 40 minutes c 24 h d slower, less-steep graph
14 a 5 b 2 Hz c 10 cm/s
15 a gravitational potential energy b 15 000 J c friction d 750 W
16 a i pointer 10 divisions to left ii no pointer movement iii pointer more than 10 divisions to left b magnetic field cutting through coils induces current in them
17 a heat flows from hot to cold b conduction c convection d cavity wall insulation, e.g. fibreglass
18 a 40% b heat warms water, which produces steam, which drives turbines and generators c National Grid
19 a total internal reflection b endoscope
20 a P waves, S waves b wave with backwards–forwards vibrations c waves with side-to-side vibrations d S waves e S waves
21 a i midday ii midnight iii dawn iv dusk b 24 hours approx.
22 a A: beta, B: alpha, C: gamma b alpha and beta c alpha d Geiger–Müller tube
23 a elastic, spring, battery b kinetic energy c can be replaced
24 a electrical, heat, kinetic b 1 Unit c 9p
25 a C b microwaves, infrared c radio waves, visible light
26 a friction between runners and ice b wear surface, heating
27 b total internal reflection c 90°, 180° d rear reflector
28 a 6000 J b gravitational potential energy c 600 W d kinetic energy e heat
29 a primary seismic waves b P: transverse, S: longitudinal c i increases; density of mantle rock increases ii decreases suddenly; waves move from solid to liquid
30 a coal, oil, gas b formed from the remains of ancient plants and animals c took millions of years to form and can't be replaced d i adds CO_2 to atmosphere ii adds sulphur dioxide to atmosphere e wind, tidal, hydroelectric
31 b to the left, opposing motion c lubrication d 25 J
32 a constant speed b stationary c 10 m/s d 6 m/s
33 a 4 b 8 c 5 d protons e electric attraction f atom (or group of atoms) which has i lost ii gained one (or more) electrons
34 b low polar orbit – Earth surface survey, geostationary orbit – communications c gravitational forces
35 a A: neutral, blue, B: earth, C: live, brown b fuse; 'blows' (wire melts) if current gets too high c extra layer of insulation e.g. plastic case d 3 A
36 a light or infrared, ultraviolet rays, X-rays, microwaves b i infrared waves ii radio waves c radioactive materials
37 a sound waves of frequency higher than 20 kHz b safer c 0.011 m
38 a chemical energy b some coal not burnt, heat from burning coal escapes, heat from hot steam escapes, heat lost with exhaust gases c wood
39 b time for half a sample to decay c 5 minutes d 213 counts per minute
40 a ray must strike inside face of material, at angle greater than critical angle d bundles of fibres used in endoscope for seeing inside body
41 a hot air rises above radiator when cooler air sinks, so heat carried round by circulating air (convection) b black is good absorber of thermal radiation c yes, but would take longer; white reflects thermal radiation d use double-glazing (two layers of glass with air between)

Index